The Tip of the Needle

Catherine O'Driscoll

In a land of slaves, rebels are hated.

*In a society ruled by lies, those who speak truth
are considered insane.*

Copyright

A CIP catalogue record for this book is available from the British Library.

ISBN: 978-0-9523048-7-6

Published by Dogged Truth Publishing.

www.CatherineODriscoll.com

Acknowledgements

Thank you – from the bottom of my heart – to Canine Health Concern members who have supported the work for so many years.

I am but one of tens of thousands of people who seek – through action – to bring positive change to this world. I hold all Peace Warriors and Truth Speakers in my heart, with love and respect.

These are the names I shall always speak: Chappie, Sophie, Oliver, Prudence, Samson, Gwinnie, Edward, Daniel, Georgie, Freddie and Ruby – the dogs who have been my friends and companions, and who have taught me that animals are people, too.

To Rob, my beautiful and conscientious husband who works so hard to keep the message moving strong, I send eternal love and gratitude.

And to you who are reading now and know that you have *done something* to help others in need, close your eyes and see me honour the Grace in you.

Dedication

This book is dedicated to Christopher Day, Veterinarian and Truth Speaker; the man who set my feet upon this path. Despite hardships and many challenges, Chris has continued to speak the Truth when others around him quivered. I am grateful that such a one as this walks the earth. I respect him and am grateful for his courage and integrity.

Foreword

Dr Jayne Donegan

I am a medical doctor, a mother, and a dog, cat and hen owner.

In 1983 I qualified in Medicine from St Mary's Hospital Medical School, where Sir Alexander Fleming famously discovered penicillin in 1928.

It was a received article of faith for me and my contemporaries that vaccination was the single most effective health intervention ever introduced. My medical and post graduate medical education seemed to confirm this. The dramatic decreases in morbidity and mortality from diseases that occurred in the course of the twentieth century were credited to the introduction of specific vaccines, with scant acknowledgement being given to improving social conditions. Despite questioning of the safety and efficacy of vaccination by reputable medical men since its introduction, debate has been, and is increasingly, discouraged. Information published in scientific journals is used to support this position, with other views being regarded as 'unscientific'.

Like all my medical and nursing colleagues, I was taught that vaccines were the reason children and adults stopped dying from diseases for which there were vaccines. Other diseases, such as Scarlet Fever, Rheumatic Fever, Typhus, Typhoid, Cholera and so on – for which there were no vaccines – were said to have diminished both in incidence and mortality (ability to kill) due to better social conditions. We never questioned whether *all* the reductions in deaths from infectious diseases might have been due to improved social conditions. The medical curriculum was so vast that we memorised what we were told: non vaccinatable diseases were placed in the social conditions box and vaccinatable diseases in the vaccines box, and then on to the next subject.

This view was reinforced by everything I was taught and read in textbooks, both before I qualified as a doctor and through all of my post graduate training.

Along with most doctors, I regarded parents who would not vaccinate their children as ignorant or, if not ignorant, sociopathic, for withholding what I then believed to be a life-saving intervention, and for putting everybody else at risk. I used to counsel the parents in the 1980s who did not want to vaccinate their children with the pertussis (whooping cough) vaccine. I told them that adverse reactions were associated with the vaccine, but that (we were told) the chances of having an adverse reaction with the disease itself was ten times greater, so any sensible parent would opt for vaccination.

Then in 1994 came the 'Measles Rubella Campaign' where seven million school children were vaccinated. The letter from the Chief Medical Officer said there was a measles epidemic coming. I discovered some time later that this was based on a hypothetical, computerised model.

Two things worried me about the campaign. The first was that someone who had already had two doses of a measles containing vaccine would still not be immune when an epidemic came. I had been counselling parents about pertussis vaccine based on the likelihood, and the stated aim, that the vaccine would, in most cases, stop their child getting the disease. But even with two shots of a one shot vaccine (with whatever adverse reactions that entailed), your child could still be at risk of contracting the disease (with whatever risk that entailed) when the epidemic came, unless they were vaccinated a third time (with whatever risk that entailed). The benefit, not to mention the efficacy was becoming much less clear cut.

The second concern was that we were being told that the best way of interrupting disease transmission was to vaccinate *en masse* and break the 'chain of transmission'. If *en masse* was the best way, then why did we vaccinate two, three and four month old babies? Why didn't we just wait three years and vaccinate everyone who had been born or moved into the area, and break the chain of transmission?

This was the start of my long, slow journey of researching vaccination, the history of medicine and disease ecology, and learning about other models and philosophies of health and natural hygiene such as those used by the great pioneers who cleaned up our cities and built clean water supplies and sewage systems. I spent hundreds of hours in libraries looking at archived journals and textbooks, and looking at government data within the Office for National Statistics (ONS). I was getting out dusty volumes from the middle of the nineteenth century to make graphs of death rates from vaccinatable diseases which, for some reason, have not been made available by the ONS or the Department of Health.

I read what prominent men of science, medical officers for health and doctors wrote about vaccination and its sequelae that never made it into today's textbooks. I found out what anyone with even a passing acquaintance with disease figures of the 19th and 20th century knew. For example, that 99% of the people in England and Wales who used to die from whooping cough had stopped dying before the vaccine was introduced in the 1950s. The same happened with measles. Even the success story of smallpox vaccination was not what it seemed: the enforcement of the compulsory smallpox vaccination law in 1867, when the death rate was already falling, was accompanied by an increase in the deaths from 100 to 400 deaths per million population.

I also started to learn about 'health' as opposed to 'disease' which is what I had studied at medical school. I began to gain an understanding of *why* people get infections and how they can be supported through them, so that they come out more healthy, rather than more ill.

My research led me to being asked, in 2002, to act as an expert witness for the mothers of two unvaccinated children whose absent fathers were applying to the Court for a vaccination enforcement order. I wrote a report based on my research, fully referenced, carefully using the methods and results of the studies I quoted to give my opinion, rather than the conclusions of the authors which are often not supported by their results.

The experts for the fathers and the children were members of the Joint Committee on Vaccination and Immunisation (JCVI). They recommended vaccination for both children. It should be noted that if they had advised that vaccination was not necessary for these individual children, they would have been seen to be contradicting government health policy based on JCVI recommendations – a conflict of interest that was not explored in the case. The judge nevertheless decided that my opinion was less valid than theirs and the mothers lost their case. When it went to appeal, one of the appeal judges called my evidence 'junk science' and on this basis I was accused of Serious Professional Misconduct by the General Medical Council (GMC) of the UK and threatened with being struck off the Medical Register, banned from practising as a doctor, and losing my livelihood (2004).

In 2007, after a long drawn out case lasting three and a half years, the GMC panel completely exonerated me. They did not merely acquit me, but said that they were, *"sure that in the reports you provided you did not fail to be objective, independent and unbiased."*

This was a very gratifying and unforeseen outcome given that my original legal team had told me to plead guilty to all the charges as they were impossible to defend and that other doctors who have publicly aired their concerns about vaccination have not been so lucky. The successful outcome notwithstanding, the case took an inevitable and heavy toll on my children, our family and my professional life.

The medical establishment is not kind to those who question its sacred dogma, but the meaning of science, from the Latin *scio, scire,* to know, is 'knowledge'. And that knowledge needs to be in the public domain so that people can argue about it, decide whether it is valid or not, provoke further research and ask good questions.

The general public don't realise that much good research is not done if there is no drug at the end of it, and research that is done may be buried if the results are not what were wanted. The peer review process, which is there to ensure quality, can also be used to reject research that rocks a particular apple cart, and now, even if the information gets as far as being published, there is that antithesis of scientific practice: the retraction of published papers so that no-one is even allowed to read them anymore.

It is like burning books.

I have not vaccinated my animals since 1994. My cats have never died of a vaccine preventable disease. My old Labrador cross Whippet friend, Jess, had no vaccines after I acquired her at the age of ten. She died at the age of 18½ years. She did not need to see a vet in all that time. She had a stroke which left her paralysed down one side when she was 15 years old. I used to carry her in and out to wee and then out in a baby carriage when I went to the park to walk the other dogs. Over the next nine months the strength in her paralysed side gradually returned and, although she always had a slight crab-like gait to one side, she walked around the park and garden on her own for the next three years. This encouraged several other owners in the park not to have their dogs put down when they had a stroke, and several lived for years afterwards, in addition to regaining their mobility.

Having read the all delightful James Herriot books that describe the horror of distemper in dogs and how they died before there was a vaccine, my 13 year-old daughter was understandably worried when she bought herself a terrier mixture puppy (Jack Russel, Patterdale, Staffie) called Poppy. Deciding that fear and anxiety weren't good for Poppy's immune system or ours (they set off the hypothalamic pituitary adrenal axis causing outpourings of, amongst others, steroid hormones. These temporarily help but over time diminish the immune response making a person more prone to disease and a worse outcome), we contacted the homeopathic vet, Christopher Day, and got nosodes – homeopathically potentised parts of the disease process – for all the diseases against which dogs are generally vaccinated. We figured that if the *least* they did was make us more confident, it would be worth it. We also followed his advice on animal feeding.

We dutifully remembered to give the nosodes every three months for two years, then we forgot. Poppy had puppies when she was three. We did the same for the puppy we kept, Golf, but in his case we forgot after six months. Poppy is now nine and Golf is six years old, both well and happy. In fact the only one in the family who is not is Archie, Golf's brother. His owner vaccinated him yearly until he was three years old and then his owner died. We took him back as the relatives were going to send him to a rescue home. He is the only one with problems of hyper arousal, changeable moods, the tendency to bite (only family, he is delightful to strangers!) and being unsettled, though he has calmed down a lot in the three years that we have had him.

Having families and animals and just being alive is an emotional experience.

Catherine O'Driscoll relates in this book how she was criticised by a vet at a homeopathic conference for being too 'emotional' in the presentation of her research, as if emotions should not be present in a book about animal or, for that matter, human health. This is not the case: intelligent compassion must be present in every step of our scientific endeavour with respect to human, animal and even plant life as well as our stewardship of the planet on which we live.

Being endowed with great brain power, in the absence of such compassion, we humans are able to propel ourselves at ever greater speed to the cold, reductionist bottom line of, 'we can do it so we will.'

The current 'scientific' model in medicine and commerce is deliberately shorn of emotion and lacking in intelligent compassion. This has brought us to a situation in which people are regarded as items to be manipulated, like players in the corporate Monopoly board. Selling a product, whether it be a drug, a vaccine, processed nutrient-empty food or the products of inhumanely, intensively raised and slaughtered animals, is more important than any benefit that might be gained by the people for whom it is marketed. Their role is merely to buy or submit to it.

As Catherine has so eloquently explained in this book, there is a huge and growing divide between rich and poor on this planet. The lack of intelligent compassion, not to mention common sense, means we spend billions of dollars every year on profitable new drugs and vaccines, when this same money spent on ensuring that every person on earth has clean water and safe disposal of sewage would have a far greater impact in terms of benefit to health.

The Bulletin of the World Health Organisation, while affirming in 2008 that: *"Vaccination has greatly reduced the burden of infectious diseases,"* goes on to say: *"Only clean water, also considered to be a basic human right, performs better"*

Yet the United nations still stated in 2013 that: *"783 million people do not have access to clean water and almost 2.5 billion do not have access to adequate sanitation. 6 to 8 million people die annually from the consequences of disasters and water-related diseases."*[1]

What a global disgrace.

---

[1] UN Water Day 2013 International Year of Water Cooperation http://www.unwater.org/water-cooperation-2013/water-cooperation/facts-and-figures/en/

It is argued that it is too expensive to enable all people to have the basic human rights of clean water and sanitation, so better to give the quick fix – namely vaccines. But vaccines are not cheap and they don't fix.

Jacob Puliyel, Head of Paediatrics at St Stephens Hospital, Delhi, contends that the $2.5 billion spent by India on trying to eradicate polio by repeatedly dosing under five year-olds with oral polio vaccines has resulted in 47,500 extra cases of non-polio Acute Flaccid Paralysis (NPAFP).

So instead of paralysis from wild polio virus there is paralysis from the oral polio vaccine, which is, *"Clinically indistinguishable from polio paralysis but twice as deadly, the incidence of NPAFP was directly proportional to doses of oral polio received."* He goes on to say, *"It is tempting to speculate what could have been achieved if the $2.5 billion spent on attempting to eradicate polio were spent on water and sanitation and routine immunisation."*[2]

Catherine also tackles the important relationship between malnutrition and infectious disease. Indeed, Hippocrates, the father of medicine, said: *"Let your food be your medicine and your medicine be your food."*

Mother's milk is a baby's first source of nutrients. UNICEF states that breastfed children have at least six times greater chance of survival in the early months than non-breastfed children due to reduced deaths from acute respiratory infection, diarrhoea and other infections, especially in those countries with a high burden of disease and low access to clean water and sanitation[3].

Nonetheless expensive Rotavirus vaccines are being added to vaccination programmes in developing countries, even though exclusive breast feeding provides infants with unique protection from diarrhoea and vomiting illnesses and even from travellers' diarrhoea when abroad. This is because breast milk is loaded with antibodies and gut protective bacteria, in addition to the *"oft forgotten non-immunoglobulin fraction in breast milk which is an additional tool of protection against rotavirus disease"*.[4]

Catherine has also examined the price of capitalism as it relates – significantly – to human and animal health, and to their callous deaths. The lack of intelligent compassion means that profit is the bottom line. Multinational companies – who have no allegiance to any country or place,

---

2   Meister H-U, Shafir, RS, Global Wealth Report 2014 p13 Research Institute Credit Suissehttps://publications.credit-suisse.com/tasks/render/file/?fileID=60931FDE-A2D2-F568-B041B58C5EA591A4 Vashisht N, Puliyel J., Polio programme: let us declare victory and move on.Indian J Med Ethics. 2012 Apr-Jun;9(2):114-7. PMID: 22591873 http://jacob.puliyel.com/paper.php?id=251

3   UNICEF Breastfeeding Impact on child survival and global situation, http://www.unicef.org/nutrition/index_24824.html

4   Prameela KK & Vijaya LR The importance of breastfeeding in rotaviral diarrhoeas. Malays J Nutr. 2012Apr;18(1):103-11.

only shareholders – develop commodities that people don't need and can't afford to buy. Low per capita income countries are stripped of their natural resources while being financially crushed under the inexorable burden of spiralling interest rates on loans that we allot them under the guise of charity, and they are thus dragged into the consumer age to create markets for more products.

The price paid by the planet is increasing levels of greenhouse gasses, pollution of the environment with synthetic herbicides and fertilisers, destruction of the rainforests, carbon sink and a massive loss of diversity – of animals, plants and indigenous peoples.

Thus 'science without humanity' and 'commerce without morality' are the partners of politics without principles as enumerated by Gandhi.

"What has all this to do with dog vaccines?" you may ask. Well, as Catherine has so beautifully illustrated, your dog's next shot is just the tip of the needle. Behind that tip lies a whole world of politics – in every sense of that word – and animal *and* human suffering.

"If all the medical and veterinary information that has been presented in this book is available in the public domain, waiting to be read by anyone who takes the trouble to look, analyse and educate themselves – why don't they?"

A good point. Vaccination is a medical procedure administered to healthy human and animal babies, children and adults, surely it behoves us as health professionals to do some independent research of our own. Why do more medical practitioners and veterinary surgeons not do so?

I cannot answer for vets, but for medical doctors, what may be the biggest obstacle to their even entertaining the possibility that the Universal Childhood Vaccination Program may not the unmitigated success it is portrayed to be, or that there may be other ways of achieving health that are better and longer lasting, is possibly the fear of stepping out of line or being seen to be different – with all the consequences that this can entail – as I know to my cost. As George Bernard Shaw said in his preface to 'The Doctor's Dilemma' 1906 :

> *"Doctors are just like other Englishmen: most of them*
> *have no honour and no conscience: what they commonly*
> *mistake for these is sentimentality and an intense dread of*
> *doing anything that everybody else does not do, or omitting to*
> *do anything that everybody else does."*

So bear in mind the next time you are in your doctor's office and you say, *"I'm worried about the safety of vaccination,"* and you are told, *"You don't understand, you're not a doctor,"* that if a doctor says, *"I'm worried about the safety of vaccination,"* they will be told, *"We're charging you with serious professional misconduct....."*

In this book Catherine O'Driscoll will take you through the gripping tale of her own personal journey, warts and all, from a blind faith in the pronouncement of experts, to the realisation that she had to do her own research and become her own expert in her animals' health. She describes the toll it took on her life, health and family and the interpersonal politics that go on in even small organisations where everyone is ostensibly devoted to the same cause.

It is a tribute to the author that she has managed to keep going in the face of so many setbacks and has never given up. She has kept on, and keeps on, in her efforts to inform people of what they can do to improve their pets' health, to protect companion animals and their owners from the avoidable suffering and heartbreak that she, her animals and countless other people and their animals, who have contacted her through the years, have gone through.

Her scope is wide. By the time you finish the last chapter, you will have a global understanding of the complex interests controlling the health and well-being of your animals, your children, and yourself – and perhaps the beginning of an inkling of an answer to the question, "Why?"

12 May 2015
Dr Jayne LM Donegan
MBBS DRCOG DCH DFFP MRCGP MFHom
London NW4 1SH, UK
jaynelmdonegan@yahoo.com
jayne-donegan.co.uk/

Foreword II

There has been a recurring theme throughout history. One where a group or a brave individual takes a stance for something for which he, she or they believe within their heart and soul to be a kinder, fairer, better or more democratic way of doing things. And, of course, this belief or movement goes against the establishment which then deems this adversary as crazy, dangerous or harmful and one which needs to be stricken from society.

I recently watched a mini-series on the History Channel called the Sons of Liberty. Based on true stories, is was a re-enactment of the major events leading up to and through the Revolutionary War and ultimately the signing of the Declaration of Independence. When viewed from the eye of the mother country, England, these colonists were nothing but nuisances, going against the grain and causing problems, needing to be squashed or even executed. But when viewed through their eyes, they were only wanting to live life fairly in exchange for their labors. The more they stood for what they believed to be just, the stronger became their opposition and oppression. But, they stood by their guns, literally, and fought for what they believed despite being hugely out-numbered and out-crafted. As is so commonly said, the rest is history as this stance ultimately gave rise to the United States of America.

I shared this here because it indicated to me as I read Catherine's Tip of the Needle; what she has been up against and the backlash she has received only because of her relentless attempts to share what she believes and knows to be true.

I have been a practicing veterinarian for over four decades and although I have established a clinic that utilizes many therapies alternative to conventional medical practice, I still highly embrace allopathic veterinary medicine and believe the integration of the two is what is currently needed for the best approach to animal health and wellness. I draw a line, however, when it comes to the practice of what we accept as standard vaccination protocol and procedure. Not because I am a researcher with reams of scientific data and statistics to prove my point. But, like Catherine, I have direct experience of not only the harmful effects which vaccinations carry but also how unnecessary it is administering them at the frequency and even dosage or potencies that we do. As controversial as this subject is, also like Catherine, my intense love for animals and wanting to do right by them made it easy for me to write this forward. This is not rocket science. This is merely trying to uphold the basic tenet of medicine brought forth by its founder Hippocrates as he wrote, through accepted translation, "Physician, Do No Harm!"

In support of Catherine's relentless struggle to question authority and to help bring positive change, I offer these common sense questions. If your mind doubts going against the long term practice of responsibly responding to those annual reminders or even now every three years by bringing your pet for his or her "shots" that are "due", ask yourself, "When was my last polio, chicken pox or measles vaccine?" And why don't I get any routine reminders for them from my doctor after childhood? Also, if university studies such as one conducted by Ron Schultz at the School of Veterinary Medicine in Madison, Wisconsin demonstrated a minimum of 7 up to 15 years duration of protective immunity to canine distemper and parvovirus after proper puppy immunization, again why am I receiving reminders every three or especially still every year? Same goes for Fred Scott's similar results at Cornell University in a population of cats for the panleukopenia vaccines that actually got published in the Journal of the Veterinary Medical Association. What about the simple question of why does a two pound puppy get the same dose of vaccine that an adult 140 pound Great Dane gets? And then, why has it been verified that this dose, due to reasons of refrigerator shelf life, could be up to ten times the potency even needed by the Great Dane?

It's for questions like these and so much more information, shared experience and logic that you must continue on and read The Tip of the Needle. Funny thing is, Catherine does and has been for years supplying true scientific data concerning the subject but, because she is not a true diploma-earning scientist or some sort or a veterinarian, much of the science she has supplied is either overlooked or used but not attributed to her. This again serves as grounds to discredit.

So, in closing, I tip my hat to Catherine O'Driscoll for her courage and especially undying persistence in continuing her struggle against adversity trying to do right by our Favorite Kingdom. And also for bringing forth this wonderful and needed text.

Marty Goldstein DVM
Medical Director, Smith Ridge Veterinary Center,
South Salem, New York
Author of Bestseller, The Nature of Animal Healing

Chapter 1
This heart within me burns

I'm in the car on the way to an evening lecture that's being held in aid of a project at Polmont Young Offenders Institute, where unruly antisocial boys are being trained to train unruly antisocial dogs.

It's below freezing and the dashboard display signals danger. I'm anxious. I don't want to hit an ice patch and slide out of control. It's dark, and I'm dazzled by car lights coming the other way. I pull off the road, turn on the light, and look at the directions. I don't know if I've come too far, whether I need to turn back to find the road to Gorebridge, or if the turning's further on. I decide to keep heading forward.

I'm thinking about my life, and how I got to be here, out in the dark on a cold winter's night, trying not to lose control. I'm thinking about the young offenders, and how they got to be where they are, their lives out of control. It seems we're all prisoners, really.

I see the Gorebridge sign, turn right at the T junction, and head up the hill looking for a church. Following the directions, I pull into the leisure centre car park opposite the church and look around. I have no idea if I'm where I'm supposed to be. This doesn't feel right. So I phone Gwen on her mobile and tell her where I am. "I'll come out to the car park," she says, and I wait until I realise she isn't going to show up. I call again. Turns out there are two leisure centres in Gorebridge, both opposite churches. Just like life: thinking we are where we need to be, then finding out we're not.

Rebecca Leonardi arrives while I'm setting up my laptop and screen. I like her straight away. Rebecca is a university student who's managed to get funding for Paws for Progress, the first prison-based dog rehabilitation programme in the UK. She explains that the aim for the young offenders is to improve their behaviour and employability, which they gain whilst helping the dogs to improve their own behaviour and rehoming-ability.

I always call a dog a 'who' and not an 'it'. It makes me sad when people refer to animals as its. Even when I'm writing scientific papers, I refer to animals as people. It's a conscious act of rebellion, even if it indicates to the scientific reader that I'm not one of them. But I refuse to deny the animals their personhood just to fit in.

Rebecca is standing out front, telling us about the scheme. I'm sitting there welling up listening to her. She's taking rejected humans and rejected dogs and putting them together, and the young men are learning, possibly for the first time, that people (dogs being people) respond to you better if

15

you don't shout at them or hit them, and if you have patience. And the dogs, possibly for the first time, are learning what they're supposed to be doing in this world, and that humans can be kind.

"This has a profound effect on the young men's lives," Rebecca says. "They often say that it helps them with their own children, because many of them father children when they're still children themselves."

Every time a dog gets rehomed, the young men celebrate. When they're released, many of the boys are offered jobs working with animals, who they have learnt to love on the back of this project. I love things that go in a circle so that no-one knows who is rehabilitating who, or who is helping who.

I want to rush to Polmont and help, but since no-one is asking me to do that, I have to contain myself.

And then it's my turn to stand at the front. I'm talking about diet, and how processed pet food is another of society's rejects. Without pet food, I say, there would be more landfill sites. It's the rejected part of the human food chain. Much of it is rancid; the feet, spleen, hides, husks and chemicals they're not allowed to put in human food. I show photographs of rendering plants, leaving out the most disgusting pictures because I don't see the point in making my audience sick to their stomachs. I talk about real food, and how the world was designed beautifully and intricately to sustain life before corporations got involved.

And then I talk about pet vaccines and how they are harming the animals, as I have been doing for more than twenty years. I state the case over and over again, to anyone who will listen. Sometimes I feel like the Ancient Mariner, stopping one of three with my obsessive story and, as the years roll by, I begin to look like him: floating upon oceans of sorrow, oceans of harm.

But until my ghastly tale is told, this heart within me burns.

My story begins at the personal level, when my little dog Oliver died and I asked why. Like a snowball, the answers expand until they embrace the whole world, and affect us all.

Chapter 2

Truth

In 1978, a pathobiologist called Dr Ronald D Schultz looked at his children who did not have to be vaccinated every year, and he looked at his dogs who *did* have to be vaccinated every year, and he asked himself why. Then he went into the laboratory and established a scientific truth: once a dog is immune to viral disease, he is immune for years, and probably for life. [1]

As I write, that's 39 years ago.

Dr. Elizabeth Curry-Galvin, assistant director of the American Veterinary Medical Association, Scientific Activities Division, and staff consultant to the Council on Biologic and Therapeutic Agents, wrote in JAVMA News, July 2003 (15 years ago):

"... the one-year revaccination frequency recommendation found on many vaccine labels is based on historical precedent, not scientific data."

She added:

"Revaccination of patients with sufficient immunity doesn't add measurably to their disease resistance, and unnecessary revaccination may increase the risk of adverse postvaccination events in some animals."

Yet dog lovers are still being warned that if they don't vaccinate their dogs annually or every three years, they will die of horrible diseases – even though this warning is not true.

But we are not just paying money to vets and vaccine companies under false pretences – we are harming our dogs. Every unnecessary vaccine increases their chance of suffering.

Chapter 3

Loss

On the 2nd September 1991, Oliver blew my world apart. He was a Golden Retriever in physical form, a clown and social networker in spirit. Oliver was my darling little man. Once John, who was my husband, looked at Oliver and said, "If I could choose my personality, I'd choose one like Oliver's."

Losing Oliver so suddenly was one of the hardest things I've had to bear in this life. He was a beautiful person who lifted up the landscape of my miserable life and kept me going. He died in the middle of a recession, when my clients were unable to pay their bills. Our leader, Margaret Thatcher, had launched thousands of small businesses onto the ocean of commerce, encouraging banks to throw money at us. Then the government cocked up the exchange rate mechanism, George Soros 'broke the Bank of England', and the banks pulled the plug and wanted their money back *now*. The small ships bobbing about on the water hit rock bottom. Interest rates rose from single to double figures, and no-one could pay what they owed to anyone else, although the pirate banks made record profits. Writing as I am in the middle of another recession, it seems that the capitalist whirlpool is destined to keep on spiralling downwards, sucking in small ships that dare to set sail.

When my clients couldn't pay their bills, I had to advise my staff to look for other jobs and paid off the small businesses, and tried to sell my house. But the housing market had crashed so there were no takers, and interest rates went to horrendous heights, and eventually I couldn't pay my mortgage and ended up losing the place where we lived, which was humiliating and shameful. There was terror, too. I was terrified that we would be homeless, and there would be nowhere to go with my dogs. You might as well have torn my heart out. My world was falling apart and then the person I loved the most and who loved me the most – a dog – just ceased to exist.

I think it was hard for Oliver, too, because our neighbour kept finding Ollie's favourite ball in his garden. I think he was trying to contact me, to tell me that his spirit had survived, because I can't think of any other plausible reason for Ollie's special ball to keep finding its way over the high dividing wall.

I don't want to hark on about the misery in my life at that time – as the Buddha said: *all* life is suffering – but I think I need to touch upon it because I believe it's one of the reasons I kept asking why Oliver had died and then obsessively trying to tell other dog lovers how to prevent it happening to their dogs.

They say that you often step onto your life path, embark upon your mission, after a tragedy in your life, and I believe that all these things coming together forced me to take the risk. It's as though my life was a massive chess game, and God swept his arm across the board and sent all the pieces tumbling so that I had no option but to start again.

But because a dog called Oliver had died, I started again in an entirely different place.

I watched myself abandon logic and common sense, and chased down the reaper who had lured my beloved to his grave.

Is it really true, as some believe, that we elect to come to this earth with a mission, and agree to endure potentially terrible events that will put our feet upon our path? It seems to me that, if this is so, then there must be a part of us, maybe a barely conscious part, that knows the world is but a stage and men and women merely players – with our exits and our entrances, culminating in oblivion. Maybe, deep down, we know that all of *this* is transient and nothing really matters – except how much we have loved.

Could it be that, if we are blessed, we find something that awakens our calling; which seems so important that we would sacrifice our lives to make Love our crowning glory?

The word 'sacrifice' means, at its root, to make sacred. It seems to me that, if the world is but a stage and we are merely players, coming and going like waves upon the shore, then we may as well make sacred the surf we elect to ride.

But even if we are merely biological events, like leaves budding, shimmering and fading on a tree, we can still choose to gift our lives with meaning.

Look around you and you will see that everything on this planet is interconnected. Nothing exists entirely for itself. We all need each other in this life. The birds need the trees, the trees need the earth, the earth needs the birds.

If we abandon the truth of life's interconnectedness, consigning ourselves to things and acquisition, satisfied with form but deprived of content, this merely leads – or so they say – to a poverty of the soul.

If the word 'soul' is an anathema to you, consider, then, that denying our interconnectedness leads to a poverty of love which, when you scrape off the layers, is what life is all about. "Teach only love, for love is what you are and all you are."

This is what I hope, anyway.

Otherwise I have made a terrible mistake.

Sometimes I wish I had chosen to become an actor or a rock god instead of an animal health campaigner. For one reason, being a successful actor or rock god pays better than writing about dogs. Dog health doesn't seem to matter much on the grand scale of things. It's not a popular calling.

People profess to love their dogs, but love hardly seems to be enough. Or else love has many depths, and we only learn to truly love when we've watched our loved-ones die.

Sometimes, though, I wonder if it's fruitless to rail against death, for death is part of the contract. We all die, sooner or later.

When people say there is no God because a god would never allow us to suffer as we do, I suspect that death has a meaning greater than loss. I suspect that, when faced with the death of those we love, we are presented with a choice. We can choose to love more, to expand, or we can choose to contract, to shut our hearts down. Therefore the gift of loss is entirely in our own hands; we can pluck its fruit or starve.

Sometimes I wonder if my obsession with death boils down to the day Oliver died. Maybe I am trying to re-write history or, as has been suggested, to find someone to blame?

But then I am not a fool. I know that Oliver's body is gone and that blame is useless folly.

Maybe it's this simple: maybe the child in me believes that if everyone knows the truth, we will stop over-vaccinating our dogs, and we will stop over-vaccinating the children, and they won't die of vaccine-induced illness, and suffering will be alleviated.

I believe that if you can think it, then it can happen.

Or perhaps, as the poet Rainer Maria Rilke wrote, "All the dragons in our lives are princesses who are waiting to see us act, just once, with beauty and courage. Perhaps everything that frightens us is, in its deepest essence, something helpless that wants our love."

Chapter 4

Nightmares

So on Monday, the 2nd of September 1991, John woke me up and told me that Oliver couldn't walk. His back legs were paralysed. I went straight downstairs to see him, and he moved the front part of his body towards me and I stroked him and felt a terrible feeling in my stomach. Chappie, Sophie and Prudence were keeping out of the room, walking past the open door but not coming inside.

We made a stretcher of some blankets and took Ollie straight to the vet. I have told this story many times before, and made many people cry, and I don't want to make anyone cry again. Suffice to say that Oliver died at the vet's that day, and John and I brought him home and buried him in our back garden.

Chappie cried when we put Ollie in the ground and for months afterwards he would go outside and sit on his grave and howl. My dogs are always doing and saying things to demonstrate that they are people, too.

I just couldn't stop crying. For weeks, all I could do was cry. I wasn't expecting to lose a four-year-old dog, my darling little boy. I hadn't made any preparations for him being there and then not being there.

I think I lost some clients when Ollie died. My eyes were red raw and I'd be sitting in meetings with managing directors, acting the part of a public relations consultant while I was nothing but pain inside. Once I sat in a client's reception crying, waiting to go into a meeting. "That's not very professional," I hear the idiot say. I think I was having a meltdown.

I telephoned the Samaritans one night when I couldn't sleep, and talked about Oliver and how he had died. The Samaritan asked where my husband was, and I told her he was asleep in bed, and she asked if everything was alright with my marriage, which I found insulting at the time, but pretty insightful in retrospect.

I wanted to know about the grief process; I find it easier to cope when I understand what's going on. So I telephoned a bereavement helpline and explained that my dog had died, and the woman on the helpline was disgusted that I should be upset about a dog dying when children, who are more important, die. So I put the phone down and cried on my own.

Oliver had many friends who mourned his passing, though. We lived in a small village, and practically every child in the village came to play with the dogs. Three of them in particular, Charlotte, Joanna and Julia, seemed to spend more time in our house than they did in their own. They'd get home from school, rush in and get changed, and then run up to our house. They loved the dogs, and they loved me, and I loved them.

For years, Charlotte, Joanna and Julia would come to my house after school, and every Saturday morning they'd clean the house from top to bottom, which was a source of constant amazement to me. I hadn't asked them to do it; they seemed to enjoy doing it. They'd have sleep-overs with the dogs, camping out in my sitting room, making beds out of sofas and cushions and sleeping bags. I will never forget the look of joy on Oliver's face, and later Samson's, as they bedded down with the children. These days we live in the middle of a field in the middle of nowhere, and I wish I could buy some children for the dogs to play with.

Sometimes we'd take the girls to the local park and play rounders, with Oliver invariably stealing the ball and running off, much to everyone's amusement. Sometimes we'd have grass fights, or I'd take them to the theatre or for their first trip on a train. Or they'd invite me to their school nativity plays and village fetes, or teach me how to bake cakes – something I've avoided getting into because I would only eat them.

I used to wait for their mothers to get angry with me for taking their children away, but they never did. I'm grateful to them. I watched the girls grow and change over the years into beautiful teenagers, until we lost the house and had to leave the village. Today they are mothers with their own children and their own dogs.

A few days after Oliver died and I was walking my three dogs down to the park, some of the village children drove by with their mother. They put their heads out of the car window and waived, and Alison asked where Ollie was, and I started sobbing in the street. "Oh poor Catherine," a little child said with all the compassion of an ancient soul.

I'm the sort of person who, when confronted with a problem, goes looking for a solution. But with death there is no solution. There's no-one to complain to or beg. You can't bring a dead person back to life. You just have to find a way to cope with it.

I don't like unanswered questions. I need to know what is happening, and why it's happening, so I can deal with life. If I know the truth, then I can try to change the way I do things so it doesn't happen again. So every time I met a new vet, I'd ask them why Oliver had died when he was only four years old. All they would do was um and ah, and no-one would give me a reason.

And then my other dogs started to get sick. Just when you think you can't take any more, you take some more. The record producer David Briggs used to say, "Life is a shit sandwich. Eat it or starve," and I think that just about sums it up. Watching the ones you love suffer and die is only bearable because you have no other choice. Eat it or starve.

Only a month or two before Ollie died, we had taken the dogs to see Roy and Pat Bartlett who had bred Sophie, Ollie and Pru. Roy made a special point of congratulating us on how well they looked. He went out of his way to praise us for their health. I was really proud.

Then Ollie died, and Sophie took to her bed and refused to get out. She was bad-tempered and unhappy. I took her to the vet many times. First he said she had strained a muscle, and told us to rest her for a couple of weeks. Then he said she had a spinal misalignment; he wanted to anaesthetise her and manipulate her spine. But something inside me didn't trust his diagnosis, and I didn't like the thought of him putting her out and messing with her spine. I'd had my own back problems and knew enough to know that doctors and vets are specialists in drugs and surgery, and chiropractors are specialists in spines.

Eventually we ended up at the Royal Veterinary College where a hotshot took Sophie outside and watched her walk around. He said she had arthritis in her front paws. She was only six. I thought a six year old dog was too young to be suffering from an old person's disease.

The solution was to put Sophie under anaesthetic and cut her front claws off, and give her non-steroidal anti-inflammatories, known in the trade as NSAIDs. They didn't help. They just made her miserable and she still refused to get out of bed.

Then an old friend said to me: "Why don't you try homeopathy dear?" This was Margaret Copley. Margaret lived to the age of 103. She was a vegetarian, a spiritualist, an animal lover, and she used homeopathy. Margaret introduced me to the writings of White Eagle. Margaret was a good friend. Although I miss her now, I know she must have had a great welcome on the other side.

But I had never heard of the word, 'homeopathy'. I had no idea what it was. So Margaret explained and suggested I go to a local health shop where there would be a book outlining the different homeopathic remedies. "Look up arthritis, and choose the remedy that seems to suit Sophie best," she said.

So I did. I picked out Bryonia, because Sophie seemed to get worse when she exercised. I gave her one dose, and she jumped out of bed and started smiling and laughing and dancing. It was thrilling to see the transformation.

I've since discovered that some people say homeopathy doesn't work, and that if anyone responds to it, it's due to the placebo effect. Bearing in mind I had no knowledge or back story regarding homeopathy, and no particular bias in favour of, or against, conventional or alternative healing systems, and bearing in mind I had just as much faith in the NSAIDs as I had in the homeopathic remedy, I can't see how my expectations, such as they were, could have affected Sophie and created the placebo effect. I was incredibly surprised when Bryonia worked so powerfully.

Then Chappie started walking like a cripple, with his back arched like a capital 'A'. The vet advised lead walking and then, after knocking him out for an x-ray, concluded that he had hip dysplasia. He said Chappie was too old for an operation, and too big. All he could offer were NSAIDs which didn't work. Chappie was in pain.

Let me tell you, I was a Gold Star Client at that veterinary practice. We'd be there at least every two weeks with one problem or another – hot spots, limps, sickness and diarrhoea, itchy ears, and lately more serious problems. The red carpet was royally rolled out every time we visited. In fact, I think the vet thought I fancied him, we were there that often.

On one of my many visits with Chappie we saw a young locum who tentatively suggested that we try homeopathy. She told me she could arrange a referral to a homeopathic vet. I agreed, bearing in mind the miracle we had witnessed with Sophie.

At which point all hell broke loose.

First I got a phone call from the senior vet – the one who, I'm sorry to point out, was forever misdiagnosing my dogs' problems. He said that homeopathy was totally unscientific, and we might as well take Chappie on a trip to Lourdes or take him to kiss the Blarney Stone. Then he sent a letter to repeat the same message, adding that he would have nothing to do with it, and would not dialogue with a homeopathic vet. He said that the rejection of homeopathy was written into his practice constitution, which made me feel sorry for the locum who had mentioned it.

At the time, I was blissfully unaware of the passionate stand-off between conventional and alternative healing systems, and I was somewhat blown away by the strength of my vet's opposition. We had been good clients for around eight years and we had never once disagreed or argued. But the NSAIDs weren't helping Chappie, and I wanted to see if anything else would. Reluctantly I changed vets, hoping for a referral to a homeopath.

The new vet was a trained radiologist, which was lucky because my previous vet wouldn't release Chappie's x-rays. Turns out that x-rays fall under photographic copyright law. I was sad that my vet would rather have Chappie risk another anaesthetic than let the x-rays go. But it turned out that Chappie didn't actually have hip dysplasia, which was good to know.

My new vet said that Chappie had excellent hips for a nine-year-old Golden Retriever. He said that Chaps had ruptured his cruciate ligaments and that he was too big and too old for an operation. All he could offer were NSAIDs which, he said, would kill my boy quicker than any cruciate problem. So once again I asked to be referred to a homeopathic vet. My new vet agreed to do this, although he pointed out to me with his tongue firmly in his cheek that no pill – homeopathic or otherwise – was going to magically repair a severed ligament.

Chapter 5

The spirit lives on

When Oliver died, I went out to find him again. You do things like this when you believe reincarnation to be a logical possibility and have read accounts of near death experiences. I was looking particularly for Oliver himself or, if that were not possible, for a dog with his wonderful personality.

Oliver was the son of Hank, and Hank was the son of Nortonwood Munro, and all three dogs had the same glorious personality traits. I found it fascinating to discover through dogs that a person's personality may not be all their own, but something that can be largely inherited.

I put calls into Golden Retriever breeders, looking for the famous Munro in their puppies' pedigrees. Eventually I was put in touch with John Seymour who had bred a litter from a Golden Retriever who had been sold by the Nortonwood kennel because she'd broken a tooth and was no longer good for showing. She got her own back for her abandonment by miraculously re-growing a new tooth.

The litter's father was Best of Breed at Crufts, and the star of a pet food advertisement. His owner confirmed to me that he fed Pedigree Chum regularly, "once a year", enabling him in good conscience to take the money. In the ad, Sebastian was shown leaping and bounding through water cascading over rocks. I fell in love with him on TV, he was so rugged and handsome.

So eventually the day came when Samson came home with us. He was a little rascal, hyperactive and into everything. Late one night, when I was exhausted from puppy sleep-deprivation and waiting for Sammie to calm down so we could all go to bed, Prudence took matters into her own hands. I was raising Sammie using positive reinforcement, so admonishing the little sod was out of the question. So Prudence went to him and barked in his face and told him to shut up, and he did.

Dogs can teach you a lot, but sometimes it's better to leave it to them. Prudence had a natural grace; she knew when to speak out and when to woo.

Once, when Samson was a little older and Chappie was wobbling about with uncertain gait, I was sitting on a bench that looked over the field they were playing in and saw a remarkable scene unfold.

I could see the young Samson deciding that it would be great fun to charge into Chappie and perhaps knock him over, and I saw Prudence observing what Sammie was about to do. She dashed in between them and beguiled Sam, inviting him to play, and he did. Then, a little later, he got it into his head again that it would be fun to bash into Chappie. For a second time, Prudence stepped in and diverted his attention with the offer of play. And then a third time, Sammie grinned and dashed towards Chappie, and Prudence distracted Sammie once more. Before then, I had no idea that Prudence was a diplomat.

The day after Samson's second puppy shot, we found him in the back garden with paralysed rear legs. I panicked, fearing that what had happened to Oliver was now happening to Sam. I phoned the vet. He told me to give Sam a Paracetamol, which I didn't know at the time could be toxic to dogs. But Samson recovered, thank God. In those days I didn't know what vaccines could do, so we made no connection and carried on.

At around this time I took myself to a spiritualist church. I was still grieving for Oliver – in fact I would be grieving for Oliver for many years to come. Samson was adorable, but even if he *was* a reincarnation of Oliver, and I wasn't sure he was, he was still only a puppy and I was still grieving. I didn't realise that it can take some time before the bond appears between a dog and his human.

So I walked into the spiritualist church for the first time. I'd never been there before, and no-one knew me. The medium at the front went around the room telling people that their Auntie Doris or Uncle Arthur was there, and then he came to me.

"I have a dog here," he said. My heart began to pound in my chest. "He's licking my ear and grabbing my arm in his mouth."

Oliver used to do that.

"You have a new puppy," he said. "I've been asked to tell you that the puppy isn't the one I have here. You must allow him to have his own personality."

So I went home and allowed Samson to have his own personality, and he grew into the most wonderful dog in the world.

Chapter 6

Dear Prudence

Christopher Day operates a homeopathic veterinary practice from his beautiful old Cotswold home near Oxfordshire. He is one of the longest-serving homeopathic vets in the UK; he is also widely respected by the homeopathic veterinary fraternity around the world. I didn't know this when we took Chappie to see him. Nor was I aware of his integrity and courage.

Chris gave us well over an hour of his time, asking questions about Chappie – his personality, his preferences, his diet, his vaccination history, his lifestyle. Chris's loving concern extended to us, too, as he asked us about our own diet and lifestyle. He gave Chappie acupuncture and some homeopathic remedies for us to take home.

Chappie walked out of the consulting room and, for the first time in months, he cocked his leg. John and I thought it was a pretty spectacular result – one that conventional veterinary medicine had been unable to achieve over a period of months.

Chris also introduced us to a radionics practitioner called Chrissie Mason, and advised us to get a hair analysis done, and he referred us to Dana Green, a McTimoney chiropractor. Dana, incidentally, discovered that Chappie's hips were misaligned and this was pushing his spine into an S curve. Vets aren't trained to be aware of the spine to the degree that chiropractors or osteopaths are. As I have already said, they are specialists in drugs and surgery. Chiropractors, on the other hand, spend years studying the spine before they are allowed to practice. It is, though, illegal for a chiropractor to treat an animal without a vet first saying they can – irrespective of their hard-won qualifications. This seems wrong and imbalanced to me.

Whilst with Chris Day, as I had done for the previous two years, I described what had happened to Oliver, and asked the vet in front of me why my darling might have died. Chris asked when Ollie died in relation to being vaccinated, and I told him. Oliver had been vaccinated towards the end of June, and he died at the beginning of September.

Chris said: "It sounds like a classic vaccine reaction to me. In my experience in practice, where the start date of an illness is known, 80% begin within three months of a vaccine event."

Chris then took us to his reception area and introduced us to some of his clients. One was a lady visiting with her dog who, they said, had vaccine-induced skin problems. Another was a breeder who no longer vaccinated. "My dogs are show dogs," she said. "They come everywhere with me to shows. I give them the homeopathic nosode instead of vaccinating, and they are incredibly healthy."

Chris asked me to keep it to myself, since the very mention of vaccine damage by a vet could get him into serious trouble at the time.

I took Chris Day's word about vaccine damage at face value, with considerable interest, but turned my attention to helping Sophie with her arthritis, and Chappie with his cruciate damage. I was also writing my first book.

As you might suspect, and like many seminal moments in the journey of life, the book was prompted by pain. The day after Oliver died, the local vicar sent out a letter to all the households in the village. It was incredibly bad timing. The letter said that people were complaining about dog poo in the park, and unless owners cleared up after their dogs, the dogs would be banned. Now this is all perfectly reasonable but, at the time, picking up wasn't something dog owners did. I couldn't see some of my neighbours complying with this edict, which meant that there would be nowhere to walk the dogs. We lived in Northamptonshire, and most of the fields were taken up with arable crops. Dogs and their owners had to share space with sportsmen and children.

When a human child dies, everyone gets to know about it. Bereaved parents will take time off work and everyone will understand. There will be a funeral, and flowers, and loving sympathy. The vicar certainly wouldn't pass a note through the grieving parents' door, complaining about generalised vandalism perpetrated by nameless children, and threatening banishment for their deceased boy.

The letter was a real blow. My little boy had died and no-one seemed to care. To them, he was just a dog. I took it very personally. I think that grief can sometimes unhinge you – but if you're only grieving for a dog it's hard for people to understand.

Added to this, my next door neighbour, who was a born-again Christian, didn't seem to notice that Oliver had died. Every day, for months, I and three dogs would walk past her door, and nothing was said about my missing friend. I was so angry with her. I realised, of course, that she had taken on the guise of God's representative, and that my anger was really anger at God. In the end I had to knock on her door and tell her that Ollie had died, just so I could walk past her house without wondering if she had noticed that a very special being had gone.

I was angry with the vicar, too, but I try to channel my anger into a positive force. So I wrote and asked if the Parish Council would consider installing a bin for dog waste, plus a pooper scooper on a stick. I said that if these were provided, I would personally pick up everyone's dog poo whilst walking in the park with my own dogs. This would get round the fact that some of the dog owners in the village wouldn't dream of doing it.

The aim of the book I was writing – in direct response to my neighbours' indifference to Ollie's death and the vicar's letter – was to demonstrate that dogs, Golden Retrievers in particular but not limited to Goldens, do a great deal to enrich human life, and that human beings owe the dogs a huge debt of gratitude.

I had no business spending time writing this love story for Oliver, by the way. I should have been rebuilding my PR business after the recession, but my heart overruled my head and my attention turned to the dogs. John, not realising at the time that few authors make a living out of writing books, gave me his blessing. I contacted Golden owners around the world and asked them to share their experiences of dogs who had filled their lives with joy. The result was *The Golden Retriever Companion, a chronicle of joy*. Through it, I met many wonderful people.

Before the book was finished, I was beginning to worry about Prudence who had started lagging behind on walks. John told me it was my imagination and not to be so bloody stupid, but my concerns increased and I took her to the vet. I couldn't be specific, but I told him that she laid down like a beached whale, which the vet thought was amusing. We chuckled about it. But he took some blood and sent it off for analysis, then phoned me with the results, telling me that Prudence had acute leukaemia. "If she was a human," he said, "she'd need a bone marrow transplant. As it is, she has less than two months to live."

"Don't worry," I said cheerily. "We'll treat her homeopathically."

I could hear the vet's puzzled silence on the other end of the phone. I have always been an optimist but, perhaps more saliently and like many of us, I can tend to numb out when bad things happen. Quite often it will take a while before I react to things that matter a lot to me. My first reaction is to keep calm whilst grasping onto a solution.

I was alone in the house when the vet called to give me the results, and a White Eagle book had just arrived in the post from Margaret Copley. I sat down and read it while the dogs played around me, trying to quell the dread that was coursing through my body. Then I took the dogs out to a local country park and watched my little Prudence playing around a log, digging up clumps of grass, her eyes sparkling with joy, while I sat on the log and silently cried, lost and in despair.

I think there's a good chance that Prudence picked up on my emotional state after that, because she went downhill very fast. We enlisted the support of Christopher Day and Chrissie Mason; we did everything we could for her. I was administering homeopathic remedies around the clock, and John and I took it in turns staying awake through the night so we could be with her.

Dog ownership isn't supposed to be like this. I cannot imagine that our ancestors would have kept dogs if they were constantly sick, or died so young and in such pain. A dog is programmed to make you love him and, if you have a heart, you surely will. Something is going wrong with the modern dog. We are doing something wrong. We are letting the dogs down.

Chris Day recommended an organic diet for Pru but, in those days, organic food wasn't easy to find. John travelled across three different counties to get organic produce for her and we offered it up lovingly, only to find that she had no appetite.

The last month of Pru's life was distressing, and tender. I was devastated yet honoured to hold her hand as she made the transition. We went for walks together, just the two of us, and she was so grateful. She took me, with determination, to all the houses inhabited by the children who were her friends. They had always come to us, but they'd stopped coming, probably as a mark of respect for Pru, or possibly because it was hard for them to see her suffering and our sorrow. But somehow Prudence knew where they lived.

I was filled with awe when Prudence led me into the heart of the village. She took me through the various streets and straight up the garden paths to the houses where her young friends lived, never once wavering. She knew precisely where she was going, even though she'd never been to their houses before. She knew it was time to say goodbye to her dear young friends.

She did something else, which took me years to understand. Prudence used to take me to a particular neighbour's house and stand outside, staring in. These neighbours had two cats, and somehow I felt that she was telling me that her leukaemia was connected to cats. When, years later, I discovered that several brands of distemper vaccines in the UK are contaminated with a feline retrovirus (and still are), theoretically capable of causing cancer and leukaemia, Prudence's pointed message fell into place. I do believe that Prudence was a highly spiritual being, and I do believe that she had access to a field of knowing, just as dogs are able to detect the presence of cancer in humans, or know when they're about to have an epileptic fit.

I washed Prudence and kept her clean, and the tenderness we shared grew. She was so grateful, and so loving. It was hard watching her struggle to survive, but we had so much hope that we might save her. Then, one night, she asked to be carried upstairs to sleep on the bed with me. I covered her in a blanket and held her, and I noticed that her paws were cold. I knew then that we had lost the battle.

So I told my beautiful friend that I loved her, and what a good girl she was, and I gave Prudence my permission to go, which she was waiting for. She thanked me and told me that she loved me. And then she was gone before the vet had time to arrive.

We buried Prudence in the garden; she was surrounded by snowdrops. I remember feeling lonely and lost, and most of all defeated. Some of my own life force had departed with my darling little girl.

Chapter 7
Gambling away God's gifts

My Golden Retriever book was published shortly after Prudence died. Because of it, a Golden Retriever lover in America called Susan Rezy sent me a scientific paper by a vet and researcher called Dr W Jean Dodds. The paper read like my life story or, more pertinently, my dogs' death and suffering stories. It described how there had been an increase in cancers of the blood such as lymphoma and leukaemia, and allergic and immune-mediated diseases such as arthritis and thyroid disease, since the introduction of MLV (modified live virus) vaccines.

One memory will always haunt me. The last time I took Prudence for a booster, shortly before she died, she looked at the vet coming at her with a needle and her eyes rolled in their sockets and she climbed up onto my back, trying to get away from the needle. I said: "It's alright darling, it's good for you," and the vet went ahead. How I wish now that I had listened to Prudence and respected her right to say no to that shot.

Later, when sharing information about the causes of canine ill health made people angry with me, the picture of Prudence dying on my bed would replay like a video recording in my head, giving me the determination to carry on.

I don't think dog owners appreciate what's in store for them when they get their first dog. We get a puppy or an older rescue dog, and pretty soon many of us are dealing with sickness and pain, and vets and horrendous vet bills.

We pay for this, and they give us that.

People mistakenly believe that love is a warm fuzzy feeling, all happiness and joy. But the ways of love also lead you to pain and ultimately to growth. Love takes your attention from the outside world, from the superficial, and callously hews a path to the core of your being where fortitude and determination reside. Pain and suffering bring wisdom.

Prudence taught me that animals have far more wisdom than we human beings can possibly appreciate. I will be accused of anthropomorphising, I know. But I stand my ground on this.

We humans are so dense. Because animals don't have the apparatus to speak as we do, we have run away with the erroneous belief that they have nothing worth hearing. We are merciless control freaks, believing we know best. We profess to love the animals while we stand with our eyes closed and our fingers in our ears, shouting 'la la la'. And even if we know that animals are more than society believes they are, we bow down in silence until a scientist tells us we can speak.

Prudence told me that she didn't want that vaccine, and in my arrogance I overruled her decision. I listened, instead, to the words that human beings have constructed to take us away from truth.

Human language was invented as a sales tool. It rarely has anything to do with truth.

Truth resides in the unspoken.

Animals are superior to humans because they didn't invent sales spiel, cunningly disguised as language.

Prudence didn't even need that vaccine. The multi-billion pet vaccine industry needed her to have that vaccine. The veterinary industry needed her to have that vaccine; it is no longer a profession, it's a trade. By the age of six, Prudence was already immune to viral disease. She was probably immune from her puppy shots.

Prudence was killed by cunning words – words that I gave too much credence, and which made me think I knew better than her.

I can't help wondering if Oliver and Prudence knew what they were letting themselves in for when they came to live with me. I can't help believing that animals, like humans, have a mission when they come to the earth; a mission – an assignment – that they agree to fulfil before they incarnate.

Did Oliver and Prudence volunteer to die as they did and, in doing so, turn me into a lioness, fighting for the survival of a species?

If so, when Prudence rolled her eyes in her sockets and climbed up on my back trying to get away from that vaccine, did she share the same emotion as Christ, as his disciples slept and he awaited his crucifixion? Did Prudence ask me, her god on earth, whether, if it be possible, this cup might pass from her?

Love is recklessness, not reason.
Reason seeks a profit.
Love comes on strong, consuming herself, unabashed.
Yet in the midst of suffering,
Love proceeds like a millstone,
hard-surfaced and straight forward.
Having died to self-interest;
She risks everything and asks for nothing.
Love gambles away every gift God bestows.

Rumi

In the end, Prudence submitted to my will, giving witness to the thousand tiny acts of love our dogs shower upon us every day. She gambled away every gift God bestowed to have me sitting here now, writing this for you.

Chapter 8
Hope and healing

Under the care of the homeopathic vet Christopher Day and the radionics practitioner Chrissie Mason, Chappie began to recover from his cruciate ligament damage. His mobility improved as each week passed.

As Jean Dodds stated, vaccines can cause autoimmune diseases including thyroid disease, and Chappie had it. Cruciate ligament injury is one of the many features of thyroid disease.

It is very hard to watch someone who loves to run unable to do so. It is hard to watch your loved-ones suffer.

Of course, neither homeopathy nor acupuncture, and not even NSAIDs are going to repair a broken cruciate ligament. If someone cuts a piece of elastic with scissors, you have to sew it back together again or replace it, which is what a cruciate ligament operation essentially does. Without the operation (which can be successful but can also fail), you're waiting for scar tissue to build up between the knee joints so that it cushions the bones as they rub together. Acupuncture, meanwhile, helps reduce the pain, and homeopathy, if the practitioner is skilful, speeds the healing process.

More importantly, homeopathy, it is said, goes underneath the presenting dis-ease and energetically sets in motion a deep healing process of the whole being: of that which caused the thyroid disease in the first place.

Chrissie Mason is an amazing lady; we've become good friends over the years. In those early days before the internet was available, we spoke on the phone or exchanged faxes almost on a daily basis. Chrissie had practiced radionics and homeopathy for many years with her husband Keith. Keith Mason achieved considerable respectability as an author and valued adjunct to a conventional medical practice. Chrissie's respectability came from the fact (amongst other things) that her clients included the British royal family, most notably working as a consultant for the late Queen Mother's animals.

Chrissie educated me greatly as to the extent of vaccine damage in animals. She works with horses all over the world, and dogs, too. It broke her heart to be fixing – or trying to fix – vaccine damage day in and day out.

Chrissie also raised the issue of animals, especially dogs, picking up and carrying their owners' emotional stresses. "Dog owners have no idea how much of their stress their dogs pick up," she told me. "Quite often they throw their arms around their dogs and cry their eyes out, not realising that the dog is soaking all that energy up. Sometimes," she said, "it becomes too much for the dog, and the end result is illness and sometimes even death."

Hilary Jupp, an amazing medical intuitive and homeopath, said much the same thing to me, but she pointed directly at me and my own stresses. Hilary told me many times that I needed to be on my List of People Who Matter, and not just *on* the list, but at the top of it. "If you don't care for yourself," she said, "then your dogs will try to help you and take your emotions on. If you want them to be healthy, you have to matter too."

These days, having put that advice into practice, I tell other dog owners much the same thing.

I found it hard to know how to matter, though. It was like telling a dog lover to prefer motorbikes. There were no frames of reference for me to go from. But I did have my dogs telling me that I was more beautiful than I could possibly know. And I have had many opportunities to learn about healing and growth for myself in the process of helping others.

One day, a few months into his treatment, at a time when we were excited at Chappie's progress, he started to limp again. I sent a fax to Chrissie, asking her to conduct another radionics analysis. She faxed back promptly: "Don't worry, it's not his cruciate," she said. "He's dislocated the third digit on his back left paw."

The next day we were booked in to see Christopher Day, so I asked him to check Chappie's paw. Sure enough, the third digit on his back left paw was dislocated, and Chris pulled it back into position. For those who require scientific proof, it must seem an unbelievable coincidence that Chrissie got it right.

Radionics uses a system of dowsing, asking questions against many detailed charts, to ascertain the causes of disease, whether it be physical, mental or emotional. Once cause has been established, the practitioner places a 'witness' (usually a hair or saliva sample) onto an electronic radionics 'box', which pulses out the correct remedy for the problem in energetic, vibrational, form.

Radionics is another of those therapies, like homeopathy, which appears to have no basis when you're looking at it from a Newtonian standpoint, although it does have a basis if you're looking at it in relation to quantum physics: $E = MC^2$ (mass is a property of all energy; energy is a property of all mass). In other words, everything that is physical has its energetic counterpart. We are energy (or spirit) long before we are physical. And, because energy has no hard edges, it has no barriers to cross. "There's no hard line in the Cosmic mind," as the genius Jon Anderson sang. Therefore you can send energy to someone across vast distances using the DNA of their hair as a witness.

For the scientifically inclined, it begins to make sense when you realise that quantum physicists have discovered that there is no physical substance inside atoms. The subunits that comprise atoms are made of powerful invisible energy vortices, and not tangible matter. Matter is energy; it's not physical. Physicality is an illusion.

To quote Bruce Lipton PhD, "Atoms are made out of vortices of energy. That means, molecules, which are made up of atoms, are vortices of energy as well; so cells, which are made up of molecules, are also vortices of energy; and finally, human beings, each of whom is made up of trillions of cells, are … vortices of energy. It is true that we look as if we are physical, but it is an illusion, a trick of the light – we are all energy!"

'Nonlocality' is another precept within quantum physics. Einstein called this 'spooky action at a distance'. Nonlocality tells us that once a quantum particle interacts with another particle, no matter how many miles apart, their mechanical states remain coupled. When the polarity or rotation of one particle's spin changes, the polarity or rotation of its twin changes simultaneously in the opposite direction – irrespective of how far they are away from one-another.

So the non-material matter represented by Chappie's hair sample could, if exposed to appropriate energies through Chrissie's ministrations in Hampshire, affect the non-material energies of Chappie's body in Northamptonshire. And it must be borne in mind that we are energy before we are matter, and that within energy lies the creative principle; therefore energy therapies are acting at the causal level.

Chrissie demonstrated that she was able to ascertain what was going on in Chappie's body, despite being a hundred or so miles away, and she was able to send energetic pulses to my dogs, and I was able to witness the dogs responding.

And yet, on a boringly frequent basis, a stranger will email me out of the blue to tell me how unscientific homeopathy is, and how I need to drop it if I want to be taken seriously.

This was, however, a time of rapid learning for me. I had entered a new world. Every morning, when I gave Chappie his homeopathic powder, 'Ferrum Phos' (which was allegedly religious mumbo jumbo), I could see him being instantly energised. It was like he clapped his hands and said, "Right, let's get on with the day."

Sophie's arthritis was also improving, and I was making my way through a range of alternative arthritis remedies to see if I could help her further. I was learning about herbs and nutritional supplements, and about arthritis itself. I'd also stumbled across the Bach flower remedies, and was using them on myself and my loved-ones, and witnessing what appeared to be very interesting results.

Because my dogs were teaching me how to help them, through their responses, neighbours started asking me for health advice. Old Charlie came to me with gout and I recommended Potter's Tabritis, a herbal blend for gout which had helped Sophie. His gout disappeared and he told me that I was better than any doctor.

But if you go to a doctor, he or she will just give you drugs, with side-effects, to numb the pain. Conventional medicine doesn't look for cause; it looks for drugs to hide the symptoms. I was so grateful to have found a way out of that system – it gave me hope for my dogs rather than a future of pain and degeneration.

What an amazing time that was in my life. By this time, rather than rebuild my PR consultancy, I had decided to put myself out as a copywriter for other consultancies. It brought in much-needed income whilst allowing me a break from the stresses of running a PR consultancy. It also gave me time, and funded my ability, to ask questions about canine health.

One of my clients was a London-based PR consultancy and the MD and I soon realised that we had a mutual love of dogs. I mentioned to her about immune-mediated and allergic diseases being caused by annual vaccines, and she replied that her mother, Elvira Vockrodt, was also questioning vaccine damage in dogs. I got in touch with Elvira, and Elvira put me in touch with Sally Cronk.

Sally had lost her dog Sadie to autoimmune haemolytic anaemia, which had left her devastated. Sally was raising funds so that the Royal Veterinary College could research the disease. Not much was known about it in those days, or so we were told. Sally put me in touch with other dog lovers whose dogs had died suddenly after their vaccines, and who were also asking questions about vaccine damage.

Through Sally I met Leslie Seymour, an opera singer whose dog had also died of autoimmune haemolytic anaemia. This disease is so brutal that it often has the dogs' owners seeking counselling and being put on anti-depressants. Leslie had been trying to get his life back on track by exploring the link between this disease and recent vaccination.

I also established contact with Hylda Reynolds whose Daschund had become very ill after his shot, and June Goose, who had bred puppies who became ill shortly after they were vaccinated. Both June and Hylda had written to the dog press, asking for dog owners with similar stories about vaccine damage to contact them.

Meanwhile, my Golden Retriever book had been reviewed by an Australian dog magazine and the editor sent me a copy. Inside was an article written by an Australian vet called Ian Billinghurst entitled 'Raw Meaty Bones'. Dr Billinghurst was talking about processed pet food versus raw meaty bones for dogs. He was saying how healthy dogs were if they were given the food that had kept the species alive for millions of years. As I read it, a lightbulb went on in my head.

Prudence was overweight, but she was always hungry. I realised from this article that I had been slowly starving my dogs to death with processed pet food. I sent off to Australia and bought Ian Billinghurst's book, aptly titled: *'Give Your Dog a Bone'*.

Pretty soon I had switched my dogs from processed pet food to raw meaty bones, meat, and vegetables. They were now having chicken wings in the morning, and meat and vegetables in the evening.

It's probable that we were the first people outside of Australia who were feeding raw chicken wings to our dogs, and we were nervous about doing it. John used to take the wings outside and bash them with a meat tenderiser to break the bones up. We'd heard so many stories about dogs being harmed by bones. But Ian Billinghurst reasoned that bones are a dog's natural diet – it's when they're cooked that they become brittle and dangerous, so we carried on. Besides, our dogs were sick and dying around us – by taking what Billinghurst said on board, we felt we had more to gain than we had to lose.

The first time Gwinnie, who we rescued after Prudence died, ate chicken wings, she was immediately sick. This is a relatively common response to a dog's first chicken wing, but because we didn't know this and John was unable to tolerate discomfort, he lashed out at me, fearing for Gwinnie's life, and punched me in the mouth. Although my lips were swollen and sore for days, I managed to keep my teeth and we persevered with the raw diet. Within two months, our vet bills had dropped by 65% and our dogs became more vibrant and less sickly.

Meanwhile, a growing group of us began to copy and post scientific studies to one-another in the mail. These scientific papers had one thing in common: they all talked about the adverse effects of vaccines on dogs. Stunningly – to our mutual outrage – we learnt that independent academics had established that we don't need to risk vaccines every year. Almost without exception, dogs were immune to viral disease from their puppy shots. For life.

Chapter 9
Money stalks

As marketing and PR consultants, John and I knew that there was a reason why vets would advocate annual shots when they weren't necessary, and processed pet food when it was causing diseases of malnutrition in our dogs. It was a no-brainer. Essentially, wealthy corporations seek to influence any areas that affect sales. This was and is standard practice. We ourselves had advised clients to establish relationships with groups, institutions and individuals that might help them get product or services to market.

We didn't consider this to be a sinister practice; it was business. These days I have turned from gamekeeper to poacher. I cannot even watch the ads on TV.

We knew that veterinary colleges would be top of the list for pet food, veterinary pharmaceutical and vaccine companies to enlist as their unofficial sales force. They would, as a matter of course, offer sponsorship, research funding, and 'expertise' to colleges. Added to this – as we knew from our own academic clients – the government had charged academia with the task of actively seeking funding from commerce to augment government funding.

In June 1999, for example, the Royal Veterinary College offered a long list of sponsors on its website, including Ceiba-Geigy, Elanco, Hill's Pet Products, Hoechst Animal Health, Bayer, Dales Pharmaceuticals, Nestle, Pedigree Petfoods, SmithKline Beecham Animal Health, Spillers Foods, VetDrug, and others.

I wasn't naïve enough to think that the government encouraged academia to take money from industry merely to save government money. I had worked during the '80s for a London PR consultancy that was owned by members of our ruling classes. While I was there, I witnessed my boss offering corporate clients knighthoods in return for donations to a political party. We even had an MP on board as an advisor. There is a very well-oiled door swinging between corporations and the political elite, and I was part of the machine.

By giving money to academic establishments, corporations buy the ability to influence veterinary students, and perhaps even the curriculum. The same applies to medical teaching establishments.

So pet food companies undertake research projects, or pay academics to undertake research projects, to 'prove' that their brand of processed food generates health and wellbeing, and this could be filtered through to

41

veterinary students in order to influence their buying decisions whilst in practice. It didn't seem to matter that the research was, to use a technical term, 'crap'. Statistically, you just can't draw anything meaningful from 26 puppies being fed a particular brand for six weeks, although the pet food manufacturers managed to extrapolate claims for 'complete and balanced' and 'good for life' from such meaningless data. Importantly, no-one seemed to question their claims.

Today, pet food companies even pay the salaries of lecturers in nutrition within veterinary schools. The homeopathic vet Richard Allport calls this practice 'reprehensible'. How can vets learn the truth about nutrition if they are being taught by people who claim that their processed food is the best, whether it is or not? Or, indeed, that processed junk food of whatever variety is better than real food.

A business colleague enlightened me further on the subject of processed pet food. He had worked within the industry, and told me that he would never feed that stuff to a dog. The picture he painted of rendering plants was the pinnacle of disgusting.

One lady also told me that her husband had been sent into a rendering plant to do some electrical work and he was sick for weeks afterwards. The stink of these places can be smelt for miles around. Vets need to go on a tour of a rendering facility before they advise their clients to feed this stuff.

Once in practice, vets are regularly visited by sales reps. Apart from introducing new drugs, reps offer discounts and deals to vets: "Buy this vaccine and we'll discount this drug". The same applies to processed pet food brands, which are stocked by veterinary practices on the basis of margins offered to the veterinary practice, and also on research introduced by reps – research usually paid for by the drug or pet food company selling the drug or pet food.

Everything is about marketing. Individual processed pet food brands are stocked by vets in one country and touted as superior, whilst the same brand might be supermarket shelf fodder in another. This has very little to do with the wonders of the food itself, and everything to do with the amount of money thrown at its marketing, and which brand got there first.

As a massive American pet food recall in 2007 illustrated, most of the brands are made in the same factory and carry largely the same ingredients. Hundreds of brands, this recall revealed, contained the same melamine to boost 'protein', causing kidney damage and death in hundreds of dogs and cats.

Additionally, pharmaceutical, vaccine, and pet food companies host jollies for vets in practice. These might be in the form of dinners in the guise of educational events, and vets are awarded training points by the corporations for attending. These points are required by the veterinary bodies to 'prove' that the vet has continued with his education. There appears to be no quality control to ascertain whether industry sales jamborees are a valid form of further education.

Contrast this with accountants who must pass tests each year to show that they've remained current on tax laws. Where money is concerned, education becomes more serious. Lives, on the other hand, are – it seems – merely means to a financial end.

Overseas trips are not unheard of, either. One vet told me that he'd been on three skiing holidays with Intervet but, "it doesn't influence my buying decisions". Yes, right. Drug companies send vets on overseas trips out of the goodness of their hearts.

All of this is unethical, and liable to corruption. It's no different to the sugar industry sponsoring research to prove that sugar is good for you, or the tobacco industry paying for school trips. We just wouldn't let them get away with it – yet the pharmaceutical and pet food industries are able to do this sort of thing with very little, if any, government or legal censure. And if you think the rules are lax for human health, they are even less rigorous where animals are concerned, and particularly the animals who don't go into humans' mouths.

Even the animal charities are open to influence, with most, if not all of them, holding their hands out to big business. Believe me, as a former marketing and PR consultant, I can promise you that sponsorship is only given by large organisations to those who offer some form of reciprocal benefit, even if it's only being featured in a press release which gives kudos to the sponsoring corporation. At its worse, sponsorship is given to those individuals, charities or organisations that are amenable to control.

So far as I could see, this was the only reason why the major animal charities, and bodies such as the Kennel Club, have not spoken out and put a stop to annual vaccination. If they truly loved the animals, and looked at the science, over-vaccination would have ended decades ago.

So, knowing that this marketing pressure is placed upon vets, and the corruption within the pet products industry, John came up with what, at the time, seemed to be a brilliant idea. John had a Master's degree in systems analysis and operational research. We had conducted research and statistical analysis for many of the world's largest blue-chip companies, and we'd been handsomely paid for it. "Why don't we do some research into the causes of health and ill health in dogs," John said, "free from commercial bias?"

If I had the gift of foresight and knew what I was letting myself in for, I would have never gone down this path.

Chapter 10
Dangerous questions

We designed a massive research project that sought to gather and analyse the experiences of dog owners. In medical circles, this might be called 'results-based research'. We planned to ask every possible question relating to a dog's diet, lifestyle, veterinary treatments, vaccine history, stress levels, breed, age and health – even the rivers dogs swam in and the proximity of their houses to overhead power cables. In all, it turned into a 26-page questionnaire. And when we had the answers, John would analyse them and we would release the conclusions, and ... everyone would listen and alter how they raised their dogs, and people like us would no longer stand over the bodies of their dead dogs asking, "Why did nobody tell me?".

We estimated that it would take six months to complete the research, and then we'd go back to rebuilding our consultancy and living our own lives. I wrote to a number of veterinary colleges in the UK to enlist their support, receiving only one answer. I paraphrase, but we were essentially told to sod off, with the shocked and incredulous pronouncement that such a research project would cost at least £90,000.

I also wrote to some of the larger animal charities, and the Kennel Club, but received no replies.

Not to be deterred, I spoke to Beverley Cuddy, editor of *Dogs Today*. I knew Beverley as I'd written articles for this magazine on behalf of one of my PR clients. Beverley gave us her immediate support and agreed to launch the survey in her magazine.

Then John spoke to Beverley and put her back up, and it all fell apart. They really didn't like each other.

So I got in touch with Paula Shires, editor of another dog magazine. *Pet Dogs* had a circulation that was almost as high as *Dogs Today*, and it didn't hurt our cause that there was some rivalry between the two magazines.

Paula and I soon became firm friends. We shared the same birthday, loved the dogs, and enjoyed talking with one-another. Importantly, Paula was aware that she might lose advertising revenue if pet food companies didn't like the research we were doing, but she was prepared to put her magazine on the line to discover the truth.

Meanwhile, I continued to contact other dog lovers who were also asking questions about the poor state of dog health. Sally Cronk put me in touch with two women who were questioning why Cavalier King Charles

Spaniels were getting swollen heads after they were vaccinated, and so I wrote to them to tell them about our survey and see if we could support one-another.

I was out at a meeting when John received a call from Simon Parsons, editor of *Dog World*, a newspaper aimed at the showing world. The Cavalier women had contacted Simon to tell him about our research. I remember coming home and John telling me about the call, and saying, "Gosh, that's great – and we haven't even launched the project yet."

A week or so later, Pat Bartlett, who had bred Oliver, Prudence and Sophie, phoned. "You're in *Dog World*," she said.

"Oh really? Great," I replied.

"Have you seen it?" she asked.

"No," I replied.

"I'd better read it to you," she said. And she did.

I was standing in the hall, leaning against the wall with the phone in my hand as Pat read the article out, and my legs slowly gave way from under me as I slid to the floor. The heading of the article was that we were conducting a 'survey'. By putting the word 'survey' in quotes, the headline implied that there were dodgy dealings afoot. The main article implied that John and I were a couple of crooks, out to make tens of thousands of pounds from a so-called 'survey' into canine health.

In retrospect I can understand why this conclusion might have been reached. Firstly, who were we? We weren't involved in the dog world. We didn't show or breed or take part in obedience or agility. We had come out of nowhere to conduct a health survey. The dog world is very hierarchical and you can get into trouble if you step out of line. We had unwittingly stepped out of line.

Secondly, if we were to achieve the aims of the survey, to realise the desired statistical accuracy, we would need around 16,000 completed 26-page questionnaires, and someone had to pay for them to be printed and posted out. Our solution was to ask participants to donate £5 to support the research, in return for which we would send them the findings. In my naïve mind, dog lovers would jump at the chance to help improve canine health, and they would be as interested as I was in the findings. If we got our 16,000 completed questionnaires, the survey would be fully funded by dog lovers for the dogs, without the taint of commercial bias. Our problem was that, rather than go cap in hand to industry to fund our research, we had sought to remain free of industry influence. This was so unusual that it was met with mistrust.

Third, we had opened a post office box. This was because we had been warned by campaigners who'd heard about our research. These were people who were fighting vivisection, or who were questioning the damage to health caused by agrichemicals, or who were looking into electromagnetic radiation. They were telling us to be careful, because if our research threatened to damage big business income, 'they' would either seek to discredit us, or we would be bumped off. It seemed safer, or sensible, not to give 'them' straight access to our front door.

So in seeking to protect ourselves, we were a magnet for attack. Oh how ironic.

Chapter 11
Perilous path

Dr Tony Page, an anti-vivisection campaigner, telephoned to congratulate us for asking questions and conducting the survey, but also to warn us to be careful. He told me about Rachel Carson, author of the seminal book, *Silent Spring* in which she raised the alarm about agrichemicals. Rachel had been subjected to a massive PR campaign funded by the agrichemical industry. They used many dirty tricks to defame her in order to save their industry. "Be careful," Tony said. "If you're too successful in airing the truth about pet vaccination, they'll either seek to discredit you or bump you off."

Another campaigner sent an article from the *Guardian* about an organic farmer called Mark Purdy who asserted that BSE, otherwise known as mad cow disease, was caused by organophosphate poisoning. Purdy's experiences gave us cause for personal concern. His story was alarming.

In 1984, a government official told Purdey that he had to comply with a warble fly eradication order and treat his herd of Jersey cows with an organophosphate (OP) pesticide. Purdey refused, arguing that the suggested dose was far too high and, in any case, his natural treatment for warble fly was effective. Before they had a chance to prosecute him, he took the government to court and won his case. Finding himself front page news, he was swamped by letters from other farmers who suspected that OP treatments had ruined their own health.

Purdey noted that the BSE symptoms not only paralleled those of chronic organophosphate poisoning, but were exacerbated by changes in environmental conditions. He logged the incidence of BSE county by county, and compared it with the designated warble-fly treatment areas. He believed there was a correlation. In the June issue of *Dairy Farmer*, a columnist wrote, "It does seem that the greatest concentration of BSE cases are in what were the worst warble areas."

Over the years, Purdey – who, like me, was not a trained scientist – had a number of papers published in scientific journals, and he cultivated international contacts. One of these, a Japanese expert on OP pesticides, wrote to him saying, "your description [linking] mad cows to organophosphates is exactly true."

After the success of his court case against the government, Purdey became embroiled in many strange events. The legal fees had been considerable and he was forced to sell his farm and buy a cheaper one. At that point, a mysterious man purchased the adjoining property. "He'd been very pally with us before he moved in," Purdy said, "but his dress, his demeanour, even his way of talking, all struck me as odd. Then he moved in, and began making our lives hell. He'd argue about everything.

"He initiated problems with electricity cables running across his land. I learned he'd been telephoning the water board five days a week, trying to get us cut off. He had eight Doberman dogs that were chasing our cows. Some nights we couldn't sleep, wondering what was going to happen next."

On a day when he'd planned to go to the House of Commons, Purdey was barricaded in his house by one of the neighbour's vehicles. "It was parked across the front of the driveway. We couldn't get the lorry in to pick up the milk."

Later, the neighbour, who had an armoury of weapons, began firing towards the Purdey family. "He riddled the base of our milking parlour with shots. We called the police, and he said he'd been shooting vermin. The policeman who came out on that occasion was very friendly. 'You realise people are employed to behave in this way,' he told us. 'I can't give you any more clues, but you were the one who took the pesticide case to court, weren't you?'"

Eventually, they managed to sell their farm and buy another but the night before they were due to move in, it was burned to the ground.

"The local police said it was an electrical fault but no electricity was on at the time," Purdy said. The troublesome neighbour put his house on the market the week they moved out.

Purdey was in the process of starting up an organic milk service with Express Dairies when, one Christmas Eve, MAFF (now Defra) suddenly claimed that his milk – which had been in the premium Band A for hygiene – was tainted. Because of the holiday period, he was unable to get an independent assessment of its quality. By the time this had been obtained, Express Dairies had cancelled the order.

The steel cable which carried his telephone line was found to be severed on the day that a news story appeared about him. On the Saturday that the Press Association put out a news release about his meeting with MAFF officials, his phone went dead. Purdey says all this left him "financially and emotionally derelict".

Purdey's farm vet also died in a mysterious car crash, echoing the strange death of his solicitor, who unaccountably lost control of his car and hit a wall.

So the *Dog World* article about our research read like an expose: a couple working out of a post office box were charging £5 to take part in a 'survey', and the couple would make a significant amount of money out of it. No account was taken of the costs associated with such a survey. The article seemed designed to put people off taking part, and to discredit us, thereby killing the project dead.

I thanked Pat for phoning and telling me about the article and went upstairs and sat on the bed clutching a photo of Prudence, who had died only two months previously, and I sobbed my heart out. How could people twist what we were trying to do for the dogs in this way? I was shocked: I had never been accused of being a crook before, and it was painful, especially on top of the grief I still felt for Ollie and Pru.

John was furious with me, saying it was my fault for writing to the Cavalier women who had pitched the story to *Dog World* to tell them about our research plans. Ironically, it wasn't big business trying to discredit us, it was a couple of competitive dog women.

I sank just about as low as I could get. I couldn't sleep and my stomach, shoulders and heart physically ached. The doctor put me on anti-depressants; I remember walking out of the surgery with my shoulders in knots, struggling to breathe. But somehow I knew that pills weren't the answer. I threw them away.

I thought it necessary to phone Paula Shires and tell her about the *Dog World* piece, offering her the opportunity to change her mind about launching our research project in *Pet Dogs*. I didn't want to damage the magazine's reputation by association.

"Don't be silly," she said. "Those bloody Cavalier women have written to me, too. If anything, they've made me even more determined to support you. I'll send you a copy of what they sent me. They wanted me to publish details of their research into swollen heads in Cavaliers, and their noses were put out of joint when I told them I couldn't because we were already featuring your research."

I was so sad when I'd read what they'd written in their note to Paula. There's a quote that sums it up: "Give me a hundred words writ by the most honest man, and I shall find you something to hang him with."

I don't use my married name (I became Catherine O'Driscoll, after my mother, when I had my first book published; it's a pen name), and they used this to imply that I was masquerading under a false name in order to defraud unsuspecting dog owners. They had also picked up on the name of my PR consultancy and contrasted it with the name we had given to our research, namely the Canine Health Census, implying again that we were obfuscating who we were. And they used the post office box as proof that we were hiding our address in order to make a quick getaway when the money came rolling in.

Paula was lovely and stood firmly behind us. Another friend, Simon, who was editor of one of our local newspapers, was also outraged on our behalf. He suggested we contact Stevens Innocent, the UK's leading libel lawyers, and get them to write to *Dog World* and demand a retraction.

I picked up the phone and spoke to one of the lawyers at the firm. He was so kind, and agreed to act for us without a fee. *Dog World* printed the usual small retraction and paid the law firm's costs.

Chapter 12

Don't give up

Meanwhile the legal process was gathering pace on our house and we were soon to find ourselves without a home. John found a cottage for rent in the Peak District in Derbyshire and we persuaded the landlord to have us, so we sold off most of our furniture and hired a van. I had spent many sleepless months worrying that we'd be homeless and that we'd lose our dogs, but Grace had different plans. Our rented little cottage stood on its own in rolling countryside. We were no longer hemmed in by neighbours, and the cottage came with three beautiful paddocks for the dogs to play in. The arm that swept across the chess board and rearranged our lives had put our feet firmly upon a new rock.

I had written an article for the *Pet Dogs* launch of our survey just before we moved. It raised questions about vaccines, pet food, veterinary drugs, environmental toxins, the role of stress on health, and many other things, and called upon dog lovers to take part in the world's largest independent canine health census. John reasoned that as *Pet Dogs* had a circulation of around 30,000, we should expect around 2,000 readers to take part. If it came much short of that, he said, it would be an indication that we shouldn't go ahead. Slowly, around 200 completed questionnaires came in and – not for the first or last time – I suggested to John that we abandon our plans. "Let's go and get on with our lives," I said. "It's too hard and too painful."

"Carry on," urged Paula. "Keep going. This is a really important project. Don't give up. I'll back you all the way, and continue to feature the survey in *Pet Dogs*. Don't give in now."

So, surrounded by unpacked boxes, I sat in my new office in the Derbyshire Peaks and typed up 650 letters to the editors of local daily and weekly newspapers in the UK in order to get the numbers up. I explained that there had been a rise in chronic and acute diseases in the modern dog, and asked dog lovers to write to us with a large self-addressed stamped envelope if they would like to take part in the survey. Around 43 readers responded, although some responses weren't as positive as we had hoped.

We started to get letters and phone calls from people who were outraged that we should 'charge' £5 for them to take part in a survey, and they too were accusing us of stealing their money. It's incredibly difficult to defend yourself against something you haven't done, or aren't doing. All you can say is, "I didn't", or "I'm not".

The irony was that, before the recession, our consultancy had put us towards the top income bracket. Had I not been side-tracked by my dogs' suffering and death, I would have rebuilt the thriving business I already had, and knew how to build – just as thousands of businesses did after the recession. I didn't need to con people out of £5. Besides, apart from printing and postage costs, data entry for 16,000 26-page questionnaires would be a mammoth task, one that would need to be farmed out and paid for.

Any sane individual would have given up at this point. All of the signs were pointing towards failure and infamy. But I knew that the dogs were being harmed by vaccines they didn't need, and I knew that processed pet food was not sustaining life. And it was very personal. Oliver and Prudence had died because I hadn't known any better. My dogs had shown me that they were people, with souls. They had demonstrated that they could suffer. And they had given me so much of their love, and sustained me and kept me going, and I felt that we dog owners owed a huge debt of gratitude to the dogs. I couldn't turn my back on them. Besides, every time I seriously thought about giving up, Prudence projected herself into my mind and I relived her vaccine-induced death over and over again. I couldn't let her down. I just couldn't walk away.

I soon learnt that I was safe, and valued, when I closed the garden gate, surrounding myself with my beautiful dogs, and shutting the world out.

Sophie, a dog, took on the role of my mother. My own mum had died when I was 17; she had been ill for as long as I could remember and she wasn't really the sort of person you could go to with your troubles. The rest of my family were, with the exception of my stepmother, estranged from me since they didn't like John. Don't ask – that's a whole other book.

So it was my dogs who protected me from loneliness, and comforted me in a harsh and unkind world.

Sophie knew about wisdom, acceptance and contentment. She knew how to play, and she was always laughing. Sophie would go into the garden and do her Tai Chi exercises, which no-one had taught her, and she'd sit and look at the light dancing through the trees and smell the air, and sigh contentedly, and wag her tail. She'd take you to another realm, just watching her.

Sophie taught me about leadership. She never once raised her voice in anger, or snapped. She never once pushed herself forward or exerted her authority with the younger dogs. Instead, she'd just look and raise her lip gently, and the other dogs would do as they were told. She had presence, and focus. She was a natural leader, more in control than any blusterer or bully. The other dogs listened to her because she was wise, and safe to follow.

I used sit alone late at night when John went to bed and the dogs slept around me, thinking about the day, with the hurtful things people had said circling in my mind. Sometimes Sophie would wake up and look at me and bark quietly, and wave her paw gently at me. For a long while I thought that she just wanted a cuddle. Then one night I realised that she only barked at me when I was thinking negative thoughts. She was teaching me to be aware of them, drop them, and be at peace. She was my guru.

Sophie was always a calming presence, but she knew about elation, too. While scientists make pronouncements about whether animals have emotions or not, Sophie would just smile, scrunching her eyes and forming her lips into a grin, and put her paws gently on my lap, and steal my tissue. She'd turn my tears into laughter. Not only did Sophie have emotions, but she was aware of mine, too, and worked to heal them.

She is still with me, in my heart. If I close my eyes, I can see her beautiful white hair and her pretty pink nose. I can smell her: she smells of flowers, and she shimmers with light. I can look into her eyes, and she sends me messages. She works with me now from the other side, bringing me peace, teaching me acceptance, helping me not to worry. She taught me that once there is a bond of love, it is never broken.

I can't prove to any scientist that Sophie speaks to me from the other side, but I know that she is a resource for inner peace, even now. While on this earth, that little dog embodied the qualities of wisdom and motherly love, and I believe that once you make contact with those qualities and have someone to anchor those qualities upon, then they are at your constant disposal.

But we were in an intriguing position. In order to persuade people to take part in our survey, they first had to appreciate that there was a problem. By and large, unless someone had connected their dog's death to a vaccine, or questioned why their young dog had died or was ill, they didn't know what we were talking about. And even if they did, it became clear to me that most people wanted to hand over the decision-making to their vets. After all, vets were supposed to be the experts: intelligent people who had trained hard, and who should know what they were talking about.

I had come across people who, like us, had a number of dogs, and who had experienced illness and death in several of their young ones. But most dog owners only had one dog at a time. If that dog died of cancer or leukaemia or autoimmune haemolytic anaemia, then it would be easy to assume that it was just bad luck, or to blame the breeder. And it would be easier still to simply go off and buy another dog or, in many cases, to decide that dog ownership and loss were too painful to repeat. Statistics showed that the average length of dog ownership in America was just five years. I wondered about the stories behind that statistic.

So John came up with another brilliant idea. "Let's produce a newsletter," he said, "and send it out to the people who have elected to take part in the survey." We felt that this would, in a small way, compensate the people who had helped fund the research that, as yet, had no hope of being completed unless other dog lovers took part. We also purchased mailing lists of thousands of dog owners, and we posted the newsletter out to them, too. The hope was that when they read about the various areas of concern they might feel inclined to participate in the survey.

Realising that our research might take longer than the six months we had hoped, we formed an organisation and called it Canine Health Concern. The aim was to research and share information about health and ill health in dogs. To help pay for the newsletters and postage (which we initially funded ourselves from my work as a copywriter), we invited dog lovers to support us by becoming members and paying an annual subscription of £6. We were incredibly heartened by the response, and soon Canine Health Concern had over two thousand members, many of whom are still with us to this day.

Meanwhile, news of our research had made its way to Steve Dean, a vet who wrote a regular column in *Dog World*. Not being a breeder or shower, I didn't read this publication, but Sally, June and Hylda sent me clippings to show me what he was saying. Boy, did I think he was a sarcastic, arrogant little bugger! He wrote in *A Vet's View*:

> My final letter is from a lady worried by all the scare-mongering about vaccination. At the risk of suffering the wrath of the homeopathy lobby, let me set her mind at rest. There is no evidence which suggests that annual booster vaccines produce disease in normal healthy dogs.
>
> Some breeds and individuals have a predisposition to disorders of the immune system which vaccines may trigger; however these are in the tiny minority.
>
> My reader rightly states that distemper is now rare, as is hepatitis, and they are so because of the tremendous success of the vaccines. In fact parvovirus is also dwindling for similar reasons. It is against this background of low incidence that other schemes such as homeopathic nosodes flourish, for if there is no infection then even water will work!
>
> I have, however, seen the results of a distemper outbreak in a rural community where vaccination was allowed to lapse, and it was not a happy event. In addition, kidney disease is still a major

problem in dogs and I would lay money on the likelihood that leptospirosis is the chief criminal in this.

So stop vaccinating if you wish but be prepared to suffer the consequences in years to come.

My reader is, however, more reasonable than this. She asks is every other year sufficient? Yes for distemper, hepatitis and parvovirus, but not for leptospirosis. Is it harmful to vaccinate old dogs over ten years – no, in fact they probably need boosters as much as any dog as they become more vulnerable to disease as they get old.

It may well be that we can expect lifelong vaccination for some of the classic diseases, like distemper and hepatitis, some time in the future and I am on record as saying we should look into this possibility. However with current knowledge, we would still need to boost immunity to leptospirosis annually. A final comment in this reader's letter intrigued me: "I have just heard that there used not to be boosters at all after initial jabs!" Who invents such misinformation I do not know.

The problem has always been getting people to have booster vaccinations for their dogs. They were always recommended. In my earlier veterinary years the uptake on boosters was less than 25 per cent and now it is much better. Perhaps that is why we see so little of the classic diseases in the modern dog in the UK.

However, whichever way you look at it, this triumph over disease is because of effective vaccines, which I use for my dogs annually, and so far not an autoimmune symptom to be seen in any of them.

My experience over the years has been that scientists, who are allegedly more reasoned and reasonable than the average human being, rarely resort to the science in defence of annual vaccination. They use inflammatory words like 'scaremongering' and 'misinformation', and phrases like, 'suffer the consequences'. In fact, they themselves scaremonger to frighten people into vaccinating, whilst accusing others – who are looking at the actual science – of scaremongering. Whether this is because they are feeling overly emotional and threatened, or they are seeking to obfuscate the scientific truth, I do not know. But as a writer, I am very aware of nuance.

But first let's correct a glaring inaccuracy: booster vaccination was *not* always recommended. At one time, the only canine vaccine was against distemper, with the first commercially available vaccine being introduced in 1950. It was given once or – at most – twice.

By the time Steve Dean wrote this column in *Dog World*, most vets and most pet owners in the UK believed that annual vaccination against distemper, parvovirus, canine viral hepatitis (also called adenovirus), kennel cough and leptospirosis was required, failing which your dog would probably die of these deadly diseases. I noticed Steve's statement that, "*My reader ... asks is every other year sufficient? Yes for distemper, hepatitis and parvovirus, but not for leptospirosis.*"

I concluded from his statement that Steve must be aware of the pronouncements of Ronald Schultz and Tom R Philips who, in *Kirk's Veterinary Therapy* way back in 1978, stated that once a dog is immune to viral disease, he remains immune for years or life. Why else would Steve concede that the viral diseases of distemper, parvovirus and hepatitis did not require annual vaccination (and grudgingly admit that every other year would do)? Why would he single out the bacterial disease of leptospirosis as needing annual jabs if he was unaware of long term immunity from the viral vaccines? And why wouldn't he make it plain that the world's leading scientists in this field had established up to lifetime immunity?

This man has an agenda, I concluded, although it is conceivable that he was shamefully unaware of the independent duration of immunity studies.

What I didn't know, and didn't know for several years to come, was that Steve Dean was recruited by the Veterinary Medicines Directorate (VMD), the government body in the UK that licenses veterinary drugs and biologics, and which is charged with the task of ensuring their safety and efficacy. [1]

Neither did I know that Steve had worked for 17 years in the pharmaceutical industry. He was also a consultant to the veterinary pharmaceutical industry before being recruited to the post of director of licensing, VMD, in 1996. He was also a past-chairman and treasurer of the Association of Veterinarians in Industry.

Steve Dean was later promoted to chief executive of the VMD, which is when I discovered his government, but not his industry, ties. Being head of the VMD pays well – one source gave a figure of between £95,000 and £100,000 a year. It's also a position which demands a higher standard of knowledge and understanding than the average vet.

When he wrote the above in *Dog World*, Steve Dean wasn't, as I suspected, just a vet. He was an industry man who became a regulator; a poacher turned gamekeeper. This isn't to say that Steve had done anything wrong – but to illustrate how the industry regulator recruits from industry.

Yet his words were wrong – they just weren't true; not just in fact but also in tone which I felt was arrogant, belittling and designed to ridicule. I was no trained scientist; I had only seen a few handfuls of scientific papers – but I knew that, contrary to Steve's claims, there was indeed evidence to say that booster vaccines can cause disease in normal healthy dogs. I knew that it was fundamentally untrue to say that, "*Some breeds and individuals have a predisposition to disorders of the immune system which vaccines may trigger; however these are in the tiny minority.*" Tiny minority my backside! From what I was seeing, disorders of the immune system were the bread of every veterinary practice, and booster income was the butter.

So I wrote a letter to the editor of *Dog World* in response to Steve Dean's column and the editor published it after demanding that I supply the scientific references to support what I had written.

Pretty soon I felt as though I was the most hated woman in the dog world.

Chapter 13

Garlic and crucifixes

Having realised that in order to encourage dog lovers to take part in what we believed to be vitally important research, conducted by dog lovers for the dogs and without commercial bias, we also needed to explain the reasons for the research. I decided that, rather than do something sensible like income-generating consultancy work or copywriting, I would spend the next few months writing a book – on a subject that few people seemed to have any interest in!

The well-received but hardly lucrative *Golden Retriever Companion* demonstrated to me that book writing was unlikely to provide any reasonable level of income (Jackie Collins or Tolstoy I am not) but I threw caution to the wind and set about writing something for a specialist market with no hope of keeping the roof over our heads.

My initial aim was to write something that covered all of the areas we were questioning: diet, vaccination, flea control products, chemicals in the environment, breeding practices, and so on. I started with the vaccine chapter but, by the time I had finished this, it had formed itself into a book in its own right – a book about pet vaccination.

Something quite interesting, and conceivably mystical, started happening during this time: whenever I had a question, the Universe would furnish the answer. Either someone would phone up out of the blue and directly answer a question I had raised, or send me a scientific paper in the post, or I'd walk into a bookshop and a highly relevant book would appear to jump off the shelves in front of me. It was quite a spectacular series of experiences.

Thorson's Complete Guide to Vitamins and Minerals by Leonard Mervyn, for example, appeared to jump forward, like a Hollywood special effect, separating itself from other books on the shelf. I learnt later that this is revered as the nutrition bible by nutritionists, and is based upon scientific research showing the functions, deficiency signs, and therapeutic benefits of each of the known nutrients. I've used it regularly for the last 25 years; it's pages are only just hanging in there.

My sister Leslie bought me a veterinary dictionary to help me in my work. With this, I was able to take the long Latin-based words and terms used in scientific papers and translate them into English.

June Goose and Hylda Reynolds gave me permission to publish the letters they had received from dog owners who suspected that vaccines had harmed their dogs. Christopher Day gave me his support and blessing. I also made contact with Dr Jean Dodds, and she generously answered any questions I had. I contacted Ian Billinghurst, the vet who wrote *Give Your Dog a Bone*, and he, along with the homeopathic vets Richard Allport and Chris Day, gave us their support by joining Canine Health Concern's panel of experts.

Sally Cronk contacted me one day with news of what was to turn into a momentous event within our small pond. In her efforts to raise money for the Royal Veterinary College to research autoimmune haemolytic anaemia, Sally had decided to organise a seminar. Because the seminar was raising funds for the RVC, they had suggested that it be held in one of their lecture theatres. Would I be a speaker? I had never given a public lecture before, but I was willing to support the cause, albeit somewhat nervously. Sally also asked the vet Richard Allport to speak, as well as Hilary Jupp, a very knowledgeable Irish Wolfhound owner and homeopath; and the vet John Burns who had started a processed pet food business.

However, a couple of weeks before the seminar was due to take place, Sally called me to say that the Appeals Office at the RVC was talking about cancelling it. "Intervet and Pedigree Petfoods have heard about the seminar," Sally told me, "and they've threatened to take their funding away from the College if it goes ahead." What more proof did anyone need about the influence of corporations on the academic world?

As it happens, it was decided that the seminar would go ahead anyway, possibly due to the fact that Sally had already sold over 140 tickets, and one or two people might have been inclined to make a stink if it was cancelled. There was a proviso, however, that the speakers had to share the stage with Intervet and Pedigree.

The day duly rolled around and I arrived with John and a handful of dog-loving friends, clasping my speech in my hands. I had been told that I'd have 45 minutes, and I had timed it to the minute. I was going to stand there and read from a script.

Intervet and Pedigree went on first. Pedigree had a flash slideshow with all the bells and whistles and, as we sat and listened, we began to believe that we were barking up the wrong tree. According to Pedigree's research, dogs were living longer than ever, thanks to processed pet food. We were stunned ... if this was true, then the theories behind Canine Health Concern were false. We were wasting our time.

John spoke to the Pedigree representative and asked if she would share the research she had based her talk upon. She agreed and took our address. We never did get sight of that research, despite letters of reminder and – as was John's way – a recorded delivery letter to focus their minds.

However, John had decided to film the day's lectures and we watched the Pedigree presentation back. With more time to take in what she was saying, the claim became clearer. Apparently more dogs were living to the age of eight! I personally don't consider eight to be a good age for a dog – do you? The implication of the presentation was, in fact, that fewer dogs were living *beyond* eight, the chosen cut-off point from which to make their sales pitch.

The speaker for Intervet was a vet called David Sutton. I truly felt sorry for him on that day, because the audience was packed with people who believed that their dogs had been killed by vaccines. Watching the video of his talk back, you could see him being slammed bodily into the back wall of the stage by the energy of the audience's anger. I wouldn't wish that on anyone.

I was the last to go on, with knees shaking and hands trembling. David Williams, the RVC lecturer who was hoping to benefit from Sally's research funding, took me to one side and told me that because Pedigree and Intervet had run over their time, I only had 15 minutes for my talk. Not having spoken in public before, I had no idea how I was going to turn 45 minutes into 15. So I got up and started reading from the script.

Whilst preparing my speech a few weeks earlier, an inner voice had prompted me to find out how much money Pedigree spent on advertising. I telephoned an organisation that monitored industry advertising spend and explained that I ran a non-profit animal welfare organisation, and could they please give me the figures. "Sure," the man said kindly. "Pedigree Petfoods spent £34,465,000.00 on advertising in the UK." That's a mind-boggling thirty-four-million, four-hundred-and-sixty-five-thousand pounds to tell you that this brand of pet food is better than any other brand of pet food. In the UK alone. In one year.

"Does that include PR, sponsorship, exhibitions, or anything else?" I asked.

"No, that's just advertising spend, in the UK, for that twelve month period."

Then I sat down and worked out how much of that year's income might be spent on manufacturing, distribution, retailer cuts, staff, plant, advertising, PR, exhibitions, and so on, at the end of which I concluded, with John's expert help, that if you paid £1 for a tin of pet food, the ingredients might amount to no more than nine pence, and possibly less – which didn't say much about the quality of those ingredients.

As for Intervet and the vaccine industry, I was no kinder. It was personal, you see – I had watched my dogs suffer and die far too young.

In retrospect, this was the day we sounded the battle cry.

Later it was rumoured that Pedigree Petfoods was planning to sue me. "Good," said John. "We'll get them to disclose in court." What he meant by this is that, if it goes to court, then both parties are able to demand that specific information be provided by the other side. John was pretty sure that very few pet food manufacturers would want the quality and source of their ingredients to be scrutinised in this way.

Meanwhile, I'm standing on the stage in a lecture theatre at the Royal Veterinary College, reading my speech out like an automaton, I was so frightened, and David Williams started dancing about at the back of the room doing time out signs. A part of my consciousness watched him in a bemused way, until I realised that he was telling me to get off. Then my mouth said to the audience: "I've been told I have to stop. You paid for your tickets – do you want me to stop?"

"No, carry on," the audience yelled. So I did.

So my first public speaking engagement was somewhat stressful. Most of us left that day with splitting headaches. It felt like we'd been on the front line in World War III. The battle lines had certainly been drawn.

After writing a couple of letters to the dog press, dog breed clubs started to invite me to speak at their annual education days. Each time I was asked to speak, I found myself compulsively going back to the scientific research available to me at the time to satisfy myself that what I said at these lectures was true. The last thing I wanted was to be responsible for a rise in viral disease outbreaks in the dog population by frightening people about pet vaccines. But each time I went back to the research, it merely confirmed that what I had discovered was true.

So I'd get in the car, or on a plane, and present the evidence that we were over-vaccinating our dogs, and harming them at the same time. Technology has moved on considerably since the early 90s. In those days I was using a projector with 35mm slides. Each of these cost £18 to produce, which meant that ten slides would cost £180, and I used about 30 or so slides for each talk. Changing the talk was therefore an expense that had to be thought about seriously, especially as I was spending more time on Canine Health Concern, and less and less time on earning an income.

I'd start by asking people in the audience to put their hands up if they fed processed pet food and vaccinated every year. Every single hand, in audiences of a hundred or more, would go up. Pretty soon people would be waving their fists at me and shouting. Some would get up and stomp out of the hall in anger. I imagine there were even people in the audience waving garlic and crucifixes in my direction. "What do you mean vaccines can cause arthritis," someone would shout, their face red with rage. "What utter rubbish," someone else would say. "You're putting our dogs in danger of viral disease," was a pretty common yell. "You're irresponsible!"

But there would also be quiet people in the room whose eyes were registering and resonating with what I was saying; I could see pennies dropping around the room. These people would come up to me after the talk and share stories of their dogs becoming epileptic, or allergic, or developing skin problems shortly after they were vaccinated, or dying at shamefully young ages of cancer.

As I look back on those days, and the anger I subjected myself to, it all seems like a strange and bizarre dream. I remember walking out and getting into the car to go home, wondering why I was doing this to myself. It wasn't as if I appeared to be making any difference, either. But something deep inside me told me that someone had to speak for the dogs and, since no-one else was, the Big Finger in the Sky appeared to be pointing at me.

Then one day – a few years into the campaign – a letter arrived from a lady called Satu Bateman. She and her husband Terry had attended one of my talks. Satu told me that I had changed their lives that day, putting them on the path of natural feeding and no vaccines. She enclosed photographs of her beautiful dogs, and thanked me for their robust good health.

Turns out that while we were sitting in our office overwhelmed with despair at the task we had taken on, change was taking place.

Chapter 14

Uncovering the science

At which point, I think it's perhaps worth sharing some of the scientific information I was learning and sharing back in the early 1990s, in the days before an enquiring mind with a set of fingers could type a few carefully chosen words into a search engine on the internet and discover far more.

John taught me many things, but one thing he said had a lasting effect: "A university education has little value other than to teach you how to research; how to ask questions," he said. Education teaches you to ask why!

You can ask questions whether or not you have been to college. Unfortunately, it seems that many people who have been to college stop asking those questions, assuming perhaps that they already know it all.

We need to remind ourselves of a very basic fact. Way back in 1978, Ronald D Schultz and Tom R Phillips published in *Kirks Veterinary Therapy* that once a dog is immune to viral disease, he is immune for years or life. As I write, that's 39 years ago, and annual vaccination is still allowed, legal and common.

I appreciate that so far, I have been telling you about me and my dogs, and the human and canine side of my story. Now I'm suddenly going to plunge you into the science of vaccine damage, and you may find this jarring. So I've summarised the pertinent points in boxes. You can choose to read the whole text, or just the boxes.

The information in this and the next chapter comes from a relatively small pool of resources that were available to me in the early 1990s, before the internet.

They include:

- *The Merck Manual*, Sixteenth Edition;
- *The Merck Veterinary Manual*, Fifth and Seventh Editions;
- The *Journal of the American Veterinary Medical Association* 'Are we vaccinating too much?', 4 August 1995;
- *Current Veterinary Therapy XI, 1992*, 'Canine and Feline Vaccines', Schultz and Phillips;
- *AKC Gazette, Vol. 107, # 7, 1990*, 'Update on Autoimmune Diseases of Purebred Dogs', W Jean Dodds;
- *Dog World, 77* [(4)]: *3640, 1992*. Dodds W.J. Autoimmune thyroid disease.

- Parts 1-3. *Veterinary Practice STAFF* 4 (1, 2, and 3): 8-10, 1, 26-31, 35-37, 2. Dodds W.J. Genetically based immune disorders: Autoimmune diseases.
- *Veterinary Practice STAFF*, 4 [5]: 19-21, 1992. Dodds W.J. Immune deficiency diseases: Genetically based immune disorders, Part 4.
- *Dog World*, 77 [5]: 4448, 1992. Dodds W.J. Unraveling the autoimmune mystery.
- *Veterinary Forum*, May: 68-71. 1983. Dodds W.J. Vaccine safety and efficacy revisited.
- *Journal of Veterinary Internal Medicine, Vol 10, No 5, 1996,* Vaccine Associated Immune-Mediated Hemolytic Anemia in the Dog, Duval and Giger;
- *Veterinary Record January 11, 1992,* Distemper encephalitis in pups after vaccination of the dam, IAP McCandlish et al;
- *Australian Veterinary Journal, Vol 68, No 10, October 1991,* Adverse reactions to canine and feline vaccines, R Brooks;
- *DVM vaccine roundtable, December 1988,* Safety, efficacy heart of vaccine use; experts discuss pros, cons.
- Vaccine industry publications, including their datasheets.
- Other publications, referenced within the body of text below.
- Various papers cited by the publication *What Doctors Don't Tell You.*

Jean Dodds' paper told me that there had been a significant increase in autoimmune and allergic diseases in the pet population since the introduction of modified live virus vaccines.

According to Dr Dodds, autoimmune diseases have four main 'triggers', namely genetics, virus or vaccines, sex hormones and stress. There are over 80 autoimmune diseases.

A vaccine can trigger autoimmune diseases in animals and humans.

Our dogs are injected with a number of different live viruses, such as parvovirus, distemper, hepatitis, and parainfluenza, Bordetella bronchiseptica (kennel cough) as well as leptospirosis, a 'killed' vaccine. (Lepto is a range of around 200 'serovars' or variations of a class of bacteria.) We were, and frequently still are, advised to inject our dogs with all of these pathogens every year. In countries where rabies is a problem, annual or three-yearly vaccination against rabies is a legal requirement.

And yet, on the basis of science, we don't need to run that risk every year.

The 'core' canine vaccines used today – for distemper, parvovirus and hepatitis – are MLV (modified live virus) vaccines. MLV vaccines are 'attenuated', which means that the viruses are cooked to supposedly render them harmless, and they're designed to multiply in the host over a period of about ten days with the aim of stimulating an effective immune response.

Dodds wrote: "… the MLV vaccine can also overwhelm the immunocompromised or even a healthy host that is continually bombarded with other environmental stimuli."

'Immunocompromised' means that the immune system is compromised: the body's defences against disease aren't working properly. The body cannot mount an effective response to disease, or to a vaccine. This essentially means that the immune system is a finite resource. It's like knicker elastic – it will only stretch so far before it breaks. Even if the individual is genetically healthy when vaccinated, if he or she is already dealing with other threats to health, the vaccine is going to cause problems.

People mistakenly believe that if you vaccinate, then you are creating immunity. But this isn't necessarily the case.

Vaccines do not always immunise, which is why vaccinated dogs can and do come down with the diseases they are vaccinated against. Vaccination and immunisation are not the same thing. It has nothing to do with how often you vaccinate. MLV vaccines only have to work once to confer lasting immunity – but they don't always work.

Jean Dodds added that underlying autoimmune thyroid disease predisposes a dog to other immune-mediated diseases affecting other target tissue and organs, especially the bone marrow, liver, adrenal gland, pancreas, skin, kidney, joints, bowel, and central nervous system. "The bottom line," she writes, "is that viruses capable of inducing immune dysregulation in genetically susceptible stock can initiate autoimmune thyroid disease".

Vaccines can cause autoimmune thyroid disease which leaves the individual vulnerable to other more life-threatening diseases. Seventy percent of the thyroid will be destroyed before you begin to see overt signs of thyroid disease. You can easily vaccinate a dog with existing thyroid disease, and risk adverse effects, without knowing what you are doing. Years down the line when the symptoms appear, you're not going to correlate the condition with the vaccine you paid for.

In another paper, Jean Dodds listed parvovirus, retroviruses, cytomegalovirus, measles and distemper, and hepatitis viruses as capable of stimulating autoimmune diseases and – specifically – the frequent use of vaccines for parvovirus, distemper, hepatitis, Lyme's disease, Bordetella and rabies.

In yet another paper, Jean stated: "Immune-suppressant viruses of the retrovirus and parvovirus classes have recently been implicated as causes of bone marrow failure, immune mediated blood diseases, haematological malignancies (lymphoma and leukaemia), dysregulation of humoral and cell-mediated immunity, organ failure (liver, kidney), and autoimmune endocrine disorders – especially of the thyroid gland (thyroiditis), adrenal gland (Addison's disease), and pancreas (diabetes). Viral disease *and recent vaccination with single or combination modified live virus vaccines, especially those containing distemper, adenovirus 1 or 2 and parvovirus*, are increasingly recognised contributors to immune-mediated blood diseases, bone marrow failure, and organ dysfunction."

> Parvoviruses and retroviruses, and vaccines containing these viruses, can cause cancer and leukaemia, organ and endocrine failure, and destroy immunity.

You can imagine my alarm when I first read Jean Dodds' papers. If you listen to most vets and the regulators, they will tell you that vaccines are perfectly safe, have passed rigorous safety checks, etc., etc., but they won't tell you that a vaccine is capable of causing death: leukaemia, bone marrow failure, organ failure, diabetes, and more. But, of course, reactions like these are very, very rare. Aren't they? Yet look at the animals walking into the veterinary practice, and ask what they are in for.

> Almost all of the conditions treated by vets on a daily basis can be linked back to vaccination.

The stunning thing about it all is that we don't need to risk vaccines every year.

Jean Dodds listed other possible triggers for autoimmune disease. She wrote that sex hormones might play a part, advising dog owners not to vaccinate their bitches whilst pregnant or during or close to their seasons. She said that stress might play a role: don't vaccinate your dog while he's under stress (i.e., fresh from his mother and litter mates and introduced to new surroundings, or straight after heavy physical exercise).

Jean also mentioned that nutritional influences might be involved in vaccine reactions: the diet might be nutritionally deficient or imbalanced, or the food might contain harmful chemical preservatives or toxins – and these factors can render vaccines more harmful.

Adverse drug reactions are another trigger – some drugs, such as some of the sulfa antibiotics, can be recognised by a genetically susceptible host as foreign invaders and trigger autoimmune disease.

Successful vaccination relies upon a competent response from the dog's immune system. The immune system is impaired by poor diet, immune-suppressant drugs, stress, genetic faults, and infections. These *should* all contra-indicate vaccinating.

The late Ed Dorosz, a veterinary friend from Canada who had written a book called *Let's Cook for Our Dog*, had given me an old copy of the Merck Veterinary Manual. He also told me of an occasion in Calgary, Canada, where he vaccinated a herd of cattle and they started dropping down dead. "Since this affected the farmers' livelihood," Ed said, "the vaccine company paid out pretty quickly."

I also purchased the Merck Manual for humans. This is far more comprehensive than their veterinary manual, and it informed me that vaccines can cause or exacerbate encephalitis (inflammation of the brain), epilepsy, skin disease, behaviour problems (from brain damage), and autoimmune diseases. Bear in mind that Merck is a vaccine manufacturer and the corporation was implicating its own products as a cause of death in its manual.

Vaccines can cause brain damage, behavioural problems, paralysis, convulsions and death; allergic reactions; and autoimmune conditions.

Anaphylactic shock and/or hypersensitivity (allergic) reactions to vaccines are well documented and known to be one possible vaccine sequel. Vaccine manufacturers' datasheets recommend that adrenaline be used to prevent the animal/human from dying. Indeed, medical practitioners, who are routinely vaccinated, always have adrenaline standing by for themselves lest they should keel over and die within minutes of being vaccinated. I wonder if the general public appreciate this when they line up for their flu shots? And in countries where people can buy canine vaccines and inject them themselves, thereby cutting out the cost of a vet, do they realise that they have no backup should anaphylactic shock ensue?

I was also seriously concerned for the human race. The Merck Manual stated that, "children should not be given the DTP vaccine *again* if a child develops encephalopathy within 7 days; a convulsion within 3 days; persistent, severe, inconsolable screaming or crying for three hours or an unusual, distinctive, high-pitched cry within 48 hours; collapse or a shock-like state within 48 hours, and immediate severe or anaphylactic (allergic) reaction to the vaccine".

I was shocked by this advice from Merck. Do parents know that when they have their children vaccinated, they might have severe allergic reactions and/or brain damage and convulsions, and scream inconsolably for hours? And do they know whether these responses might cause long-term problems?

According to Merck, "Noninfectious causes of encephalitides (inflammation of the brain) include . . . vaccine reactions: many." I presume the 'many' in that sentence means many different vaccines can do this.

Merck also stated that epilepsy can be caused by, "CNS (central nervous system) infections (meningitis, AIDS, encephalitis . . .)"; and also by a foreign serum or drug allergy [vaccines contain serum], or by convulsive or toxic agents – and vaccines contain a variety of toxic agents, including mercury, aluminium, formaldehyde, peanut oils, bacteria, and more.

I discovered, also, that:

> Paresis is a symptom of encephalitis (inflammation of the brain), which can be vaccine-induced. Paresis means paralysis of one or more limbs – which is what happened to Oliver the day he died.

If Oliver had encephalitis, he may have had lesions throughout his brain and spinal cord, slowly eating his body up. I looked back to the weeks and months before Oliver's death, and remembered that his hair was falling out in clumps either side of his spine, and around the feathers above his back legs. I wondered if this was a sign of central nervous system problems, and a portent of what was to come.

> Seizures are another symptom of encephalitis, which can be vaccine-induced.

British government research showed that the DTP (diphtheria tetanus pertussis) and MMR (measles mumps rubella) vaccines could increase the risk of seizure five-fold. Whilst the American government was reassuring Americans that the measles vaccine was perfectly safe, its Public Health Laboratory Service Statistics Unit had found that the combined two produced seizures three times more than was previously reported, and that the DTP schedule is responsible for a four-fold increase in seizures. (*What Doctors Don't Tell You*, vol 1, no 8.)

I reasoned that dogs and humans both come from the earth; we are all made of the same stuff. Canine and human DNA is an 89% match; we all have blood cells, immune systems, organs and brains, and we can all have inflammatory and autoimmune responses. It was no surprise, then, that I was also seeing similarities between acknowledged human vaccine reactions and what was happening to the dogs.

There was specific research to prove the vaccine-epilepsy link in dogs: Writing in *Veterinary Record* during 1992 (130, 27-30), AIP McCandlish et al state: "Post-vaccinal encephalitis is a recognised complication of the administration of certain strains of live attenuated canine distemper vaccine (Hartley 1974, Bestetti and others 1978, Cornwell and others 1988)." The study detailed puppies who suffered seizures as a result of their mother's shots.

US evidence, incidentally, showed that the DTP vaccine caused convulsions in infants less than a year old, usually three days after they had been given the dose. The MMR vaccine took longer to cause convulsions – between 15 and 35 days. *The Lancet*, in 1989, reported that one in 400 children given the MMR vaccine would suffer convulsions; and in 1995, that children given the MMR jab were three times more likely to suffer convulsions than those who didn't receive it. It should be noted that the measles and distemper viruses are, to all intents and purposes, the same virus.

I also discovered from Merck that, "autoimmune diseases may be initiated by the encephalitis that can follow rabies vaccination in which an autoimmune cross-reaction probably is initiated by animal brain tissue in the vaccine". Yeuk, we're injecting animal brain tissues directly into our bloodstreams, and our pets' bloodstreams, and this can cause brain damage and autoimmunity.

> Vaccines are typically cultivated on dog, cat and monkey brains and kidneys; chick embryos, hamsters and guinea pigs, and even human embryonic tissue – all of which can be described as 'foreign protein', which can cause an allergic reaction, allergies, autoimmune diseases and encephalitis when injected directly into the bloodstream.

Further, the *Merck Veterinary Manual* confirmed that modified live parvovirus vaccines were suspected to cause autoimmune haemolytic anaemia in dogs (a life-threatening autoimmune disease). So Sally Cronk's fundraising initiative for the Royal Veterinary College – well, the research had already been done.

Ronald Schultz stated on the subject of over-vaccinating, "The client is paying for something with no effect or with the potential for an adverse reaction. I believe that adverse effects are increasing, because we are putting more and more components into these animals."

A paper entitled, "Effects of Vaccines on the Canine Immune System" by Tom R Phillips, et al, published in *Can J Vet Res*, 1989, stated:

"... the results of this study demonstrate that the majority of polyvalent canine vaccines significantly suppress lymphocyte responsiveness to PHA. . . . in certain circumstances, even a relatively short duration of suppression could become clinically significant especially if the animal was in a partially immunosuppressed condition (e.g. nutritional deficiency) . . . This is the first report of individual vaccine components which are not immunosuppressive by themselves causing an immunosuppression when inoculated in combination. Thus, the results of this study may have implications for other species which receive polyvalent vaccines".

Combined vaccines (distemper/parvo/adenovirus plus leptospirosis plus whatever else you want to throw in there; or, say, a MMR cocktail) work together to suppress the immune system temporarily and leave animals and humans open to disease. There is also a clear association between the suppression or absence of an immunologic function and an increased incidence of cancer.

Note that multivalent vaccines for humans and animals are still common, over twenty years later. Indeed, Dr Andrew Wakefield's concerns regarding the potential link between autism and the MMR vaccine were centred on the fact that the triple vaccine had not been tested and proven to be safe. Manufacturers had obtained a license for their cocktail by saying that individual components of the vaccines had been tested – not together but individually.

International pharmaceutical giant, Merck, stated in the *Merck Veterinary Manual*: "Some viruses induce immunological deficiencies, usually via effects on the bone marrow. Examples are human immunodeficiency virus (the cause of AIDS in man) . . . . . and human and canine parvoviruses . . .

"Bone marrow suppression with transient (21 day) or chronic/latent erythroid dysplasia in the presence or absence of thrombocytopenia and neutropenia, Coombs' positive haemolytic anaemia, and immune-mediated thrombocytopenia have been associated with (i.e., may prove to be caused by) both retroviral and parvoviral infections in man and other species. Also, modified live parvovirus vaccines in dogs . . . are suspects as causes (in genetically susceptible animals) of such haematological diseases."

Translation: Some viruses, including parvovirus and HIV ... and some vaccines, cause deficiencies in the immune system. HIV is associated with Simian Immunodeficiency Virus (SIV), thought to be introduced to humans via monkeys used in vaccine manufacture. There is strong evidence to say that canine parvovirus was caused by vaccine manufacturers who cultivated the distemper vaccine on cat kidneys that were infected with feline enteritis.

Blood and bone marrow diseases can also be vaccine-induced. Both viruses and the vaccines we inject in order to avoid the viruses can cause bone marrow suppression and erythroid dysplasia – a condition in which immature red blood cells in the bone marrow are abnormal in size, shape, organisation, and/or number. This is associated with thrombocytopenia (bleeding, poor blood clotting, bruising); neutropenia (destruction of white blood cells, associated with leukaemia, cancer, infections and autoimmune diseases); and haemolytic anaemia (where antibodies attack the person's own red blood cells; death can occur within days).

Tizard's Veterinary Immunology, 4th edition, stated that the cause of autoimmune haemolytic anaemia was unknown, although they postulated some cases may result from the alterations on the surface properties of erythrocytes (red blood cells), perhaps induced by drugs or viruses. There is evidence, they said, for a genetic predisposition to the disease in some animals. However, "its onset may be associated with obvious stress such as vaccination using modified live virus, virus disease, or hormonal imbalances such as pregnancy or pyometra."

Another piece of evidence to confirm that autoimmune diseases can be initiated by vaccines was supplied by the insert within the Rabdomun rabies vaccine box, which a dog lover posted to me from overseas. This stated: "Because Rabdomun is produced on an established cell line, it has safety advantages over inactivated brain-origin rabies vaccines. Tissue-origin vaccines contain extraneous protein in addition to rabies antigen that can lead to autoimmune disease."

This struck me as an interesting sales pitch: our vaccines aren't cultivated on animal parts, so they won't cause autoimmune diseases (unlike our competitors' vaccines which will cause autoimmune disease).

I also noticed that scientists are continually conducting research in order to confirm what is already known but largely ignored. I wondered what use this research was if it was just consigned to a dusty shelf with no-one acting upon it. Generally, scientific papers ended with: "more research is needed". This, it seemed to me, was just a convenient way for corporate-funded academia to maintain the status quo and keep the money rolling in.

Then I was sent *The Journal of Veterinary Internal Medicine* (Vol 10, No 5 (September-October) 1996), with a paper entitled: 'Vaccine-Associated Immune-Mediated Haemolytic Anaemia (IMHA) in the Dog'. The paper stated: "This study provides the first clinical evidence for a temporal relationship of vaccine-associated IMHA in the dog."

But it wasn't the first evidence that vaccines can cause this fast-acting harbinger of death. Merck had already confirmed that vaccines can do this to humans in its Manual, and *Tizard's Veterinary Immunology* had already alluded to it.

The paper went on to state: "Because vaccine components can remain in the body for extended periods of time, chemical reactions caused by these vaccine components may continue to occur later than with other drugs that are excreted or metabolised more quickly."

> Vaccines can cause reactions some time after the jab – when no-one will suspect a link. Vaccine reactions can appear days, weeks, months and years after a shot. This in turn implies that vaccine reactions are vastly under-reported, making them appear safer than they actually are.

Later the paper stated: "Vaccine-associated IMHA has been reported after diphtheria-pertussis-tetanus vaccination in children."

And later: "The vaccines reported in this study are commonly used canine vaccines (DHLPP, rabies, Borrelia, Bordetella and coronavirus). They included modified live viruses, killed viruses, and killed bacterins. Any of these components, as well as the adjuvants used in these vaccines, may stimulate or disrupt the function of the immune system or elicit increased antibody production that could lead to IMHA."

> Any vaccine may cause autoimmune haemolytic anaemia – it's not just the rabies vaccine, or the lepto vaccine. It's all of them, alone or combined.

The authors concluded that, because not all cases were reported to the manufacturers (none of the cases in this retrospective study had been reported), the prevalence of vaccine-associated IMHA was likely to be underestimated. This in itself gives a lie to claims made by regulators and governments that vaccine reactions are rare. In fact, they're just rarely reported.

I received a phone call from a man who owned a pathology lab. He'd heard through one of my vet friends that I was researching for my book *What Vets Don't Tell You About Vaccines*. He said: "I wanted to tell you that I've seen many cases of dogs coming down with autoimmune haemolytic anaemia just after they're vaccinated, to the stage where I know there's a link. Each time I've telephoned the relevant vaccine manufacturer to alert them to the problem. In every case, they have replied, 'oh, we've never seen that before'.

"Look," he said, "I am a scientist. And when someone alerts a scientist to what is a very worrying pattern, the correct response is to say you will look into it. But the vaccine manufacturers never say this. They just brush it off. In my opinion, it's all about money, and this is just wrong."

I asked the pathologist if I could quote him in my book. He said of course, but asked me not to identify him. "I rely on referrals from vets," he said. "If you publish my name in relation to this, I'll lose business." This conversation was to join a steady line of conversations where the truth speaker asked to remain anonymous for fear of reprisal.

Meanwhile, a vaccine manufacturer placed an article in *Veterinary Practice Nurse* in 1996, saying: "Despite scaremongering amongst certain canine journalists (that would be me, then), there is no evidence for the mythical disease coined 'vaccinosis' in boosted dogs, and there is no evidence of harm in any breed of cat or dog from giving a full booster every year."

At which point it became clear that I was dealing with an organised bunch of lying bastards.

Chapter 15

More unsavoury truths

I purchased a copy of the NOAH Compendium. NOAH is a trade association representing the veterinary vaccine and pharmaceutical industry in the UK (with the misleadingly kindly and authoritative title, 'National Office of Animal Health' – this is a trade association concerned with selling product, after all). The Compendium carries the datasheets that accompany veterinary drugs and biologics. It's now available for free on-line.

> When an organism mounts a huge allergic reaction to a foreign invasion, which is what a vaccine is, the reaction can lead to death.

I discovered that vaccine manufacturers warned, within the data sheets accompanying their vaccines, that dogs can suffer hypersensitivity reactions following vaccination, contradicting their advertising propaganda. They further advised that adrenaline be administered in this event. Adrenaline is there to stop them dying.

> Vaccines are often contaminated with bacteria and viruses, and these can cause illness in vaccinated individuals.

I was sent details of vaccine recalls. Schering-Plough Animal Health, for example, recalled stocks of its Intrac canine Bordetella bronchiseptica vaccine (kennel cough) during 1997, after routine testing revealed that it had fallen below the product specification for live bacterial count within the shelf life of the product. The likely explanation (they said) appeared to be in the supply of bovine serum albumin and gelatine from non-UK sources – imposed as a consequence of BSE regulations. These vaccines were, therefore, recalled because they were contaminated with bacteria above *acceptable limits*. Clearly, some contamination was acceptable, then. It's perfectly fine, it seems, to inject contaminated vaccines into a dog's body, providing the contamination isn't too contaminated.

As an aside, I discovered that British government officials had a meeting about cow blood products in vaccines when mad cow disease raised its head in the UK. They agreed that bovine serum could theoretically cause Creutzfeld Jacob disease (CJD) in vaccinated humans (the equivalent of mad cow disease) but chose to say and do nothing about it in case it caused panic among the populace. Their chief concern, it appeared, was that vaccine levels should not fall. Tough luck if you got CJD, though. And don't expect anyone to tell you what caused it, or to compensate you for being at the wrong end of their decision.

This link – Justice for Andy – http://justice4andy.com/whats-to-blame/vaccines – gives a more contemporary view of the situation.

Believe me, I was swimming in shock at what I was learning. When I started to research *What Vets Don't Tell You About Vaccines*, I knew that annual vaccination was unnecessary, but I didn't know whether or not I would vaccinate my new puppies. By the time I had finished researching *What Vets*, I was terrified of what vaccines could do. There was no way I would willingly inject this stuff into my dogs. The carnage just kept on coming.

I was contacted at this time by a woman in America whose puppy had died. Through training classes and mutual friends, over a hundred puppy owners – whose puppies had suffered the same fate – got together and compared notes. The only common denominator was that the puppies had all received the same batch of the same brand of vaccine. They contacted the manufacturer, but the manufacturer naturally denied any link. They wanted to get the vaccine tested (in America, pet owners can inject their own self-purchased vaccines), but no-one with the authority to do it would do it. They asked me if I knew anyone who could test it.

I was, by then, in contact with Professor Richard Lacey, a respected microbiologist, and he agreed to do the tests. He came back to me saying that the vaccine tested negative for bacterial contamination, which meant that it was a process problem. "This means that it's the way the vaccine is made, and other puppies will be at risk," he said.

There were dogs in *What Vets Don't Tell You About Vaccines* whose owners had seen their friends' skin splitting; there was even a child whose story was reported in one of the British tabloids. Their skin literally began to split after they were vaccinated. One dog was pumping out green gunk from his body. They – the dogs and the little girl – required extensive skin grafts, and the girl was left with crippling arthritis. In several cases the damage was so severe that the dogs had to be put to sleep.

In scientific circles, these souls are relegated to the status of 'anecdote', which offends me to this day. Because no-one has written up a scientific paper on their deaths, they become stories which should be dismissed. But maybe we should think of anecdotes as data with a soul?

The science exists to confirm that what happened to these living beings shortly after vaccination can indeed be induced by vaccines. But their owners couldn't expect anyone to tell them, either.

The Merck Manual stated that serum (used in vaccines) can cause Type III
hypersensitivity reactions, including a highly inflammatory skin condition
involving painful local lesions leading to tissue necrosis (skin death); as well as
widespread vascular injury. Vaccines cause other skin diseases, too.

In 1983, two scientists named Frick and Brookes assembled a group
of dogs who were genetically pre-disposed to develop atopic dermatitis
(atopic means an allergic or hypersensitivity reaction, dermatitis means
inflammation of the skin). Atopic dermatitis is considered to be an
hereditary predisposition, but genes merely load the gun. Vaccines pull the
trigger in most cases.

The dogs were divided into two groups and the first group was
exposed to pollen (which is an allergen), and they were then vaccinated.
None of the genetically pre-disposed dogs developed the allegedly
hereditary condition.

The second group was vaccinated first, and then exposed to pollen.
All developed the 'hereditary' disease. There are scientists who have gone
looking for the genetic marker for this hereditary disease, by the way, and
they have yet to find it. [1]

Vaccines sensitise an organism, setting them up for allergic disease.

The post-vaccine allergen could be pollen, or it could be house dust
mites, or it could be fungal spores, or the petrol fumes your dog, horse or
cat breathes in post-vaccination. Or it could be the food he's evolved to eat.
Get your dog vaccinated, and suddenly he's allergic to life.

Chapter 16
Big hearts, fried brains

I have observed that animals, like humans, are evolving along their own spiritual paths. Samson was highly evolved. When you talk about a person like Samson, no words exist to describe his energy. You'd have to sit with him, in the silence, to understand fully. Awesome, limitless, sublime, pure love – these words only come close to describing the experience of being with Samson.

Samson was devoted to me. He didn't want to be anywhere where I was not. He took care of me. If I was working too hard, and was tired, he'd come to me and take my arm in his mouth and walk me through the house and up the stairs and into the bedroom, and he'd guide me onto the bed and tell me to get some sleep. He really did this. I find it significant that just a dog should be aware of my energy levels and do something to correct them.

Samson lived inside my head. If I was sitting at my desk, typing away, his mind was in my mind. Once I thought it would be nice to have a biscuit with my tea, but we don't keep biscuits in the house because I'll only eat them. I thought – only thought – about walking up to the village shop. Straight away, Samson had his front paws on my lap, asking to come too.

Sometimes, when we were out walking, he'd be so overcome with joy and love for me that he'd fly at me and wrestle me to the ground, with the heather providing a soft landing, and – helpless with laughter – I'd lie there while he kissed me.

Samson was very mindful of time, and very keen on order. He liked to ensure that routines were kept in the home, and that enough time was allocated to rest and relaxation. "Stop work now", he'd say. He was always on my side, wanting the best for me – and when I failed to attend to my own self-care, he told me that I mattered, and insisted I listen. As such, Samson was concerned with my spiritual growth.

Samson was a dog with a very big heart, and a very big brain. A very big soul. He embodied unconditional love. I have access to that love, still. I just have to close my eyes and he is with me, shimmering with light, wrapping his love around me.

If you have never experienced what it is to be fully, completely and unconditionally loved, you have never had a dog. That is, unless a vaccine has fried your dog's brain.

Sharon Webley wrote: "Smudge was a very normal, happy, lively Border Collie puppy who I was training for obedience competitions. A friend had an unrelated puppy of the same age and I remember chatting to her when the pups were about five months old and she was saying that her's was difficult to train and had a very short attention span and I said I was thrilled with Smudge and he was coming on really well.

"When Smudge had been vaccinated at 10 and 12 weeks old, he was very ill afterwards. He had bad sickness and diarrhoea. He recovered and I thought no more of it. Then I read in *Dog Training Weekly* about two puppies (litter brothers) who'd been vaccinated but developed parvovirus and both died from it. The vet told the owner that the vaccines hadn't taken. The owner said that both the pups had had sickness and diarrhoea (parvo symptoms) after the jabs, just as Smudge had.

"I took Smudge back to the vet to be blood tested. He was just over six months old by this time. The test showed no immunity to anything and the vet gave him a booster.

"Gradually over a period of months, Smudge's behaviour changed. He wouldn't be cuddled, wouldn't make eye contact, wouldn't interact at all, didn't like going outside, had strange blank episodes like his brain had shut down. If we moved any furniture, he'd freak out. If anyone came to the house, he'd run around yapping uncontrollably and then hide behind the settee. If he wasn't hiding, all he wanted to do was fetch toys, he'd do it for hours non-stop. I gave up training him, my mum tried but then she gave up. He had no attention span and couldn't even remember how to sit most of the time.

"He lived to 13 in his own little world. I saw a documentary about autistic children and it suddenly dawned on me that Smudge was autistic. I was told that dogs don't suffer from autism, then years after Smudge had died, I saw an article in the *Daily Mail* which talked about another dog becoming autistic post-vaccination."

Chapter 17
Widespread damage

Viera Scheibner, a formidable vaccine researcher, hearing that I was researching a book on canine vaccination, came to visit and offered her help. She gave me a paper prepared by Hans Selye entitled, 'A Syndrome Produced by Diverse Nocuous Agents', (Selye H, 1936, *Nature*, July 4 138:32). This was the first important work to describe the syndrome of non-specific responses to injury.

The scientifically revered Selye reported that the non-specific response to stress includes enlarged adrenal cortex; intense atrophy of the thymus, the spleen and all lymphatic structures; signs of petechial bleeding (bleeding into the skin or mucous membrane) – into the lungs, thymus, pericardium and other internal organs, and intrathoracic cavity (the cavity in the vertebrate body enclosed by the ribs between the diaphragm and the neck and containing the lungs and heart); ulceration of the lining of the stomach and duodenum; disappearance of the eosinophil cells (a type of white blood cell produced in the bone marrow) in the circulating blood; a number of chemical alterations in the constitution of body fluids and tissues; changes in the viscosity and clotting properties of the blood, and signs of derangements in body temperature control (overheating or under heating).

> Selye demonstrated that living organisms have a general non-specific reaction pattern to stress: a general defence mechanism with which they meet damage caused by a variety of potential disease-producers. Vaccines are designed to stress the body, causing it to mount an immune response. Sometimes the stress can overwhelm the individual, leading to chronic disease or death.

The clinical symptoms of what Selye termed General Adaptation Syndrome include general feeling of malaise, nausea, coated tongue, reflux (a back flow of liquid against its normal direction of movement), otitis media (ear infections), upper respiratory tract infections, runny nose, sticky eyes, clamminess, deranged body temperature, rash, tenderness of the liver and spleen, diffuse pains and aches in the joints, gastro-intestinal disturbance with loss of appetite and weight, diarrhoea and/or constipation.

Generally, an animal or human cannot maintain a continuous state of alarm. If they're confronted with an insult so damaging that their normal defence mechanisms are unable to mobilise and complete a healing response, the individual will either sustain chronic damage or respond with death. If the defence mechanisms are not normal, that is, if the individual's immune system is already stressed and dealing with other challenges, chronic or acute disease will result – either that or death.

And this is what underlies a typical vaccine reaction. Vaccines are *designed* to stress the body. Viruses, bacterins, and adjuvants (which are essentially toxins or irritants, there to provoke a stronger immune response) tell the body that it's under attack and must react with the immune response. Vaccines are a declaration of war, and the individual's defence abilities are what predict a good or bad outcome.

This is precisely why vaccines are licensed for use in healthy animals and humans only. They are not designed for those who are physically under-par. The datasheets specifically state: 'for use in healthy animals only' or 'do not use in unhealthy animals'. They state this because, when the vaccines were licensed, the regulators told them they had to. And the regulators specified this because vaccinating a sick individual could make them sicker or kill them. Besides which, you need a functioning immune system in order to recognise the vaccine virus and develop antibodies.

And yet vets and doctors often have the peculiar belief – despite licensing stipulations – that if an individual isn't well, they need the vaccine even more. This is why they vaccinate sick and elderly dogs and humans: because they (rightly) believe that these individuals are more susceptible to viral disease. The problem is that they are also more susceptible to having a vaccine reaction. And you deliberately inject a vaccine, whereas you may not encounter a disease threat.

> So many signposts point to the conclusion that it would be more sensible to refrain from vaccinating and bring the individual to health so that they are able to either withstand the vaccine challenge, or to naturally overcome a viral assault.

Vaccines essentially cause damage wherever there is a weak point in the individual's body. However, it's not like the Thalidomide drug where babies were born without limbs after their pregnant mothers took it. It's not like pricking your finger with a needle and you bleed. Vaccines can cause destruction in any system within the body – whether it be the immune system, organs, skin, brain or endocrines. There is no single disastrous outcome. There are myriad potential disastrous outcomes. As for vaccines being (as is commonly said) more dangerous to those with genetic faults – we are mostly ALL genetic defects.

There is no test to prove vaccine damage. You can know that vaccines are scientifically proven to cause a particular disease, but you cannot prove that a vaccine caused your particular dog's disease.

If money was my only concern, and I were a sociopath, I'd go looking for such a product to sell – a product that people were frightened to go without, and which caused harm in any system of the body but without any easily recognisable proof to pin the blame on. Then I'd make drugs and claim that they alleviated the problems my product originally caused. And to support all this, I'd buy off the medical and veterinary professions, charities and governments, and live above the law.

And here's the kicker: there is no conventional cure for autoimmune or allergic diseases. All the conventional medical system is able to offer is a lifetime of drugs with side-effects.

In the alarm stage of Selye's General Adaption Syndrome, the cells of the adrenal cortex discharge hormone-containing granules into the blood stream. Under certain conditions, an excess production of the hormone called mineralocorticoid desoxycorticosteron (DOC) causes brain lesions. When this is coupled with vascular lesions, also characteristic of Non-specific Stress Syndrome, it may lead to the destruction of large parts of the brain.

Selye's research on its own explains why vaccines can and do cause brain damage. They deliberately stress the immune system, causing inflammation, in order to provoke an immune response. Many vaccines also include toxins such as aluminium, mercury, formaldehyde, peanut oils and much more, because without them the vaccine won't work. At the same time, these 'adjuvants' increase the stress the body is subjected to, and many of them are neurotoxins.

Selye's seminal paper was published in 1936 and the world is still not listening.

Sally Cronk gave me a book called, *Vaccination Social Violence and Criminality* by Harris L Coulter. Coulter built a compelling argument to suggest that (human) learning disabilities, autism, dyslexia, aggression, hyperactivity, and sociopathic behaviour are largely rooted in vaccine damage. He also noted the high incidence of allergies, seizure disorders, appetite disorders, a lack of control of bowel and urinary functions, breathing problems, and nervous disorders in autistic and minimally brain damaged children. He traced all of these conditions back to neurological damage, or encephalitis (brain inflammation).

Coulter contended that the most common cause of encephalitis in modern day America, where childhood vaccination is mandatory, is vaccination itself.

I so wish parents and pet owners would read Harris Coulter's book before they submit their children and pets to vaccination.

I mentioned Polmont Young Offender's Institute at the beginning of this book. Some years ago on TV, it was reported that a high percentage (I believe from memory that the figure was either 60 or 80%) of Polmont's inmates are dyslexic, which is of course another neurological condition that is highly represented in autism. This is not to suggest that all dyslexics are autistic, but that dyslexia is one of many features of autism. Encephalitis is what I would call a spectrum disease. It can be undetectable and mild, all the way through to brain dead, and indeed dead. Its symptoms can also differ between individuals because the lesions in the brain can appear anywhere in the brain.

Could it be that our prisons are full of people who have been damaged by vaccines and, due to the poverty many of them were raised under and the nutritional inadequacies of processed food, they suffered early malnutrition which, itself, can damage the brain and render vaccines more dangerous?

I was also reading a book by Geoffrey Cannon called *The Politics of Food*. Mr Cannon was a former health journalist who turned his attention to nutrition. He described how Margaret Thatcher's government had commissioned scientists to look into the eating habits of UK children. The scientists were horrified, learning that children were eating little more than crisps, chips and chocolate. They threw their arms up in horror, warning that our hospitals would be full of cancer patients, and our prisons full of people who, through malnutrition, had poorly developed brains.

Margaret Thatcher's government suppressed the report. Eventually, due to protest from the scientists, an abridged paper was eventually pushed out quietly through a side door. If industry's interests are seemingly put ahead of the health of our children, then what hope our dogs?

It hadn't taken me long to realise that health is contingent on a small number of factors, which included our interaction with the physical world, and the wellbeing of our internal world. Indeed, even Intervet's vaccine datasheets state that: "A good immune response is reliant on the reaction of an immunogenic agent and a fully competent immune system. The immunogenicity of the vaccine antigen will be reduced by poor storage or inappropriate administration. Immunocompetence of the animal may be compromised by a variety of factors including poor health, nutritional status, genetic factors, concurrent drug therapy and *stress*."

Why do they have to use such arcane language? All they are saying is that the vaccine might not work if the animal is ill, malnourished, is taking immune-suppressant drugs, or stressed, or if the vaccine isn't stored properly or is administered inappropriately.

In fact the scientific discipline called 'psychoneuroimmunology' has discovered that the immune system is greatly influenced by our emotions. If we are happy, we are less likely to succumb to viral disease. Similarly, if we are unhappy or stressed, we are less likely to develop immunity when vaccinated.

Demyelination was another factor within Harris Coulter's thesis, and demyelination can be induced by a vaccine. The Merck Manual states: "The myelin sheaths of many nerve fibres promote transmission of the neural impulse along the axon. Many congenital metabolic disorders affect the developing myelin sheath. Unless the innate biochemical defect can be corrected or compensated for, permanent, often widespread, neurologic deficits result.

"In acute disseminated encephalomyelitis (post infectious encephalitis)," Merck says, "demyelination can occur spontaneously, but usually follows a viral infection or *inoculation* (or, very rarely, a *bacterial vaccine*), suggesting an immunologic cause. The neuroparalytic accidents and peripheral neuropathies that can follow rabies vaccination with brain tissue preparations . . . are similar demyelinating disorders with the same presumed immunopathogenesis."

Accidents?

Merck is a vaccine manufacturer admitting that its own products can cause serious diseases, starting with tingling in the hands and feet all the way through to sexual dysfunction, incontinence, paralysis of the brain, heart disease, and sudden death!

Does anyone tell you that before you have your baby or puppy vaccinated, or when they're persuading your grandmother to have a flu shot? Do you think they should?

Vaccines can cause demyelination. This damage impairs the conduction of signals in affected nerves. In turn, there are deficiencies in sensation, movement, cognition, or other functions depending on which nerves are involved. Symptoms include blurred vision, clumsiness, weakness, paralysis, fatigue, incontinence, speech and hearing problems, neurological damage, and more.

So far, most of my research back in the 90s had come from conventional scientists: Drs Schultz, Dodds, Phillips, the Merck Manual, a few scientific papers, and the vaccine company datasheets themselves.

But out in the field, at the coalface, American holistic vets also seemed to have their fingers on the pulse. This is largely due to the fact, I believe, that homeopathy recognised vaccine damage over a century ago, so vaccine damage is part of a holistic vet's training. Therefore, they are more likely to observe cause and effect.

I was sent a copy of an article that appeared in *Wolf Clan* magazine. Pedro Rivera, DVM, was quoted as saying: "In our practice, we have seen hypothyroidism, chronic yeast ear infections, immune-mediated diseases and worsening of them, joint maladies, and behavioural problems as secondary reactions to over-vaccination."

Pat Bradley DVM observed that behaviour problems such as fearfulness or aggression often begin shortly after vaccination. Stephen R Blake DVM noticed that, "There are a lot of chronic conditions that develop some time after vaccinating. Some of these conditions that I see are digestive problems, seizures, skin problems, and behavioural problems."

Other holistic vets gave similar observations.

Pet owners were also asking questions regarding the onset of illnesses in their pets and their relationship to a recent vaccination. In fact, there have been vaccine dissenters since vaccines were invented. But still, vets like Steve Dean were ridiculing those who asked questions, and minimising any links.

To cap it all, Tom R Phillips and Ronald D Schultz wrote in a paper appearing in *Current Veterinary Therapy XI, 1992*: "Incomplete vaccine attenuation or vaccination of an immunosuppressed host can result in modified live vaccines causing the disease they are designed to prevent. Examples of this problem are feline respiratory vaccines causing a mild upper respiratory tract disease after immunisation, and the development of post vaccinal encephalitis subsequent to canine distemper vaccination. An even more alarming example is vaccine induction of clinical rabies (Esh et al., 1982, Pedersen et al., 1978)."

Double take: vaccinate your dog and he could actually get the disease you're vaccinating against, or long-lasting symptoms of the disease itself! Does your vet warn you of this possibility in the 21st Century?

Chapter 18
Hate mail

For the attention of Catherine O'Driscoll:

Having read the absolute nonsense that you have published, regarding vaccination, I would like to invite you to put your money where your very irresponsible mouth is:-

Take yourself off to any (or all) of the disease-ridden areas of the world, without immunising yourself (i.e., using any of the vaccines you have comprehensively rubbished) and live among the diseased communities – let's say, for two years. If you are in any way short of funds for this essential piece of scientific research, please let me know and I will be delighted to chair the fund-raising committee.

Yonni Wilson

Chapter 19
Insignificant and deluded

I had stumbled across scientific information which made me seriously concerned about vaccines, and specifically that we were encouraged to vaccinate our pets every year despite there being no science to support this practice. In fact, there was legitimate independent, but largely hidden, science to say that annual vaccination was neither necessary nor safe. This came from leading *pro-vaccinating* scientists in the veterinary field.

Back in the 90s, most people believed that their dogs' vaccines were safe. Even if we were over-vaccinating, what's the harm? For this reason, I felt it necessary to enlighten dog lovers so they might consider vaccinating less frequently.

Yet when I started to repeat this information, in an attempt to prevent other dogs suffering from vaccine-induced disease, I was attacked. Apparently I had become a liar, a crook, mad, a 'woo woo lady', and all sorts of other unpleasant appellations.

The world has many divisions and, as I was to discover, few elicit more emotion and disharmony than the schism between pro- and anti-vaccinators. The pro-camp asserts that vaccines have saved billions of lives; the anti-camp asserts that adverse effects do not justify the use of vaccines; they (we) also assert that good nutrition is a legitimate alternative to a jab, but without the risks, and that there are other safer alternatives to vaccines.

Generally speaking, the pro-vaccinators appear to consider themselves to be the true scientists, and they believe anti-vaccinators to be deluded.

The website 'rationalwiki.org' [1] has much to say about people like me. Apparently the "anti-vaccination movement (or vaccine hysteria) is an irrational trend of mistrust of vaccination. There are many ideas, not supported by any accepted evidence, that vaccines are inherently harmful. These beliefs often stem from other ideological positions; for instance, vaccination programs are seen as excessive government interference, or as an implementation of socialized medicine, although it's hardly just a conservative thing, as a look around *The Huffington Post* will tell you, and New Age woo is another reason some oppose vaccines.

"This particular pseudoscientific belief is unlikely to go away soon, despite the evidence attesting to the efficacy and safety of vaccines. ... Despite the hysteria and media coverage, there is no evidence linking currently popular vaccines and serious medical conditions."

There is no evidence linking vaccines and serious medical conditions? *No* evidence? Really? What a strange assertion from people who consider themselves to be rational.

Rachel Dunlop, in *The Guardian*, even put forward the argument that the media should not publish information from those who consider vaccinations to be unsafe. Her rationale was that there are more people who think they're safe than those who don't. [2]

The website slate.com [3] discusses an article from the medical journal *Vaccine*. [4, 5] Ironically, I used to write for Elsevier before I changed sides.

> "…the global anti-vaccination movement … is a loose coalition of rogue scientists, journalists, parents, and celebrities, who think that vaccines cause disorders like autism—a claim that has been thoroughly discredited by modern science.
>
> "The Vaccine article contains a number of important insights. First, the anti-vaccination cohort likes to move the goal posts: As scientists debunked the link between autism and mercury (once present in some childhood inoculations but now found mainly in certain flu vaccines), most activists dropped their mercury theory and point instead to aluminum or said that kids received "too many too soon." "Web 2.0 facilitated the debate of these new theories in public forums before their merits could be examined scientifically; when they were studied, the theories were not supported," notes the Vaccine article.
>
> "Second, it isn't clear whether scientists can "discredit" the movement's false claims at all: Its members are skeptical of what scientists have to say—not least because they suspect hidden connections between academia and pharmaceutical companies that manufacture the vaccines. (This, in itself, is ironic: In 2006 the British investigative reporter Brian Deer revealed that Andrew Wakefield, the British scientist who famously "showed" the connection between vaccination and autism in a now-retracted 1998 article in the Lancet, was himself handsomely compensated by trial lawyers who were readying to sue the vaccine manufacturers.)
>
> "In other words, mere exposure to the current state of the scientific consensus will not sway hard-core opponents of vaccination. They are too vested in upholding their contrarian theories; some have consulting and speaking gigs to lose while others simply enjoy a sense of belonging to a community, no matter how kooky."

I can't help pointing out that the publication *Vaccine* is a pro-vaccinating journal, almost certainly read and supported by people in the vaccine industry and vaccine researchers (i.e., people who make a living from vaccines, and corporations that make and sell vaccines). The clue is in the title.

However, if it's you or your loved-one who has what they call a rare serious side-effects, then the word 'rare' becomes a rather moot point. The majority of 'anti-vaxxers' were once pro-vaccinators, after all.

Those of us who take our doctors' or vets' advice have a right to know what the benefits and risks are, but if the industry is hiding the risks, how do we make an informed choice?

I don't recognise myself from any of these analyses, either. They seem, in fact, to be casting aspersions in order to dismiss the carnage.

There is also the little matter of truth. Point of fact: The veterinary vaccine industry has been insisting that vaccines need to be administered every year (against disease to which they are already immune) or your dog or cat might die. This is not true. What else isn't true?

It seems to me that there's a high level of arrogance in what these people say and how they say it. One 'scientist' even believes that people like me should be censored in the allegedly free press. The general public is to be denied information.

It seems to me that arrogance is always accompanied by ignorance – which is the act of ignoring. Yet how can you claim to be a scientist unless you engage in the open pursuit of truth? "Information is the currency of democracy," said Thomas Jefferson.

So here's some information that you need to know: vaccines are not always without harm. They can cause serious, debilitating, disease. They can even kill you. This is the truth that pro-vaccinators wish to stifle.

Open-mindedness – a spirit of enquiry – is one of the fundamental aims of education, but education itself frequently prevents individuals from questioning the information handed down to them. Ask any open-minded vet who's been through college. They're worked so hard that they don't have time to think for themselves. Dissenting viewpoints are quashed. This is the antithesis of education. As Vasudev said: "The sign of intelligence is that you are constantly wondering. Idiots are always dead sure about every damn thing they are doing in their life."

The problem pet owners and parents face is based upon the unfortunate fact that very few vets or doctors know very much about the subject of vaccination, and what they think they know is frequently incorrect. The shame is that their education has misled them into believing that they know more about all aspects of health than everyone else, even when they don't.

This is a tragedy for *everyone* concerned.

The other problem is that vets and doctors often (like the rest of us) latch onto snippets of information to support their views. One of my vets, for example, is clearly against any alternative healing systems and even real food for dogs. If I try in any way to turn her views into a discussion (i.e., state facts that may not agree with her views), her whole body tenses and turns away from me. The door is closed.

Education is defined as 'systematic instruction', and it depends very much on who is doing the instructing, and why. Having been put through an educational programme doesn't necessarily equate to knowing what is true; it could have as much to do with politics, funding and influence as it has to do with the truth.

Intelligence and wisdom, as opposed to education, are intrinsically allied to the questions you ask: why, why, why?

Doctors and vets are taught that vaccine reactions are very rare, yet they are not schooled in vaccinology – which is one of the complaints made by Ronald Schultz who has sought to end over-vaccination in companion animals through his involvement in the World Small Animal Veterinary Association Vaccine Guidelines Group. Ron has gone so far as to say that vets aren't qualified to advise on vaccination.

From what I can gather – and feel free to correct me if I'm wrong – vets are taught how to lift the skin around the neck and stick the needle in. They are taught about anaphylactic shock (where the animal will die if adrenaline or equivalent is not administered). Full stop. Go forth and vaccinate.

Vets are unable to tell you if a dog who has organ failure within days or even months of being vaccinated is vaccine damaged – because no-one teaches vets that vaccines can cause organ failure. Nor are they taught that vaccines can cause brain damage, epilepsy, arthritis, autoimmune diseases, leukaemia or cancer. If they do find out about these *accidents*, they are able to dismiss them as rarities because the *system* has decided that vaccine adverse effects should be hidden from us. Perceived coincidence, and a body of scientific research to say that such outcomes are possible are all we have to go on. And in order to know about the research, you have to go looking for it.

Vaccinology is a complex specialisation. Veterinary education is a generalisation. People specialise because it's impossible to know everything there is to know about everything. There just isn't enough time. The vet you visit with your pet is a General Practitioner.

Why do doctors and vets believe that vaccine reactions are rare? Because it is politic for them to believe this. Why is it politic? Well, on the surface it's because people believe that vaccines have saved the world from viral and bacterial diseases like polio, smallpox, distemper and parvovirus. I wouldn't dream of arguing that vaccines don't protect against disease, although I would add the caveat that they don't always do this. Ron Schultz, for example, has demonstrated that vaccinated dogs develop immunity to the diseases they are vaccinated against, and if they have circulating antibodies in their blood, they simply won't get the disease. But not all vaccinated dogs develop antibodies.

There are many instances where highly vaccinated populations nevertheless experience epidemics (for example, 6-18).

But because no-one wants anyone to die from preventable diseases, people close their ears to people like me who suggest that these reactions aren't as rare as one might think. Believing that vaccine reactions are rare, what would the harm be in giving animals annual shots, especially as the booster provides the opportunity for an annual health check (and coincidentally boosts practice income)?

Since unnecessary vaccinations are (they are taught) unlikely to cause harm… because reactions are very rare… it would be natural to close your eyes and ears to anyone who believes that vaccines are potentially harmful. Or, indeed, that they're just not necessary.

The problem, though, is that any reaction to a vaccine that is not needed is unacceptable.

Nevertheless, I read pro-vaccinators' analyses of so-called anti-vaccination campaigners, and sit back on my heels and ask myself if I'm misleading myself, and trying to mislead the dog world. Self-doubt *must* underpin the pursuit of truth. The day you think you know it all you stop learning.

Which is what makes the Dunning-Kruger effect so interesting [19]. This is a cognitive bias wherein relatively unskilled individuals suffer from illusory superiority, mistakenly assessing their ability to be much higher than is accurate. This bias is attributed to an inability of the unskilled to accurately evaluate their own ability level. Conversely, highly skilled individuals may underestimate their relative competence, erroneously assuming that tasks that are easy for them are also easy for others.

Not having been trained as a scientist, I suffer from a lack of confidence – which is why I rarely make assumptions and am always asking further questions. Further, when my writings go into print, I think I'm open to far more challenge than the average convention-touting scientists. People with titles and letters can easily fall into the trap of thinking they know more than they do.

Chapter 20

Truth doesn't make money

So back in the 90s, Steve Dean, who became head of the British government's veterinary medicines licensing body, kept making comments in his 'vets view' column in *Dog World* to the effect that anyone who questioned pet vaccines was scaremongering and worthy of ridicule. So John, in direct response, came up with another bright idea: "Let's break the larger survey (the one we had been unable to get off the ground due to a shortage of people willing to complete the questionnaire) into smaller surveys," he said. "We'll be able to fund those ourselves. And we can start with a vaccine survey."

With the help of Jean Dodds and the homeopathic vet Christopher Day, John designed a short questionnaire. It took up two sides of A4 paper. One side explained the questionnaire and left room for the dog's name and the owner's address, plus vaccination history, and the second side carried a grid. At the top of the grid was a timeframe (this illness arose within one day, one week, one month, etc., after vaccination), and down the left side of the grid was a list of canine diseases. Pet owners merely had to tick a box if their dog was ill, and indicate when that illness began in relation to his shot. We were, in fact, testing Chris Day's observation in practice that, where the start date of an illness was known, 80 percent began within three months of a shot.

In answer to people who claimed that we were in it for the money, participation in the survey was free: we funded it ourselves and did the work for free. In order to increase the number of dogs covered, and also to reduce any bias, many glorious and wonderful members of Canine Health Concern took survey forms to the park and asked fellow dog owners to complete them, and knocked on neighbours' doors and encouraged them to participate. Additionally, we paid the full advertising rate (£600 at the time) to have the questionnaire printed in *Dog World*.

Then one day the telephone rang. "Are you sitting down, Catherine?" Nick Mays, a dog journalist, asked me. "Yes, why?" I replied.

"I have bad news, he said. It's about Paula Shires." Paula, you will remember, was the editor of *Pet Dogs* magazine. "Paula and her husband are dead," Nick told me.

Naturally I was distressed. "Oh God. Was it a car accident?" I couldn't think of any other reason for both Paula and her husband to die together.

"No," Nick said gently. "Paula's husband killed her and their dogs, and then he killed himself. They were expected at Paula's father's for dinner but didn't show up, so he and her brother went to their house and found them."

I couldn't imagine how horrible this would have been for Paula's family. It flashed through my mind that they had been bumped off for featuring the Canine Health Concern survey in the magazine, but this is the thing with the mind: lots of thoughts come up from our left-brain filing systems. It's better to observe those thoughts and then look for any corroborating evidence. We shouldn't believe these thoughts immediately.

The horror of this tragedy coursed through my body.

I later learnt from Paula's assistant Fiona that her husband was violently abusive and an alcoholic, and she had found love with someone else. Her husband had discovered this and murdered her and the dogs, and then he killed himself.

The dog world was rocked; it was such a tragedy. And I missed Paula very much on a personal level. Sharing the same birthday and both of us living with violent men unnerved me, too.

As far as CHC was concerned, though, Paula's loss presented us with difficulties. Remember that my profession was public relations. I knew how to get stories into the media – to illustrate the point, I have to say I was good at it. PR is time-consuming and expensive; clients want and demand solid measures of success. My clients got their success.

Yet whenever I contacted any of the dog magazines to raise the issue of canine health, and as a consequence implicate the multi-billion pet products' industry, I got the brush off. Editors who used to speak to me openly and happily stopped taking my calls or, if I actually got through to them directly, spoke in a clipped and uptight way, and got rid of me as quickly as possible. Getting a press release published, which I knew how to do and – as I say – I had been very successful at, became almost impossible.

We reasoned that either the editors were not ready to question pet vaccines and processed pet food, or they were concerned about losing advertising revenue. Besides, I wasn't a vet, and I was seen as contentious and a trouble-maker. Suddenly I had social leprosy.

Pet Dogs, meanwhile, was being kept going by Paula's assistant Fiona until a buyer could be found, and I was asked to contribute regular articles. "It's coming up to flea season," Fiona said one day. "Can you write an article about flea control products?" So I did.

By the time I had finished writing the article, I was literally shaking; I was in shock. I had discovered, by cross-referencing (using the book *C is for Chemicals*, Green Print) the ingredients listed in the NOAH datasheet compendium, that flea control shampoos, sprays and spot-ons for dogs contained chemicals that could cause cancer and other serious health issues.

Piperonyl butoxide, for example, is 'highly toxic if absorbed through the skin, less so if swallowed. It has been shown to cause cancer in animals, although the US Environmental Protection Agency has concluded that it is not carcinogenic (will not cause cancer) to people.'

There were flea collars containing a chemical called Carbaryl. The World Health Organisation (WHO) listed Carbaryl as 'moderately hazardous': it is a mutagen and carcinogenic and teratogenic in laboratory animals (this means it can cause mutations in cells; it can induce cancer, and it can cause birth defects when absorbed in pregnancy). It was also more toxic to dogs than other animals.

One spot-on contained Permethrin, which the US FDA listed as a possible carcinogen. Manufacturers warned that dogs shouldn't be allowed to swim for 12 hours after treatment because the product is 'extremely dangerous to fish'. People shouldn't handle the treated area on the dog for three to six hours, and treated dogs shouldn't be allowed to sleep with people, particularly children.

Another capsule contained an organophosphorus compound, a class of chemicals, 'some of which are considered to be the most toxic chemicals ever manufactured'.

"The high acute toxicity of organophosphates stem from their action against a vital enzyme in the body that regulates the functioning of the nervous system."

A flea spray listed Dichlorvos as an ingredient. WHO listed Dichlorvos as 'highly hazardous'. It's poisonous if swallowed, absorbed through the skin, or inhaled. It is a mutagen and possible carcinogen, and a potent anticholinesterase agent (blocking the transmission of nerve messages).

The manufacturers stated that the product was designed to have a high margin of safety, before advising that "if signs of toxicity appear, administer the antidote atrophine sulphate at 0.1-0.2mg/kg intravenously or intraperitoneally and apply artificial respiration". I wondered how you could prevent your dog from inhaling and swallowing the spray, and how it would fail to be absorbed through the skin since it was sprayed onto the skin.

I stated in the article that there are safer ways of dealing with fleas. Garlic repels fleas, as does apple cider vinegar. Those of us who champion the natural diet believe, from our experience, that raw meaty bones help keep the immune system healthy, and a dog with a healthy immune system is unattractive to fleas. Certainly, my dogs have not had fleas since I started feeding the natural diet over twenty-five years ago.

There are also safer homeopathic remedies, and herbs that are said to combat fleas and worms.

I took Sammie to the vet whilst my mind was still swimming with this information, and took the opportunity to ask the vet in passing if they studied the toxic properties of flea control products in college.

"Oh yes," he said, "but you don't want your dog to get fleas".

"I give my dogs garlic," I replied, "and they don't appear to get fleas."

"Oh but Staffordshire fleas are big strong fleas. Garlic won't work here," he replied in a macho and patronising sort of way, his chest literally puffing with male pride.

I only just stopped myself from retorting that I expect Staffordshire vets have great big willies, too.

Shortly after submitting the article, I got a call from a freelance dog journalist. "I'm really embarrassed to be calling you," he said, "but I've been asked to write an article to replace your article about flea control."

"Really?" I said. "Why?"

"Because they want to run an advertising feature alongside the article, and they won't get advertisers with your article. I thought I needed to tell you."

My heart sank and I have to admit to feeling extreme disgust. Had Paula been alive, this would never have happened. She was a dog lover with integrity, and she would have wanted her readers to know if the products they regularly used on their dogs had the ability to harm them. I was sad, too, that another journalist, and a dog lover, would be prepared to write an article to please the advertisers. But, then, as Oscar Wilde said: "None of us is perfect; I myself am peculiarly susceptible to draughts."

Besides, I was learning quickly that the world is full of people who are willing to sell our loved-ones out. You just have to recognise it and let it go. You can make yourself ill condemning other people.

But if the article wasn't going to be published, we could at least alert the other dog magazines and even the national papers. I wrote a press release and sent it out. Within two weeks, the British government announced that it was withdrawing Carbaryl – which we had featured in the release – from head lice shampoos for children. Soon, someone at the VMD anonymously sent us paperwork to show that the VMD had held a meeting with the manufacturers of flea control products and agreed to give them 18 months to use up their Carbaryl stocks.

This made me sit back on my heels a little, with a big question mark fluttering over my head. The VMD is the official body in the UK – the government department – charged with the task of ensuring the safety of veterinary products. And yet the government was putting the financial interests of manufacturers ahead of the potential cancer risk to dogs. The implications of this were, it seemed to me, enormous. It implied that the government regulator was more interested in corporate profits than animal safety – and if this applied to flea control products, it would also apply to vaccines and drugs.

Meanwhile, a paper [1] determined a significant link between the use of pet anti-flea sprays and brain tumours in children who were exposed to them, both in the womb and after birth. The risk was 70% higher for children exposed whilst in the womb, and particularly where the child was diagnosed as having a brain tumour before the age of five, where it was 150% higher. The risk doubled when the pregnant mother had prepared, applied or cleaned up flea/tick products herself, and when people didn't follow product instructions. The researchers recommended that further research be conducted to identify the specific chemicals to blame.

It was becoming clear that the government's policy in terms of chemicals and drugs was one of pragmatism and corporate profits. So long as toxic products are used on animals that don't enter the human food chain, then humans would be safe.

Except they're not. Flea control products can cause brain tumours in children.

Chapter 21

Samson in my head

When Prudence died of leukaemia, I panicked. Oliver had died when he was four, and Pru died when she was six. Chappie had thyroid disease and ruptured cruciate ligaments, and Sophie had incredibly painful arthritis. Sometimes it felt as though I was constantly throwing medicines and remedies into my dogs, and worrying about them. My dream of sharing my life with dogs had turned into a nightmare.

I was now worrying about our young Samson, even though he was a handsome, strapping, young man. So I asked Chrissie Mason to conduct a radionics analysis for him, just to be sure that he was alright. I fully expected the analysis to come back with glowing praise for my beautiful boy, but Chrissie instead said that she would like him to have a blood test because she wasn't confident that all was as it should be. This was duly arranged, and Christopher Day reported that "Samson is waging a battle within his immune system". Sammie had autoimmune disease. He was two years old.

You will remember that Samson had a reaction to his second puppy shot, and we found him in the garden the next day with paralysed back legs. The next year Samson received a booster because I still, at that time, knew nothing about vaccine adverse effects. That night his head swelled up like a football and he ran around the house all night screaming. I telephoned the emergency vet and she told me to bring him to the surgery the next day where he was given an injection. I didn't ask what my dogs were being given in those days – I trusted my vet's superior knowledge implicitly. The swelling went down, and we carried on as if nothing unusual had happened.

Eventually, I began to learn about the adverse effects of vaccines and stopped vaccinating, and then we moved to our rented cottage in Derbyshire. I wasn't overly worried for Sam – he was being treated holistically for an autoimmune disease that showed no overt symptoms, and I asked Rolf Gordon of Dulwich Health to test the new property for Geopathic Stress and was extremely relieved to discover that it was clear. Ironically, it had high radon levels instead!

Due to the distance, we moved from Chris Day's practice and became clients of a local homeopathic vet, Peter Gregory. By this time we had our dogs on Ian Billinghurst's raw diet, and the improvements in their health gave us great hope, and much to be thankful for. We were surrounded by fields and cattle and sheep, and there was an abundance of rolling grassy slopes upon which we could walk our dogs. The garden wrapped itself around the house, and we had three paddocks the dogs could play in. This was especially wonderful for Chappie and Sophie who, by this time, were quite elderly and content to pootle in the paddocks rather than go on long walks.

The young dogs, on the other hand – Samson and Gwinnie – enjoyed massive long walks amidst hills and valleys, and swam in the nearby rivers. Most of the year, except during tourist season, we had all of this mostly to ourselves, too. It was heaven. So my mind and heart decided that I shouldn't worry too much about Sam. He was in good hands.

Whilst still in Northamptonshire, we had noticed something interesting about Samson. Whenever one of us was away, Sammie appeared to know when we were coming home: he would rush to sit panting at the door at the exact same time as either of us decided to return.

This continued when we moved. On one occasion I had gone back to our old village to see friends, and John asked me what time I had set off home, as Sam had been waiting expectantly at the back door for some time. Northampton was over 90 miles or around two hours away. I hadn't looked at my watch when I left, so I telephoned my friends and asked them what time I had set off for home, carefully avoiding saying that Sam had indicated the time. "Mum," Joanna shouted, "What time did Catherine leave?"

"About 4.30," her mum replied. John confirmed that this was the time Sam had waited at the back door for me.

He did the same thing when we returned from a holiday in Greece, which was a few thousand miles away. The plane had taxied up the runway to take off and then came to a halt and we were left sitting on the plane for an hour while a repair was made. Our doggie sitters reported that Sammie had run to the garden gate and waited for us when the plane had first taxied up the runway, and again when it actually took off. Clearly Samson was inside our heads – even at that great distance.

Reading about research being conducted by the biologist Rupert Sheldrake who later wrote the book, *Dogs Who Know When Their Owners Are Coming Home*, we contacted him and offered to take part in his study. Rupert sent a researcher along. His research assistant Pam put a video with a timer pointing towards the back door and took me off on a random drive and we stopped off at a pub. Sure enough, the exact time she said: "We'll go back now," Samson woke up from a sleep and rushed to the back door panting in anticipation.

Samson ended up on a TV programme about Dr Sheldrake's work called *Strange but True*. On the day of the shoot, My darling Samson impressed everyone. Not only was he incredibly handsome, but he was also incredibly intelligent. I had never formally trained Sammie – we just talked with one-another and he cooperated willingly. He did take after take just as he was asked, and I was incredibly proud of him. It was as though he knew exactly what he was doing and why.

At the end of the day, as we were walking towards the car to come home, I looked at him and received a 'knowing' that Sammie had done what he had come to this earth to do, and that he would leave us very soon. Denial is a very strong driver, so I put this thought to the back of my mind.

Chapter 22

Corporate power

CHC, and my enquiries into vaccine adverse effects, were causing a stir in the dog world. The phone was virtually ringing off the hook. It would ring and I would answer, and I'd spend maybe an hour talking to someone about their dog's illness and vaccine adverse effects, and I'd put the phone back down only for it to immediately ring again. Frequently I was spending almost entire days on the phone, which of course no-one was paying me to do. I was writing *What Vets Don't Tell You About Vaccines* in between these calls, and fitting in some paid copywriting work to try to keep the roof over our heads. There was very little time to care for myself or the dogs properly.

We had also arranged to import copies of Ian Billinghurst's book into the country and were selling these and ploughing the profits back into promoting CHC, Ian's book, and the natural diet further. This in itself took up a lot of time – raising invoices and parcelling up books, and dealing with enquiries from people who wanted to know more about natural feeding.

People started calling in on us at home out of the blue, too. They might have read one of my articles in the dog press, or they'd read my Golden Retriever book and just called by to say 'hi', or they wanted us to answer questions about natural feeding, or even to ask us to demonstrate how to use a kitchen processor to mash up the dogs' vegetables. Usually they called when I hadn't had time to dust for a few days, and I'd be sitting there entertaining visitors whilst squirming inwardly at the dust on the bookcase.

One day a woman came up to me when I was out walking the dogs. "Are you Catherine O'Driscoll from Canine Health Concern?" she asked. Soon she was visiting me in my home, and mentioned that her brother worked in the pet food industry.

"I expect someone will offer you a lot of money to go away," she said one day.

"We wouldn't take it," my mouth replied very quickly without allowing time for my brain to engage. I don't know if she was sounding me out to see if I could be bribed, but it was a 'no' from the depths of my soul. John insisted that we break off contact with the lady, which was a pity if her brother's career and her comments about bribery were innocent rather than an approach from industry. I hope she didn't take it personally.

John got in touch with the local Trading Standards officers and asked them if they would be prepared to investigate the claims made by pet food manufacturers, particularly the claim that their food was 'complete and balanced'. The officer was really interested, and extremely positive about putting processed pet food through tests in the lab. He went off, saying he'd be in touch. But we waited weeks and nothing happened.

So John got in touch again, eventually sending a recorded delivery letter asking whether they were going to do the tests. In the end the officer telephoned and asked to come back for a meeting, perhaps to avoid putting what he had to say in writing. He explained that corporations have massive budgets for legal cases, whereas the Trading Standards Authority had a limited budget. "What happens," he said, "is that the corporation in question will say, 'Fine. We'll be using this hotshot firm of lawyers. We'll have six lawyers on the case, costing hundreds each per day, and the action will last at least two years.'

"We just don't have a budget to match corporations." He confirmed that the only way that Trading Standards could admonish a pet food company would be if a can or packet didn't carry what was stated on the side of the can or packet. For example, if it had an elastic band in it.

So in terms of the contents of their cans and packets, and their advertising claims, it seemed that the pet food industry was above the law and wielded more power (aka money) than governments.

Another man came to gossip about the fate of David Williams, the RVC professor who had worked with Sally Cronk to set up the seminar in 1994, which we were told was to raise money so that David could research autoimmune haemolytic anaemia. Sally had received a very unhappy letter from David, saying that he had not received the money she had raised for his research. It had gone to some other project, he said, nothing to do with autoimmune haemolytic anaemia. He had also been told that under no circumstances was he to write a glowing report about the seminar, and especially not to show interest in the presentation Richard Allport had given on homeopathy.

Our visitor told us that Professor Williams had been head hunted by the Animal Health Trust in the UK, a charity that relies heavily on research grants from industry and boasts vaccine development as one of its skills. He told us he was very friendly with this organisation, and had been told that David was, in fact, being punished for his involvement in the seminar. He had been 'put in a back room and had his funding removed'.

I have often wondered what really happened to him. All I knew for sure is that he wrote a disgruntled letter to Sally because he hadn't received his funding, and I knew that he had moved to the Animal Health Trust. Someone later said that he had gone to America so he could get some research funding.

It seemed an extreme punishment for someone who had done nothing other than get himself involved with a fundraising seminar in order to continue with his work.

I tracked David Williams down and had a chat with him on the phone, merely to ascertain whether the rumours were true. He had become an eye specialist, and was lecturing at Cambridge University. "No," he confirmed, "I never did get the research funding Sally raised. But I was delighted to go back to the Animal Health Trust."

Sally subsequently wrote to the RVC and they replied that the funding had been re-allocated back to its original purpose.

David told me on the phone that he was fairly certain that vaccines last for longer than a year, but that the vaccine industry wouldn't fund research to prove it, and no independent scientist would be able to get funding. David didn't give me the opportunity to tell him that the research had been done by Ron Schultz, back in the 70s, no doubt because he was a professor and I was just a dog owner, and he probably didn't think I had anything worth listening to. So I emailed him the references later.

I have to admit that I was disturbed that a professor who taught veterinary students was unaware of the duration of immunity studies. They had become a central tenet of my work – how come, in 2013, veterinary lecturers were still oblivious to the science?

Chapter 23

Samson's light

One day not long after Samson's television appearance, John came back from an early morning walk and said: "Sam seems to be dragging behind on walks."

I burst into tears; all the energy draining from me. I knew, I just knew that this was serious. I prayed to God that if He wished to take Samson back, please give me the strength to cope with his loss.

Samson was already on a regime of homeopathic remedies for his autoimmunity, and we were keeping a regular eye on him. In addition to seeing Peter Gregory, our local homeopathic vet, Samson was also registered with a nearby conventional veterinary practice where they could deal with cuts, sprains and any formal tests that were required, such as bloodwork and x-rays. I took him for a check-up but was told there was nothing wrong with him.

So I took Sammie to a local spiritual healer in the hope that this might help him. She said that she could feel something untoward in his stomach region and suggested he get an x-ray. So John took our boy to our conventional vet again, asking for an x-ray. Whilst in the reception, two men who said that they were very experienced dog owners commented on how healthy and vibrant Samson looked. The vet again said there was nothing wrong with him and sent John home with a packet of antibiotics, presumably as a palliative for a dog owner who might expect to come home with something. The vet refused to do an x-ray.

Two days later, Samson collapsed against my leg groaning. Although Peter Gregory was away on holiday, we decided to take Samson to the practice that rented Peter his veterinary rooms. If our own conventional vet wouldn't conduct an x-ray, perhaps this one would?

So we arrived at the practice with Sam, explaining what had happened, and asked if they would please x-ray him. Vets, of course, have a system of etiquette where they won't treat another vet's patient without the previous vet's permission. They weren't willing to do it. Sometimes John's rudeness came in handy, though. He basically kicked up a stink, pointing out that they had no ethical or moral right to refuse to look at a sick animal.

"Well, leave him here," the vet said, "and come back around 3 o'clock. We can't do the x-ray yet, we've got other patients to see."

"Not good enough," John said with a considerable amount of aggression. "He needs to be x-rayed now."

"Don't speak to me like that," the vet said indignantly.

I tried to calm things down and pacify everyone, pointing out that, rather than argue, it would perhaps be better if someone would please take a look at Samson. The vet thankfully heard me and looked at him, and saw that his gums were paper white. "Oh my God," she exclaimed.

Samson was taken for an immediate x-ray without anaesthetic. He didn't need an anaesthetic because he didn't have the energy to move and spoil the shot. Sometimes you wonder what it takes for someone to listen to what you have to say.

The results were devastating: Samson had a massive tumour on his spleen: a haemangiosarcoma. This is a rapidly growing, highly invasive type of cancer that arises from the lining of blood vessels; it's hard to stop it spreading elsewhere in the body. Frequently the tumour can rupture, causing the patient to swiftly bleed to death.

We were sent home with Samson and told to bring him back the next morning for an operation to remove his spleen, and we were overjoyed when we heard that the operation had been successful, although the tumour had been unusually large. Later I was told by a vet friend that it was quite wrong to send Samson home as the spleen was dangerously close to rupturing. Jean Dodds also warned me that she had rarely come across a dog who survived for any length of time with haemangiosarcoma, even with an operation.

But we had great faith because we had more in the tool box than the normal conventional veterinary client. We had homeopathy.

When Samson was diagnosed with cancer, Hilary Jupp telephoned me. Hilary, you will remember, is a medical intuitive and a homeopath who has spent her life studying health and healing systems. Immediately she began to speak on Samson's behalf:

"I am so sorry that I have cancer," Samson said through Hilary. "I want you to know that I intend to beat it. You have had so much sorrow in your life, and we all love you so much, and I don't want you to suffer any more. I will do everything I can to heal this cancer."

Curiously, Sammie had been sleeping in the sitting room when Hilary phoned and I was further along in my office. He came into the room as she was speaking and looked at me, wagging his tail and barking. It seemed that he was telling me that it was indeed him speaking.

Not long after Sammie's operation, however, I was in the house alone with the dogs and Sam came up to me panting, and then he collapsed. That moment is seared into my soul, because he was dying in front of me, doing what is often called the death rattle. I got down on the floor and begged him not to go. "Please Sammie, don't go," I pleaded. "We'll go walkies, and play, and I'll give you beautiful dinners. I love you so much. Please don't go."

And he decided not to go.

That wonderful dog sat up and bore the pain because I had asked him to. It is this which seared my soul, and confirmed to me that dogs are far more than most people give them credit for. They are the embodiment of love. And, as Samson demonstrated, the greatest masters are the greatest servants.

I phoned Peter Gregory and he agreed to call in on us shortly, on his way home from work.

"I wouldn't normally suggest this," said Peter, "but I think he's got an infection, and he needs antibiotics."

Homeopaths don't tend to use antibiotics due to their sometimes dire side-effects – but there is a place for everything in this world. Peter made the half-hour drive back to the surgery where he obtained antibiotics from his conventional colleagues, and then drove back and gave them to Samson. He left us after 10 o'clock that night.

Two or three weeks later, Samson and Gwinnie came walking with us, up on a high ridge in the stunningly beautiful Peak District. My wonderful boy strode around with all the beauty of the most ruggedly handsome dog in the world, and I was so proud of him, and so grateful that he had made a full recovery. But this was before he stopped eating.

My sister Leslie had taken her dog, Polly, to a spiritual healer working from Richard Allport's homeopathic veterinary practice near London. Charlie Siddle had achieved spectacular results for Polly who had Addison's disease. After her first session, Leslie and Glenn had taken Polly out for a walk and she had run like the wind, as she had done before Addison's was diagnosed. I booked Sammie in to see the healer.

"It's such a pity he had the op," said Charlie. "It's very hard to heal cancer once the body has been opened up. It makes the cancer spread."

But you cannot change what has already been done, so I did what I *could* do, and booked Sam in for another session. Although it was a hundred mile drive, I was keen to do anything for Samson that might alleviate his suffering and even keep him alive.

Unfortunately, the next time we made the trip, Charlie had been kicked in the head by a horse and couldn't make the appointment. We had set out too early for the phone call that would have prevented us from going, and mobile phones were not the norm in those days. So, disappointed, I put Sam back in the car and set off back home.

Still Sammie wouldn't eat, and he had very little energy. We continued with the homeopathic remedies, trying desperately to save him. I slept on the sofa downstairs so I could be with him through the night as he was no longer able to walk upstairs.

Two months after the operation to remove his spleen, Samson asked to go outside at night. The frost was thick in the garden, but all he wanted to do was lie in the freezing cold, so I slept on the floor by the open door to be with him until he was ready to come in.

When John woke me the next morning, I immediately went to Samson and he shimmered with light. Beautiful white light streamed out of him, illuminating the room, and he wagged his tail to see me. It was as though he had waited for me to wake up, and was saying goodbye. I kissed him and stroked him, then dashed upstairs to get dressed while John phoned the vet. We agreed that it was time to let our darling go.

Samson died while I was upstairs.

John and I just sat and sobbed our hearts out.

Then we gathered our little boy's body up and took him to the car, and drove to a local facility where we had arranged to have his body cremated. Arriving at the agreed time, we discovered that there was no-one there to meet us, so we waited for an hour until we realised that no-one was coming. We drove home, still with our boy in the back of the car.

When we got home, Peter Gregory and his lovely wife Cher were waiting outside the house. John had phoned Peter to tell him that Sammie had gone, and they had driven over in the hope of seeing him. He was such a special dog that this wonderful vet and his wife wanted to see him one last time.

Eventually we drove our darling boy to a pet cemetery in Wales, where he was honoured and his body was cremated.

I missed my Sammie so much, so I asked Hilary to speak to him; my sisters had been spiritualists and I was no stranger to the belief that the spirit lives on. I wanted to know why he had died when he was only five years old. I believe that Oliver and Prudence died to put my feet on this path; there was no need for Samson to die. I was already doing what I came here to do. Why?

"He wants you to tune into him yourself," Hilary said. I had no idea how I would do this. "Just sit quietly and think of him," she told me.

John was away, so this gave me the chance to do as Sammie had asked. I sat quietly all weekend, apart from walking and playing with the dogs, and finally, at 7pm on Sunday evening, he came to me. He wrapped his love around me and projected a knowing into me. "I died for my love of humanity," was all he said.

This seemed strange to me; I didn't understand. Why would he die for his love of humanity? Did he have a mission to help humans, as well as the animals? Certainly he was a being of great love, and great intelligence. Certainly he had seemed to know precisely what he was doing when he was filming to show that dogs are far more than we know they are.

And certainly I am not one of the people who loves dogs because I don't love humans. I love humans very much, and have great compassion for our species. For me, alerting dog owners to the dangers of over-vaccination and processed pet food was as much for the humans as the dogs. I didn't want people standing over the bodies of their dead dogs asking why, and coming up with no answers. Perhaps Sam and I had been working as a team? Perhaps Sam had died to show that one shot is all it takes – for his vaccine damage started with his puppy shots. And maybe he had a message for homeopaths who still vaccinate and imagine that homeopathy can cure vaccine damage?

Months later, Cher phoned me, very excited, because another Golden Retriever who looked just like Sam had been signed up with the practice. "He's full of love, just like Samson," Cher said.

I wanted to hit Cher because Samson was gone, and I wanted to hug her because she knew. She knew that Samson was a being of love and light. She knew that he was a spiritually evolved being whose only wish was to serve humankind.

Chapter 24

One consciousness

I have spent most of my life living with dogs, and I recognise them as my best friends. Over the years they have taught me that animals are spiritual beings.

Chappie, my first born, taught me that We Are All One.

Sometimes Chappie would stick his head around a corner, and I would think I was looking at myself. Our energies had merged, and we were the same being. There was no me and him; there was no separation.

We are all One – everything that has life is made of the same Source energy. That Source energy, the energy that holds us all together, is Love. Love is the Creative Principle.

When another living being suffers, we all suffer – because we are all connected.

My dogs taught me this.

While I was researching the damage caused to dogs by vaccines they did not need, it was natural for me to also look at the damage caused to human children, and the science behind it. Maybe this is why Samson accepted his fate of death by vaccine. Was it because of his love for humanity and the path his death would open up for me?

We are constantly told by governments and the media that vaccines are safe, and that those of us who question the assertion of safety are … well, misguided.

So alongside reeling at the vaccine-related illnesses and deaths of countless dogs, I was also being exposed to similar stories from parents of human children. As I have already stated, humans and dogs share blood, tissue, cells, immune systems, and genes, and both species are capable of having inflammatory and autoimmune reactions to drugs and biologics.

One such victim of the lie that vaccines are safe is Michael Belkin who testified In 1999 before America's Advisory Committee on Immunization Practices, Centers for Disease Control and Prevention. Michael's daughter, Lyla Rose, had died within 16 hours of receiving a mandatory hepatitis B vaccination.

Michael was formerly a quantitative strategist at Solomon Brothers, and an advisor to some of the largest financial institutions in the world. As such, he was qualified to analyse and make conclusions about statistics.

"Based on that experience," he testified, "I am astonished that the scientists on this Committee would disregard or cover up data showing the number and severity of adverse reactions to this vaccine. Science is observing and learning from what is observed. The assertions of the CDC that the many reported reactions to this vaccine do not exist or are coincidences violates the basic principle of science, which is rooted in the observation and analysis of data.

"A benefit/risk analysis of the hepatitis B vaccine for the average infant in America, not born to infected parents, must conclude that the VAERS data on adverse reactions shows the real-world risk of a newborn infant dying or being injured by the hepatitis B vaccine is a greater threat than the remote chance of contracting the primarily blood-transmitted disease.

"At her death, Lyla had four of the eight highest-reported symptoms in the VAERS hepatitis B vaccine adverse reaction data. The NY Medical Examiner observed brain swelling at the autopsy but refused to record that or mention the hepatitis B vaccine Lyla received in the autopsy report.

"I hold each one of you who participated in the promulgation or perpetuation of that mandated new-born vaccination policy personally responsible for my daughter's death, and the deaths and injuries of all the other beautiful, healthy infants who are now victims of the hepatitis B vaccine. Your negligence is the proximate cause of my daughter's death and you have failed to exercise reasonable care.

"At the NVIC, we are overwhelmed following-up constant new reports of deaths, seizures and autoimmune reactions following hepatitis B vaccination. Because the CDC refuses to acknowledge this large number of serious adverse reactions, hospitals and doctors who have been misled about the risks continue to administer the vaccine and then deny any vaccine connection when children die, get ill, or have seizures within hours or days. CDC officials tell parents they have never heard of hepatitis B vaccine reactions.

"This is a lie. For this government to continue to insist that hepatitis B vaccine adverse reaction reports do not exist is negligent, unethical – and it is a crime against the children of America.

"It is a sad day for the US when the nation's children need protection from the official medical authorities who are charged with protecting them from disease."

Chapter 25
Hidden influences

Samson once came to me and took my arm in his mouth, and led me up the hall towards the dining room. He let go of my arm at the end of the passage and nodded towards the dining room floor where the puppy Gwinnie had left a poo. We didn't use the formal dining room much, and Sammie knew that I would want to clear it up.

Samson had intelligence, and he knew I would listen to him.

Gwinnie was a precocious pup, a punk. She taught herself to go upstairs but lost her nerve for the way down. I was below her on the stairs, trying to persuade the little princess to summon the courage to walk down, and Samson walked up the stairs past me and looked at Gwin, turned around and walked down, telling her over his shoulder to follow him. She was too scared, so he walked up the stairs again and showed her how it was done, saying gently, 'follow me'. But she was too scared. So he walked up a third time and urged her again, and she followed him down.

When she was older, and Gwinnie was in the snow-clad garden, and Samson was sleeping by my side, he woke up suddenly and came rushing to me, urgently wanting to tell me something. I followed him, and he led me to the garden. Gwinnie had jumped the wall again and was off running through the fields. Samson thought I should know. How, I wondered, did Samson know that Gwinnie had absconded when he appeared to be sleeping by my side?

Not long after Samson died, I read an article about Reiki. Reiki, the article explained, is a system of energy healing, but also a spiritual practice, that was developed by a Japanese monk called Mikao Usui. The article spoke of incredible healing achieved through the laying on of hands.

Immediately I was reminded of Christ's promise that, "All I do shall ye do and more". I had often wondered, and still do, how Christ was able to heal the sick and even raise people from the dead, and I trusted that humanity would one day see his promise fulfilled: that one day we would also know how to heal. It seemed to me that maybe Reiki was taking us nearer to Christ's promise. I found a Reiki initiation course nearby, and booked onto it.

I remember sitting cross-legged on the floor with the other initiates, answering the Reiki Master's question as to why we were there. And I remember tears streaming down my face, saying that Samson had died and that I had driven miles to see a healer, and that I wanted to be able to heal

– or at least do something – for my dogs myself.

I also remember saying that the phone was constantly ringing, and that people were sucking the energy out of me. I hadn't planned to say that – it just came out. Sometimes the soul knows when healing is available, and jumps at the chance to receive it.

The Reiki Master taught me a technique to prevent 'energy vampires' from draining the energy from me. "Draw a circle and a cross with your hand around all of your Chakras," she said.

In the break, I started chatting to a man who had come for a Reiki initiation. His name was Brian James, and he was a former BBC documentary producer. Brian was now freelance and interested in what I had to say about pet food and over-vaccination, and he said he might be prepared to produce a documentary on the issue.

It's said that when you undergo a Reiki initiation you can experience great shifts in your life, and I certainly did. I met up with Brian later and told him the story and gave him all of my contacts – including the details of key players who disagreed with me – and left him to it.

Chapter 26
A brush with the regulator

Meanwhile, *What Vets Don't Tell You About Vaccines* was delivered to us from the printers. We hadn't tried to get a publisher for it, feeling that its contents were too contentious and that it would potentially leave us open to be sued. We couldn't see a publisher taking it on. Instead, we published the book ourselves. We also found a printer who was using what was then new-fangled technology, printing direct from a computer. This meant that the costs were lower than previous methods which required a huge investment in printer's plates. We could order a small print run and reprint extra copies if we managed to make any sales.

I had previously sent the manuscript to Simon, a friend who was editor of a local newspaper. He'd had formal training as a journalist and understood the law as it applied to the written word. He phoned me after reading it.

"You can't publish this," he said. "You just can't publish it. They'll sue your arse off." (Simon was always prone to colourful language.)

"The vaccine manufacturers will get hold of it, and it will go straight to their legal departments, and they'll go through it with a fine toothcomb looking for reasons to sue you. Publish this," he said, "and you can kiss goodbye to everything you own."

The results of our vaccine survey were in the book. I had already completed the manuscript before we decided to conduct the survey, and I vowed that if the findings didn't support what I had already written, the manuscript would go in the bin. I didn't care that it had taken me months to write it; what I cared about was that we stop harming the dogs.

As John analysed the data, though, we started to feel like Archimedes who had displaced water in his bath, and jumped out running through the streets naked shouting, "Eureka!".

Although we kept our clothes on, our excitement was hard to contain. Our research fully supported Chris Day's theory that, where the start date of an illness is known, a high percentage start within three months of a vaccine event. So far as we were aware, no-one had ever looked at illnesses arising post-vaccination. No studies had ever been conducted to measure vaccine adverse effects in this way. We were even able to break it down into individual illnesses, and how they were highly represented in the days, weeks and first few months after the dogs were vaccinated.

But after hearing Simon's worried warnings, I went to bed and woke up in a hot sweat, my stomach in knots and my entire body jangling with fear. Simon's words, "they'll sue your arse off," were coursing through my cells and pores. And then a thought came strongly into my mind: "Someone has to speak the truth." I felt the thought as a deep conviction, deep in my heart. Besides, what did we have to lose? *Things?* I would rather die than protect mere things above life.

Then I put the light out, and went to sleep. John, too, was not for turning. Publish and be damned. Shortly after the book was published a beautiful, clear, voice woke me in my sleep. The voice said: "It is done. Annual vaccination is a thing of the past." Unfortunately, I think they got the timing wrong – but I have no doubt that I will see the end of annual vaccination in my lifetime.

Soon, we were contacted by the Veterinary Medicines Directorate which wanted our base research material for scrutiny. Already suspecting that the VMD was in the pockets of the veterinary pharmaceutical industry, John agreed ... so long as they nominated an independent scientist to scrutinise our research.

The VMD came back, naming the scientist who was to conduct the review. John looked him up. He was a consultant to the veterinary vaccine industry, and received research grants from the veterinary vaccine industry. So John got back to the VMD and repeated his request for an independent scientist, suggesting a professional body involved with statistics or data analysis. The VMD refused.

Interesting ... why would a government department refuse independent scrutiny of research?

The VMD had also started sending CHC invitations to attend various committee meetings, and John decided to go along to discuss a European Union directive concerning the traceability of veterinary medicines. Traceability would enable manufacturers to recall faulty products because they'd know who the hell they'd sold them to. To John, it was also an excellent opportunity to implement a computer system that would log adverse vaccine reactions, as well as reactions to other veterinary drugs.

He went along with full proposals for a system, pointing out that it would be very inexpensive to implement, with software being rolled out to individual veterinary practices which already had their own computers.

John was the only representative from an animal welfare organisation in attendance; the rest were from industry. He got voted down, and the entire EU directive was voted out. Seems they didn't want to trace their own products or monitor adverse events, and the UK government wasn't keen to let them.

Had this system been implemented, we could have stopped arguing about whether or not vaccine reactions are rare – we'd have had the figures to show us exactly what happens post-vaccination. Why, do you think, the industry and British government agents weren't keen on such a database?

Chapter 27
Anecdote, ha ha

When a parent or dog lover says that their child or dog suffered or died shortly after receiving a drug or vaccine, the scientific convention is to dismiss their experiences as anecdote. The word 'anecdote' is defined generally as 'a narrative of an interesting, amusing, or biographical incident'. The question is: how many amusing stories do we need before scientists stop brushing suffering aside? Anecdote may be at the bottom of the evidence pyramid, but let's stop dismissing it, hey?

In fact, I'm not the only person saying this. One team of researchers, writing in the *Indian Journal of Medical Ethics*, stated:

Medical professionals forgetting their role

Basic defects inherent in the medical community underlie the issue of the HPV vaccine. In 2004, Sheldon Krimsky pointed out the increasing influence of commercialism in academic science and biomedical research in his book, *Science in the Private Interest*. He wrote, "…the mix of science and commerce continues to erode the ethical standards of research and diminish public confidence in its results."

In the 13 years since the publication of the book, his warning has become a reality everywhere in the world, not only in the USA. Originally, public health and pharmaco-epidemiology were the scientific fields that aimed to protect the health of individual patients and the public. However, the current reality is very far from the ideal.

Science is now misused to protect the interests of the pharmaceutical industry, and has been used to deny the causal relationship between the drug and its adverse reactions. Many researchers and experts are attempting to exclude inconvenient truths from consideration. "The taxonomy of diseases represents the nearest science has got to nature, but it remains a theoretical construct. It is the theory that should be discounted when the patient's symptoms refuse to fit, not the patient's account of the reality of their experience." This means that doctors must be more humble and scientifically honest. Today's diagnostics and therapeutics were created by listening to patients' voices and conducting careful examinations. It is irresponsible to dismiss a patient's complaint as a psychogenic reaction or a general phenomenon among young women without conducting a thorough examination. [1]

Dear Catherine

I have had Keeshonds since I was a young child in 1949. The early ones, only having initial vaccines, led healthy lives on the whole. As a result of reading your comments in *Dog World* and my own suspicions, the present dog (now six years old) has been on nosodes since he was one year old, having had the initial vaccination.

I had a lifetime of problems with the previous dog (Oliver), and as a result of reading the articles and your book, I am now certain they were vaccine induced.

After the initial vaccine when he was a 10 week old pup, he soon developed skin problems followed by various inflammatory conditions, including ear problems which eventually resulted in an ear re-section. After the first booster he started with ulcerative colitis; both the skin problems and the colitis were lifelong, treatable, but incurable problems.

At one stage he had small tumours in the mouth which needed cryogenic surgery. His temperament became quite unlike a normal Keeshond, he would hide under furniture and growl when shown his lead, almost agoraphobic. He was much more hyper than any of our other dogs had been. We loved him to bits but he was a daily battle and a worry.

At about eight years, Oliver was very ill shortly after a booster. Blood tests revealed severe liver failure and we feared he would die then. Vast amounts of medication pulled him round again and he gradually improved, but he was on pills for life. Still the skin trouble and colitis flared up periodically.

Because of all this he was almost 10 when the vet said he should have another booster. Within days of this he was very ill with total kidney failure, and he died less than three weeks later. Perhaps we were fortunate (if you can call it that) that he lived for so long. It was not all gloom and doom but his quality of life was severely impaired so many times and, looking back, he must have felt pretty rotten.

It is only since getting our present Keeshond that I have become aware of the vaccine controversy and I am absolutely certain that Oliver was indeed vaccine damaged. He suffered and eventually died through my belief that the 'expert' must be right. Hopefully I have saved Charlie from a similar fate. I am now very grateful for your articles and the book, and will pass the book on to my dog-owning friends.

Yours sincerely
Maureen Croft

Chapter 28
Misunderstandings

The phone rang one day, in the early days of CHC, and a woman with a thick Yorkshire accent said: "I've just read your article in the dog press. I've been blaming my next-door neighbour for poisoning my dog for the last fifteen years, and now I know it was a vaccine that did it. I want to help."

I was taken aback. This was the first time anyone had told me that they wanted to help. "I'm going to put a seminar on for you," the woman said. "And we'll raise funds for CHC."

I couldn't have been more delighted. We hadn't been running CHC for long, but already it was creating a very large body of work, and it was also proving difficult to fund; John and I were ploughing every spare penny we had into it. So I drove up to Yorkshire to speak at the seminar and meet up with the lady and her son.

"Come on in," she said, showing me into her sitting room. "This is my son Bertie. He's helped me to set the seminar up." They had also arranged for the Leeds-based homeopathic vet John Saxton to speak alongside me.

The seminar was a great success. Bettie and Bertie had attracted a large audience, and they donated all of the profits from ticket sales to CHC. The next week, Bertie telephoned to say that his mum wanted to do more.

"Well," I said, "there are people around the country who are talking about starting CHC branches to spread information about vaccines and natural feeding on a local basis. The trouble is, I'm spending so much time on the phone trying to set it up that I don't have time to get other work done. How would your mum like to be our branch manager?"

Bettie leapt at the chance, and Bertie wanted to help, too. We arranged for the telephone to be diverted to volunteers, leaving me with the time to write for CHC, and get on with freelance work to provide me with an income. Bettie was responsible for liaising with the volunteers. Things were starting to go well.

John Saxton, one of the UK's leading homeopathic vets, Christopher Day, and Peter Gregory thought that I should be invited to speak at the annual homeopathic veterinary symposium. Having by now been pilloried by a number of conventional vets for my work in the vaccine field, and having had my personality ripped to shreds by vets and dog lovers who thought I was scaremongering or downright lying about vaccine adverse effects – and saying what I was saying in ways they considered unacceptable

– I was really pleased to be invited to speak at the symposium. I would be amongst friends, I thought. It was going to be lovely; everyone in the audience would have studied what is known by homeopaths as the 'vaccine miasm' (inherited vaccine damage). I would be singing to the choir.

'Vaccinosis' was a term coined by the British homeopath, J Compton Burnett, in 1884. His original treatise on the subject, a book called *Vaccinosis and its Cure by Thuja*, is core to homeopathic training. In it, Burnett takes the reader through human cases of horrible suffering that wouldn't yield to the treatments of his day, even those homeopathic treatments that seemed certain to work. These people didn't get well until he considered vaccines in his patients' history, and treated specifically to undo the illness that had begun from that procedure.

So John and I drove to the venue. It was a lovely summer's day, and we were so pleased that Canine Health Concern's work was being recognised by the British homeopathic veterinary fraternity. We had been invited to be there during the entire conference, and they were putting us up in the hotel overnight.

I got up to deliver my lecture and was met on stage by a homeopathic vet. "I've read your book," she said. "It's far too emotional."

"Oh."

I had deliberately included emotion in the book, illustrating what it feels like when your much-loved dog dies as a result of a shot he didn't need. I was tired of the vets who were trying to tell me that emotion has no place in science, reasoning that this was a control measure imposed upon scientists to disconnect them from what they were doing. I wanted to make graphically clear what can happen when we over-vaccinate, and I wanted to relate to the dog lovers who saw their dogs as people with feelings and the ability to suffer.

So feeling slapped before I started, I began to speak to a roomful of around a hundred homeopathic vets. Suddenly I started crying, and I had no idea why. I was standing on the stage, overcome with emotion, tears rolling down my face. 'What the heck is going on?' I asked myself. I had to turn my back, compose myself, and start again.

That night in the bar, all became clear. One after the other, homeopathic vets sat down next to me and explained why they were still vaccinating despite the vaccine miasm.

"I got into homeopathy because I had vaccine-induced asthma as a child," one of them said. "I was cured by a homeopath who treated me for vaccine damage. Now I can't feel my fingers, and I'm terrified that I'm getting vaccine-induced MS. My sister has vaccine-induced autoimmune disease, too. I cry every time I vaccinate an animal."

"But why do you do it?" I asked.

"Because when I started up my practice," he replied, "I was given a loan by Intervet. Now I'm tied into buying their vaccines."

As the evening wore on, and reason after reason was given to explain why they still vaccinated – none of which appeared to relate to the health of the animals in their care – I began to understand why I had started crying on that stage.

As an empath, I pick up the energies of the people around me, like a sponge (although I have learnt how to control it better now). I imagined that I had been picking up the thoughts and emotions of the homeopaths in the audience who vaccinated animals despite knowing the damage they were doing. I guessed that maybe I was picking up their anger – because no-one likes a messenger – or maybe I was picking up on their discomfort and sorrow. Or maybe they just didn't like me, or I said what I said in the wrong way. Whatever it was, the tears were not from my own emotions, because when an emotion originates from yourself, you know what caused it.

I went to bed in a very confused and wounded state.

As my head hit the pillow, Samson came to me. I appreciate that if you have never had an experience like this, I will sound like a crazy woman. All I can do, though, is tell my truth. I hadn't been thinking of Sammie. I was just upset. And I put my head on the pillow and Samson surrounded me in his love, like a loving mother wraps her arms around a child.

I fell asleep comforted in Samson's love.

Twenty years later, I met up with a homeopathic vet who holds a senior position within the British Association of Homeopathic Veterinary Surgeons who nevertheless still vaccinates. We discussed the issue and she mentioned that she had been at that symposium and she looked at me in a sort of disparaging and disapproving way as she said it. I wondered why, so I asked my homeopathic vet friend Peter Gregory to tell me what he remembered about my 'performance' on that day, asking him not to spare my feelings.

"I remember it well," he said. "I don't feel the need to be diplomatic with you, especially about something that happened so long ago, so here is my version of events!

"My recollection is that you seemed quite angry and came across a bit aggressive; also you were disappointed that so many homeopathic vets should be unsympathetic to what you were saying about vaccines – I don't think it was all as universally accepted in those days and I got the impression that the feeling was 'who is this woman to tell me how to run my practice?' I remember you being very upset that you didn't get a better reception.

"We could discuss for hours the whys and the wherefores but that is how I remember the event."

People say that first impressions count, and they certainly counted on that day. I have spent years wishing that the homeopathic veterinary fraternity in the UK would stand up and say more on the vaccine issue, and years wondering why they called me 'contentious' when I was merely speaking the truth.

I had made a serious mistake. I had gone to the symposium with the impression that British homeopathic vets didn't vaccinate, having studied the vaccine miasm; that they were aware of the harm caused by vaccines and, like Peter Gregory, James Newns, John Saxton and Chris Day, they didn't vaccinate. I was wrong, and I would have delivered my lecture differently had I known.

Yet looking back through 20 years of Canine Health Concern newsletters to mark our 20th anniversary, through the distance of time, I could see that anger was a driving force behind me in those early days. I'd like to think that it was righteous anger, arising from the belief that real harm was being committed. Our dogs were dying and suffering because we were being persuaded to pay for a veterinary procedure that was neither necessary nor safe. The veterinary vaccine industry was, it seemed to me, covering up the carnage and bald-faced lying about it.

We had been sent letters by a number of dog owners who had written to the same vaccine manufacturer to detail their dogs' deaths shortly after vaccination, and even though many of the accounts detailed the same adverse effects, the vaccine manufacturer was claiming it had never seen such a reaction before. Further, the industry was being quoted in the press, saying that vaccine reactions were very rare and in some instances they were denying known vaccine reactions.

I couldn't comprehend how vets could be unaware of the duration of immunity studies conducted some quarter of a century earlier, or why they were still over-vaccinating our dogs and cats. And I couldn't understand why homeopathic vets, who presumably studied the vaccine miasm (aka vaccine damage), were still vaccinating at all.

And yet here was Peter saying that he didn't think that vaccine damage was so universally accepted in those days.

Human communications are so darned difficult. I have often felt that if we had the opportunity to sit down and truly communicate – no matter how much we disliked or disagreed with someone – then we would find something to love them for.

My feeling is that although we believe ourselves to be self-determined and rational, we are far from it. I sincerely believe that we are largely the result of our 'programming'. Our life experiences are stored in the brain, much the same as software and data are stored on computer hard discs. When something happens, our brain searches for relevant data (experiences) and we respond with whatever the brain throws up, based upon our experiences and the values handed down to us by our early caretakers. And because no-one has complete data or even fully accurate data, our actions, thoughts and responses can be incredibly misplaced.

I went to that symposium with faulty data. I assumed that all homeopathic vets knew where I was coming from. From memory, I think I also assumed that they wouldn't feel that my anger was directed at them, but at the vaccine industry which was misleading vets and pet owners – because I assumed that these vets knew the damage vaccines can cause. I wasn't able to look at myself as others saw me, or accordingly modify how my presentation was made, because I had made an assumption about who I was speaking to.

But I also believe that God can use our faults, because the anger I felt on behalf of the dogs and their owners, and the very personal love and grief I felt for my own dogs, provided the fuel which enabled me to wipe the sand off my face and keep on keeping on.

Chapter 29
The danger of blind belief

Pam Morris wrote:

Lisa was a Golden Retriever, typical of her breed, loving and lovely, but sadly she was vaccine damaged and was stolen away long before her time.

Lisa became hemiplegic [paralysis which affects one side of the body] in September 2001 following her annual vaccination. She was immediately written off as a totally hopeless case by the conventional vet who had administered the vaccine to her. After battling against the odds for two months, I found a wonderful homeopathic vet who got her mobile again using a combination of homeopathic remedies and acupuncture.

Through a chance meeting in this vet's waiting room, I met a very kind lady who also had a severely vaccine damaged dog, so she was well placed to understand my anguish. She introduced me to many other complementary therapies and recommended an excellent hydrotherapy pool where the lady swam with and manipulated Lisa in the water to help her rebuild her muscles. Both my dogs also started to go to an animal healing group in Yeovil where the gentle, peaceful atmosphere helped us all.

Looking back, it was after her very first vaccination that Lisa developed severe eczema and had appetite loss. She suffered an upset stomach and was really off colour, even appearing somewhat brain-damaged, but on expressing my worries to my vet, he just put it all down to coincidence.

The second booster led to the same result, but the vet yet again said it was pure coincidence. I shudder as I look back and realise that, with each successive vaccination, Lisa's reactions became stronger and stronger.

When Lisa was four years old, I read an article by Catherine O'Driscoll of Canine Health Concern which really did worry me, as everything she said simply underlined what Lisa had gone through.

On the strength of this I really badgered my vet (which was unusual for me as I'm not really a pushy person at all) but, once again, I was assured that vaccination was quite safe and, to be fair, my older dog always seemed fine. So I kept on putting Lisa through it, even though I remained really concerned.

I feel consumed with guilt for allowing myself to be so browbeaten when, in my heart, I knew something was going wrong and getting worse each time.

Then came the jab which paralysed my beautiful Lisa and the awful realisation of what I had done to her. Later on the same day that she had received the vaccination, Lisa was wobbly and the next day she was even more wobbly, until on the third day she became paralysed. Now the vet had to finally acknowledge that the problem was a direct result of the vaccination. But he also admitted that he could do nothing to help her, so euthanasia was the only answer. It was a desperate, desperate time made worse by my terrible feelings of guilt.

Needless to say, Lisa never had another vaccination and neither would her best friend Emma, who now has the homeopathic nosode instead.

Lisa had fifteen good months but sadly relapsed at Christmas. Despite losing her mobility in her last three months, being a typical Golden Retriever, Lisa still remained loving and happy until the end when, to preserve her dignity, the final, awful, decision had to be made.

If Lisa's life is not to be in vain, I would urge dog owners and vets alike to please take note of what happened to her and to question anything which worries you, rather than just blindly believing.

She was on this earth for such a short time but she gave me so much love and guidance. I love you Lisa and miss you so much. You will be in my heart forever.

Chapter 30
Eminent support

By now, my book *What Vets* was getting out there. It was being purchased by CHC members, and they were recommending it to other dog friends. In no time at all we had ordered a second, then a third, and then a fourth print run.

John was also getting busy on the internet – a new phenomenon that I was steering clear of. He was contributing to the newly emerging discussion groups, promoting Ian Billinghurst's raw meaty bone diet, and getting metaphorically kicked in the teeth for his troubles by people who had been taken in by the advertising propaganda and believed that processed pet food was 'complete and balanced' and created by scientists. The raw diet had one-and-a-half people and a monkey in its camp, and John was experiencing what it felt like to be pioneering a new concept on his own.

He'd come into my bedroom every morning with a cup of tea, and sit there with a cloud of depression hanging over his head. He was learning that people can be very rude and abusive on these groups, although I'm sure he gave as good as he got.

A Canadian woman called Sandra Brigola, however, was interested in what he had to say. She published a natural rearing magazine in Canada, which was hard going for her because natural rearing magazines in those days were decidedly short of advertisers. In the early 90s, dog lovers had a choice of conventional drugs or conventional drugs, or they had to find their way into the underground to buy natural products from small companies that were struggling to survive in a disinterested market. These companies couldn't afford to advertise – and magazines stay in business chiefly through advertising revenue and not, as you might suspect, through reader subscriptions.

I wrote a number of articles for her magazine and we started to correspond. Pretty soon there were lots of people in the UK and North America who heard us and who had put their dogs on Ian Billinghurst's diet. In fact, Ian soon achieved superstar status in the dog world. We decided to invite him to come from Australia to the UK and put him on a seminar tour.

That was fun!

Ian came across to the UK with his fiancé Ros, who is now his wife, and we asked our homeopathic vet Peter Gregory to speak, too. I did a talk on the vaccine issue, and Peter talked about canine epilepsy and how he had treated it successfully with homeopathy, noting that if the dog was revaccinated the epilepsy would start again.

The tour took in Manchester, Somerset, Birmingham and London, with over a hundred people attending each event.

We all met up for the first gig in London. Jane, who was helping out, had booked us into a cheap hotel, chiefly because it accepted dogs and was close to the venue. Little did any of us know in advance that we were booked into a doss house.

John and I parked the car and went straight in, knowing that Ian and Ros would already be there, having spent the previous few days in Paris. As we walked into the lounge, we could feel our feet sticking to the decidedly shabby carpet. Around us were various stained chairs and melamine tables with chunks missing, exposing some rather unattractive wood chip. The air was permeated with cigarette smoke and beer.

"Oh gosh," I said. "Not a great start. Ian will be wondering who he's gotten himself involved with."

As it happens, Ros had burst into tears when she saw the place and, later that night, covered her stained pillows with a towel she had brought from Australia. Jane remarked incredulously that her dog towels were in better nick than the ones supplied here. Our own bedroom contained around six scruffy single beds of various design, randomly scattered around the room to provide maximum overnight dossing potential for drunken revellers. Peter's room was positioned above the bar and because the other residents were having a rowdy time into the early hours of the morning, he decided it would be better to walk the streets of London than lie in bed trying to sleep over the noise.

Luckily none of us died, and so we laughed instead. The horrible hotel became the butt of many jokes, and we got to know each other amidst raucous laughter over dinner in a nearby restaurant. Thankfully, as the tour progressed, our accommodation improved, and at the end of the tour we put Ian and Ros up in a country house hotel. They went from the ridiculous to the sublime and I hope we redeemed ourselves.

When it came to the seminars, Ian Billinghurst was the star of the show. John and I had worked hard to ensure that most of the audience had transferred their dogs from processed junk food to raw meaty bones, and their dogs' health had improved dramatically. Women were lining up in front of Ian, cooing and aahing, delighting in his every word. Ian, meanwhile, took great pleasure in exercising his Australian sense of humour.

"Dogs have always acted as human refuse collectors," he told them. "So if you come home from a party and chuck up on the stairs, don't worry – the dog will clear it up for you."

Ew, the ladies squirmed. Ian was a big hit.

Those new to raw feeding commonly ask how much they were

supposed to feed their dogs – raw meat, bones and vegetables don't come in a packet with feeding guidelines for different sized dogs. Ian had a simple answer to this dilemma ready prepared. He presented a drawing of an emaciated dog with the word, 'more' underneath, followed by a picture of a fat dog with the word, 'less' below it.

Richard Lacey, the microbiologist who had alerted the world to BSE, also added his support, agreeing wholeheartedly with me on the vaccine issue. He contributed his voice to our tour when we hit Manchester.

Richard Lacey was Professor of Clinical Microbiology at Leeds University. He had a degree in medicine from Cambridge University and a PhD in clinical microbiology from the Faculty of Medicine at the University of Bristol. As well as publishing over 200 papers in scientific and medical journals, Professor Lacey lectured extensively overseas and appeared frequently on radio and television. His work had won him a number of prizes for his contribution to medicine and science. He was an advisor to the British government and was widely recognised as a world authority on BSE.

He told me that the government had asked him to sit on the Veterinary Products Committee for four years from January 1986 to December 1989. He also told me that the interests of big business were put ahead of the interests of the animals the VPC was supposed to protect. The VPC is part of the VMD, about which I myself have a huge beef (if you'll pardon the pun considering the BSE scandal).

Richard Lacey expressed concerns about BSE, otherwise known as mad cow disease. He was hugely critical of the government's stance on BSE and the consequent risk to the health of the British public. "We have a terrible crisis on our hands," he said – but he found it hard to find someone who cared.

"Evidence that the Government was less than concerned about the risk to the British public comes from the Tyrell Report," he wrote. "For example, this said that the brains of cattle normally sent for slaughter should be checked to see if some animals had BSE and were not yet ill with it. This would have shown how big the problem really was. Not surprisingly, this has never been done, despite numerous requests from the UK Parliament, because it would have been 'too expensive'. Too expensive for the meat industry, that is. Once consumers realised that they were eating infected meat, profits would have plummeted."

Time after time, I was learning, business interests are put ahead of life.

We issued a joint press release saying that veterinary vaccine manufacturers are without proper control:

"The Veterinary Medicines Directorate and the VPC are totally reliant upon data supplied by the manufacturers themselves," Professor Lacey said, "but no-one makes them supply that information. It is my belief that serious side-effects are far greater than the number reported. There is no proper monitoring system, no independent check, and there should be."

Professor Lacey confirmed to CHC that only vaccine manufacturers are able to test vaccines, which means that if there are any problems, no-one except the vaccine manufacturers need know about them. Professor Lacey further confirmed that bovine products are used in vaccine manufacture which, he believes, "could certainly pose a risk of cross-species spongiform encephalopathy (BSE)."

Professor Lacey echoed statements from top US veterinary immunologists that once immunity to a virus exists, it generally exists for the lifetime of an animal. "Vets and kennels are demanding that pets are vaccinated unnecessarily," he says, "and the owners are being fleeced. The veterinary profession and the vaccine manufacturers should be subject to adequate external monitoring."

He added that, in his opinion, the leptospirosis vaccine should be withdrawn, confirming that there are over a hundred strains of the leptospirosis bacterin, and you can't get all of those in the needle. "It is a useless vaccine," he told CHC. "Besides which, leptospirosis is extremely rare. Considering the risks of side-effects posed by the vaccine, it is causing more harm than good."

Richard telephoned me shortly after the press release went out. He'd received a menacing and threatening call from a member of the veterinary vaccine industry whose name I won't repeat because I can't prove a telephone conversation. "I wouldn't be surprised if they sued us," Professor Lacey told me.

Of course we weren't sued, since – once again – it's a bit risky to sue someone who is telling the truth.

I lost contact with Richard Lacey after a while, but a *Guardian* interview in 2001 explained how he had fared. Turns out that he became the scourge of the very establishment he was a prominent member of. He was vilified by politicians, civil servants, and the food industry. In March 1996, the government finally admitted the link between BSE and CJD. Lacey said he wasn't a conspiracy theorist until BSE.

By late 2000, when the Phillips report into BSE was released, at least

80 people had died of CJD in Britain. The report vindicated Lacey. He tried to warn us that by producing meat on the cheap, we put our health at risk. He says exactly the same is true for foot and mouth, and that until we have a return to small scale local production there will always be a chance of national catastrophe.

Richard Lacey went into retirement at the age of 58. The Tory government and its farming friends didn't like the message so they decided to destabilise the messenger. What a criminal waste of integrity and honour.

In 1994, his department at Leeds University was 60% funded by the Health Service. One morning a service manager turned up and announced that all of his staff were going to be transferred to another authority. It meant he couldn't do any work.

The University, which remained loyal to him, worked out a package. The health service advanced his pension and agreed to reemploy him as a consultant in a small hospital for three years. The total cost to the health service was half a million pounds. However, he only had about ten minutes of consultancy work to do a day: he was paid half a million to lie down.

How badly did all of this affect him? "Not really at all. Well, it did slightly. I suppose it changed my personality a bit. I think I became withdrawn. They tried to damage me, but I don't think they've actually succeeded."

And here was Professor Richard Lacey standing on a stage in Manchester confirming to the audience that I was telling the truth about the pet vaccine issue. I doubt very much that many in the audience had the slightest understanding of the courage and integrity of this wonderful man. As the years rolled on, and I got to know more and more scientists, I began to discover how dangerous it was for them to speak the truth if it interfered with big business interests.

The tour ended very badly for us. We were so pleased at the success of the tour that we all stopped off at a pub outside Birmingham for a celebratory meal. Whilst we sat and congratulated each other, thieves were busy in the car park robbing the contents of our car. They took Ian's lecture slides, Ros's electric hair rollers which she had cherished for years and which were now irreplaceable, and the PA equipment we had hired without thinking to insure. That landed us with a bill of £4,000, ensuring that the tour made John and me a massive personal loss. Bearing in mind that I was only copywriting part-time, we weren't being paid to run CHC, and John hadn't earned a penny since our PR and marketing company had been blighted by bad debt, it was a bitter blow.

We also fell out with Ian Billinghurst who, despite this, will always have my gratitude. I don't think the constant stress was particularly helpful for me, either – because when you're under a lot of stress, it can affect your ability to handle life calmly. I picked up the phone and, at great expense, telephoned Ian in Australia and told him what I thought of him. I don't think it went down that well. Then I telephoned a woman in the UK (let's call her 'Mary') and with great emotion and somewhat unreasonably, had a go at her. Her sin? She was one of the retailers Ian was selling the book to while we were under the impression that we had an exclusive arrangement – and of course it wasn't her fault. She did manage to get me back, though.

I'm glad to say that Ian and I are now back in touch and working together in small ways to help the animals.

But there was also a great deal of excitement and enthusiasm in those days, too. Everything was new. Although there had been dog lovers quietly raising their dogs naturally since the beginning of time, and although some used herbs and homeopathy for their dogs, no-one had sought to get the news out there for everyone to hear. We were making homeopathy and other alternative therapies vastly more popular, promoting the natural diet, and sharing information about vaccines, environmental toxins, stress, and other factors which might adversely affect our dogs' health. We were pioneers, and despite the criticism and censure, we also got to experience the excitement and joy with the people we had positively influenced.

Then one day I was out mowing the lawn when John rushed out. "I've got a contract," he said. He'd been applying for short-term contracts in the IT industry, and it had finally paid off. I remember distinctly that the weight literally lifted off my shoulders. I actually felt the weight lift.

Making ends meet had become increasingly difficult. We were slowly going under. This contract made a huge difference. It also meant that John would be flying to Scotland from Derbyshire every Sunday night, returning home on Friday evening. I would be running CHC, copywriting, and looking after the dogs, with John flying home at weekends to manage the CHC membership and deal with the accounts. Suddenly things were about to get a whole lot busier.

Chapter 31
Real food and no vaccines

Dear Catherine

I have been a member of CHC for about a year now, since my Bernese Mountain Dog was seven months old. I read Ian Billinghurst's book, as you recommended, and put Dan straight onto a natural diet at that point in time. He had, back then, awful digestive problems and had developed large bare inflamed patches under his neck, belly and underarms. He constantly had a runny nose and mucous around his eyes. He spent most of his days in a corner under the stairs. I can honestly say I didn't think he would make it to adulthood.

He was vaccinated at eight weeks and eleven weeks – that's when the real problems started. After reading your book, *What Vets Don't Tell You About Vaccines* – I realised he had vaccinosis.

Dan is now on a natural diet, no boosters – I used nosodes this time. He now has loads of energy (too much sometimes), bright eyes, a beautiful coat, and he positively shines. I didn't connect the symptoms he had to vaccines until I read your book. I lost a beautiful Bearded Collie at four years with autoimmune disease – he was always ill after boosting.

I must tell you that whilst Dan was so ill, he would strip the branches from the conifers in the garden and eat the bark. The type of conifer was Thuja. I noticed in your book that Thuja is a homeopathic remedy for vaccinosis.

I would like to say I am deeply grateful to you and all CHC members who point the way forward for dog owners and guardians of the animal kingdom – who instinctively knew something was wrong but didn't have the simple truth to put it right. Many thanks for showing us the 'Light'. Barbara Storey, another CHC member, and I try to spread the word as best we can when we're out on our doggie walks.

Jane Marshall

Chapter 32
My decision to stop vaccinating

Sue Hawkins was a Golden Retriever breeder and show judge who lived not too far away near Coventry. She also ran a boarding kennels. Sue telephoned me one day, having heard about CHC and our aim to reduce the vaccine load on companion animals.

"I haven't vaccinated for years," she admitted sheepishly. "To be honest, it was impossible to afford them for all my dogs. Then I began to notice at shows that other breeders had sickly dogs who were beset with health problems, whereas my own dogs were incredibly healthy."

Due to the prevailing group delusion that we must vaccinate our dogs every year, Sue was unable to go public on her lack of vaccination. Her dogs travelled all over the country with her and, as well as being healthy, they hadn't died of viral disease either. Neither did living on top of a boarding kennel make them sitting targets for viral disease, as you might expect.

We talked about breeding and I mentioned to Sue that I had never seen puppies being born. I was too busy to breed dogs myself, and I also knew that I'd have great difficulty in finding puppy owners who would see dogs as more than 'just dogs'. I have always felt great sorrow when people treat dogs like dogs, making them sit in the corner and behave themselves, shouting at them and bullying them, and never stopping to listen to what they have to say.

"I've got a litter due soon," Sue said. "Why don't you come down and see the birth? I can phone you when it starts – you'd be here in plenty of time."

Samson was seriously ill, in his last days. "I'll come if I can," I said, not really thinking it would be possible; I wasn't going to leave my darling boy.

A litter arrived the night before Sammie died – I never did make it to see the birth, but Sue invited me to go and look at the pups a week or so later. It was very healing to see new life as we grieved the loss of our beloved Samson.

On the day of Samson's death, ironically, the veterinary vaccine industry was hosting a conference for vets, with a retired vet as a key speaker, to deny the claims made in *What Vets Don't Tell You About Vaccines*. There they were in the dog press, making unfounded claims, like 'experts say that there is no correlation between vaccination and epilepsy'. Which experts? I asked – but never did receive an answer. If these alleged experts really did exist, then they weren't experts.

Samson had paralysed rear legs after his second puppy shot, an allergic reaction which made his head swell up like a football and scream all night on the night of his first booster, a diagnosis of autoimmune disease by the age of two, and he died of cancer aged five. I was pretty convinced that Samson was yet another vaccine victim. The vaccine industry conference sickened me; I made a solemn vow to Samson, Oliver and Prudence that I would not stop working towards vaccine reform until annual vaccination was a thing of the past – even if it killed me.

So John and I went along to Sue Hawkins' place and we cuddled the puppies, and we looked at each other and smiled, and we both knew that we'd be having one of those pups. "Can we have one?" I asked John.

"Why not have two?" he said. We ended up with a boy from this litter, and another boy from the next litter which arrived two weeks later. This made our family into seven – five dogs and two humans.

Edward and Daniel were remarkable pups. They were so calm. People kept asking, "Are you *sure* they're puppies?" They were the first pups we decided not to vaccinate – at all. Instead, they had the homeopathic nosode, a pill containing a minute dilution of the diseases you might otherwise vaccinate against. Sue had started them on nosodes in liquid form when they were a few weeks old, dropping it into their mouths through a pipette.

Sue told me that people always commented on how calm her dogs were. I don't know if this was genetic, or whether it was down to the fact that Sue hadn't vaccinated for generations. She also gave her dogs tripe alongside kibble, so at least they had some real food. Either way, they were the most wonderful puppies in the world.

Edward was the oldest; he came to us two weeks before Daniel. Sue had given us a bag of Eukanuba and advised us not to switch Edward from this puppy food straight onto raw: "It will upset his tummy if you change his diet too quickly," she said. So I moistened the Eukanuba and added scrambled egg, and took it out to the garden for him as it was a beautifully warm June day. Edward sniffed at the food and turned his nose up, refusing to eat it. Gwinnie was most put out that the pup was being offered food when she wasn't, so I gave her a small scoop of Eukanuba from my hand. She took it into her mouth and spat it out, a look of utter disgust on her face. Princess Guinevere was used to real food. I couldn't help but laugh.

Then I brought Chappie, Sophie, and Gwinnie their raw chicken wings into the garden. Before I knew it, Edward had jumped into Chappie's bowl and literally sucked in all of his wings. I didn't have a chance to stop him, he was so quick and determined. I was horrified – whereas Edward was chuffed to bits. He was having a whale of a time, and he'd fallen in love with Chappie, following him around like a little baby duckling. By this time Chappie was 13 and no longer prepared to put up with a puppy biting his neck, so while Edward sucked up to him, Chappie was busy telling him to get lost.

Later that night, I took Edward to bed with me. I've done this since Oliver and Prudence were pups – I just couldn't bear listening to puppies crying in the kitchen, desperately wanting to be with me. So puppies sleep with me on my bed and, if they move in the night, I always seem to manage to wake up and either place them on some newspaper, or take them out into the garden.

At around 12 o'clock, this little puppy started panting so much that the bed was heaving up and down. "Oh my God," I though, "I've killed my puppy. He's eaten all those chicken wings (probably three), and he's about to die." I was seriously terrified for him and considered phoning the vet, wondering how on earth I was going to explain that I'd allowed my puppy to eat all those chicken wings. In those days there wasn't a network of raw feeders to ask for advice – we were on our own.

I picked Edward up in my arms and took him outside into the dark night, frantically going through the options in my mind. But Edward simply had a pee, and we went back to bed and he slept through the night and – no – he didn't die. In fact, this was the start of his lifelong love affair with bones.

Then we collected Dannie, my sweet little man. I sat in the back of the car with him on my lap, wrapped loosely in a blanket. He didn't like the car; he felt nauseous and disorientated, so I sang *Dannie Boy* to him and he linked in with my energy and settled down. Always, when I sang this song to him, my Dannie knew it was his song.

He was such a funny little pup, into everything and instantly lovable. I put Dannie straight onto the raw diet, too, and he took to it like a dog to … well, like a dog does to his natural, biologically appropriate diet.

I also failed to worm Edward and Daniel, which is the standard procedure for pups. Instead, I kept an eye on them and looked out for signs of worms, but it never seemed necessary. The theory is that processed pet food is full of ingredients that are biologically inappropriate for dogs, including an abundance of carbohydrates, and this leaves lots of gloopy residue in the gut – perfect for worms to eat and thrive on. Raw meat and bones, on the other hand, are biologically appropriate, and the dogs are able to metabolise them quickly, with a very small amount of waste. This leaves worms nothing to thrive on, and so raw-fed dogs tend to be worm-free.

A wonderful homeopathic vet, James Newns, confirmed that, in his view, my instincts were correct. He told me that intestinal parasites, in the right balance, have a purpose – with one sentinel worm protecting the gut and eating up toxins and worm larvae that a dog might ingest on his travels. "If you use harsh wormers," he said, "you destroy the sentinel, which leads to an infestation."

Managing two older dogs on my own – Chappie and Sophie were getting on by this time – and the two-year-old Gwinnie, as well as two young puppies, was full on to say the least. The older dogs needed quiet attention and cuddles, the younger dogs needed training and walks and play. I was split in several directions.

I had been told that it would be safe to take the puppies into the wider world after two weeks on nosodes, so I started to walk them round the fields and up into the village so they could get used to roads and cars. I was pretty surprised that neither Edward nor Dannie pulled on the lead and, if they were off-lead in the fields, they would immediately come to me if I called them. There was no effort involved in training them at all. They were intelligent children, and did precisely as I quietly asked. Chewing wasn't a big problem, either. Also, my sister Leslie, who I was back in touch with, came to stay with me for the first two weeks, helping me with the pups and older dogs.

Knowing that vaccines cause inflammation in the brain, and that pet food is often industrial waste cleverly marketed as 'food' likely to induce further inflammation in the body, I wondered whether their absence made these puppies so easy to deal with. Normally, you can expect puppies to turn your life upside down and even leave you crying in a corner for the first few weeks and months until they understand how to settle into family life. But Edward and Daniel were a delight.

Meanwhile, it turned out that the British Pet Food Manufacturers' Association wasn't happy with us, and was planning to spend lots of money with a major PR consultancy to counteract our efforts to popularise real food for dogs. Someone anonymously sent us minutes of one of their external affairs meetings which was held on June 2nd, 1998. The committee proposed that, "a list of friendly journalists be drawn up so that the industry is able to provide accurate information in response to such adverse publicity as the CHC seminars."

The meeting was informed that Grayling Public Relations had already started a friendly journalist list. The secretary reported that a CHC seminar was scheduled to take place on 10-11 October, which would include speakers such as Wendy Volhard and Chris Day.

Members of the PFMA committee also noted that, "a list of veterinary contacts is to be compiled by the PFMA to supply to the various pet press to ensure that a wide range of vets and nutritionists were in contact with the media to help with articles on petfood nutrition and other issues."

"That's interesting," I thought, whilst leafing through a PFMA sales brochure which boasted that, without the pet food industry, there would be many more landfill sites.

Chapter 33
Kennel cough and whooping cough

It was coming up to Christmas and old Sophie was looking a bit of a mess, so now that John was earning good money and we had more cash to spare, I decided to book her into a grooming parlour for a wash, trim, and brush up. Shortly after, Sophie started coughing and sneezing – she had kennel cough.

I had stopped vaccinating Chappie, Sophie and Gwinnie, but Edward and Daniel were still on nosodes. There was thick snow outside, it was freezing, and the windows and doors were being kept tightly shut. Chappie came down with kennel cough next, and then Gwinnie. But Edward and Daniel – by now nine months old – didn't cough or sneeze once.

At around the same time, Ronald Schultz and holistic vet Susan Wynne were conducting a nosode challenge trial, giving puppies a strange regime of nosodes and then injecting viral disease into them to see if they survived. They didn't. According to this research, nosodes don't work. According to my own impromptu and unplanned in-house experiment, they did. Otherwise why would two nine-month-old puppies not succumb to an air-borne disease that was literally staring them in the face?

True, vaccines were also tested in the same way as Schultz and Wynn tested the nosodes. If a dog survives having a virus injected into him post-vaccination, it's a pretty good indication that the vaccine worked. Maybe nosodes worked against natural infection, but not unnatural injection? It was a puzzle.

Chris Day had also been invited into a boarding kennel in Oxfordshire that was experiencing a kennel cough outbreak. He very cannily invited a vaccine manufacturer to take part in a trial. The results showed that dogs who received neither nosode nor vaccine fared better than vaccinated dogs, and that nosoded dogs either didn't get ill, or recovered faster than the other two groups. In fact, the vaccinated dogs fared the worst of all in the trial. [1]

Despite a vaccine manufacturer being involved, and despite (or probably because of) the findings, conventional scientists insist upon calling it a badly designed trial, and therefore irrelevant. This always seems to be the way – if you don't want to agree with the results, just say it's a badly designed trial and dismiss it.

But the fact of the matter is that kennel cough vaccines actually give dogs what the datasheets call a 'mild' form of kennel cough. Mild or not, they then become infective and can give kennel cough to other dogs. Many canny kennel owners and groomers now refuse dogs who have recently been given this vaccine, knowing that the vaccine itself starts outbreaks in kennels.

More worryingly, Bordetella bronchiseptica (kennel cough) is virtually the same virus as Bordetella pertussis (whooping cough). Bordetella bronchiseptica datasheets (available from the NOAH website) warn that immunocompromised humans should avoid contact with dogs who have received this vaccine for up to seven weeks, since the vaccine can make these sickly humans ill. But this only hints at the fuller story.

I mentioned this at one of my evening lectures, and a woman in the audience came up to me afterwards to tell me that she was just getting over whooping cough, and that – yes – it started just after her dog got a kennel cough vaccine.

One study gives credence to the notion that this lady may have contracted what we call kennel cough from her vaccinated dog. The study states that *B pertussis* and *B. bronchiseptica* are nearly identical and the gene detection kits for pertussis infection in humans can mistakenly identify a significant proportion of human B. bronchiseptica infections as whooping cough. [2-5]

Expressed another way, humans who are told they have whooping cough might actually be suffering from 'kennel cough', contracted from their dog and/or the dog's vaccine.

Another paper states: "B. bronchiseptica infection in humans is considered rare but has been documented in both healthy and immunosuppressed individuals. In healthy individuals, pertussis-like illness and chronic respiratory infection have been reported. Some cases of pertussis-like illness in humans have followed exposure to sick pets or farm animals. The disease is more likely to be severe in individuals who are immunocompromised, such as those with Hodgkin's disease, cystic fibrosis, or HIV infection. Pneumonia, sepsis, and death have been reported after infection." [6]

The paper goes on to state: "*Bordetella pertussis, Bordetella parapertussis*, and *B. bronchiseptica* are closely related species that all may cause respiratory tract infection in humans and other mammals and may express many similar virulence factors... With the advent of aerosol vaccination [up the nose] in veterinary clinics for companion animals, human exposure to *B. bronchiseptica* has likely increased in recent years. Physicians should ask patients presenting with pertussis-like illness whether they have visited a veterinary clinic or have been exposed to a sick or recently vaccinated animal during the week before the onset of symptoms.

If the potential for exposure to *B. bronchiseptica* is present, performance of cultures should be considered before antibiotics are administered.

"Even when administered properly, there may be opportunity for human exposure, especially if the animal sneezes, which is a common occurrence after intranasal administration of a liquid. In addition, the animal may be able to transmit the vaccine strain during the period of active infection."

Double take: kennel cough vaccines can give humans a whooping-cough like illness.

One paper queried why pertussis (whooping cough) vaccines fail, and gave as one of its reasons the possibility that other Bordetella species might cause a coughing illness.

In other words, the kennel cough vaccine you give to your dog could give you 'kennel cough' which is so bad they think it's whooping cough! Further, a significant number of human kennel cough cases are misdiagnosed as whooping cough in lab tests.

Considering the kennel cough vaccine causes kennel cough and starts outbreaks, you have to wonder why anyone wants to use it. It looks like a public health risk to me.

Here's another fact: naturally-occurring B. bronchiseptica gives dogs permanent immunity, whereas the vaccine blocks permanent immunity. What's the point of this vaccine?

Chapter 34

Getting the word out

I was working with Brian James and his researcher to bring their TV project to fruition. They had been commissioned by Granada TV's World in Action documentary series, so it was full steam ahead.

I gave Brian all my contacts and it was made very clear that my involvement would be limited. Brian's background as a BBC documentary maker had taught him, as well as TV regulations, that impartiality was key. In the media, however, 'impartiality' generally means that if someone spouts the Establishment line, there is no need for the other side to be put, whereas anyone questioning established wisdom has to be put down.

The researcher was amazed when he spoke to Hal Thomson who runs a pathology lab at Glasgow University. I had given Brian Professor Thomson's name as I thought he might be the closest we have in the UK to a Ron Schultz equivalent. Ron Schultz, you will remember, had conducted duration of immunity studies which showed that once a dog is immune to viral disease, he is immune for years or life. I had never spoken to Hal Thomson, but I was confident that the science was the science and, if he was an honest man, he was bound to speak the truth.

As it happened, the researcher was pleasantly surprised. Hal practically endorsed everything I had told Brian. There was chuckling all round when it was reported that he'd called the VMD 'three little monkeys' – see no evil, hear no evil, speak no evil, which I took to mean that the VMD was in the pocket of industry.

A camera crew was sent along to do an interview, but it turned out to be a waste of time. Hal just wouldn't repeat anything on-camera that he'd said to the researcher on the phone. Later, NOAH's David Sutton was quoted in *Dogs Today*, crowing that although Hal Thomson had been filmed for the programme, none of his material had been used. I wondered how he knew, and whether Hal had been got at?

Interestingly, a CHC member had taken it upon herself to telephone one of the veterinary vaccine manufacturers after reading my book, *What Vets,* and she was put through to scientists in a lab. "You'll never believe what this scientist said," she told me. "He said that they'd all read your book, and you were right. I asked him if he'd come and do a talk for our breed club, and he agreed to do it. Then he called me back an hour later to say that he was in terrible trouble with his boss, and would I please forget that we'd had the conversation."

I was invited to speak at a seminar down in Somerset by a dog lover called Allison Lovell. Allison's GSD puppy, Cougar, had received only the leptospirosis vaccine as she was frightened to give the full puppy series. She showed me a photo of Cougar the day before his lepto shot, where he was bright-eyed and bouncy, and another the day after. Cougar was very clearly brain-damaged, you could see it in his eyes – there was no-one home. Allison reluctantly, and with utter devastation, agreed to put Cougar to sleep.

The World Small Animal Veterinary Association Vaccine Guidelines Group has since come out to say that the lepto vaccine is the one most likely to provoke severe reactions, and that toy breeds in particular are at risk from this vaccine. A GSD is not a toy breed. This is a BAD vaccine. There are now support groups on Facebook for people whose dogs have, they believe, suffered adverse reactions to the new four-way lepto vaccine.

Allison invited her vet, David Holmes, to attend my talk. As I stood in front of the assembled audience, I could tell that a man in the front row was a vet – he sat with his arms and legs crossed, and his tongue firmly in his cheek. But at the end of it he came up to me and said: "I don't agree with everything you say, Catherine, but you've said enough to make me believe that we vets need to look into what you're saying. Our local vet group holds regular meetings above a pub – would you be prepared to come and talk to us?"

"Of course," I said. "I'd love to."

I put David's name up to the documentary production team, and he subsequently, and generously, appeared in the documentary to say that I needed to be listened to.

I also gave Brian contact details for Ann Martin who had recently had a book published called *Food Pets Die For*. She and I had struck up a friendship and were emailing regularly as we were both on the circuit talking about canine health, and working to improve the health of dogs in the face of big business influence.

I also gave Brian Chris Day's contact details, plus those for other holistic vets; Ian Billinghurst's details, and the contact details of another vet, Michael Fox, who had written the foreword for Ann's book.

John, however, decided that he didn't want to be involved in the programme. "It will be a set-up," he said. He was convinced that the media was biased in favour of big business, that Granada relied upon advertising revenue from pet food manufacturers, and that the truth would be distorted.

I, on the other hand, judged Brian James to be a decent man. I was prepared to give him the benefit of the doubt and risk it. If we could get information about vaccines and pet food out to the general public, it could well do the job for us. We'd succeed in getting the news out there so quickly that we'd be able to shut CHC down and leave the dog world to its much needed reformation.

While the production team continued their research, John and I flew off to British Columbia, Canada. Sandra Brigola had organised a seminar for us to speak at and, since John was now working and very well paid, he funded the trip.

I guess you don't need me to tell you that Canada is the most beautiful country. We met some really lovely people and had the greatest time. John was white-water rafting in the Rockies on his 60th birthday, and we went horseback riding, too. We took Sandra and her husband Alex on a sea safari in Lyon's Bay – one of the most wonderful experiences of my life. The seminar was also a huge success. Ironically, I heard a member of the audience say during the break that it takes someone from England to tell the truth in North America, but to my mind, it has taken the North Americans to tell the truth about pet vaccines. With fewer than a handful of British vets speaking out, I despaired of my own country.

We had also slipped-in a seminar in St Louis, Missouri on the way to Canada. This was arranged by an anti-vaccine group for human children. Unfortunately, it turned out that their supporters weren't interested in vaccine damage in dogs, so we were collected off the plane and taken straight to the venue, only to be greeted by an audience of one. I was massively jet-lagged and accidentally managed to shorten my talk from an hour and a half into about 20 minutes, while our audience of one snored loudly from the front row. At least I managed to bomb in relative privacy!

Chapter 35
Coincidence?

Whilst in Canada, I was in my hotel room when a news item came on the TV. A plane had crashed off the Canadian coast. A thought came into my mind rather urgently: *"find out who was on the plane"*. I didn't think much about it – besides, how would I find out who was on the plane? But the crash, and that urgent thought, stayed with me.

A few years later I read an article in the *Sunday Times* about what appeared to be a seedy and highly unscientific AIDS vaccine research project, where extra funding had been blocked by a WHO official. That funding, according to the Sunday Times piece, was finally granted after the official died in a plane crash.

The article made me wonder if it was the same plane crash I had heard the 'voice' about, and if the vaccine industry was such that the passengers of an entire plane might be sacrificed in order to get one incalcitrant WHO official out of the way. But, again, I didn't know how I could look into this.

Thanks to internet search engines, I looked it up recently. The flight in question was Swissair Flight 111, which crashed on September 2nd 1998. On board, in addition to Jonathan Mann, a former head of the World Health Organisation's global AIDS program and his wife, were various Saudi royals, a physicist, a peace negotiator for the UN, a cardiovascular geneticist, and a former MI6 agent, all of whom might conceivably be the subject of a hit. All 229 people on board died. The flight was nicknamed the 'UN Shuffle', due to its popularity with UN officials, business executives, scientists and researchers.

Shockingly, sabotage was suspected. In September 2011, a CBC program *The Fifth Estate* reported allegations that an incendiary device might have been the cause of the crash. This came from a former Royal Canadian Mounted Police (RCMP) officer, sergeant Tom Juby, who claimed that suspicious levels of magnesium and other elements associated with arson were discovered in the wiring. [1]

Juby said he was ordered to remove references to magnesium or a suspected bomb from his investigative notes.

CBC later reported that the magnesium was explained by the long exposure of the wires to seawater. Makes you wonder why an RCMP officer might put himself on the line and appear in a TV documentary after being told to keep quiet if he wasn't convinced of his evidence. [2]

Back in the early 90s, just as I was beginning to ask questions about pet vaccines, and people had warned me to be careful, I was asked to write a brochure for a company selling systems to protect against terrorist insurrection. I took the opportunity to ask my client if he ever got involved in industrial espionage. He turned pale and shivered, and said, "No way. That's the sort of business where you stand at a bus stop and get mowed down."

I thought it was interesting that my client felt it was safer to deal with terrorists than the corporate world.

It seems that involvement with microbes, viruses, biowarfare and vaccines is a high-risk career choice, with a good chance of sudden, inexplicable, or even violent death. Verifiable accounts involve hit and run accidents, violent attacks and even shootings, a bombing, numerous car and airplane crashes, alleged suicides, 'accidental' infection with deadly viruses, torture and mutilation.

Rense.com came up with a list of bio-scientists who had met untimely ends. Here are some of them, all of which I've verified:

- Leonid Strachunsky, microbe expert, died June 8, 2005– fatal blow to the head. Investigators speculated that Strachunsky's murder was linked to a sudden outbreak of Hepatitis A which afflicted more than 500 people in Russia, and which some believed was caused by a biological weapon.
- David Banks, principal scientist with Biosecurity Australia, died May 8, 2005 – airplane crash.
- Tom Thorne and Beth Williams, experts in chronic wasting disease and brucellosis, died December 29, 2004 – killed in a crash.
- Professor John Clark, biotechnology, died August 12, 2004 – found hanged.
- Bassem al-Mudares, drug company chemist, died July 21, 2004 – tortured and mutilated.
- Paul Norman, chief scientist for chemical and biological defence at Porton Down, died June 27, 2004 – plane crash.
- Assefa Tulu, bioterrorism expert, died June 24, 2004 – found face down, dead in his office.
- Antonina Presnyakova, bioweapons expert at the Russian Vector, the former Soviet bioweapons facility, died May 25, 2004 – accident with a needle laced with Ebola.
- Mohammed Munim al-Izmerly, chemist, died April 2004 – in American custody from a blow to the back of his head.
- Richard Stevens, haematologist, died January 6, 2004 – disappeared; apparent suicide. In a Telegraph article concerning Stevens' death,

Peter Mossman was described as a 'fellow haemophilia campaigner'. Mossman links Stevens to an independent enquiry concerning the transfusion of blood to thousands of patients containing Hepatitis C and HIV. Successive governments refused to acknowledge any fault. [3, 4]

- Robert Leslie Burghoff, microbiologist, died November 20, 2003 – hit and run accident.
- Michael Perich, vector-borne disease expert, died October 11, 2003 – one-vehicle car accident.
- Steven Mostow, America's leading infectious disease and bioterrorism expert, died March 25, 2002 – plane crash.
- David Wynn-Williams, astrobiologist and microorganism expert, died March 24, 2002 – hit by a car while jogging.
- Ian Langford, leukaemia and infection specialist, died February 12, 2002 – found dead in his blood-spattered and ransacked home.
- Vladamir "Victor" Korshunov, microbiologist, died February 9, 2002 – found dead with his head bashed in.
- Benito Que, AIDS researcher, died December 6, 2001 – found comatose in the street after what was called a mugging.
- Vladimer Pasechnik, bioweapons expert, died December 23, 2001 – stroke.
- Don Wiley, expert in Ebola, HIV and influenza, vanished December 16, 2001 – his body was found floating in the Mississippi river a month later.
- Set Van Nguyen, vaccine scientist, died December 14, 2001 – found dead in walk-in laboratory refrigerator; the room was full of deadly gas.
- Avishai Berkman, Amiramp Eldor, and Yaacov Matzner, experts in haematology and blood clotting, died November 24, 2001 – airplane crash.
- Elizabeth A Rich, MD, AIDS research, died July 10, 1998 – traffic accident.
- Tsunao Saitoh, expert in Alzheimer's disease, died May 7, 1996 – shot and killed along with his young daughter.

I remember hearing the BBC news one morning about a biological weapons expert called David Kelly who, according to the news report, had in no way committed suicide. By the time the same story appeared on the evening news, it had definitely become suicide.

David Kelly died July 18, 2003. The British biological weapons expert was said to have slashed his own wrists while walking near his home. Kelly was the Ministry of Defence's chief scientific officer and senior adviser on biological weapons to the UN biological weapons inspections teams. He was also, in the opinion of his peers, pre-eminent in his field.

He came to public attention in July 2003 when an unauthorised discussion he had off the record with a BBC journalist about the British government's dossier on weapons of mass destruction in Iraq led to a major controversy. Kelly became known as the source and was called to appear before the parliamentary foreign affairs select committee. He was questioned aggressively about his actions and found dead two days later.

Previously, in June, he had been quoted as 'a British scientist and biological weapons expert who had examined the trailers in Iraq,' saying: "They are not mobile germ warfare laboratories. You could not use them for making biological weapons. They do not even look like them. They are exactly what the Iraqis said they were – facilities for the production of hydrogen gas to fill balloons."

Many doctors and prominent figures publicly challenged the verdict of suicide, with one former KGB agent even saying that Kelly had been 'exterminated'. Richard Spertzel, a UN weapons inspector, said Kelly was on a "hitlist" in the final years of his life. [5]

Fast forward to March 2014, and a Malaysian plane, flight MH370, mysteriously disappeared. The night before the news broke, I woke from my sleep with the image of a nose-diving plane. On the plane were 20 members of a US technology company, Freescale Semiconductor, which makes powerful microchips for industries, including defence [6]. All sorts of conspiracy theories ensued, including one from Beforeitsnews.com, which reported: "It is conceivable that the Malaysia Airlines Flight MH370 plane is 'cloaked', hiding with hi-tech electronic warfare weaponry that exists and is used. In fact, this type of technology is precisely the expertise of Freescale, that has 20 employees on board the missing flight."

Former Proteus Airlines boss Marc Dugain has even suggested the plane was shot down by the United States after being remotely hacked – and he cites some of the islanders' accounts in his findings [7].

In July 2014, another Malaysian plane was shot down, this time above war-torn Ukraine, with none of the sides taking responsibility [8]. A leading HIV researcher, Joep Lange, was amongst those on board [9]. In fact, 108 people from the international Aids research community were on board. The victims included staff from WHO and medical researchers, health workers and activists who were due to attend the twentieth International Aids Conference.

Dr Lange was a former president of the International Aids Society and had been researching HIV for 30 years. He helped lead the fight for the availability of affordable treatments across Asia and Africa. Also on board was Glenn Thomas, Director of Communications for WHO and a leading expert in Aids and Ebola.

What percentage of plumbers or electricians die in car or plane accidents, or of violent attacks, or are the percentages higher for bio-scientists, virologists, and those involved with warfare?

So I'm listening to BBC Radio 4 one morning in 2014, and relatives of the victims of the Lockerbie bombing, which happened back in December 1988, are talking about how the tragedy has affected their lives. In addition to 243 passengers and 16 crew being killed, more than 11 residents of the village of Lockerbie lost their lives when the plane landed on their homes [10].

I wondered, rather belatedly perhaps, if there was anyone involved with viruses or the bio industry on board that plane.

Turns out that there's a big conspiracy theory surrounding one of the passengers. This was the UN Commissioner for Namibia, Bernt Carlsson. He'd been interviewed in a World In Action TV documentary, 'The Case of the Disappearing Diamonds', where he warned that the UN would take action against those who were illegally exploiting Namibia's natural resources. According to the *Namibian Sun* of 8 January 2014, a British-based mining company may have been behind his 'assassination'.

Just over three months after the UN Commissioner for Namibia had been killed at Lockerbie, prime minister Margaret Thatcher made a point of visiting the Rössing Uranium Mine in Namibia as part of a tour to countries in Southern Africa. She was accompanied by David Cameron, a subsequent UK Prime Minister. Mrs Thatcher was so impressed with the Rössing Uranium Mine that she declared it made her "proud to be British", a sentiment echoed by David Cameron.

The trip by Mr Cameron in 1989 was funded by a firm that lobbied against the imposition of sanctions on the apartheid regime. A spokeswoman for Mr Cameron said: "Yes, he did go to South Africa. He met with anti-apartheid campaigners, he met opposition politicians when he was out there, including Zeth Mothopeng, the head of the PAC.

"It was a fact-finding mission that happened 20 years ago. He met union leaders and was shown around mines. The position of the Conservative Party at that time was against sanctions." [11]

All of this ties in with allegations that British and American interests, along with international corporations and whoever's behind them all, are empire-building in the developing world. See the book *Confessions of an Economic Hit Man* by John Perkins.

However, also on board the Lockerbie flight was Irving Sigal who had been called a 'spectacular scientist' as the senior director of molecular biology at the Merck Research Laboratories in New Jersey. Sigal had made a major breakthrough, finding a drug that could treat Aids. Although the drug was nearly shelved after Sigal's death, Merck went on to spend more than $700 million racing two other firms – Abbott Laboratories and Hoffmann-La Roche – to make it. [12]

Several terrorist groups were quick to claim responsibility for the bomb. Colonel Muammar Gaddafi admitted Libya's responsibility and paid compensation to the victims' families in 2003, though he maintained that he never personally gave the order for the attack. Palestinian organisations were also thought to be in the picture. Security forces had also been alerted to a potential terrorist attack in advance.

Abdelbaset al-Megrahi, a Libyan intelligence officer, was found guilty of the bombing and sentenced to life imprisonment, although the Court of Criminal Appeal in Edinburgh found he "may have suffered a miscarriage of justice". Amidst calls from grieving relatives for an independent enquiry, which was denied, alternative theories emerged.

The Guardian's Patrick Barkham listed the theories in 1999. There were allegations that Libya was framed. One theory suggests the bomb on the plane was detonated by radio. Another theory suggests the CIA prevented the suitcase containing the bomb from being searched. Iran's involvement was alleged. The US Defence Intelligence Agency alleged that Ayatollah Mohtashemi, a member of the Iranian government, paid US$10 million for the bombing.

In 2009, it was revealed that a security guard had reported that Heathrow's Pan Am baggage area had been broken into 17 hours before flight 103 took off. Police lost the report and it was never investigated or brought up at trial.

One of the British relatives, Martin Cadman, alleged that a member of President Bush's staff told him: "Your government and ours know exactly what happened but they are never going to tell." [13]

Fast forward to June 2015, and Dr Jeff Bradstreet, who helped families whose children were believed to have been vaccine damaged, was found dead under what many were calling 'suspicious circumstances' [14]. He was found floating in a North Carolina river. Bradstreet, a medical doctor, was a prominent autism researcher and vaccine opponent. He was also parent of a child who developed autism after vaccination.

A fisherman found his body in the Rocky Broad River in North Carolina. "He had a gunshot wound to the chest, which appeared to be self-inflicted, according to deputies," reported Fox News Carolina.

Bradstreet ran a private practice in Buford, Georgia, which focused on treating children with Autism Spectrum Disorder and related neurological and developmental disorders. Among various remedies, Bradstreet's Wellness Center reportedly carried out mercury toxicity treatments, believing the heavy metal to be a leading factor in the development of childhood autism. Bradstreet is said to have pinpointed the cause of the disease after his own child developed the ailment following routine vaccination.

In addition to treating patients, Bradstreet offered expert testimony in federal court on behalf of vaccine-injured families and was founder and president of the International Child Development Resource Center, which at one time employed the autism expert Andrew Wakefield as research director. The circumstances surrounding Bradstreet's death were made all the more curious by a multi-agency raid led by the FDA on his offices.

Social media pages dedicated to Bradstreet's memory were filled with comments from families who said the deceased doctor impacted their lives for the better. Despite his family requesting the public to refrain from speculation, many were nevertheless concluding the doctor's death was part of a conspiracy.

"Self-inflicted? In the chest? I'm not buying this," one person in the WHNS comments thread stated. "This was a doctor who had access to pharmaceuticals of all kinds. This was a religious man with a thriving medical practice. Sorry, but this stinks of murder and cover-up."

Another commentator had a more definitive conjecture: "He did NOT kill himself! He was murdered for who he was speaking against, what he knew, and what he was doing about it. He was a brilliant, kind, compassionate doctor with amazing abilities to heal. He was taken. Stopped. Silenced. Why would a doctor who had access to pharmaceuticals and could die peacefully shoot himself in the chest???? And throw himself in a river?? THIS IS OBVIOUS! MURDER!!"

A second Florida doctor, who held a PhD in nutrition from Harvard, died less than two weeks later. Bruce Hedendal died suddenly on Father's day. He was found in his car, but there was no car accident and the car wasn't running. Then a third holistic doctor, Teresa Ann Sievers, was found dead in Florida. Lee County Sheriff's Office declined to discuss the case, saying it was an ongoing homicide investigation.

In fact, at time of writing, more than 80 doctors have died suspiciously in America [15]. The speculation from Catherine J Frompovich is that these doctors had been investigating the fact that nagalese increases in the body post-vaccination, leading to inflammation, and that this surge can be treated with GcMAF, a chemical normally produced by the body.

Frompovich states: "Shortly after I emailed this blog around to colleagues, I received an email from Richard Sacks, the host of "Lost Arts Radio" wherein he provided me with the link to the interview he did with David Noakes, founder of the company producing verifiable-by-test pure GcMAF that physicians were using, but had his business, Immuno Biotech, Ltd., the manufacturer of GcMAF, closed by British MHRA authorities.

"On 4 February, the UK's Medicine and Healthcare products Regulatory Agency (MHRA) staged a raid on the manufacturing plant of Immuno Biotech, in Milton, Cambridgeshire and made off with 10,000 vials of the stuff, claiming the manufacturing process had been 'contaminated'.[16]

"One has to wonder why doctors, who were using GcMAF in the USA and getting dramatic improvement-to-cure rates with patients, have been found DEAD. Furthermore, Dr Bradstreet was about to publish a paper detailing his success rate in reversing/curing autism using GcMAF."

Blimey, I thought that this sort of stuff was largely Hollywood fantasy. I find it interesting that most people, in the UK at least, know that wars are waged in areas where there are valuable natural resources [17]. But there also seems to be a suspicious propensity for bio-scientists to die in plane crashes, and for holistic or free-thinking doctors to die in suspicious circumstances.

According to CBS News, May 2009, for example, Merck made a "hit list" of doctors who criticised a discredited drug called Vioxx, according to testimony in a Vioxx class action case in Australia. The list, emailed between Merck employees, contained doctors' names with the labels "neutralise," "neutralised" or "discredit" next to them. [18, 19]

I personally received an email from a scientist I cannot name, because names would put him in danger. He was frightened. A high-ranking government official, who I know but cannot name, had written to his university after the scientist had presented an honest research paper, which I cannot describe. The government official was furious from the tone of his letter. The scientist, as demanded by the government official (from a *different* country that I cannot name), had all of his research funding withdrawn, making it hard to continue with his work.

The research concerned something that you and I need to know in order to protect our dogs from terminal illnesses. But the scientist has been put out of business by a government source. No wonder he was frightened.

It seems to me that science is no longer the open pursuit of truth, and that it's been hijacked by political and multi-billion interests. You cannot trust science anymore; you cannot trust your government; you need to ask who speaks, and why they speak.

Although I was warned by concerned onlookers and, importantly and significantly, a top UK government official who told me (on the phone so I cannot prove it) that he feared for me if I continued to expose the untruth surrounding pet vaccination, I am still here.

Alarmed at first, and following me around, the veterinary vaccine industry soon learnt that dog owners were reluctant to listen. But if you speak the truth over and over again, first one, then two, then one hundred, then two hundred people, then ten thousand people hear … and then the world begins to understand.

Just don't get on a plane with me, or anyone involved with the bio-industries!

Chapter 36
Arguments and tragedies

I was invited to join a panel of experts discussing threatened legislation. Dog owners had successfully campaigned to have passports granted to pets so they could go on overseas holiday with their owners. The downside was that globe-trotting dogs would have to have rabies shots. One option under consideration was that every dog in the UK would have – by law – to be vaccinated against rabies. Rabies is not an issue here; the issue would be animals coming back into the country after having been potentially exposed to rabies – which is a real threat because no vaccine can be guaranteed to immunise.

The discussion was taking place at the Animal Health Trust's premises in Suffolk; it was part of the British Veterinary Nursing Association annual conference. The idea was that each member of the panel would have ten minutes to put their view, after which the discussion would be opened up to the audience.

I arrived the night before, only to discover that there was a grand ball being held. For some reason the programme and itinerary hadn't been sent to me, so I had to sit in my hotel room feeling like Cinderella No-Mates while everyone else got to go to the ball. I read through the material that should have been sent to me previously, only to discover that the whole event was sponsored by Intervet. I wondered whether it was truly a mistake that the paperwork hadn't been sent to me in advance, as it had been to everyone else.

So the next day a line of about eight of us are sitting on stage giving our ten-minutes-worth, and there are a man and a woman in corporate suits sitting in the front row. Pretty soon, the man from Intervet had grabbed the mic and was delivering a monologue about vaccines being safe, calling upon the assembled veterinary nurses to attest to the 'fact' that they'd never seen a vaccine reaction – which would be difficult if their education hadn't told them what a vaccine reaction looks like.

I looked at the meeting's chairman, and then pointed to my watch. The panel members had been given ten minutes to speak, but Mr Intervet was on his feet delivering a lengthy oration. It was frustrating, because I didn't have permission to respond to his claims. Eventually the chairman indicated for the mic to be taken away from the man, and we sat and stared each other out. I think I won on the eyeballing front, anyway.

A few days before we were due to fly home from Canada, we

received a call from Brian James, the documentary producer. "You need to come back a few days early," he said. "We plan to film you the day after your arrival back in the UK, and we don't want you to be jetlagged. So home we reluctantly flew, only to be confronted with a press release issued by 'Mary' claiming that the documentary was based on Ann Martin's work (Ann was author of *Food Pets Die For*). I told you 'Mary' would get me back, illustrating that one should never telephone someone when under stress – people you piss off frequently have long memories.

Granada's lawyers went ballistic, and so did Brian's team. They hastily sent out another press release to refute the allegations.

Brian had chosen to invite a vet to discuss the complaints about pet food rather than Ann Martin. The media is like this – they're less interested in what a layperson has to say than they are in what a qualified professional has to say which, as a layperson, I know only too well. They had initially invited the vet Michael Fox to fly across from America to talk about pet food, but he'd nominated Jean Hofve DVM, an holistic vet, to take his place. I had urged Brian to get Ann Martin across, but he hadn't bitten the bullet.

Michael Fox, incidentally, had written the foreword to Ann's book. When he returned to work as head vet for the Humane Society in America, he was demoted. Turns out that the Humane Society was in the process of negotiating a large sponsorship deal with a pet food manufacturer, and Michael's involvement with Ann Martin's book put the deal in jeopardy. Michael speaks plainly about this, saying that he was effectively dismissed. When a new head came to steer the American Humane Society, Michael received an apology.

So presumably disgruntled and falsely believing her work had been stolen from under her (the vet Wendell Belfield had written much the same as Ann a decade or so earlier), my friendship with Ann was over. I'd wondered why her emails had dried up just before we went to Canada.

And then the day came for the programme to be aired. John had tried to forcefully persuade me not to take part, but even he could tell when to give up. Nevertheless, I sat in front of the TV and shook the whole way through it. We hadn't been allowed to see the programme before it aired and half of me was expecting a set up and half of me hoped it wouldn't be. True, the documentary had – as was required by TV rules – heard spokesmen from the 'dark' side, with the Royal College of Veterinary Surgeons defending over-vaccination and dissing our vaccine survey, and the Pet Food Manufacturers' Association defending pet food – but the general feedback was that they didn't seem to be that relaxed or convincing about it. I certainly wouldn't have bought a used car from any of them.

Spectacularly, Brian James had found a dog trainer who was consulted by the owner of a vicious German Shepherd. He told the owner to go away for two weeks and feed real food (aka raw food) to the dog. It took only one week on real food for the snarling, angry dog to transform into a mild-mannered pussy cat – and this was without any training intervention. Brian had also interviewed a zoo keeper who confirmed that they couldn't feed their wild canine inmates pet food because it made them ill.

On the whole, I was delighted with the programme.

When the documentary ended, viewers began to call. One after the other told us how their dog had died or become ill shortly after being vaccinated, some on that very day. Others wrote:

"In June 1998, our 15-month-old Border Collie, Holly, was given her annual booster, which included kennel cough. Within a couple of days we noticed she was snorting and almost breathless at times. We contacted the vet for advice and they said it was normal for a dog to do this following a nasal injection. A few days later her condition worsened – diarrhoea, a temperature of 105, breathless, and very unstable on her feet. A vets appointment was made immediately. To us these were some of the symptoms shown in the documentary after a dog's annual booster.

"After numerous vet visits, they could not resolve the problem and Holly was referred to the Royal Dick Veterinary Clinic in Edinburgh on 13th October 1998, where she spent nearly four weeks. All kinds of tests and treatments had been carried out and advice from America was given. Her illness was not diagnosed.

"Not being able to see Holly, as she was in Edinburgh, she died on the 8th November 1998, which was very devastating to us both after trying to fight her illness for five months. We would be very grateful if you could give us any advice relating to the vaccination."

A letter from the Royal Dick School of Veterinary Studies, copied to us by Holly's parents, stated that pathological opinion indicated that Holly had a very serious disease of her bone marrow. Jean Dodds has noted a rise in blood and bone marrow-related diseases since the introduction of MLV vaccines. Case notes supplied by the vet noted a possible vaccine reaction. Although the Royal Dick failed to establish a vaccine link, the vaccine was – to me – an apparent contributor to Holly's death.

Ann Marston wrote:

"I saw the recent World in Action programme and felt I had to tell of my recent experience. Until just before the programme I had three beautiful healthy cats. One was a Russian Blue just eight years old, who had never had a day's illness in his life. I took them for their boosters on Friday October, 2nd. The vet examined them before the injection and pronounced them fit and well. When we took them out of their baskets after a 25 minute car journey home, the Russian Blue was dead. The vet did a post-mortem but could offer no reason for the death. He said that the cat was healthy and had no disease.

"As the cats live indoors, I would have certainly thought twice about having annual vaccinations had the programme gone out a week earlier, and Blue would still be alive today."

I replied to the grieving lady:

It's quite probable that Blue suffered an adverse reaction to the vaccine. Unless the vet thought to fill in a yellow form (MLA252A) and send it to the VMD, no official link with the vaccine and Blue's death will have been established. If your cat was given LSD and died within 25 minutes of taking it, it would be assumed that the LSD killed him. But because it is a vaccine, the coincidence is ignored.

T Fudger-Sherrington wrote:

"After seeing you on the World in Action programme, I just wanted to write and tell you about my own experience.

"Up until Easter this year I owned a male Great Dane. On the 9th of April, when we got up at 7am, he was yelping when he got on or off the sofa. By 11am he was really squealing, so we took him to the vet, and were told he had pulled a muscle in his back. He was given an anti-inflammatory injection and pain relief tablets.

"When we got home, he lay down to rest and never got up again. By 3pm he had started fitting, and we called the vet out immediately. When they arrived they tranquilised him and took him to the surgery where, despite anti-epileptic drugs, he just got worse: screaming in pain, fitting, going rigid, biting his lips, and messing himself.

"By 7pm we were told that there was no way that he could be saved, and that he would have to be put to sleep there and then.

"I am telling you this is because he had his annual booster on the 20th of March, and was vomiting intermittently for about a week afterwards. I know that in this case nothing can be proved, but I now have two new Danes and I want to be as informed as possible, so I can make judgments about their health and safety.

"We loved him so much, and he had such a beautiful nature. It was a terrible shock to lose him at only four years old. I never want to see another dog die in that much pain and suffering again."

I replied, saying that encephalitis is a known sequel to vaccination, and that epilepsy is a symptom of encephalitis.

M Davies wrote:

"We watched World in Action last night and what you said has concerned us so much that I feel I must tell you of recent events in our life.

"We had two Rottweilers who had annual boosters. The elder, a bitch called Heidi, was 11 years old. On 20th August we took her for her booster and check-up. She had arthritis which made her stiff until she got going, and one or two fatty lumps, but she was fine otherwise. The vet said she was pretty good for her years.

"The day after her booster, Heidi ate very little. This was unheard of as she was always greedy. During the next two weeks we encouraged her to eat by offering chicken and other treats which she normally enjoyed. She didn't regain her appetite, simply picking at her food or eating tiny amounts. At the same time, her stiffness became worse and she managed very little exercise.

"On the 7th September, our vet was concerned and prescribed steroids. For a few days she did improve, seeming brighter, moving more freely and eating a little with enjoyment. After a few days' improvement, Heidi deteriorated again. The vet prescribed strong anti-inflammatory drugs and painkillers. This time there was no improvement. Heidi could not go out to toilet herself unaided and she would stand only for her back legs to give in. She ate nothing for a couple of days and only drank sips of water.

"Sadly, after talking to our vet, Heidi was put to sleep on 16th September. We are heartbroken but could not let her suffer any more.

"We could not believe how quickly her health deteriorated and had said how strange for her to be so well when she had her booster, and for the end to follow so soon.

"Now, after hearing you on the television, we wonder if the booster was the cause. Of course, nothing can bring our Heidi back, but we feel desperate to know more about the possible harm of boosters in order to make up our own minds when our other dog is due to have his booster."

Vaccines are licensed for use in healthy animals only, which would – in my view – contraindicate Heidi receiving a booster (which, at 11, she didn't need anyway). Loss of the use of her back legs would also indicate encephalitis. The First International Veterinary Vaccine Symposium, held in 1997, issued guidance stating that geriatric dogs should not be vaccinated. They defined geriatric as over eight years of age. Heidi was almost certainly already immune.

Another lady wrote:

"We have just watched World in Action and were so amazed by the similarities in our own dog's life. Our dog, Leo, is a three year old Shih-tzu. He was a healthy, bouncy, typical puppy. He was given a clean bill of health by our vet when he had his first vaccination but we started having problems after his second set of puppy vaccinations. He had to be taken back to the vets suffering from vomiting and diarrhoea.

"He also had problems with his skin, he was scratching incessantly and his skin was covered with large, weeping, sores.

"When he had his first booster in March 1996, he had a severe bout of diarrhoea and vomiting. He was passing blood in his motions and he had to be kept in by the vet and was on a drip for two to three days. The vet told us that our dog was suffering from colitis and until we watched the programme this evening, we had not connected it with his boosters. He also had three fits, which our vet informed us were nothing to worry about as they were of short duration and occurred very intermittently.

"He has continued to have his boosters each year and, thinking back now, after each one we have had to return to our vets two or three times within five or six weeks after the booster, with digestive or skin problems."

Vaccines are of course known to cause reactions in the skin, vomiting, diarrhoea, and convulsions.

In fact, many letters flew to us in the post with similar stories. We replied, offering information, recommending homeopathic veterinary surgeons who at least acknowledged vaccine damage, and urging respondents to become members of CHC and support the work. Sadly, very few actually did. They agreed with us, were grateful for the information we shared, but helping us get the information out there was clearly a step too far.

Chapter 37

Duff me up, why don't you?

The day after the documentary aired, I drove down to Somerset to speak at the seminar organised by Allison Lovell's vet, David Holmes. It had morphed from a discussion with vets above a pub into a massive seminar sponsored by Intervet. I had pleaded with David not to do this: "Please," I said, "Let's for once do something that isn't sponsored by the vaccine or pet food industry." It seemed vets and scientists can't blow their own noses without being sponsored to do it.

David – for whatever reason – insisted upon receiving Intervet's sponsorship, though, and the seminar ended up being me in a battle versus Intervet, although David had also, at my suggestion and very kindly, invited Chris Day along to put the dissenting vet's view.

On the way there I met up with my branch managers, Bettie and Bertie, who were attending the event. Over a cup of coffee in a motorway service station, they outlined a brilliant plan. "Let's get hundreds of members to phone the VMD and the RCVS over and over again on the same day," said Bertie. "We'll jam their switchboards in protest."

"No, I don't think so. That's not what we're about," I replied cautiously. "We're not here to cause problems or to destroy. We're here to tell the truth." I don't think they liked my response.

Peter Shields, managing director of JCB, acted as an impartial chairman to oversee the conference to vets. Before we went on, the speakers stood in a huddle at the front of the room agreeing terms of engagement. "Is there anything you don't want to answer questions about?" Peter asked us all.

"Yes," I said. John had instructed me not to answer questions about the statistics behind our vaccine survey. I was not a statistician, and if I got into that debate I could easily get the figures wrong. "I don't want to answer questions about statistics as I'm not the statistician, but we are happy to answer any questions in writing."

Intervet/NOAH's David Sutton put his fingers to his lips and stuttered: "You're not answering questions about statistics?" The look on his face was a picture – he was clearly not happy.

"No," I said.

The room was packed. The middle front row was taken up by CHC supporters from the Bristol area, and the remaining hundred or so were vets, as well as veterinary students who I think had been shipped in from

Bristol University for the talk.

David Sutton claimed that my research was gathered from the tabloids. He put a cartoon up of a sinister vet in dark shadows injecting a dog with a needle, and claimed that we used illustrations such as this to discredit vets. It was hard sitting there listening to this distortion, and eventually I tried to refute what he was saying from the audience. David Sutton roared at me with frightening force and ordered me to shut up.

That same illustration appeared in the pro-vaccine article David Sutton, I suspect, placed in *Dogs Today*, and it also raised its head some years later when *Veterinary Times* contacted me to comment about a presentation by a pathologist who had suggested we used this kind of illustration. Ironically, it seems to me that the only people who used sinister pictures in relation to vaccination appeared to be the vaccine industry and its supporters – I imagine in an attempt to make dissenters like me look bad. This, in a crazy sort of way, illustrates how impeccable I must have been at the time, because it would have been more effective had the industry highlighted the error of something I had actually done or said.

Then David Sutton talked about the research "we" (meaning, I assumed, he and the veterinary vaccine industry) had commissioned the Animal Health Trust to conduct, although in a report to NOAH – the veterinary drug trade association – David Holmes referred to this research as BSAVA/AHT research.

This research "proved" that vaccines don't cause autoimmune haemolytic anaemia in dogs. It seemed to me that this research had been commissioned by the veterinary vaccine industry in response to the independent study I mentioned earlier which proved that vaccines do indeed cause AIHA in dogs. But the vets and vet students in the audience lapped up everything David Sutton said, cheering him loudly on, questioning nothing.

I can't find any trace of that research the industry appeared to have paid for now. It seems to have disappeared, although it is mentioned in a document NOAH (the trade association that represents veterinary vaccine companies) posted to vets to refute the concerns raised about over-vaccination in the World in Action documentary.

My part of the evening was pretty unpleasant for me; I had twenty minutes in which to try to condense the body of research I was then aware of, which I had complained about before the event.

There was a tall dark stranger in the front row heckling loudly. He was on his feet demanding – extremely loudly – that I answer questions about statistics and waving his fists. The vet students in the audience were helping him along. Later I tried to find out who this man was, but nobody

I spoke to had seen him before. I guessed he was a plant, and felt that this was why David Sutton was knocked off balance when I told the chairman I wouldn't answer questions about statistics. If so, John had pre-empted their tactics well. No-one bothered to write with their questions.

I presented my slides – none of which had been garnered from the tabloid press – but practically everything I said was met with boos and jeers. Frankly, I felt that this was a disgraceful response to a veterinary client who presented evidence to show that their procedures were causing harm. "Aw shuddup, so what if I killed your kid?"

A little oik, younger than the kitchen knife I bought when I had my first apartment, made a speech from the audience with his chest out and his chin in the air about how he told his clients to vaccinate annually. By this time the stress of the evening had taken its toll and I replied: "You *tell* your clients? Who do you think you are – God? Dog owners aren't stupid, and many have a great deal of knowledge. You don't *tell* them to do anything; you offer them informed consent."

Later Chris Day advised me that being rude wouldn't win anyone over. I didn't respond, but I thought, "They're killing our dogs, and we have to be polite?" Besides, no-one in that room was open to being won over.

Intervet was paying the speakers a fee and putting them up in the flash hotel overnight, but I wasn't prepared to accept a vaccine industry fee or their hospitality. Their money was everywhere, it seemed.

I asked Bettie and Bertie to escort me back to my humble B&B. Having been unnerved by the evening's events, I put a chair below the door handle in my room, imagining men in hoods with baseball bats storming their way in.

The evening was covered by *Veterinary Times*, which published a photograph showing the line-up of speakers. I looked like a fox cornered by hounds which, depending upon how veterinary readers wished to view me, could have been interpreted as me looking deranged.

According to *Veterinary Times*, I gave an impassioned but 'statistically challenged' presentation. "Catherine O'Driscoll claimed that these data [from our vaccine survey], although by her own admission somewhat anecdotal, showed that current veterinary vaccination programmes were flawed and were causing widespread suffering and disease in cats and dogs, especially the young, the old and those individuals with a compromised immune system."

The journal added that Chris Day used elegant analogies gleaned from mediaeval warfare. "In summary," he said, "We are seeing things that could be attributed to vaccination. We may not accept them but we should ask for more research. We should at least treat Catherine O'Driscoll's findings with respect."

David Sutton was described in the same article as, "David Sutton, who not only works for a major vaccine manufacturer (Intervet), but is also intimately involved with the licensing of vaccines and the reporting of suspected adverse reactions".

"Dogs need booster vaccinations," he said.

So I gave a statistically challenged presentation, Chris Day used mediaeval analogies, and David Sutton was practically a scientific deity – according to *Veterinary Times'* David Watson.

But, as we all now know, the deity was wrong. Dogs do not need booster vaccinations. In 1998, when that conference took place, dogs were being given the full cocktail wombo combo every year. Which they didn't need, and never had needed.

A few years later, veterinary bodies in America went public with the statement that "vaccines are not without harm" – which is also what I was saying that night. The WSAVA repeated that same truth a few years later.

Now then, John, in his wisdom, made a Freedom of Information Act request upon a number of bodies acting within the animal healthcare field, one of which was NOAH. Their Catherine O'Driscoll/Canine Health Concern file was large. It included our newsletters, our press releases (which must have been passed to them by one of the journals we sent the release to), and – thanks to a press clipping service via Graylings Public Relations – more press clippings about us than we had ourselves.

It also included a document written by David Holmes. David told NOAH, "I was invited to attend a meeting of local dog breeders and kennel owners where Catherine O'Driscoll was speaking. Catherine gave a powerful and extremely emotional presentation outlining the views of CHC regarding the prevalence and significance of vaccine reactions in dogs... I was impressed with the depth of feeling she expressed and the effort she had put into her research".

On the subject of the Bristol vet conference, David said: "All the speakers gave valuable presentations but it is difficult at this stage to judge how the audience felt. The one thing that really came out from the questions was that many people could not handle what they perceived to be the poor science of the CHC survey."

Bless David Holmes, for he tried to give an honest, open and unbiased precise of his feelings. He stated clearly that our research should not be dismissed, but was swayed towards it being unscientific. Well, I guess you see what you want to see. The majority of vets are, after all, still not even listening to WSAVA vaccine guidance.

At the end of the conference, CHC members attempted to hand out the ten-page document we had prepared for vets in attendance, realising that twenty minutes wouldn't be enough to say what was needed to be said. It contained statements taken from Intervet's vaccine data sheets; a quote from Ron Schultz and Tom Phillips in *Current Veterinary Therapy XI, 1992*, in which they state that MLV vaccines can cause the disease they are designed to prevent; quotes from Dr Larry Swango, associate professor of virology at Auburn University and Dr Ian Tizard, professor at Texas A&M University; data concerning dietary factors relevant to infection and disease; genetic factors relating to vaccine contra-indications (taken from Merck), quotes from Merck relating to vaccine-induced epilepsy and encephalitis, immunosuppression and vaccine adverse effects; stress and vaccine adverse effects from Dr Jean Dodds; and the science (from Merck) relating to vaccine-induced autoimmune diseases. It also contained references from proper peer-reviewed research papers relating to vaccine-induced allergies and arthritis.

Our handout finished with the words, "Thank you for taking the time to read this paper. It means a great deal to your clients."

CHC members were shocked to discover that the majority of vets and student vets leaving the conference pushed the paper away, refusing to take it, not even out of courtesy or to look at it at all.

I didn't know the terms then, but I do now: 'confirmation bias', and 'cognitive dissonance'. The scientists in the audience were simply not open to the truth. If they refused to look at the science we presented, then they could of course continue in the belief that we were unscientific.

The good news is that, following the World in Action documentary, vets were having to spend an inordinate amount of time explaining to clients that their dogs did indeed require annual shots, and many clients were phoning up and cancelling their booster appointments.

I also appeared on several BBC radio channels. When you're a phone-in guest on the radio, you get faded out a lot. So I was invited to explain the contents of *What Vets Don't Tell You* in two minutes, and then I'd be faded out and have to listen to a vet telling the listening millions that annual vaccination was absolutely mandatory (or your dog will die), and that adverse vaccine reactions were very, very rare. There was no recourse – I had no chance to speak after that.

I was also invited to be interviewed by BBC local radio, and this was to be networked across all of the BBC's local radio stations. Having been faded out on the phone, I agreed to go into the station one dark damp night; I was also assured, before I agreed to go in, that there wouldn't be a vet on the programme to argue with me. After all, if a vet issues a press release or engages with the media, I'm not invited on to put the other view. What vets and doctors have to say – no matter whether they're right or wrong – is taken at face value.

A vet friend had previously passed me a copy of the document NOAH had issued to refute the documentary programme. It was posted to all the vet practices in the UK in anticipation of pet owners having had their eyes opened. It naturally defended annual vaccination and downplayed adverse effects. Unfortunately, CHC didn't have the funds to post letters to every vet in the UK to share the *actual* science.

So I arrived at the BBC studio, only to be informed that there would be a vet on the show after all. He appeared to be cribbing from the NOAH sheet, and although he wasn't in the studio, he didn't keep getting faded out! My mind flashed back to the evening in Bristol where I noticed an Intervet employee listening into a conversation with a CHC supporter where I mentioned that I was going to be networked on BBC local radio. Darn it – I'd probably allowed the show to be nobbled by opening my mouth in public.

The same Intervet employee had proudly told me that Intervet's David Sutton sat on a VPC committee that decides whether a vaccine reaction is a vaccine reaction or not. I was horrified, telling him that a vaccine industry employee had no right to be on that committee. It would be like a robber filling a jury with his friends and family. We wrote to the VMD and asked if this was true, but it took many weeks, and several reminders, before they replied that, no, David Sutton wasn't on that committee. Of course I wonder why an Intervet employee told us he was, and why it took so long to say he wasn't? And why did *Veterinary Times* say that he, "not only works for a major vaccine manufacturer (Intervet), but is also intimately involved with the licensing of vaccines and the reporting of suspected adverse reactions"?

Chapter 38
Conflicts of interest

In May 2001, a large brown envelope was dropped through the letterbox. I looked at it and was strangely engulfed in rage – having had so many aggressive and accusatory letters in the post, I seemed to have developed a sixth sense before opening them. This particular envelope contained a document entitled: 'Final Report to the VPC: Veterinary Products Committee (VPC) Working Group on Feline and Canine Vaccination.' [1]

The VPC is part of a government department called Defra ... Department for the Environment, Food and Rural Affairs.

I turned immediately to the page which stated who the members of this working group were. There were four people. The first was Rosalind Gaskell from the University of Liverpool. Searching revealed that Gaskell was an Intervet shareholder and received research funding from the vaccine manufacturer Intervet.

The second was George Gettingby from the University of Strathclyde, who had financial and research assistance from Intervet and its sister company Organon.

Number three was Mrs Sheila Graham BSc, billed as a lay member.

And the fourth was Mr David Skilton, a veterinary surgeon, who could be contacted via the Veterinary Defence Society Ltd, and of course vets were, and still are, benefitting from booster income. David Skilton later chaired the VPC.

Not surprisingly, the Working Group proclaimed that we should carry on vaccinating annually.

The Veterinary Products Committee is billed as 'an independent scientific committee established under Section 4 of the Medicines Act to give advice on the safety, quality and efficacy of veterinary medicines to the UK licensing authority (Health and Agriculture Ministers) and to promote the collection of information relating to suspected adverse reactions for the purpose of enabling such advice to be given'. [2]

Independence is of course vitally important, otherwise we'd have drug, chemical and vaccine company yes men and women making judgements about their own sugar-daddies' products. This would make the industry its own regulator. Yet try to find the VPC Register of Interests through an internet search. For some reason they're not wishing to shout this little baby out to the rooftops.

In July 2000 the *Sunday Express* reported on the issue, pointing out that top vets were taking cash from drug firms. "There is a growing concern that committee members of the Veterinary Medicines Directorate – who decide whether to license products or take them off the market – may have conflicts of interest". More than half of the directorate's experts – 26 out of 48 – were part-funded by drug companies.

"Richard Young, of the Soil Association, said: "There is a cosy pro-industry culture which runs throughout the regulatory framework. Because of this there is a tendency for committee members to look upon products in a non-critical way.""

Gaskell and Gettingby who, through a VPC working group, proclaimed that we should carry on vaccinating annually whilst claiming independence, were also receiving funding from, and even owning shares in, a vaccine manufacturer. History tells us now that they were wrong.

Nothing much has changed. The VPC is still staffed by individuals who appear to be industry shills. Remember, the VPC is there to provide 'independent' assessment regarding the safety of veterinary products. You are welcome to check out the Register on-line via the VMD website, or email the VMD to ask them where they've hidden it.

The 2013 VPC 'declaration of interests' document listed its members and potential conflicts of interest:

Dr Claire Bryant was a consultant for Astra-Zeneca, and received research funding from Astra-Zeneca, GSK, and Zoetis. Mr Peter Cargill enjoyed consultancy fees from Intervet Schering-Plough, Pfizer and Vaxxinova, amongst others. Mr Stephen Lister was a consultant to Elanco Animal Health. Professor Jacqui Matthews was a non-executive director of WormVax. Mr Robert Morris was a company secretary with shareholdings and a pension from Roma Pharmacy. Mr Declan O'Rourke benefitted from a long list of consultancies for the likes of Bayer, Pfizer, Eli Lilly and Boehringer Ingelheim, etc. Professor Andrew Peters also had consultancies with Bayer, Elanco, Pfizer and others.

The purportedly independent VPC committee appears to be staffed by people whose research and livelihoods are closely related to the industry they are allegedly protecting us from.

After the TV documentary and the VPC working group report, the British Small Animal Veterinary Association (BSAVA) proclaimed on its web site that it supported the informed choice of clients, but that there was not enough evidence to discontinue annual shots. This is, of course, a continuation of the vaccine-associated ostrich disease I diagnosed in my book, *What Vets Don't Tell You About Vaccines*. Of course there's enough evidence – in fact there's zero scientific evidence to *support* annual vaccination! And when do vets *inform* clients that the shots they are about to give are probably unnecessary, and that vaccines can cause harm? There *is* no informed consent.

The British Veterinary Association (BVA) and the BSAVA followed up the World in Action documentary by issuing a joint statement. There was much bluster about vaccines preventing major epidemics; how highly skilled and trained veterinary surgeons are; and how the profession must adhere to the best scientific information, which was widely deemed to be annual shots.

"The VPC's working group recommended that there is insufficient justification to alter current data sheet recommendations." The statement went on to say: "The fact remains that we still do not know enough about the true duration of immunity in individual animals and .... whilst (titre) testing is possible it incurs extra expense to the owner."

Actually, titre testing could be considered an inconvenience to the veterinary vaccine industry. It would act as a sales prevention tool. If dog owners were able to test and discover that their dogs were already immune, then they wouldn't need to make that annual or three-yearly pilgrimage to get boosters.

This government-endorsed statement came despite the fact that I, through CHC, had sent circa 24 letters to my MP who forwarded them on to the Defra Minister, who forwarded them on to the working party, and we included piles of duration of immunity studies, which it seems were ignored!

And then, amidst the media furore, it was the turn of members of the VPC working group to pipe up. In a letter to *Veterinary Times*, Rosalind Gaskell claimed that the VPC working group report on feline and canine vaccination was not actually an industry report, but an independent report. Prof Gaskell gave her academic standing and quoted the academic standing of Prof Gettingby, a fellow working group member, and she claimed that they were both independent. However, Rosalind Gaskell failed to mention that, according to the VPC declaration of interests, both she and Gettingby enjoyed financial support from the veterinary vaccine industry, or shareholdings.

And I kept getting letters from the Minister responsible for Defra to the effect that members of the VPC, and the people in the working group recommending annual vaccination, were individuals of the highest integrity and repute.

This may have been the case. I just don't think we should be asked to make assumptions about their integrity. Rather, I think we should have people manning these committees and making decisions on our pets' behalf who have no ties with, and no financial assistance from, the industry they are allegedly protecting us from.

Meanwhile, the veterinary vaccine industry paid the Animal Health Trust (a charity that also boasts vaccine development as one of its activities) to investigate vaccine reactions and, in my view, their idea was to not find many vaccine reactions at all. They called this the POOCH study, and looked at veterinary records around the UK. They concluded that, actually, not only were there hardly any reactions, but vaccinated dogs were healthier after their shots.

The survey methodology itself was strange. Can you, for example, understand why older vaccinated dogs were deleted from the research? Is this because old dogs cannot possibly suffer vaccine reactions? I'd be very interested to look at the deleted data and see how this might affect research findings. This question aside – why delete any dogs from the research in the first place? Since vaccines can have adverse effects on any individual, then any individual should be studied – unless, of course, it isn't in your interests to look at certain individuals.

In another letter to *Veterinary Times*, a representative of the Animal Health Trust stated that I was malevolent for suggesting (in another letter to *Veterinary Times*) that the Animal Health Trust research was far from independent, having been sponsored by the vaccine industry.

It was befuddling. People kept on asserting, over and over again, that the POOCH study, paid for by the veterinary vaccine industry and conducted by a vaccine developer, was independent. I could only conclude that my understanding of the word 'independent' is different to that held by government, industry, animal charities and the veterinary profession, although looking at a dictionary, it appears to mean 'free from outside control; not subject to another's authority', and 'not depending upon another for livelihood or subsistence'.

I don't believe it's necessary to be malevolent to point out that members of the VPC, with funding and shares in the industry it's supposed to be protecting us from; or the Animal Health Trust, which gets a lot of its funding from the pharmaceutical industry and boasted in its report and accounts that it is a vaccine developer, might not be particularly independent.

Chapter 39

Rumours and betrayal

A vet called Tom Lonsdale wrote to me from Australia, sending articles about his raw diet for dogs [1]. Tom was a veterinary dental specialist who had conducted research to show that dogs fed on processed pet food suffered from what he termed, 'diet-induced Aids'. His published paper described how he had taken dogs and cats into his practice who suffered from periodontal disease. He took blood and administered antibiotics to deal with gum disease, and extracted rancid teeth. Then he gave them raw chicken wings to eat, and took more blood.

Tom concluded that by eating from a can or packet and never having their teeth cleaned, dogs and cats were literally swallowing a bacterial soup which went on to suppress the immune system and cause organ failure. He said that raw meaty bones were Nature's toothbrush for carnivores, and that by feeding them processed mush we were submitting our pets to horrendous harm. He challenged his veterinary colleagues to eat out of cans and packets for two weeks without cleaning their teeth so they could know what it felt like.

Tom wrote a book called *Raw Meaty Bones* and we offered him our support by publicising his book and a seminar tour he was planning in the UK.

Tom came to stay with us in our home for a few days and we worked with him to refute the claims made by Pedigree Petfoods which was marketing a new product called the 'Rask'. This was a carbohydrate-based biscuit that claimed to clean dogs' teeth. Tom had been given background notes from a presentation to vets about the Rask. What the veterinary notes stipulated, but the consumer marketing didn't appear to, was that the trial which 'proved' the Rask's efficacy included cleaning the dogs' teeth with toothbrushes. Any measurement of benefit was therefore … what's the technical term? Dodgy?

We contacted the national media and secured an article in *The Telegraph*, which helped to promote the natural diet further.

At the same time, we issued a press release with Tom entitled, 'chalky white dog poo' – explaining that our grandmothers' dogs used to have chalky white poo because they ate lots of bones. The white poos soon crumbled into the earth. Modern junk food-fed dogs, on the other hand, produce copious wet, smelly, brown poo. As well as sending the release to the press, we sent it out over the internet. One man emailed me demanding that I should never send him such a press release again, presumably because talking about poo was offensive to him. In contrast, raw feeders love talking about poo since the state of a dog's poo reflects their state of health!

Tom dedicated his life to educating both the veterinary profession and the owners of carnivores to feed a biologically appropriate diet to their patients and pets. While visiting, he asked us if we were in this for the long haul, warning that it would take many years before change would come. He also pointed out that our research, showing a high percentage of illnesses arising in dogs shortly after their shots, would end up on a dusty shelf somewhere and no-one would look at it.

Tom, being English at birth, campaigned for many years to become president of the BSAVA on the raw food for carnivores campaigning ticket. As a result, many of his veterinary colleagues disassociated themselves from him, although some offered their support.

Years later, Tom tried to persuade me to drop the vaccine issue, arguing that diet was responsible for good health, and improper diet was responsible for vaccine reactions. I actually agree with him to a very large extent – the problem, though, is that whilst pets are being fed 'crap in a bag' and are still over-subjected to the vaccine challenge, vaccines still represent a huge threat to health. Sadly, Tom's views were so strong on the matter that he later tried and failed to prevent me from speaking at a seminar in Germany.

Meanwhile, Bettie was continuing to manage the branch network. One day I had a call from one of our volunteers. She'd been talking with three other volunteers and they felt they needed to talk to me. "Catherine," she said, "you need to know that Bettie has asked us to leave CHC and help her set up a competitive organisation. She's saying all sorts of things about you. We thought you should know."

"Oh! What sort of things?" I asked.

"That you're closing CHC down. That you're taking money from pet food companies. That you're living a life of luxury on the back of CHC."

"Really?" I replied, my heart sinking.

"And she's also saying you've been phoning vets up and swearing at them."

As things began to unfold, the extent of the problem became clearer. I telephoned Ainsworths, the homeopathic pharmacy, to buy some remedies. Its owner Tony Pinkus came on the line: "What's this about you closing CHC down?" he asked.

Christopher Day wrote to me, asking why I was taking money from pet food companies (which I wasn't).

It seemed everyone I spoke to asked about me closing CHC down.

Sally Cronk was taken in hook, line and sinker. She got on the phone and repeated Bettie's rumours to Hylda Reynolds. Hylda phoned me: "I've just had a call from Sally. She says you've been doing all these things! She said that you told Bettie that you wouldn't trust Sally to organise a seminar because you think she's too stupid. I told her to stop spreading these rumours straight away. I can't believe people should be saying such things about you, Catherine, I don't believe a word of them."

Hylda was the only person who gave me her support. The only person.

Bettie had mentioned several times that she loved telling people about vaccines and pet food at dog shows: "It makes me feel like Jesus," she said.

Well, I was feeling like Jesus, too – betrayed, abandoned, and crucified!

I was devastated, utterly and completely devastated. Everyone I spoke to was repeating these rumours back at me, and it seemed as though everyone believed them. I was wearing myself out running CHC, answering phone calls and letters to help people help their dogs – without anything in return – and suddenly the people I had thought were with me were almost without exception against me. Alternatively, like Pontius Pilate, they had washed their hands of me.

Bertie and Bettie, by the way, are not their real names. This isn't a getting-even exercise. But watch your back if you stick your head over the parapet, and don't assume that the people on your side are actually on your side.

Chapter 40
Politics and propaganda

While I was experiencing the political power games associated with the dog world, a medical doctor in the UK was experiencing a political power struggle on a larger stage. As a gastroenterologist, this doctor had seen a number of children with inflammatory bowel disease who also experienced autism-like developmental regression. The majority of these children's parents believed that they began to regress shortly after they had been given a measles, mumps and rubella (MMR) jab. The doctor's name is Andrew Wakefield.

Wakefield and colleagues from the Royal Free Hospital in London published extensively on the possible causes and mechanisms of inflammatory bowel disease. But when a paper by the team appeared in *The Lancet* in 1998, it was to herald the end of Dr Wakefield's reputation and career.

The Lancet paper was a case series, designed to observe a pattern of common features in patients with the aim of raising a hypothesis that can subsequently be tested in the appropriate design framework. A case series is a precursor to a case-control study, and is not designed to investigate possible causes. Wakefield and his team did not state in their paper that the MMR jab caused autism, but that the majority of parents in the case series had implicated the MMR jab. As such, Dr Wakefield included information, appropriately, that might have a bearing on any future investigations.

Dr Wakefield had separately been asked to act as an expert witness by Richard Barr of Dawbarns law firm. Specifically, he was asked to review the safety of measles-containing vaccines and to design a study that would help determine whether there was or was not a legal case against the manufacturers of measles-containing vaccines. A research proposal was submitted to the Legal Aid Board and approved.

This is an important crux: In his book, *Callous Disregard* [1], Wakefield claims that he didn't know at that time that Professor Sir David Hull, the then-chairman of the Joint Committee on Vaccination and Immunisation (a British government department), had "contacted the dean of the Royal Free Medical School to ask the dean to bring to bear whatever pressure he could to stop Wakefield from acting as an expert witness in the case".

Let's be clear: a British government agent appeared to be involved before Andrew Wakefield was ever 'discredited', seeking to put a stop to honest research aimed at helping children and the parents of autistic children, and to hide any potential damage caused by the MMR vaccine.

You might also be interested to know that the Urabe strain of the measles vaccine was causing meningitis in an unacceptably high number of British children. Only after knowing for a couple of years that brain damage was being caused was its license revoked by the British government, and another license was granted so that this dangerous vaccine could be sold and injected into the bodies of children in Brazil. [2]

Does the British government want to cause brain damage in children, or is it putting pharmaceutical industry profits, or pro-vaccine ideology, above life? If an alternative to the Urabe-strain vaccine was available yet the unsafe vaccine continued to be used, this removes ideology from the equation and leaves only the profit motive – or genocide.

The Royal Free dean, Arie Zuckerman, apparently responding to government influence, suggested to Dr Wakefield that he had a conflict of interest, but failed to specify what that conflict might be. Yet universities rely upon funding from industry ... if that isn't a conflict, then how can legal aid funding be a conflict?

Then two men entered the story, apparently campaigning to discredit Dr Wakefield. One was a freelance journalist, Brian Deer; the second was editor of *The Lancet*, Richard Horton. Brian Deer was working for the Murdoch-owned *Sunday Times*. The Murdochs have vaccine industry interests, with James Murdoch even sitting on the board of GlaxoSmithKlein. [3]

A little word about the Murdoch family. As you know, the media is increasingly owned by rich and powerful people who have views on how you should live your lives. The media baron Rupert Murdoch, for example, is politically active in the UK, America and Australia, and widely thought to heavily influence who rises to government. Murdoch was also a major backer of the Iraq war.

According to 'Offshire Simple', a company offering to help rich people escape their tax bills, Rupert Murdoch is an exemplary example of tax evasion: Murdoch's "News Corp has mastered the use of the offshore tax haven in its many international transactions. The company reduces its annual tax bill by moving profits through multiple subsidiaries in offshore tax havens like the Cayman Islands. For example, the overseas profits from movies made by 20th Century Fox, go into a News Corp subsidiary in the Caymans, where they are not taxed, according to one insider familiar with the transactions. Mr. Murdoch has taken advantage of the differing tax regimes around the globe and so has been able to make sure his companies keep more of what they earn. Mr. Murdoch provides an excellent example of the proper use of tax havens in business strategy for all to follow." [4]

What, you might ask, has this to do with us, concerned as we are with our dogs' and children's health? Bear with me, the plot will unfold, but on the most basic level it has everything to do with us, as these massive corporations use the infrastructure we pay for through our taxes. Their vehicles use our roads, and their employees use the rail network. Corporations benefit from the education we tax payers have paid for. We also pay for health services enjoyed by their employees, and our tax revenue pays for vaccines, from which the Murdoch family presumably benefits through shareholdings.

Rupert Murdoch [5] was a co-chairman of the Partnership for New York City [6] which has many super-rich backers. The partnership invests funds in a variety of ventures, including biopharmaceutical companies, web-based services helping pharmaceutical companies to grow sales, a company offering capital-efficient investment in and the management of biotechnology opportunities, the New York genome centre, PIN Pharma, and Vivaldi Biosciences, focused on influenza and pandemic flu vaccine development. So you can guess where Rupert Murdoch's 'interests' might reside, and speculate as to why the media is so keen to scare us about flu pandemics that don't materialise.

Wakefield's other persecutor, Richard Horton, worked for Crispin Davis. Crispin Davis was Chairman of Reed-Elsevier, which owned *The Lancet*. There have, incidentally, been criticisms of Reed-Elsevier's involvement in the arms trade alongside medicine [7]. In 2003, Crispin Davis was made a non-executive director of GlaxoSmithKline [8], manufacturers of the MMR jab. In 2004 he was knighted.

Between them, Horton and Deer appeared to sow the seeds of professional misconduct against Wakefield and his team.

In a meeting in February 2004, three specific claims were made by Deer to Horton, the editor of *The Lancet*. He claimed that *The Lancet* study was funded by Legal Aid money; that the children reported in the paper were sourced by lawyers; and that Wakefield had hidden his involvement with Dawbarns, the firm of lawyers involved in the MMR litigation. None of these claims, according to Wakefield, was true.

Within hours of his meeting with Brian Deer, Horton stated publically that the paper was "fatally flawed." He further claimed that had *The Lancet* been aware of Wakefield's involvement with Dawbarns at that time, the paper would never have been published. The paper was later retracted. Wakefield, however, asserts that he made his involvement with Dawbarns clear to Horton before publication of the paper, and the editor had not seen a problem.

Deer, a journalist, called for a General Medical Council (GMC) hearing. As a result, Wakefield and his colleague Dr John Walker-Smith were struck off the medical register amidst claims of medical fraud. The trial is detailed in Andrew Wakefield's book, *Callous Disregard* and it is clear that, from his perspective, witnesses were got at or were obfuscating the truth, and that evidence was distorted. Deer wrote unflattering articles about Wakefield and his research, and the rest of the media laid down. Andrew Wakefield was no longer called Dr Andrew Wakefield. His new name became 'the discredited Andrew Wakefield'.

Have you noticed that Andrew Wakefield's name is never used in the media without the prefix 'the discredited' attached to it? Polly Tommey, Editor-in-Chief of *The Autism File*, threw light on why this might be in a 2010 editorial [9]. She was warned not to print any more articles by Andrew Wakefield, and not to invite him to speak at their conference. Some organisations warned her that they would drop her if she continued to support and publish papers by Wakefield. Advertisers told her they were under pressure to pull advertising from the publication. And a number of celebrities, high earning individuals, journalists and scientists, told her that it was more than their jobs were worth to be associated with Wakefield.

"The circumstances surrounding my "warnings" are remarkable in a country like Britain," she wrote.

> In the first case, very recently, I met with a senior representative of a leading autism organization. We met, at his request, not at his office, but at a café in London. He told me that he was aware that at our recent UK conference, I had introduced Dr Wakefield and had openly declared my support for his research to continue. This, it seems, had presented his organization with a serious problem. The message I was very clearly given at this meeting was that if The Autism File magazine continued to publish Dr Wakefield's work, if I continued to support him publicly, and if I allowed him to speak at our conferences, then they could not work with either me or The Autism File. He also reminded me, very pointedly, that they worked closely with the Department of Health and were the decision makers regarding many important issues relating to autism . . . .
>
> In the second case, some time ago I interviewed a notable academic from the UK autism community, and I invited him to join our scientific advisory board. He was keen but stated he could only do so if certain existing members – specifically including Andrew Wakefield – were removed from it. He then bluntly warned me that if The Autism File continued to support Dr Wakefield it would be

"shut down". Despite his standing and expertise, his concern was such that ultimately he chose not to even write for our magazine because, he said, "it is too controversial," and, given that he is funded by the government, he felt that if he did, then his funding would be at risk."

Polly Tommey also wrote that when she appeared on the Wright Stuff television chat show on Channel 5, the host Matthew Wright said that he had been told by the show's lawyers that if Wakefield's name was mentioned, he had to say that Wakefield was "discredited." Matthew said that he had no choice – these were his lawyers' instructions . . . "When I was on GMTV they said pretty much the same thing, and we have all read the same in many newspapers."

Don't you think it strange that the British government is seen attempting to hide potential vaccine damage, and to put scientists out of business for conducting honest research? Is it acceptable to silence scientists for asking questions? And since all these individuals, bodies, and even advertisers feared reprisal, isn't this a conspiracy against him?

The *Wall Street Journal* subsequently reported that James Murdoch, son of beleaguered media mogul Rupert Murdoch, whose empire is embroiled in scandal, had stepped down from the GlaxoSmithKline board [10]. In addition, Sir Crispin Davis, former Chief Executive of Reed Elsevier, which owns *The Lancet*, was leaving the GSK board after a nine year tenure. Heading a massive medical publishing business and sitting on a drug company board is surely a conflict of interest, Sir? [11]

James Murdoch came under fire from MPs who questioned him about signing off out-of-court settlements to hacking victims at the *News of the World*. In September 2012 James was criticized by the British Office of Communications [12], which concluded that he "repeatedly fell short of the conduct to be expected of as a chief executive and chairman" and that his lack of action in relation to phone hacking was "difficult to comprehend and ill-judged".

The *News of the World* editor, Andy Coulson, was found guilty in June 2014 of a conspiracy to intercept voicemails and sent to jail.

Coulson became the Conservative Party's director of communications in July 2007. In July 2011 the *Mail on Sunday* alleged that the prime minister David Cameron had been about to appoint the BBC's Guto Harri, but was persuaded by Rebekah Wade, also of the *News of the World*, to appoint Coulson. The paper quoted 'an individual intimately involved in Mr Coulson's recruitment' as saying "Rebekah indicated the job should go to Andy. Cameron was told it should be *someone acceptable to News*

International. The company was also desperate to find something for Andy after he took the rap when the phone hacking first became an issue. The approach was along the lines of, 'If you find something for Andy we will return the favour'." [13] Elsewhere, Rebekah Brooks denied any involvement.

What we are seeing here is that the man who apparently set out to destroy Andrew Wakefield was a director of the company manufacturing the MMR vaccine; we also know that his morals were under investigation, and that one of his editors at *News of the World* was apparently foisted on the prime minister of the British government by his father's company, News International, before being sent to prison.

I remembered my father's response when Tony Blair went to visit Rupert Murdoch before being elected prime minister of the UK in 1997. My dad felt that the Labour Party was finished and, for the first time in his life – highly disillusioned – he didn't know whether to vote.

Tony Blair flew to meet Rupert Murdoch in Australia's Hayman Island in 1995, and two months before he swept to power, Murdoch's *Sun* newspaper dramatically swung behind him. After stepping down as prime minister, Blair was asked to be godfather to one of Murdoch's young children. "There's something fundamentally wrong about any politician having that kind of secret friendship with someone in that position," said Tom Watson, a former Labour election fixer.

In his book, *The Establishment And how they get away with it* [14] Owen Jones writes: "The media is made up of self-evidently exceptionally powerful political actors, projecting the opinions of their oligarch owners into British political life, helping to forge the political direction of the nation."

But Britain is not the only nation whose politics are influenced by Murdoch and his assets. America, Australia and China have also benefited from his donations. And then we expect his media outlets to deliver unbiased, democratic, reportage?

When James Murdoch stepped down from the GSK board he received a ringing endorsement from the MMR manufacturer according to Reuters news agency. GSK insisted that Murdoch had made "a strong contribution" to the group and received share payments worth $158,000 in 2010. Murdoch, it turns out, was appointed to the board of the pharmaceutical manufacturer with a brief to *"review...external issues that might have the potential for serious impact upon the group's business and reputation".* [15]

The Murdoch press, especially via *Sunday Times* journalist Brian Deer [11], had been on a mission since 2003 to disparage gastroenterologist Andrew Wakefield, MBBS, who noted a correlation, asserted by parents, of an MMR vaccine–autism link. In May 2010, Dr Wakefield was struck off the UK medical register. In January 2012, James Murdoch retired from the GSK board [16], his brief presumably fulfilled.

But $158,000 is chicken feed to someone like James Murdoch. What lies beneath?

Out of interest, Professor Denis McDevitt, who was originally proposed by the GMC as chair of its fitness to practice investigation into Wakefield and colleagues, was himself a member of a 1988 government safety panel which approved Pluserix MMR vaccine as safe for vaccine manufacturer Smith Kline & French Laboratories (later GlaxoSmithKline). This was revealed in previously secret government minutes that were disclosed by the MMR litigation brought by parents of alleged MMR-damaged children. Also, at the time that the panel approved the vaccine, McDevitt was being paid as a research fellow by MMR vaccine manufacturer, Smith Kline & French Laboratories. [17]

If the vaccine/autism link interests you, see also reference 18, which provides 132 research papers supporting vaccine/autism causation.

It seems to me that Andrew Wakefield wasn't just stitched up; he was made into a patchwork quilt, dunked in acid, and squeezed through a ringer. Meanwhile, ordinary people are being led to believe by the media that Andrew Wakefield has been legitimately discredited, and that the MMR vaccine is safe. They are being duped, and their children's bodies are the ultimate victims.

In March 2014, the *New York Times* reported on a new book [19] by the French economist Thomas Piketty. They called it the most important economics book of the year — and maybe of the decade.

> Mr Piketty, arguably the world's leading expert on income and wealth inequality, does more than document the growing concentration of income in the hands of a small economic elite. He also makes a powerful case that we're on the way back to "patrimonial capitalism," in which the commanding heights of the economy are dominated not just by wealth, but also by inherited wealth, in which birth matters more than effort and talent. Six of the 10 wealthiest Americans are already heirs rather than self-made entrepreneurs, and the children of today's economic elite start from a position of immense privilege.
>
> As Mr Piketty notes, "the risk of a drift toward oligarchy is real and gives little reason for optimism."

Oligarchy means rulership of the few, most notably the rich. I would take it further and suggest that we are already living in a tyranny created by the rich, where we are misled into submitting to drugs and vaccines with unacceptable, hidden, side-effects, and we are forced to eat pesticides and environmental toxins that none of us want on our food or in our bodies. All of this, and more, is supported by a media that is owned and censored by the rich – who might also have major shareholdings in the very companies that are selling dubious vaccines and life-threatening chemicals.

According to mediareform.org.uk:

> Just three companies control nearly 70 per cent of national newspaper circulation – Rupert Murdoch's News UK; DMGT (The Daily Mail group), chaired by Jonathan Harmsworth, 4th Viscount Rothermere; and Trinity Mirror. Five companies control three-quarters of regional daily newspaper circulation and five control more than 70 per cent of online news consumption (measured by browsing time).
>
> If we were to do the same at the global level, it would not get much beyond Amazon, Google, YouTube and Facebook. So, despite the proliferation of websites and social media, power and influence is still concentrated in the hands of the few – super-rich billionaires, multinational corporations and governments.
>
> Politicians of all parties paid homage at the court of Rupert Murdoch – understandable when his newspapers made up 37 per cent of the newspaper market and whose boast was that they could deliver election results.

Jonathan Harmsworth, by the way, became the controlling shareholder of Associated Newspapers after the death of his father. He was a supporter of the Conservative leader David Cameron; has non-domicile tax status, and owns his media businesses through a complex structure of offshore holdings and trusts which result in him paying almost no UK tax on his income, investments or wealth. [20]

Sir David and Frederick Barclay were named the richest people in media in Britain with a £6bn fortune by the Sunday Times Rich List of 2014. Their businesses have also been accused of tax avoidance by placing assets under ownership of companies registered abroad and controlled through trusts. According to BBC News online [21], "The owners of the Daily Telegraph, Sir Frederick and Sir David Barclay, are under the spotlight after allegations over the way their newspaper treats stories that impinge on commercial interests."

Chapter 41

Manipulation, cover-ups, and lies

The information you hear about vaccines being safe and effective is not so much about the science but about politics and propaganda. By 2000, more evidence of the government seeking to gag information about the MMR jab came to light. This time the Scottish health boss, Ian Jones, was trying to gag MMR revelations.

According to press reports, senior clinicians, including a former medicines regulator at the department of health, were about to publish a paper in the *Journal of Adverse Drug Reactions*, saying that the MMR vaccine shouldn't have been licensed in 1988 because of insufficient evidence of safety. [1]

Writing in the paper, Peter Fletcher, senior medical officer for the department of health in the early 1980s, said, "Being extremely generous, evidence on safety was thin, being realistic there were too few patients followed up for sufficient time."

The editor of the journal, John Griffin, also a former head of the medicines division of the department of health, said: "I think this is an attempt to put pressure on me not to publish the article and I resent that. We are going to publish the article. We are not going to be deterred by threats. I think putting pressure on us not to publish is despicable."

An article in the *Daily Mail*, 22 March, 2006 [2], reported:

"After agreeing to be an expert witness on drug-safety trials for parents' lawyers, he [Peter Fletcher] had received and studied thousands of documents relating to the case which he believed the public had a right to see. He said he has seen a "steady accumulation of evidence" from scientists worldwide that the measles, mumps and rubella jab is causing brain damage in certain children. But he added: "There are very powerful people in positions of great authority in Britain and elsewhere who have staked their reputations and careers on the safety of MMR and they are willing to do almost anything to protect themselves."

In March 2010, Andrew Wakefield's colleague, John Walker-Smith, won his appeal against the United Kingdom's General Medical Council regulatory board that had ruled against both him and Andrew Wakefield. Walker-Smith was returned to the status of a fully licensed physician in the UK [3].

Justice John Mitting ruled on the appeal by Walker-Smith, saying the GMC's conclusions were based on "inadequate and superficial reasoning and, in a number of instances, a wrong conclusion." The verdict restored Walker-Smith's name to the medical register and his reputation to the medical community. While John Walker-Smith received funding to appeal the GMC decision from his insurer, his co-author Andrew Wakefield did not — and was therefore unable to mount an appeal in the high court.

However, Mr Justice Mitting observed in his judgement exonerating Walker-Smith: 'There is now no respectable body of opinion which supports (Wakefield's) hypothesis, that MMR vaccine and autism/enterocolitis are causally linked'.

Really?

The Canary Party optimistically issued a press release calling for the UK government to investigate corruption at the GMC.

"It is quite obvious to me that James Murdoch, Brian Deer and GlaxoSmithKline orchestrated the smear attack on Andrew Wakefield," said Ginger Taylor, executive director of the Canary Party. "A judge has now ruled that the GMC hearings were a farce. Parents are waiting for journalists to find their spine and start some honest reporting on the character assassination of doctors that is blocking medical treatments for vaccine injured children, and the role that GSK and Merck may be playing to protect their profits on the MMR vaccine"

I would emphasise that Professor Sir David Hull – the government agent who approached the dean of the Royal Free to pressure Andrew Wakefield into withdrawing as an expert witness – played an important role in Wakefield's downfall. He will come back into the picture later.

In his book, Wakefield cites Stratton K, et al (1994), Adverse *Events Associated with Childhood Vaccines: Evidence Bearing on Causality.* He writes:

> "Where a child with regressive autism has received more than one dose of measles-containing vaccine, exacerbation of existing symptoms or recurrence of transient symptoms associated with the first dose is frequently reported. Properly documented, the Institute of Medicine's Vaccine Safety Committee accepts the 'rechallenge' effect as evidence of causation."

In simpler language, if children given an MMR booster (second jab) had more severe reactions than those given one dose, this indicates a causal link. The same principle should apply to dogs and other animals who get ill after one vaccine, and sicker after a second, third, fourth, fifth, and so on.

To say that there is no evidence to support the MMR-autism-vaccine link is yet another of the downright untruths that clouds every aspect of vaccine safety. For the media to constantly parrot the phrase "the discredited Andrew Wakefield" every time measles or MMR is mentioned … well, that stinks of media or state manipulation, and is not synonymous with a free media. The case against Andrew Wakefield appears to be a fabrication.

Move forward to August 2014, and a whistleblower finally stepped forward to confirm cover-ups surrounding MMR vaccine safety in America.[4]

The whistleblower, Dr William Thompson, came forward after a Freedom of Information Act request for original data on an autism study was filed. CDC documents and discussions with the whistleblower revealed widespread manipulation of scientific data and top-down pressure on CDC scientists to suppress a causal link between the MMR vaccine and later autism diagnosis, particularly in a subset of African-American males who received their immunisation "on-time" in accordance with the recommended CDC schedule.

Documents from the CDC show that in 2003 a staggering 340% increase in autism in African American boys related to the MMR vaccine was hidden due to pressure from senior officials. CDC researchers recalculated their results by removing an age group to get the desired results. [5]

Dr William Thompson had worked for the government agency for over a decade and confirmed that "the CDC knew about the relationship between the age of first MMR vaccine and autism incidence in African-American boys as early as 2003, but chose to cover it up." He alleged criminal wrongdoing by his supervisors, and expressed deep regret about his role in helping the CDC to hide data. [6]

Thompson's revelations call into question the nine other studies cited by the CDC as evidence denying a link between vaccines and autism. They also spurred a change.org petition to have a fraudulent study retracted from the *Journal of Pediatrics*, which published it in 2004.

The background to Thompson's admissions is horrifying, as documented and referenced by ageofautism.com. [7]

From 1987 to 1989, scientists set up a centre near 30 remote villages in Senegal to research the effects of two high titer measles vaccines. Children who received the high titer vaccine were significantly more likely to die at 41 months than children who had a lower titer measles vaccine. But they weren't dying from measles – most of the deaths were from other common childhood diseases. They had lowered immunity, making them more susceptible to diarrhoea, dysentery, malaria, malnutrition, respiratory illness, and other infectious diseases.

Children who received the high-titer Edmonston-Zagreb vaccine died of other diseases at a rate of 80% higher than children who received the standard vaccine. There were 75 deaths for every thousand babies vaccinated. One in every six babies given this vaccine died within three years.

Despite WHO and the CDC knowing about high mortality associated with this vaccine, they decided to see if it would have the same effect in babies in the developed world, so trials in Los Angeles began. By 1991 the Los Angeles trials were halted, but not before nearly 1,500 minority babies were experimented upon.

What is the matter with the people who conducted these life-threatening studies on human children, knowing already that the vaccines posed a high risk of death? What were they thinking?

The Helsinki Declaration [8] states that: The Declaration of Geneva of the WMA binds the physician with the words, "The health of my patient will be my first consideration," and the International Code of Medical Ethics [9] declares that, "A physician shall act in the patient's best interest when providing medical care." It also states: "It is the duty of the physician to promote and safeguard the health, well-being and rights of patients, including those who are involved in medical research. The physician's knowledge and conscience are dedicated to the fulfilment of this duty."

By vaccinating African American babies, knowing that the vaccine had already been shown to harm a high percentage of vaccinated children, these physicians crossed the line. To me, at least, it seems that the line is crossed as a matter of routine.

It brings the Milgram experiment to mind where volunteers were instructed by an authority figure to administer successively higher electric shocks to an actor when they got answers to questions wrong. Milgram summarized the experiment in his 1974 article, "The Perils of Obedience":

> Ordinary people, simply doing their jobs, and without any particular hostility on their part, can become agents in a terrible destructive process. Moreover, even when the destructive effects of their work become patently clear, and they are asked to carry out actions incompatible with fundamental standards of morality, relatively few people have the resources needed to resist authority.

Which makes me question how amenable the veterinary profession is to control when the VMD issues warnings to 'follow the SPCs' (datasheets), even though annual vaccination is neither necessary nor safe.

A study by Dr Brian Hooker PhD was accepted for publication in the peer reviewed *Journal Translational Neurodegeneration.* It found a 340 percent increased risk of autism in African American boys receiving the measles-mumps-rubella (MMR) vaccine on time. [10]

This was going to be the abstract before it was retracted:

"When comparing cases and controls receiving their first MMR vaccine before and after 36 months of age, there was a statistically significant increase in autism cases specifically among African American males who received the first MMR vaccine prior to 35 months of age. Relative risks for males in general and African American males were 1.69 and 3.36, respectively. Additionally, African American males showed an odds ratio of 1.73 for autism cases in children receiving their first MMR vaccine prior to 24 months of age and thereafter. The present study provides new epidemiologic evidence showing that African American males receiving the MMR vaccine prior to 24 months of age or 36 months of age are more likely to receive an autism diagnosis."

Again, I have to ask: what were they thinking? But, then, even this is contested. Apparently Hooker is incompetent, and Thompson was backtracking. [11]

Meanwhile, Jerome Burne and Sally Beck wrote in the on-line Rescued Media [12], Thompson has of course come in for sustained and aggressive attack on social media since then.

"This very active pro-vaccine blog portrays Thompson as a lone figure who was only complaining because his personal pet result had been ignored. This was described as an 'almost certainly spurious finding'. It was that in a sub-group of African American boys, vaccination was associated with an increase in autism. The blogger than asserted that the 'increased risk was seen in no other subgroup and disappeared when proper correction for cofounders was made.'

Makes you wonder.

However, Scienceblogs.com has a different take on it all, complete with highly scientific name-calling, ridicule and sarcasm. [13]

See also references 14-79.

Chapter 42

Once it gets personal

It's interesting that scientists themselves do not always agree on the vaccine issue. I received an email from a veterinarian whose story is harrowing. She remains anonymous upon her lawyer's advice in case speaking out jeopardises the compensation she received for her daughter.

"My own daughter was a victim of the MMR vaccine five years ago," she wrote. "She suffered from severe encephalitis and is permanently brain injured. She received compensation from the vaccine fund here in the USA.

"I am now out of typical veterinary practice and do only surgery, dentistry and in home hospice/euthanasia. I was never taught in school how much damage we were doing to animals.....I guess this was God's way of opening my eyes.

"I have tried talking to veterinarians, but they have the mentality of 'if it ain't broke, don't fix it' as far as their businesses go. As far as their personal beliefs – many of them do not vaccinate their own dogs or cats after puppyhood. This seems hypocritical to me. I had such a moral issue with working for practices who felt this way that I quit my job in typical practice. Most of my colleagues agreed with me that vaccines are over-used and can cause injury, but they would not change hospital protocol. When my boss went out of town for two weeks, I took it upon myself to start checking titers on those dogs whose families would listen – and every single one of them came back protective. I showed this to my boss when he got back, and he was extremely angry with me for going against protocol.

"I turned in my notice a few weeks later – walking away from close to $100K a year. I now make maybe $25K a year – all very part time. It's all I can find. I need to make more money, but I refuse to go back to typical practice unless I am able to share what I know with the clients.

"Until we get the owners to question the veterinarians, nothing is going to change. It is so frustrating. And to live with the reality of the situation: screaming, crying, tantruming, in my face every day with my daughter and her permanent severe disability, I find myself in a constant state of sadness and anger and feel I need to do something to educate people – but many don't want to listen. I have lost many friends who think I have gone over the edge."

Oceans of sorrow, oceans of harm.

I was very distressed by this vet and her daughter's plight, and wondered what I could do to help. I know many holistic vets, especially in America, who refuse to vaccinate and as a result suffer severe financial consequences. Perhaps it was time we had another article, like an earlier one in *Wolf Clan* magazine, where the voices of dissenting vets could be heard? The subsequent article was published in *Dogs Naturally* magazine.

Many vets expressed their views and the article was given twelve pages in the magazine [1]. For those who don't have internet access, here's a representative extract from Stephen Blake:

> I emphatically do not believe that I was taught adequately with regard to the vaccine issue. I was taught to believe vaccinations were synonymous with immunization. They are two separate entities.
>
> I was taught vaccines were safe and it was implied there had been safety studies done on them before they were used on the general public. They are not safe and there have not been any safety studies done on any of them.
>
> I was taught that if something adverse happens within a few hours after immunization it was related to the vaccines but, if it happened later than that period of time, it had nothing to do with the vaccines. The truth of the matter is vaccines can set up a latent condition that may show up within a few hours or years after immunization.
>
> I was taught you needed to vaccinate every year to boost animals' immune systems. There are no studies to show that annual boosters are ever indicated or that there is any science to support annual vaccines to boost an animal's immune system. I was never taught that mercury and aluminum hydroxide, which are in the vaccines, can cause cancer, are neurotoxins, and can trigger autoimmune disease.
>
> When I first went into practice, I noticed some animals developed fevers for a few days, became lethargic, lost their appetites, developed ear infections, seizures, pruritus, UTI, musculoskeletal issues, and behaviour issues after vaccination.
>
> As time went on, I observed that otitis, UTI, autoimmune disease complexes, gingivitis, allergic dermatitis, IBD, asthma, aggression and phobias, convulsions, paralysis, cancer, chronic conjunctivitis, liver disease, kidney disease, cardiac disease, arthritis, anterior cruciate rupture, hip disease, and corneal lesions can be correlated with vaccine damage.
>
> Pet guardians are being misinformed. There is no scientific evidence that annual vaccines are needed or indicated.

I feel there is pressure at all levels of veterinary medicine that we are not to say anything negative about vaccines which would alarm the public and make it harder to sell the vaccine concept. There is no informed consent information presented to the pet owner prior to vaccination because they do not want to alarm the owner and make it difficult to promote vaccines. It has been known for over 20 years that rabies vaccines can cause terminal cancer in the feline and I have yet to meet a client who was informed of this scientific fact by their attending veterinarian. This should be made public to all cat owners prior to rabies vaccine so the owner is aware of the low risk of getting rabies compared to the high risk of getting cancer from the rabies vaccine.

I love the practice of veterinary medicine with an oath to prevent suffering and do no harm. I do not support my profession's over-use of drugs, chemicals and vaccines as we know them today. I feel my profession needs to be the leader in breaking away from the dangers of these products and show the human medical profession this is not healing. It does cause harm.

I feel the pharmaceutical industry finances the veterinary schools and the veterinary profession. I feel they are the fox in the hen house that sets policy for the practice of medicine as we know it today in our country.

The pharmaceutical industry has too much influence in veterinary teaching. Their approach to medicine prevents any other modalities of healing from being available in our veterinary schools. This is done so they have no competition for the pet industry dollars from unpatentable means.

Conventional veterinary medicine, with its reliance upon vaccines, steroids, NSAIDs and antibiotics is doing more harm than good.

The main causes of ill health in animals are vaccines as we know them today; drugs that are needed in an emergency situation; use of chemicals to treat fleas, ticks, lice, and heartworm; herbicides, pesticides, radiation, artificial dyes, flavouring, poor quality pet foods, contaminated water, and cleaning chemicals in homes.

I have a dream. My dream is that alternative veterinary medicine will no longer be 11th hour medicine and that it will be the first choice of medical care for our friends the animals before I leave this world.

Chapter 43

The blind leading the blind

Dear Catherine

I am writing to tell you about the death of one of my much loved dogs which has now made me search for answers.

On Monday, 20th August 2001, Pippin, a Collie cross, didn't want her breakfast and seemed depressed, so I immediately phoned for an appointment at the vets because Pippin was normally bright and full of life. As I was putting her collar on I noticed her gums were very pale. The vet checked her over, took blood, and gave her antibiotics and steroids. The vet said she could have one of two problems but the blood tests would confirm what was wrong.

I took her home but that night I had to ring the emergency vet as she seemed to be getting worse and panting. She was put on a drip and the next day I took her home but returned two hours later because I wasn't happy with her condition. The vet had the results of the blood tests which showed Pippin had autoimmune haemolytic anaemia, and her body was killing her red blood cells.

The vet explained what was happening and said that she was a very sick dog, but he also said they had another Border Collie in three weeks ago with the same condition and it was fine now. I then asked "When did it have its booster vaccinations?" The vet very quickly replied, "We vaccinate thousands of dogs every year – it's got nothing to do with it."

Pippin was kept on a drip and given steroids to try to kick start her body into working properly. On the Thursday night they gave her a blood transfusion because her blood count was going down. I went to see her on the Friday and took her some chicken. She wagged her tail and wolfed down the chicken and seemed a lot brighter. I was pleased to think she was on the mend.

I went to see her on the Saturday but I was worried because she seemed to have deteriorated again. The vet said they would do more blood tests to see what was happening. On Sunday morning I received a phone call to say her blood count was critically low. The critical point was 10% and hers was down to 9%.

I immediately went to see her and the vet told me her condition was not even stabilising at a low count but still going down and now her organs were starting to fail. The vet said she could die at any time. She was having difficulty breathing and she looked up at me as if to say, "I've had enough", so I had to make that awful decision we all dread but I was with her to the end. I couldn't bear the thought of her dying while I wasn't there.

One week before I had a perfectly healthy dog running and playing and now she's gone. She was only ten years old, which is not old for a Collie type and she was very fit and healthy because we did competition, obedience and agility. She became ill exactly three weeks to the day after her annual booster.

Pippin is my first (and last) dog to have annual boosters.

I have bought your book and spoken to many people, and the more I find out, the more convinced I am that Pippin's booster caused her to get AIHA. I have written to my vets to question the necessity of annual boosters, although I know I will not get an answer, but at least I am putting my point over to them.

All my friends are very worried and are going to request blood tests before boosters. One friend had a very sick dog on a drip in hospital for five days two weeks after his booster but we didn't make the connection until recently. We all want to help you in your cause.

Yours sincerely,
Gloria Fountain

Oceans of sorrow. Oceans of harm. Since Gloria Fountain's vet blankly denied any connection between Pippin's recent vaccination and the onset of AIHA, no adverse event report is known to have been forwarded to the VMD which claims to monitor adverse reactions in the UK. And as you know, vaccines *do* cause this disease. [1, 2]

Chapter 44

Human nature

In the middle of Bettie and Bertie's attempt to destroy CHC, John decided we should move to Scotland. He was exhausted flying between Scotland and England, and spending all weekend catching up with work for CHC, and he had seen a house for rent near Dundee. His contract, too, had become long-term, making relocation to Scotland more sensible.

I went up and had a look at the house he'd found, and we packed our bags. Chappie, Sophie, Gwinnie, Edward and Dannie came with me in the back of my old Volvo estate – and they were delighted to see that, once again, we had a wrap-around garden and a paddock for them to play in.

The house was bigger too. It was an old granite farmhouse with a big kitchen with a range, and three reception rooms, meaning a larger office for CHC. The icing on the cake was the fact that Scottish property is very much cheaper than property in England. Edward and Daniel had a great time, with us chasing each other around the house, benefiting from the extra space, and Chappie and Sophie were still able to pootle about in the large garden.

Gwinnie was another matter. Poor little Gwin had a problem: we couldn't let her off the lead. I hated this; my instinct has always been to ensure that my dogs have plenty of exercise and freedom. But if we let Gwinnie off the lead, she would be off over the hills. In fact, we'd had a terrible job keeping her in our garden in Derbyshire. She was an athletic dog and she'd jump over the dry stone walls to chase rabbits. She had cost us a fortune in extra fencing, but it was still nearly impossible to keep her on the property.

I'd arranged for deer fencing to be added to the property in Scotland – the man who erected it commented that it would be cheaper to shoot the dogs. But the house was on a main road and we couldn't take the risk.

Meanwhile, all the rumours about me continued to circulate. We issued a rebuttal in the CHC newsletter, and Bettie and Bertie formed their rival group with a number of our volunteers, who I had foolishly allowed Bettie to 'manage', jumping ship. She had told each of them a story, personal to them, that made it seem as though I had been truly horrible about them. She even told one of our phone volunteers that I had installed a system to spy on the phone calls they took for CHC and was, bizarrely, believed! Bettie's group soon imploded in on itself and disbanded after two weeks.

Devastated, I looked at my dogs, and I looked at myself, and I said, "enough". Deep inside me a conviction arose that I would no longer sacrifice us for everyone else. We were going to matter, too, and I was no longer prepared to spend every working hour of the day providing free time and advice to people who were prepared to abandon me at the drop of a hat. I would not answer the phone every time it rang; I would issue fact sheets to answer the questions that people wrote to me with, rather than writing long individual letters. Enough!

Then we took the dogs to a nearby beach and decided to try Gwinnie off the lead (the sea being a natural barrier), and she stayed with us! Hilary Jupp had told me that Gwinnie was showing me how necessary it was to erect boundaries. By this, she explained, she meant that I had to learn to say 'no'. It took Bettie and Bertie's betrayal to make me put those boundaries up – and as soon as I did, and I said 'enough', Gwinnie reformed. Instantly, we could let her off the lead without losing her.

In many ways I have a lot to thank Bettie and Bertie for! They brought with them a huge storm, but the silver lining was bigger – although painfully accrued.

After we issued our denouncement of Bettie's accusations in our newsletter, a CHC member telephoned me to say that many dog lovers in their town had been worried when they heard that Bettie was involved with CHC. "She's done the same to several dog clubs in the area," my caller said. "She joins them, is very enthusiastic, and then she shuts them down, walking out with lots of members in tow. Then they all fall out, and then Bettie goes looking for some other organisation to join and destroy.

"I wanted to warn you," the caller said, "but I didn't think you'd believe me. Also, I have to admit I was frightened of what she might do if she found out I had warned you."

"You're right," I said. "I'd probably have said that she seemed alright to me, and I wouldn't have wanted to condemn her on rumours." Unfortunately, one of the features of people like Bettie – who I now suspect to be a sociopath – is that they can be very charming when they want to be and I was taken in, as were the CHC supporters she lied to.

Not long after starting CHC, I began to notice that the consensus on Catherine O'Driscoll was split between those who imagined I was a living angel, and those who imagined I was the devil's daughter. Vets, I was told, referred to me as "that awful woman". Which is all very interesting if you're able to step back and observe.

John's contract in Perth had come to an end and he started to get new contracts for ridiculous amounts of money around the world. Our bank account was brimming over. He announced that I could take the rest of the year off from copywriting work. For the first time in my adult life, I had three whole months to do just as I liked. So I kept CHC ticking over but also had time to recover from the stress that had been mounting.

Chapter 45
Another road to healing

Cher Gregory had jumped in her campervan with her beautiful Collie, Taz, when her marriage with Peter, our homeopathic vet in Derbyshire, was ending. She came to stay with me for a while. It was lovely having Cher around, and she became one of my dearest friends. I also joined the local complementary therapists' group and got to know amazing women in the area who were healers and therapists.

A man who had watched the *World in Action* documentary got in touch. His name was Anthony Artus, and he wanted to show me a healing technique he had devised called Animal-Links. It was based upon BodyTalk, an energy therapy for humans.

Before he came up, Anthony told me that he was formerly an SAS soldier and the paranoia within me wondered if he might have anything to do with the vaccine industry. I watched the dogs' reaction to him very carefully when he got out of the car and was relieved to see that they seemed to like him.

Anthony was a natural philosopher, an incredibly inspirational man. After retiring from the SAS, he had become a Reiki Master and BodyTalk practitioner. He spent four days with us, treating me, John, and the dogs and, when he left, Sophie, who had been deaf for the past two years, could hear again. He treated us all for vaccine damage, and me for the belief that everyone I love dies (boy, did that have me in floods of tears).

The three telephone lines into our house went dead while Anthony was with us. The telephone engineer was bemused, saying it's most unusual for three separate lines into one house to all go dead at the exchange at the same time, whilst the rest of the lines in the exchange didn't. Anthony said, with his SAS training behind him, that our phones were tapped.

Anthony became a firm friend and I set up workshops for CHC members to learn his healing technique. Animal-Links involves muscle testing to ascertain where there are blocks or breaks in the energy flow between organs and endocrines in the body. Once discovered, you link them together energetically and tap the top of the head and the sternum until the flow is resolved. The general treatment takes at least an hour – but it's very powerful.

Anthony phoned one beautiful summers day to say that he'd like to come and visit us again, and I was really looking forward to it. Sadly, before he had time to come, Anthony died in his sleep of heart failure. Apparently he had been to the doctor with chest pains, but action hadn't been taken quickly enough. There are many times, years later, when I would dearly love to pick up the phone and speak to this inspirational man. I hope he looks in on us from time to time from the other side.

While he was still on the planet, I told Hilary Jupp about Animal-Links and she came on one of his courses. She also suggested that another energy therapy called Emotional Freedom Technique (EFT) ran on similar lines, but was less complex.

I'd been told about EFT a few years before but in order to find out more about it, I would have had to master the internet. Eventually I went online and ordered the training pack from America. When it arrived, I sat down and read the manual, then watched the first video. I was planning to go out and mow the lawn after that but my hayfever arrived with a bang before I had the chance. I had learnt that when you are about to treat something using EFT, you need to work out how bad it is using a subjective zero-to-ten point system so you can measure progress. Zero means it's non-existent; ten means it's unbearable. I put a seven on it, and did my first round of tapping.

With EFT, you tap 13 points on the body while naming the problem. These points correspond to energy line (meridian) endings as accepted within the Chinese medical system, and used within acupuncture. A round of tapping takes about 60 seconds, and it's very simple.

Much to my surprise, after one round, my hayfever subsided. I decided it had gone down to a three in terms of discomfort, so I tapped another round and the hayfever disappeared. I went outside and mowed the lawn without so much as an itch or a sniffle.

This was utterly amazing to me. I had tried everything available for my hayfever, bemoaning the fact that it wasn't fair. I absolutely loved being outside in Nature – why me? But now I didn't have it anymore, and haven't had it since that day in 1998. EFT delivered a permanent cure in less than three minutes. Imagine the impact it might have on the drug companies selling hay fever tablets and sprays if we all cured our own hayfever using an energy therapy. [1]

At which point I became an EFT fanatic. I was tapping on everything. EFT is good for physical ailments such as hayfever, aches and pains, and even – some report – as a cure for cancer. It also treats emotional disturbances. You can use it on traumatic memories, and emotions such as guilt, resentment, fear, a lack of self-esteem – anything and everything that bothers you. I also worked out that you can use EFT on animals, and put it to the test.

Dannie had a hotspot. Although he had never been vaccinated (I just wouldn't take the risk), I suspected that this was inherited vaccine damage. So I adapted a protocol from Animal-Links to EFT, and treated Dannie for inherited vaccine damage. Within two hours the swelling had gone down and the wound had dried up. Hair began to grow back the next day.

By this time Sophie was around 15 years of age, and the arthritis she'd developed at the age of six had taken its course: her front paws were painfully knotted and deformed. I sat opposite her at the other end of the room – about 15ft away – and tapped myself whilst saying: "Sophie's arthritis".

Like a Hollywood special effect, Sophie's deformed paws normalised. I hadn't even touched her, but tapped myself on her behalf. The energy therapy worked over distance, normalising Sophie's paws in front of my eyes. Show me a drug that will do that!

It was such a far-out response that I actually discounted it. It wasn't until my sister Leslie was visiting a few weeks later, and Sophie's paws deformed again, that I saw it happen again – but with a witness. This time, EFT appeared to provide a permanent cure: Sophie's paws never deformed again.

EFT also resolved a problem we were having with Edward and Daniel. I would put their food down for them to eat, but they were reluctant to eat it. One day John came into the room and started haranguing me, saying that it was my fault and I was getting their food from the wrong place. My stress levels rocketed, at which point Edward and Daniel swiftly walked completely away from their bowls.

I sat and tapped on my anxiety and, like a light switch going on, the boys went back to their bowls and started eating. Of course this illustrates that our dogs pick up on our stresses and if we deal with our own stress, this will positively impact our dogs' behaviour.

Many amazing EFT experiences ensued. One involved a problem I had when in crowded places. Maybe you'll relate to this but, believe me, it was a huge problem for me: I'd be walking in a busy shopping centre and people would bodily push me out of their way. On one occasion I was walking along a pavement with shopping bags in my hands, when three girls walked towards me and sent me flying, and my shopping flew all over the road. They walked on as if I hadn't existed.

I was telling a PR client about this sort of thing happening to me as we were driving towards a railway station to collect a journalist. When we got out of the car and walked towards the station, two men came towards us and, yet again, I was sent flying off the pavement. My client was incredulous: "Blooming heck," he said, "I thought you were exaggerating, but I've seen it with my own eyes."

So I sat and tapped on these horrible people and felt much better about it – but the most amazing thing followed: people actually stopped bumping into me in crowds or pushing me off the pavement. EFT changed my internal landscape, which changed my external world and the behaviour of others. This has huge implications. Take time to contemplate this: if you change yourself, you change the world.

Chapter 46

Farewell my noble friend

Not long after we arrived in Scotland, Chappie's back end began to go. By now he was sixteen, and I had to help him up off the floor, and occasionally pick him up if his back legs gave way in the garden. We put him on homeopathic Causticum, which is the classic remedy for old dogs, and added a herbal blend called Anima-Strath to his food. When the vet came for a follow up visit and conducted a reflex test, he literally stepped back in amazement, exclaiming, "This dog has improved! I would normally expect an old dog like this to go downhill fast with CDRM – but he's improved."

I tried to explain what I had done to help Chaps, but the vet changed the subject.

Gwinnie was now allowed to run off the lead as she was no longer wanting to disappear – and what did she do? She went and ruptured a cruciate ligament. It was a bitter blow – for me as well as her. Finally she had achieved freedom, only to have it curtailed by this crippling disability. The receptionist at our local vet's told me, "I shouldn't be saying this, but there's a vet in Kirriemuir who does acupuncture, and there's an animal physiotherapist who might be able to help."

I telephoned the physio and John, on one of his trips home, took Gwinnie along for a consult. The advice was not, as a vet might suggest, to rest Gwinnie. Rather, I was to exercise her on tarmac for five minutes a day, slowly, on-lead, and to increase the amount of time, distance and speed over several months. In the end I was riding a bike with Gwinnie running alongside me.

I also booked Gwinnie in to see Gavin Durston at Thrums veterinary group in Kirriemuir for acupuncture. Gwins had acupuncture once a week for a while, then once a fortnight, then once a month, until eventually she was signed-off.

Gavin turned out to be one of the best vets I've ever had the pleasure to consult. He was young, handsome (like Brad Pitt's younger, slightly weedier, brother), open-minded, and he seemed to have great sympathy for my stance on the vaccine issue. He was also kind. When the practice opened their new building, the ribbon was cut by the head of the BSAVA. Apparently the fact that I was a client came up, and she commiserated with Gavin for having that 'awful woman' as a client. "No," Gavin told her. "She's really nice."

Thanks Gavin!

The other thing I liked about Gavin was that he didn't recommend treatments to boost practice income. He always gave the pros and cons for any particular form of treatment, often erring on the side of 'don't spend the money'. He was also open to the alternative therapies I used on my dogs.

The animal physiotherapist advised me to purchase a supplement for Gwinnie from a lady called Sally Spencer who had written a book on the Morgan horse. The supplement was generally used on horses, but I was told it would be good for Gwin. It was chondroitin – something in common use today, but little heard of in those days.

Sally became a firm friend, introducing me to Archangel Gabriel, no less. Gabriel was channelled by a woman called Karen Cook in America, and I loved listening to the tapes Sally gave me of his channelled lectures. His message was simple, but loving and kind.

It may be that Archangel Gabriel was not being channelled through Karen Cook, who knows? But anything that gives a person hope and comfort, and helps them to get through life without harming anyone else is good enough for me.

Within a few months, Gwinnie had regained a lot of her mobility although, like Chappie, she would never return to the condition before her cruciates ruptured.

Over the next year or so, Chappie's CDRM eventually deteriorated until, one day, he collapsed outside the back door. This was the end of my darling Chappie's ability to enjoy the thing he loved most in life: charging around with his nose to the ground, picking up rabbit scents. Mentally he was fine, but I couldn't see my boy enjoying life parked in the sitting room. With a heavy heart I realised that it was time for me to help him cross over to the Great Mystery.

John and I called the vet and we took Chappie out to the garden, where he could hear the birds singing and smell the earth, and we gave him fruitcake, which he loved but wasn't allowed once I learnt that raisins are poisonous to dogs. I stroked him and cuddled him and told him what a good boy he was, and then the vet came.

Chappie was my noble friend, a kind, sensitive, intelligent and loving person. It broke my heart to say goodbye to him. I guess it doesn't matter when a dog dies – young or old, and Chappie had reached the grand age of 17 – it still breaks your heart.

A few months later I developed an extremely painful frozen shoulder, so I set about using EFT to clear it. With EFT you name the problem while you tap meridian line endings, but nothing seemed to work. So I sat down quietly and put my attention on the pain, and asked myself what emotion lay behind it (this is based upon the premise in alternative therapies that most physical ailments have an emotional root cause). As I sat quietly waiting for an answer, the thought of Chappie and grief came up. So I tapped on Chappie and grief, and the frozen shoulder disappeared.

Chapter 47

Another house move

About eight years into the CHC campaign to end over-vaccination and popularise raw food for dogs, I witnessed a change in energy when I was invited to speak at a breed club education day. Although half of the committee had refused to support my attendance and had stayed away, I was sitting drinking a cup of tea in the break when I heard enthusiastic and excited voices behind me. Listening in, I realised that they were talking about how healthy their dogs were now that they'd stopped vaccinating and were feeding real food.

We had turned a corner.

One day the man who owned the farmhouse we were renting told us he was putting it up for sale, so we looked around for another to move into. We found one advertised locally and it seemed to fit the bill, so we set up a viewing and found ourselves entering the Carsegray Estate through stone pillars and tall iron gates, past a gate lodge, and up a pristine tarmac drive bordered with rhododendrons and magnificent trees. "Blooming heck," I said. "This is a bit posh. Too posh for us." I felt genuinely intimidated.

We swept up the mile-long drive, passing a cluster of whitewashed cottages, until we saw what could only be described as a mansion house. "Crikey, this is it," I said. It hadn't looked nearly so grand in the particulars. We thought we'd come to see a more ordinary house. We got out of the car and let ourselves in through the garden gate. Charles Gow, the estate manager, greeted us with a handshake in his country gent's uniform of tweeds and brogues and opened the huge studded door, motioning us inside.

The place was freezing. It was November and the house was empty and unheated. Charles showed us room after room – 43 in all if you counted the sculleries, anterooms and bathrooms. The place clearly hadn't been decorated for what looked like a century, but it was dotted with gilt-framed oil paintings and antiques. Then he led us into a very large room on the first floor.

"I could run seminars here," I said, which clinched our decision to move in.

Outside, the gardens were stunning. Even in November, with the leaves off the trees and grey clouds in the skies, they were stunning. Actually, it was more of a park than a garden, with trees and shrubs gathered by Victorian ancestors from every corner of the globe. It had been designed in sections, as though they were rooms in a house. There were oaks and chestnuts and sycamores and redwoods, and all sorts of happy shrubs that I had never seen before. "The dogs would love it here," I said.

We were asked to dance through hoops and sign declarations in blood to convince Charles Gow that we were good enough to rent the property. Finally we were invited to meet the owner, Hamish, to also convince him of our worthiness. We sat in our coats on ancient chairs in a cold upstairs room and eventually Hamish said, "Well, I should be jolly pleased for you to come and live in my house".

Hamish was a real toff. He owns an estate in Warwickshire in addition to the Carsegray Estate which itself boasts around eight farms and over twenty cottages.

"Thank you," John and I said.

"Splendid," said Hamish.

"Did you live here as a child?" I asked, just to make conversation.

"No, this was my grandmother's house," he replied. "We used to come up for the summer."

"That's better than a caravan in Clacton, innit," my mouth said before I could stop it.

Hamish looked at me with surprise, but thankfully he didn't rescind his offer to allow us to live there.

The greatest thing was that the rent was relative peanuts, significantly less than we had shelled out on our mortgage in the glory days, and about the same someone in London would pay for a one-bedroomed apartment. What we didn't appreciate was that the cost of heating the place would be astronomical, with oil prices continuously rising.

But I was crippled with insecurity, feeling that I – who had grown up in a council house in Hemel Hempstead – had no right to live in such a beautiful place. They would find out I was common and eject me, I was sure of it. I'm not joking – I went through agonies before we moved into Carsegray. My stomach – the centre of self-esteem – was in knots. I did a lot of EFT to even begin to feel remotely worthy of living in that beautiful, beautiful place.

Since John was away on contract, it fell to me to organise the move, and I absolutely loved it. John had agreed that if I was to run workshops there and generate an income, it needed some serious upgrading. I called in a professional team of decorators and had practically every room in the house painted. I had new showers and sinks installed, and turned the large downstairs gunroom into another bathroom; and curtains were made. A ground floor room, along from the gunroom, had been used as a carpenter's workshop and I had it transformed into another large bedroom and sitting room.

We also had to buy furniture to fill up the rooms. It is to John's credit that he allowed me to make my way through tens of thousands of his pounds in order to turn Carsegray House into a warm and welcoming place for seminar delegates. We went to auctions and picked up furniture, and bought towels and bedding and crockery and glasses. I would walk around the house in awe, over and over again, taking in its beauty and the energy of graceful living that had built up over centuries.

The first night was not as planned, though. I had left the dogs in the farmhouse with a friend looking after them during the move. Then I drove back and loaded them into the Volvo, and brought them to Carsegray. It was the beginning of March and there was thick snow outside, and Sophie, now 16, didn't cope with the move well. She had terrible diarrhoea and there was no hot water to wash her with, so I did the best I could with cold water and soap. There was no heating oil, either, and the house, which had been empty for some time, was absolutely freezing. We settled ourselves into the downstairs wood-panelled sitting room, making use of an electric heater that the decorators had left overnight.

Sophie by now was shaking with cold, so I dug out a hair dryer and warmed her with it, and coddled her in a padded sleeping bag.

Edward and Daniel thought the house was great, though. I rolled balls for them to chase along our lengthy new back passage, and we chased each other up the massive formal staircase, past oil paintings of aristocratic ancestors, along the length of the house, and down the servants' stairs. Outside, they were able to run and sniff and play in their own private park. I was so sad that Chappie was no longer with us – he would have loved pacing around the garden with his nose to the ground.

As John was working abroad during the move, I concentrated first on the office, making it ready for his arrival at the end of the week. I must have walked miles, emptying boxes and taking items to the many different rooms. It was great because, instead of sitting at my computer writing all day, the exercise had the weight falling off me.

I was so excited for John to see how much I had done, but he walked around looking at all of the boxes that needed to be unpacked, and said: "We've moved into a white elephant". He was filled with misgivings, sure we'd made the wrong move. And he wasn't in the least bit impressed that I'd done it all without his help. EFT had subtly transformed me into someone who was self-reliant and confident. While I was glowing with happiness, loving these gracious surroundings, John was miserable.

He began to complain about everything, small problems and large, and took to worrying, which was unusual. John normally had nerves of steel. I was worried for him.

After a few months at Carsegray, Sophie, who was now 17, began to have more serious problems with her back legs and I had to help her into the garden. Sophie was so content – happy for cuddles when they were available, and accepting her old age and infirmities with serenity. She was so kind, sending me love and approval, even though I wished I could do more for her. But she carefully taught me that old age is a transition and not a disease.

Eventually, my old girl refused food and I knew it was time for her to go. I called the vet and sat beside her on her bed and fed her illicit chocolate biscuits as he helped her to leave the planet. We buried my beautiful darling in the dogs' graveyard within Carsegray's magnificent garden. Her grave, with its own gravestone, rests under abundant wild flowers and yew trees which symbolise the immortality of the soul. There is a star on her gravestone: my Sophie Bright Star.

Somehow, Sophie's contentment and acceptance of all that came, and the fact that she was a good age, made it easier for me to let her go, although this didn't mean there weren't floods of tears. There is a beautiful photograph of Sophie above the TV wherever I live now, and I speak to her every night. She is like a mother looking down on me, wanting the best for me, and accepting me no matter what.

Now we were down to three dogs – Edward, Daniel and Gwinnie – and I spent hours with them wandering around the beautiful Carsegray estate, breathing in the energy of the trees, finding indescribable peace in nature.

Chapter 48
Finally, vets speak out

As the 20th Century turned into the 21st, the American Veterinary Medical Association Council on Biologic and Therapeutic Agents presented their consensus at the July, 2000 Annual AVMA Convention. They announced:

> "When an annual booster vaccination with a modified live virus (MLV) vaccine (i.e. Distemper, Parvovirus or Feline Distemper) is given to a previously vaccinated adult animal – no added protection is provided. Modified live virus vaccines depend on the replication of the virus for a response. Antibodies from previous vaccines do not allow the new virus to replicate.
>
> "Antibody titres are not boosted significantly, memory cell populations are not expanded. No additional protection is provided.
>
> "Vaccine Manufacturers' label claims should be backed by scientific data. There is no scientific data to support label directions for re-administration of MLV vaccines annually."

My memory is that it was stated that vets needed to take this information on board, since a 'campaigning group in England' was effectively ensuring that the veterinary profession would have egg on its face if it didn't reform its vaccination policies. Since CHC was, I believe, the only pet vaccine reform campaigning group in the world (i.e., it is the only organisation, although there are many individuals who seek to effect change), the AVMA was probably referring to us. You have no idea how fulfilling it is to know that our work has had at least some effect.

Their pronouncement also meant that, at last, it wasn't just me raising these issues. I had a legitimate veterinary body now saying what I had been saying for the previous six years. I had an official organisation to quote.

Meanwhile, Richard Ford from North Carolina University was invited to address the British Small Animal Veterinary Association 2000 Annual Conference, and I was sent a recording of his address:

"You now vaccinate cats with rabies on the right leg, as low as possible on the leg, and leukaemia on the left leg, as low as possible. That's in order to determine whether it's leukaemia or rabies [vaccine] that's causing the cancer. Some veterinarians are vaccinating cats in the tail. Now the only question I have to ask is that most owners are a little bit smart about this and they recognise that that's not conventional. And they might ask you why you are vaccinating my cat in the tail? And you're gonna have to tell them, "Oh, when it gets cancer in its tail I can cut the tail off". This is not the way to sell vaccines.

"But the reality is we are causing cancer, and I'm embarrassed, honestly, to see ... the bulk of the energy going into fibrosarcomas today is how to treat these things rather than how to prevent them."

It's worth noting that there are studies confirming that vaccines can also cause vaccine-site cancer in dogs and also in ferrets.

The BSAVA Colloquium chairman said at the Conference: "The debate within the veterinary profession in North America has been much more open than over here. In the States it was probably the feline vaccination site sarcoma issue that triggered the debate, whereas in the UK it is the pressure groups against vaccination that appear to have stimulated the debate."

How rude (smile)! There were no pressure groups – there was only one group, and that group was Canine Health Concern. If I quote the conventional veterinary and scientific communities, at least I have the decency to acknowledge the folks who did the work! However, vets in the UK are still vaccinating when they don't need to.

When I was a child, my mum, dad, brother and I were travelling to Wales to get the ferry to Ireland, and we stopped off for breakfast in a small hotel. My brother asked for a large bowl of cornflakes but the waiter told my dad that a large bowl of cornflakes wasn't on the menu; he could only have a small bowl. My dad retorted: "Well, change the menu, then." We were all naturally embarrassed at my dad's assertiveness.

A homeopathic vet also quoted my work but again refrained from attributing the work to its author. I wrote to him to ask why, and he told me that it wasn't the convention.

Well, change the convention, then. If it's good enough to quote, then it's worth acknowledging that pet owners might also have something worth hearing.

Chapter 49
When parents are blamed for killing babies

Alan Yurko was in prison in America, tried and found guilty of killing his baby son, also called Alan. According to the law, he had shaken his baby to death. His only answer was that he hadn't – which wasn't much of a defence, considering the baby had bleeding in his brain and several broken ribs. Doctors could think of only one plausible cause, and this they called 'Shaken Baby Syndrome'. Alan was serving life without parole, plus ten years, which meant that he would never be free again.

Desperate to prove his innocence, Alan wrote to many medical doctors and scientists, and discovered an important coincidence: his baby died shortly after he was given a cocktail of vaccines, and there was strong scientific evidence to suggest that Shaken Baby Syndrome was, in the majority of cases, caused by the vaccines these babies had been given. Death usually occurs around ten days after their shots, depending on body weight. Essentially, vaccines can cause a huge release of biochemicals, as described by Selye's 'non-specific response to stress' and other research relating to the cytokine storm, which can lead to bleeding into the brain and eyes.[1]

When I was helping Alan, there were 50 parents in American jails who had been accused of shaking their babies to death shortly after they were vaccinated.

Alan had heard about my work with the dogs, and added me to his list of contacts and supporters. My heart truly went out to this man. I couldn't imagine how awful it would be to lose your child, and then to be falsely blamed for their death. Nor could I imagine how awful life was in an American prison. Alan wrote regularly, telling me how the other inmates would beat him up and throw urine and faeces at him, a convicted baby killer.

He had many supporters in the UK. We had featured Alan's plight in the CHC newsletter, and a number of our members had donated to the campaign. Well over a hundred medical doctors and scientists from around the world also actively supported him.

Alan told me that Sally Clark, the well-publicised lawyer who had been convicted of killing her two sons, also had a vaccine link. Sally's eight-week-old boy Harry died five hours after being give the DTP vaccine, and her other son a week after being vaccinated. But medical experts who testified at her trial refused to tell the truth about the vaccine-cot death link due to fears that airing vaccine risks in a high profile court case could undermine public confidence.

An article in *The Spectator* on the 19th May 2007 [2], reported that the DTP vaccine both of Sally's two sons received has been especially implicated as a cause of permanent brain damage and death: "The evidence was spelled out in an unpublished 150-page report to the Department of Health by Dr Gordon Stewart, emeritus professor of public health at the University of Glasgow and a world authority on vaccine safety.

"Professor Stewart's report, first submitted at the request of the chief scientist in 1983 and updated in 1998 and 2006, also shows that, unlike the other vaccines, pertussis is ineffective — there has been widespread recurrence of whooping cough in fully vaccinated children in Europe and the USA. For these reasons several countries, including West Germany, Italy and Japan, removed it from their infant vaccination schedule. The report calls on the UK to do the same."

Sallyclark.org states: "In the case of Sally Clark's children Christopher and Harry, vaccination seems to be suspiciously associated with [both] their deaths."

Brian Deer (who went gunning for Andrew Wakefield), on the other hand, has an article on his website refuting the fact that the DTP shot causes brain damage [3]. Also check the appendix for relevant studies.

Sally Clark was eventually exonerated but died prematurely, no doubt due to the stress of losing her sons and being falsely imprisoned for their deaths. Her heart had been broken.

Before moving to Carsegray, I took on a three-month contract as a technical writer, and a curious coincidence had put me in touch with a specialist at Dundee's Ninewell's hospital who could help Alan Yurko. I had been sitting in my client's reception waiting to go into a meeting when I saw a front-page newspaper article about a doctor who had returned over seventy babies to their parents after they had been accused of breaking their bones.

Dr Colin Paterson, a senior lecturer in medicine at Dundee University, called the condition "temporary brittle bone disease". [4, 5]

"It is a very distinctive syndrome, the symptoms of which mimic the symptoms of non-accidental injury. It has often been misdiagnosed as child abuse. It is more common among twins and premature babies," he said.

The doctor had proven that premature babies (which Alan was) suffer from an enzyme deficiency, having failed to adequately mineralise during their shortened term in the womb. As a result, even the gentlest handling could result in broken bones. I contacted the doctor and he agreed to look at the medical records and slides, and subsequently added his support to Alan's campaign.

Dr Paterson called me one day to tell me about another case he was dealing with. A baby had died, and his father had been accused of killing the child and, yes, the baby was vaccinated on the 17th of March, and had died on the 27th.

On another occasion I had taken Edward to visit John McManaway, a healer famed locally for fixing animals' backs. His friend sat in on the session, and somehow the conversation got round to Shaken Baby Syndrome. "This is incredible," John's friend said. "I have a friend on one of the Scottish islands who's just been arrested for shaking his baby to death."

"Well go home and ask whether the baby was vaccinated before this happened," I advised.

Sure enough, the man called me that night and the baby had been vaccinated a week before. I put him in touch with people in the network who might help, including Dr Viera Scheibner who had many years previously noted a correlation between cot death and a recent vaccine. See also references 6-23.

Carsegray was made for large gatherings so we invited Alan's wife Francine and her daughter for a holiday, which John funded, and some twenty people came to stay in the house over a weekend to meet them, including the consultant Dr Paterson and various campaigners and their children.

Lyn Thomson, a vet, also came along with her husband. Lyn had telephoned me a few years previously to offer her help. She also felt that vaccine damage in animals was more common than the reports suggested, and had tried to persuade her veterinary boss to drop annual vaccination, even lending him my book.

One day she telephoned me, brimming with excitement. Her boss hadn't read my book, but he had read one of my letters in *Veterinary Times*, complete with the references I provided. He was shaken, having finally looked at a small selection of the science, and told her that they would stop vaccinating annually, and he also gave her permission to look through practice records to see if there was any correlation between recent vaccination and the onset of illness.

Two weeks later, however, Lyn phoned again. Her boss had been thinking, and told her that, apart from losing booster income, the practice would also lose patients if there was no vaccine damage to treat. He told her to shut her mouth and refrain from enlightening clients on the vaccine issue. She was devastated.

Unfortunately, after Francine's visit, it came to light that as a teenager, Alan Yurko was charged with burglary. He says he'd been associating with a group of teens who got into trouble, and served about six years before being released on parole in the summer of 1996. Alan met Francine in Ohio after his release but she moved to Orlando as her stepfather was dying of cancer. She was pregnant with baby Alan, and Alan made the unwise decision to leave Ohio without permission so he could support her. He had two months remaining on his parole. Pro-vaccinators made much of this.

Eventually, Alan was successful in his appeal. This wasn't on the grounds of vaccine damage but because the prosecution had made such a mess of the case, even filing medical records for a baby that was not Alan's child.

Alan maintains he did not kill his son, and there is significant scientific evidence to support the view that vaccines can and do cause sudden infant death.

Shortly after Francine Yurko's visit, my world fell apart again. John became enraged with me, claiming that I was in love with Alan; I was nonplussed and bewildered at the strength of his accusations which, to me, were utterly bizarre. John was absolutely furious and swore to destroy Alan.

As events unfolded, it transpired that he had declared his love for Alan's wife Francine and asked her to leave Alan and set up with him. It seems that John was projecting his confusion onto me. Projection, I discovered, is a defence mechanism that involves taking our own unacceptable qualities or feelings and ascribing them to other people.

I felt embarrassed and ashamed as Alan's supporters contacted me to persuade John to back off: He was posting damaging information about Alan on the internet, but he was beyond my control. It was a nightmare – my husband appeared to be losing his mind. It was a frightening time, too, since I had no idea whether John, in such an irrational state, might finally finish me off.

Soon I discovered that John was internet dating and when I broached the subject with him he asked me for a divorce. I had mixed emotions. On the one hand I feared for John, yet I couldn't see myself carrying on a relationship with someone I could no longer trust. Despite his violent behaviour, I also knew that he was a vulnerable and damaged individual. I also had no idea how I could keep CHC going without his support, or where I and my dogs would go. My sister Leslie invited me to live with her, but it would have been difficult to foist myself and three big dogs onto her and her husband Glenn in their own small multi-dog household.

So John and I staked our claims within the mercifully large house we were renting, and I – at John's request – set divorce proceedings in motion. We both tried our best not to get drawn into arguments and an unsteady truce ensued.

Chapter 50

Guidance

In 2003, the American Animal Hospital Association issued its vaccine guidelines [1], stating that, once immune, dogs would remain immune to the core canine diseases (distemper, parvovirus and hepatitis) for years, and probably for life. They called for an end to annual vaccination, and confirmed that vaccination was not harmless.

Nine years after the formation of Canine Health Concern, a second veterinary body had added its weight to what we had been saying all along.

Because life had to carry on despite the upheaval I was going through with John, and because I needed an income, I advertised Emotional Freedom Technique workshops in *Cygnus* magazine. As a result, I had lots of delegates.

Carsegray offered a beautiful setting, and the workshops went extremely well. EFT is such a powerful technique and delivers such stunning results that delegates witnessed and experienced miracles every time.

We also ran courses on canine health. We provided lovely home-cooked food, and delegates were able to walk and enjoy the beautiful grounds. Carsegray also had its own ancient stone circle, and we'd often take people there, or to the walled garden, or to many of the spectacular fields and woods surrounding the property.

I was grateful to be doing something with my life that brought peace to others, falling in line with the Buddhist 'Eightfold Path', which includes right livelihood – doing work that doesn't harm others and which is helpful to them. I also can't help believing that we live in a beneficent universe, and that I was graciously placed at Carsegray so that Nature could support me through another life upheaval.

To help me through this difficult time of separation from John, my friend Sally Spencer arranged for me to have a private telephone consult with Archangel Gabriel. Gabriel told me that I would be very happily married in the future which, as you might imagine, wasn't something I was particularly pleased to hear whilst in the middle of a divorce.

"I don't think so," I told him, Archangel or not. I could think of nothing I would like less than to get married again. I was having a ball as a single woman, doing what I wanted to do when I wanted to do it. Life was great, if somewhat stressful.

"Oh yes," said Gabriel. "And he will be younger than you."

"I can't see that," I said, trying not to be rude to the Archangel. I had always gone for men who were older than me.

"It works well," he said, "because men don't tend to live as long as women, and it will give you longer together."

OK, I thought, I'd better go along with it. "So will he be spiritual?" I asked him. John had always poo poohed my leanings towards spirituality.

"Yes, and he loves the dogs as much as you do."

"Does he like music?" I asked.

"Yes," said Gabriel. "He even writes his own music."

Ah, a musician, I thought. I hoped he played the guitar, being a sucker for a guitar riff.

Gabriel told me that my future husband would be my 'divine complement'. I asked him what that meant.

"It's someone you feel very comfortable with," he said, "like a pair of old slippers. You've been together in over 2,000 lifetimes. He wasn't planning to come back this time, but then he heard that you had volunteered so he volunteered to come along to help you."

I often meet people on my travels who have difficulty accepting the basis of energy therapies such as homeopathy and EFT, and I certainly meet people who think I am nuts for having a private consult with an alleged Archangel, *and* telling people about it. But I'm not particularly interested in the approval of scientific types who have allowed their profession to be bought and sold, and I personally believe that there is far more to the world than science is yet able to prove.

It turns out that I did meet a man who is younger than me, who is a musician who composes his own music, and who loves the dogs as much as me.

Chapter 51
My dogs demonstrate complex emotions

Since starting CHC and writing *What Vets Don't Tell You About Vaccines*, I was frequently invited to be a guest on internet discussion groups to speak about pet vaccination and vaccine damage. One of these groups was called DogRead. The idea is that the several thousand group members are supposed to read an author's book, and the author makes herself available to the group to answer readers' questions.

I soon discovered that very few people on DogRead had read my book, but they certainly had their opinions about it. Many of the contributors were interested, courteous, and kind but, as is often the case, a group of about four women decided that it would be fun to roast me on a spit.

It didn't matter what I said, or which scientific references I posted (it was, apparently, always 'badly conducted research'), I was met with name-calling and ridicule. The trouble is, if you are representing a cause, you don't have the luxury of giving as good as you get. This would merely have the movement for change I represent allied to abusive behaviour. So I had to suck it up and remain calm in the face of incredibly spiteful abuse.

Besides, when Oliver died and pretty much everything else in my life was horrible, I recognised that life for all of us is pretty painful, and I decided that I don't want to contribute to anyone else's suffering. This isn't as easy as you might think, and sometimes I fail, but the desire to do no harm underlies the way I try to live. So giving as good as I got wasn't an option.

Around that time I was having terrible shoulder and back pain and a friend suggested I visit Dr Wei, a doctor of Chinese medicine in Dundee. I went for several massage and acupuncture sessions. On one visit, Dr Wei put needles in me and I began to sob on his treatment couch. I just couldn't stop crying. I cried in the surgery, and I cried in the street on the way to my car. Then I cried in the car, cried as I drove home, and cried when I got home. He must have released something in me.

I cried so much that I frightened myself, so I made a very rare visit to the doctor – and I cried there too. He diagnosed 'reactive depression' which, he explained, meant that I didn't have a depressive personality, but that I had reached a point where I could no longer cope. Running CHC, losing Sophie, going through a divorce with John, not knowing where I would live or how I could care for my dogs in the future, and dealing with abuse on the internet, had combined to place me beyond my limits of endurance.

My dad was also suffering from dementia at this time. Thankfully, now that John and I were divorcing, I had been welcomed back into my fuller family and so I was visiting as often as I could. It was hard to see this once vibrant, intelligent, man of integrity pacing the floor and living in fear.

Then I had a call from my sisters and brother who were at my dad's bedside. They put the phone to his ear and I was able to say goodbye to him, and he was gone. My dad died on a Friday when people were arriving for a workshop, and I had no choice but to carry on. It's amazing what you can do when you have no choice.

After my outburst of tears, Dr Wei began the process of 'cupping'. This is where the practitioner puts suction cups on specific parts of the body. He placed the cups on my back, around my heart, and the suction changed my skin to a dark mahogany brown, drawing out the heartache that I was feeling during this time. Dr Wei explained that if there is no dis-ease, then the skin will not change colour.

But still I kept CHC going, banging out newsletters, answering emails and phone calls to help people with their dogs, and managing our discussion group. Dr Wei expressed surprise after I had cried in his surgery, saying that I was one of those people who, they say in China, 'lives life behind a curtain'. He explained that (even though I'm a Sagittarian who is supposed to wear her heart on her sleeve) I put on a good show. I think, rather, that I am pretty well able to compartmentalise life, living in what is happening now.

I learnt how to do this as a student of practical philosophy when I was in my 20s. The School taught me mindfulness, where you observe the circling thoughts in your head and live in the present moment. I was also initiated into Transcendental meditation. I discovered, through this, that I am not my emotions, my body or the thoughts in my mind. I am a spiritual being. Always, it's possible to know that there is an observer observing the thoughts and emotions – and this observer is the Self. With this knowledge and experience comes a certain degree of detachment. However, I had reached my limit.

Something unusual happened between Edward and Daniel while John and I were going through our divorce. While we were being polite to one-another, there were nevertheless many emotions under the surface. Edward took to lying on the bed in John's room during the day, and Dannie stayed on mine. Then they started fighting one-another. It was pretty harrowing to watch, and difficult to pull them apart, especially with the pain I was feeling in my shoulder and arms. I had the idea that perhaps they were mirroring John and I, so I decided to do EFT on it. I tapped for Edward mirroring John, but I didn't even get a full tapping round done before my boys put their ears down and went up to each other and made friends again.

On another occasion, during an Animal Communication and EFT workshop at Carsegray, Dannie came into the workshop room and walked across the floor as though it was going to cave in on him. We asked what was wrong, and he told us that he was fed up being the under-dog. So we used EFT to resolve this problem for him.

(Communicating with animals is something that I had been increasingly doing since the day I sat and tuned in to Samson. I've written about this in my book, *The Animals' Agenda*.)

That night, as we were all sitting downstairs in the panelled sitting room, Edward, as he usually did, told Dannie to get out of the room. Dannie just sat there quietly refusing.

Edward howled, although howling isn't quite the right description. It was more like a mournful cry. Some of the delegates laughed at him, and we discussed whether he was upset at being knocked off the top dog position. We resolved to work on Edward's problem the next day.

So the next day I invited Edward to join us in the workshop. He resisted, looking ashamed and humiliated. Eventually I persuaded him to come in, but he sat looking out of the window with his back to us. He looked so pitiful that once again a couple of the delegates laughed, at which point he stood up abruptly and walked out of the room. I had to go out and apologise to him and urge him to come back in.

We tapped on Edward being knocked off the top dog position, after which he seemed much happier. We left the boys to settle back into their own pattern, and they were fine.

On yet another occasion, Colleen Steed and Liz Jay, who are both dog groomers, came to another workshop at Carsegray and brought their grooming tools. They'd decided that my shaggy dogs needed a haircut. They trimmed Edward first, and Dannie was delighted, and laughed at him. Edward was deeply upset. It wasn't until Dannie also had a haircut that Edward returned to his normal happy self.

People frequently say that animals have no egos. I think they do. They are perfectly aware of themselves as distinct thinking and feeling entities, and they often have what Eckhart Tolle describes as 'pain bodies'. Animals, just as much as humans, are on their own spiritual paths.

Chapter 52

Meeting my divine complement

Spookily, immediately after John asked me for a divorce, I met a musician who composes his own music, is younger than me, likes the same music as me, loves the dogs as much as me, and who is as comfortable to be with as an old pair of slippers.

John had asked me for a divorce the day before I travelled to England to speak at a lecture for Bearded Collie breeders. I was being put up for the night by Angela Pedder along with my fellow speaker, Neil, who majored on canine diet. Angela told me later that I had a very calming presence and that her dogs had quietened down when I entered her house, adding that Neil, my fellow speaker who was normally quite hyper, was also calmer in my presence. None of us can see ourselves as others see us, so it was interesting to hear that despite my life being in turmoil, I had a peaceful effect on those around me. (I only mention this to redress the balance, since I've shared many of the occasions where I've been reduced to tears and you'd be forgiven for thinking that I lived my life in a constant state of drama!)

That evening, I got on a train to Bristol, where I was teaching an EFT workshop the next day. One of the delegates was a man called Rob Ellis. As he stood next to me in the garden during a break, I though what a kindly and gentle soul he was. And then I went home, thinking no more of him.

Some months previously, Rob had sent me a letter to say that both of his dogs, Samson and Jazar, had died within three weeks of one-another. He thanked me for the information I had provided through CHC, saying that before he became a member and adopted my advice, his friends were in a really bad way, and Samson was close to death. I distinctly remember thinking what a nice man he was when I read his letters. He was kind and compassionate, aware of me as a human being rather than just someone who might answer his questions.

The health of Rob's dogs improved dramatically and they lived a further four years on raw food and no more vaccines. Samson's immune system had been collapsing; he had colitis, muscle wastage, and severe hip dysplasia. Within months of starting the raw diet with supplements and homeopathic remedies, Samson was running along the beach with Rob and his health problems had disappeared. Jazar's ear and skin problems cleared up, and his immune system rallied round.

A few months after we met at the workshop, Rob emailed me to say that he had been awarded an advanced diploma in canine psychology. He wanted to work *for* the animals and asked me if I had any thoughts. I offered what advice I could, saying ultimately that he should follow his heart, and then asked him about something that had been troubling me lately.

"I'd like to ask you something," I said. "The thing is, people keep talking about anthropomorphism, and how we shouldn't attribute human emotions to animals. But as far as I can see, animals DO have human emotions. What are your views on this as a behaviourist?"

We began to correspond, each day answering one-another's emails and putting our own points of view. He was equally kind by email, and each email made me like him more. I think I began to fall in love with Rob through cyberspace; it allowed us to get to know one-another without the physical side of attraction getting in the way. In fact, we might have both run in opposite directions if we hadn't been able to make friends first. Rob, too, had been badly emotionally battered in a previous marriage.

I invited him to Carsegray so he could meet Edward, Daniel and Gwinnie, and see how they demonstrated their thoughts and feelings in person. Rob telephoned to confirm that he'd booked his flight, and I couldn't help but notice that his voice was full of light. And he was funny – he was bringing his guitar and talked about providing in-flight entertainment on the way.

We had a lovely weekend together, talking about dogs and life, and he played his guitar and sang to me. We also liked the same music. How many people are 'Yes' fans? It's not the sort of music that gets on the mainstream radio but is spoken about in a derisory manner as 'progressive rock' – but we both put *Nous Somme du Soleil* from the Topographic Oceans album at the top of our Desert Island Discs list, and we both love Neil Young. I have to also mention that he's an absolute Led Zeppelin freak and has won me over on that.

Rob also loved the Carsegray environment, and the fact that the dogs had so much freedom to run off lead in so many beautiful places. Pretty soon, it was clear that Gabriel was right. He was my divine complement. As a boy, Rob's nickname was 'Evil' – because he wasn't. He has the soul of a Golden Retriever.

Rob has made me happier than I have ever been in my life. He is funny and kind, and he's thoughtful and respectful of others. My dogs immediately adored him.

Edward took up football – they'd go onto the croquet lawn in Carsegray's splendid garden and spar with one-another. I can still see my beautiful Edward now, filled with happiness and delight to have a man to play with. Dannie, too, was overjoyed. My sweet little man was shy and tentative with Rob, but he was all smiles to be in his presence.

Gwinnie, though, wasn't quite so pleased because Rob took her place on the sofa next to me, but in time they became firm friends. Rob has written and recorded a song for each of them, all beautiful and poignant.

For the first time in my life I felt dizzy when someone kissed me – it's like a hit straight in the pineal gland, also known as the third eye. I have the same effect on Rob – and it hasn't diminished over the years; even a hug will do it. Gabriel told me that this was because our energies are so closely matched.

We took advantage of cheap flights between Edinburgh and Somerset, and visited one-another as often as we could. After a few months, Rob gave up his job in Somerset, handed over his life savings to keep CHC going, and joined me at Carsegray. John, realising that it was time to leave, found a flat and moved out, which filled me with sadness. I wished him well.

Interestingly, the day John moved out, the pain I had felt in my hips over the past few months simply lifted. On an emotional root level, hip problems relate to a feeling that you're unable to move forward in life. Since Rob moved in the day after John moved out, it all made perfect sense.

Rob and I were, and still are, very happy together. We'd get into bed at night, chatting and laughing, and just as we closed our eyes the dark room would be flooded with light, as though the sun had arrived with a burst. "Did you see that?" one of us would say to the other. "Yes," the other would say. The next time I spoke to Gabriel I asked him what that weird light was, and he told me it was God sending us a blessing.

With Rob by my side, Canine Health Concern came back with renewed vigour.

Initially Rob had planned to get himself a job in Scotland so that we'd have food on the table and a means of keeping the roof over our heads, but his heart was aching. He dearly wanted to work for the animals, and helping to run CHC fulfilled that need. In the end we both threw caution to the wind and, with Rob committed to keeping CHC going, I returned to the work with enthusiasm. We had no idea how we'd survive financially but trusted that, if we were doing what we came here to do, then somehow we would be supported.

I went back to Dr Wei shortly after meeting Rob. Dr Wei put the suction cups on my back again, and my skin refused to change colour. Rob's love had healed my heartache. And for the first time in my life, I now felt safe in my own home.

Having spent most of my adult life with a man who was difficult and unpredictable, I was overflowing with gratitude and joy to be with Rob. And yet there is also sadness that we didn't meet sooner, and that our time together is limited and therefore incredibly precious.

I was also sad for John. He had been a major force in my life for 20 years, and no-one is all one thing. There were many reasons to love John and to be grateful to him; I feared that he would be lonely and hoped that his wishes would come true.

I can't help feeling that God has a plan for all of us, and that He holds us gently in His loving arms. Although life – as it is for all of us – had been difficult and challenging, the metaphorical arm had always seemed to sweep across my own particular chessboard in order to place me where I need to be to do the work I do.

Rob came with the skills that would enable him to take over where John had left off. It was almost as if I had made him myself as a perfect fit for my needs. He had worked in accounts for most of his career so he took on the management of CHC, which required the ability to manage the membership and the somewhat dire finances. It was also wonderful to have him answering the phone, knowing that he would be polite and kind.

Rob has grown to become a real driving force behind CHC. He's always thinking strategically, looking at what we need to do next to end over-vaccination and promote real food and natural healthcare for dogs.

John, it turned out, had left me with enormous debts, and Rob had the nerve-wracking task of trying to sort this out with nothing in the way of a handover. Despite my many charms and sexual magnetism (said with tongue in cheek lest anyone take that seriously), many men would have walked away from such a mess, and I shall always be grateful to Rob for taking me and CHC on.

Although John had offered me a settlement, and to repay some of the debts when his next contract came up, nothing ever materialised. Sandra, my stepmother, turned into my Fairy Godmother and volunteered to pay the rent for us, which we paid back on a monthly basis until, one day, she telephoned to say that she didn't need or want us to repay any more. Sometimes people do such kind things that there is nothing on earth that can ever repay them. Thank you Sandra.

Nevertheless, our days at Carsegray were numbered – turns out I really was too common to sustain that sort of lifestyle. Although it was a fabulous place to be in the summer, the winters in this big beautiful house were cruel. We would scream at the cold sheets when we got into bed and we could only afford to heat the room we were using. Every other room was unheated and felt colder than the snow- and ice-drenched Scottish landscape outside. My mansion-acquired stiff upper lip was quivering with the cold.

Then, to cap it all, and despite having spent tens of thousands on modernising the place, the rent was put up beyond our means. We knew we'd need to find somewhere else.

Chapter 53

Extra effort required

Someone passed me a copy of a letter that had appeared in the UK's *Veterinary Times*. It was signed by 31 vets, most of them homeopaths, calling for an end to annual vaccination [1]. I burst into tears of relief when I read it, overjoyed that UK vets were finally coming out in public and stating the truth.

For a long time I'd felt that homeopathic vets like Chris Day, John Saxton and Peter Gregory had escorted me to the front line and offered to hold my coat while I jumped out of the trenches and took the bullets. Despite these three having the courage to tell the truth and eschew vaccine income, I felt that other homeopathic vets with a strong understanding of the damage and suffering caused by vaccines should do more. American holistic vets were far more vocal.

It was difficult for me to sympathise about vets losing their jobs for speaking the truth, because I had consciously sacrificed my own career and the majority of my income to try to resolve the destruction caused to our beloved animals by unethical businesses. But at last – with this letter – I was no longer fighting the battle on my own in the UK.

And then my heart sank, knowing they wouldn't see it through. It would be incredibly difficult for them to do so. This one letter was significant, but it wouldn't on its own put an end to over-vaccination. In order for real change to occur, many more small droplets would be needed to fill the ocean.

Some months later I telephoned many of the vets who had signed the letter, looking for support. They had mostly all decided to put their heads back under the parapet. Some told me that they relied heavily on referral business. If they spoke out too much, that business would dry up. There had also been calls from the conventional fraternity to have the signatories struck off, meaning they would no longer be able to practice. There was even talk of them being bumped off. Some added that they didn't want to be associated with me, since I was too contentious.

One homeopathic vet even came to one of our weekend workshops but was unable to attend on the Saturday when I gave the vaccine lecture. Much to my consternation, he stood up and made a speech about how wrong I was on the vaccine front, grossly misrepresenting our stance and the lecture I had given the day before which he hadn't been present to hear. The next week he emailed Rob to tell him, essentially, that I must change and become someone else. For some reason I have terrible trouble remembering this vet's name. My psyche has cancelled it out.

Unbeknownst to me, Chris Day was also in big trouble at the time. He was being prosecuted by the RSPCA for allegedly allowing an animal to suffer unnecessarily. He went through two painful years of defending himself and when the RSPCA failed in their bid, his veterinary association took over and also tried to put him out of business. Neither was successful; he was completely exonerated. Some believe that Chris may have been singled out and punished for his association with me and his willingness to discuss vaccine damage. Some also believe that, had he been successfully convicted, it would have signalled the end of veterinary homeopathy in the UK.

Years later I met up with Chris at an evening lecture and he told me that he suffers significant financial hardship because he cannot ethically bring himself to vaccinate. "I just can't do it," he said. He speaks out whenever he has the opportunity. We who love the animals have a great deal to thank Chris for. Richard Allport has also spoken the truth about vaccine damage on a public scale, with frequent references to it in his *Dogs Today* column. I think that, given the media opportunities, he would do more.

But I stood there in my office, looking at the letter in *Veterinary Times*, and realised that rather than move the campaign forward, it would require extra effort from Rob and me – and active CHC members – to see the job through. We couldn't rely upon the British veterinary fraternity to effect lasting change.

A guiding thought came into my head as I stood there with that letter in my hand: "Get out on the road with the Foundation in Canine Healthcare workshop". The whole concept arrived in one insight, complete with title. By talking to people about the issue face-to-face, I believed that we would build an army of informed dog lovers who would speak to other dog lovers. Rob and I talked about delivering a course in natural canine health around the country, and I sat and wrote it.

At the same time I wrote the follow-up to *What Vets Don't Tell You About Vaccines*. Called *Shock to the System*, it updated the vaccine issue, included cats and horses, and explained the other factors that affect health, namely genes, diet, environmental toxins, conventional veterinary meds, and stress. I worked flat-out to finish the book before the upheaval of a house move, and succeeded.

We had received a donation of £500 from a lady called Teresa Maxwell who had been left a large sum of money by her late mother. Teresa was an idealistic lady who didn't want to use money raised by her mother through dealings with the capitalist system – so she looked for causes to distribute her legacy amongst. We were fortunately one of these, and this enabled us to reprint CHC leaflets, which we were missing dreadfully.

Teresa also funded the publication of *Shock to the System*. Soon after this, Dogwise – a dog book distributor in America – agreed to take it on. By this time, *What Vets Don't Tell You About Vaccines* was out of print and I had little hope of finding the money to reprint it. Second hand copies were selling on the internet for around £90, so I reasoned that there must still be a market for it. Once again, Dogwise stepped in and we worked out a publishing deal. Both books have sold in the thousands and are, depending upon whose definition you accept, official 'best sellers', selling steadily and consistently over the decades and, I am proud to say, helping to change the outdated over-vaccination paradigm.

A warning for all aspiring writers, however: over a hundred thousand titles are published every year, and the vast majority are pulped, having failed to make sales. Only a tiny minority of books make their authors rich, or even make them a living. A few hundred pounds every few months, if you're lucky, will not keep the roof over your head. For people like me, book-writing is about communicating something that we feel needs to be heard.

Meanwhile, Rob was busily setting up a workshop schedule. Getting 'delegates on seats' is always the hardest part of putting on any lecture or weekend workshop unless you're Madonna. Travelling from Scotland to various parts of the UK makes it harder; since you don't have the local contacts who can network and tell others that the event is taking place. It's so much harder to publicise an event from a distance, unless you have a healthy marketing budget.

Chapter 54
Money censors what you may know

One day I received an email from Beverley Cuddy, editor of *Dogs Today*. You may remember that John and Beverley had fallen out with one-another, so that was the end of any opportunities we might have had to publicise the over-vaccination and raw feeding messages in her magazine. Beverley's email came out of the blue, saying something about her email account being down. I thought this was pretty synchronous and replied, telling her that John was no longer on the scene. As a result I was asked to submit articles for publication and was even offered a regular column.

Another magazine asked me to be a regular contributor. This was an on-line publication called *Dogs Naturally* which soon became successful enough to go into print. Its editor Dana Scott was wowing me with her professionalism and determination to move important canine health issues forward. I was also being asked to write articles for other dog magazines. All of this gave me a reason to research the vaccine subject further.

Initially I was paid to write articles for but another recession saw an end to this. With advertising revenue falling, magazines simply couldn't afford to pay their writers. Nevertheless, I couldn't stop myself from taking advantage of these opportunities to get the word out there. Thankfully things are a little better now; sometimes I get a financial bonus.

Some scientists like to mock the Internet as a source of dodgy information on medical and vaccination issues – but the internet is also a rich source of academic peer-reviewed papers. If someone makes an unsubstantiated claim, or I'm researching a particular area, I like to go back to basics and check the science.

There is, however, a problem. A lot of the scientific papers are only available for a price. You have to pay to access them. Unless you work for academia or industry, you often don't have the funds to pay for access. And unless you pay, you have to go from the abstract (a short summary), or you have to find someone to forward the full paper to you for free.

Even the so-called *free* research sites can limit access to information if you're not an industry or academic researcher. The free on-line resource ResearchGate.net [1] carries one of my articles, presumably considers me to be a researcher, but refuses to allow me access to complete scientific papers. I can't even read my own article on their site:

"Thank you for your interest in ResearchGate. Unfortunately we were unable to approve your account request. ResearchGate membership is limited to those who are part of the scientific or academic research community."

As I pointed out to Bazil, the ResearchGate Access Prevention Officer, I have published best-selling books on the subject featured in my article held on the ResearchGate database; I have written hundreds of researched articles which have appeared in publications around the world. Why would they restrict my access to their free website?

I am aware that vaccine science is complex, and it would be easy to get it wrong. This is why I like to keep asking questions, and quote peer-reviewed scientific research. So why would these people try to stop me accessing that free research?

It is an absolute fact that vaccines can and do cause serious life-threatening adverse effects. Silencing and marginalising people like myself who genuinely feel that there are serious problems that need to be addressed – well, to me that is dishonest. Dishonesty is about lying and cheating; but it is also about withholding critical information. Where there's money involved, it becomes fraud. Fraud itself has been defined as 'seeking to gain financial advantage through deception'.

So I asked Bazil who funds ResearchGate, the free-to-some scientific research site. The site appears to have a large staff, and someone has to pay them if no-one is paying to access the research.

You see, in the twenty years I've been researching vaccines, I keep coming up against industry funding, which severely limits the open pursuit of truth. You have to be in the same club, and share the same viewpoint, or you are a social leper. Unfortunately Bazil chose not to tell me who funds the site, so I researched ResearchGate.

Ijad Madisch, MD, PhD is a co-founder of ResearchGate. He holds a PhD in Virology from Harvard Medical School. When seeking funding for ResearchGate, Madisch was reported in *TechCrunch* as saying that ResearchGate aims to help "free knowledge from the Ivory Tower, to digitize it and make it accessible for everyone in order to accelerate scientific progress."

Everyone except me, it seems.

But I'm not the only one who's worried about a lack of access to scientific research.

The Lancet recently published a paper calling for wider availability of data. [2] However, according to *The Lancet*, these are rarely available and studies are plagued by selective reporting. "When full information about studies is inaccessible, billions of dollars in investment are wasted, bias is introduced, and research and care of patients are detrimentally affected."

Translated: we only get to see the research the industry wants us to see. Truth doesn't live here anymore. The bottom line is that lives are jeopardised.

I wasn't surprised to discover that Microsoft co-founder Bill Gates, one of the world's richest people, helped lead a $35 million investment in ResearchGate [3]. And now ResearchGate – rather than making information accessible to all – is censoring access to information, at least as far as I'm concerned.

If you're concerned about vaccine adverse effects, you also need to be concerned about – or at least question the activities of – Bill Gates. During 2013, it was announced that Bill and Melinda Gates, and WHO, had funded a group to spy on vaccine 'misinformation'. Once concerns were detected and analysed, they planned to implement an 'early response' and engage with the public to ensure sustained confidence in vaccines and immunisation [4]. The word 'propaganda' springs to mind.

Apparently, "despite the historic success of immunisation in reducing the burden of childhood illness and death, episodes of public concerns and rumours around vaccines have occurred around the world, spreading quickly and sometimes seriously eroding public confidence in immunisation and ultimately leading to vaccine refusals and disease outbreaks".

Did you know that there has never been one single industry-funded long-term study to assess the effects of vaccine programmes? And yet there's money in the coffers to assess risk associated with people like me talking about vaccine adverse effects and to counteract those of us who have experienced the harm vaccines can do.

Bill Gates is a rich man, which means that he will be living in an ivory tower. Ordinary people won't have access to Bill. I'm not likely to meet him at a cocktail party, or to sit around the pool or boardroom table to discuss the risks associated with vaccination. I can't look in the telephone directory and pick up the phone and have a chat.

Does he know, for example, that the Japanese Health Ministry issued a nationwide notice that cervical cancer vaccinations should no longer be recommended for girls aged 12 to 16 due to unacceptable adverse reactions? The vaccines in question are Cervarix and Gardasil, which have resulted in permanent paralysis of many human beings, destroying their lives [5].

Has Mr Gates seen the Cochrane Collaboration report on flu vaccines, which found no benefit in them? [6]

The media was reporting that polio has been eradicated in India, thanks to a Bill and Melinda Gates oral polio vaccination drive encompassing nearly 170 million children. [7] However, the vaccine used a live virus that is linked to vaccine-induced polio paralysis. [8] More precisely, there were 47,500 known cases (and possibly more) of non-polio acute flaccid paralysis in India, a polio-like condition that is clinically indistinguishable from polio paralysis but twice as deadly, linked to the oral polio vaccine. Do Bill's employees tell him when this sort of thing happens?

Does Bill know that vaccines alone don't eradicate disease? Polio spreads largely through faeces-contaminated water [9], so ignoring poor sanitation and lack of clean water in developing countries, along with the lack of healthy food to support their immune systems, is bizarre if the goal is really to eradicate disease. I didn't see any news reports saying that anyone was planning to help the people paralysed by the polio vaccine, either.

Instead, *the Telegraph* reported in February 2014 [10]: "Bill Gates, founder of Microsoft and the world's biggest charitable donor, has hailed the Indian government's eradication of polio as the greatest health achievement he has seen.

"India became polio-free last month on January 13th, three years after its last victim, four-year-old Rukhsar Khatun, was diagnosed with the disease in West Bengal.

"A labour-intensive and coordinated campaign led by the Indian government, Rotary, the Bill and Melinda Gates Foundation and the Global Polio Initiative deployed two million staff to vaccinate 170 million children throughout the country on two dates to help finally wipe out the disease."

Someone had forgotten the 47,500 paralysed victims of the Indian polio vaccine campaign when they wrote the press release. Later estimates put it at 53,000. [8,11,12]

Ahead of the prestigious Dimbleby Lecture by Bill Gates on 29 January 2013, the BBC acknowledged serious concerns about the safety and usefulness of the Foundation's polio vaccination campaign. In his article "Bill Gates: The world can defeat polio" [13], the BBC's medical correspondent Fergus Walsh refers to the study by Indian paediatrician Jacob Puliyel, MD, et al. in the *Indian Journal of Medical Ethics*: "The polio eradication programme epitomises nearly everything that is wrong with donor funded 'disease specific' vertical projects, at the cost of investments in community-oriented primary health care (horizontal programmes)…"

The paper opened with these words: "It was hoped that following polio eradication, immunisation could be stopped. However the synthesis of polio virus in 2002, made eradication impossible. It is argued that getting poor countries to expend their scarce resources on an impossible dream over the last 10 years was unethical." [8]

Billions are spent on profitable new drugs and vaccines, when the same amount spent on clean water and sanitation – many contend – would have a far greater impact in terms of benefit to health.

In a new development in early February 2017, India's National Technical Advisory Group on Immunisation announced it has cut off all financial ties with the Gates Foundation due in part to "conflict of interest issues" relating to its links with pharmaceutical companies. [14]

Because Mr Gates has funded a system to spy on vaccine dissenters on the internet, I wrote an on-line letter to him, pointing out known vaccine adverse effects: encephalitis and brain damage, a massive increase in autoimmunity, allergies, cancer and leukaemia – and a huge body of scientific research showing how vaccinated individuals come down with the diseases they're supposed to be protected from.

I asked if he understood that you need a healthy immune system to be able to respond positively to vaccines, and that starvation and malnutrition make it difficult for the immune system to fight disease or, indeed, the negative effects of a vaccine. "In this light, are you aware that some people fear that massive vaccine programmes in the third world are some sort of exercise in eugenics?"

Bill didn't reply to me. And I'm still not allowed to access research on the Gates-funded ResearchGate.net.

Meanwhile researchers from Yale and Penn State universities published a paper confirming that they've found a disturbing association between the timing of vaccines and the onset of certain brain disorders in a subset of children. Analysing five years' worth of private health insurance data on children ages 6-15, these scientists found that young people vaccinated in the previous three to 12 months were significantly more likely to be diagnosed with certain neuropsychiatric disorders than their non-vaccinated counterparts.

The study, which raises important questions about whether over-vaccination may be triggering immune and neurological damage in a subset of vulnerable children (something parents of children with autism have been saying for years), was published in the peer-reviewed journal *Frontiers in Psychiatry* [15].

Children who had been vaccinated were more likely to be diagnosed with anorexia and OCD than their non-vaccinated counterparts. Vaccinated children were also more likely to be diagnosed with an anxiety disorder and with tics compared to the controls.

In a carefully worded conclusion, the researchers caution making too much of these results while also urging further investigation. "This pilot epidemiologic analysis implies that the onset of some neuropsychiatric disorders may be temporally related to prior vaccinations in a subset of individuals. These findings warrant further investigation, but do not prove a causal role of antecedent infections or vaccinations in the pathoetiology of these conditions."

Analysing the study, Robert F Kennedy Jnr wrote, "We all know that correlation (in this case, vaccine administration in the previous 12 months and new diagnoses of brain disorders) does not necessarily mean causation. But if certain vaccines or a combination of vaccines are actually triggering brain disorders, it is imperative that we figure out which vaccines, or combination of vaccines, are the culprits and what risk factors may make some children more susceptible than others.

"Of particular concern is the influenza vaccine. In this study, influenza vaccination was strongly correlated with both anorexia and OCD. At the same time, new research by CDC scientists has shown the mercury-containing preservative thimerosal to be as toxic and as brain damaging as other forms of mercury [16]. Yet multi-dose flu vaccines still contain thimerosal, and flu vaccines are recommended for pregnant women and infants in America despite questions about efficacy and the scientifically documented risks.

"While new discoveries about the human immune system are being made all the time, it is well understood that the immune system plays a role in brain development and in certain psychiatric conditions, including attention disorders, eating disorders, obsessive disorders and depression.

"It is also well understood that the body's immune response involves inflammation, which is when tissue swells in response to harmful stimulation. Harmful stimulation includes infectious diseases (that is, illnesses themselves), environmental toxins like mercury, and allergens like pollen or dust mites (which are actually benign, though an over-stimulated immune system perceives them as threats).

"We further know that vaccination can cause inflammation, which is part of the body's natural response to foreign substances. Previous scientific studies have shown that when an immune reaction causes inflammation, it can negatively affect the brain. So it is scientifically plausible and more than reasonable to investigate whether vaccination itself, which provokes inflammation, may also negatively affect the brain."

Your brain is really important. Without a working brain, your life is basically stuffed. Harris Coulter wrote much the same in his book, *Vaccination, Social Violence and Criminality* in 1990. Vaccines are dumbing the population down, to say the least, and could be responsible for societal aggression. In the worst-case scenario, vaccines can turn your bright child or pet into a brain-damaged husk. Or it can kill him. Take your pick.

Chapter 55

Population, hygiene, malnutrition and infection

There have been assertions that Bill Gates is secretly hoping to reduce the world's population through his vaccination programme; the internet is awash with what some consider to be evidence of this. But I prefer to look for the good in people. It's entirely possible that Mr Gates and his charitable foundation are seeking to alleviate and prevent human suffering by vaccinating against vaccine-preventable diseases. He could be one of the good guys.

Nevertheless, there are some worrying coincidences which don't help in terms of public relations and potentially faulty perceptions.

Bill Gates' father, William H Gates, has long been involved with *Planned Parenthood* – claimed by some to be a "rebranded organisation birthed out of the American Eugenics Society". [1]

In a PBS interview with Bill Moyers [2], Bill Gates admitted that his family's involvement in reproductive issues throughout the years has been extensive, referencing his prior adherence to the beliefs of eugenicist Thomas Robert Malthus, who believed that populations need to be controlled through reproductive restrictions. So apart from being a money magnet, Bill is also an idealist, following an ideology ingrained into him as a child.

Gates also said in the interview: "as you improve health in a society, population growth goes down", and he talked about the horror of viral disease in third world countries. Therefore, his aims – believing as he apparently does in the ability of vaccines to alleviate suffering – would be two-fold: to eradicate disease, and to reduce the population by making people healthier. This obviously sounds contradictory – how do you reduce the number of people by preventing disease? Surely they'd die quicker if they didn't have vaccines to protect them? The answer lies in his assertion that people in third world countries won't produce so many children to care for them in old age, since fewer children will die.

Bill Gates' hero, Malthus, was not associated with the sinister side of eugenics, by the way. He didn't seek to reduce the population by murdering 'undesirables'. More sinister attempts to mitigate problems associated with overpopulation in the early 19th century focused on forcefully sterilising people thought to have undesirable traits. Methods included forced abortions, birth control, marriage restrictions, and segregation of the mentally disabled.

The eugenics concept was expanded in Nazi Germany to exterminate undesirables, most notably the Jews, Gypsies, homosexuals, and the disabled. This became genocide, also known as murder.

The vaccine industry has arguably been involved in eugenics, having been caught lacing vaccines with chemicals that cause sterility in women, proven in the Philippines, Nicaragua and Mexico. In March 2014, the Catholic Church in Kenya publically questioned whether a national tetanus vaccination campaign targeting women aged between 14-49 years was aimed at sterilising these women. [3,4,5,6,]

For people who believe that the world is overpopulated and that we have a right to make choices about whether or not we create new life, there is nothing sinister in Planned Parenthood. It also has to be said that there are serious concerns that the world is over-populated, and that some believe we can't sustain increasing population rates.

Here's the scale of the problem: More than seven billion people currently inhabit the planet, compared to only three billion in 1967. Every year 80 million are added to our global population, an increase of about one United States every four years. Almost half are under 25 and their decisions during their reproductive years will determine whether we have 6 billion or 14 billion people by 2100.

The InterAcademy Panel Statement on Population Growth, circa 1994 [7], said many environmental problems, such as rising levels of carbon dioxide, global warming and pollution are aggravated by population expansion. Other problems include the increased demand for resources such as fresh water and food, starvation and malnutrition, consumption of natural resources faster than the rate of regeneration, and a deterioration in living conditions. However, some believe that waste and over-consumption, especially by wealthy nations, and especially by America, are putting more strain on the environment than overpopulation.

On this basis, I have to concede that Bill Gates could be motivated by a desire to reduce human suffering. Bill's side of the story is in the appendix [8,9].

But it's unfortunate that the pro-vaccine movement denies and obfuscates vaccine-induced suffering, even limiting access to information that might shed light on the science.

Planned Parenthood believes we have a right to choose over our reproductive abilities; but do we also have a right to choose not to die from experimental, unnecessary, ineffective, or dangerous vaccines? And should oligarchs or government agencies have the right to make you sterile against your knowledge or wishes?

It is an absolute fact that vaccines are not without potential harm. Therefore we need information that will enable us to decide whether the risk of an individual vaccine outweighs the risk of perceived disease threats. We also need free access to information that promotes vaccine alternatives. What we don't need are lies or censorship. Who has the moral authority to force you to take risks with your life without informing you of the risks?

It worries me that one of the wealthiest people in the world, with a known desire to reduce the population, is funding massive vaccine programmes in the third world when vaccines are licensed for use in healthy individuals only. When people are drinking out of dirty, polluted puddles and where food is scarce, surely there would be a greater need to give them clean water and nutritious food? Then, and only then, might the vaccines be deemed to be 'safe'. Malnutrition and infection compromise the immune system, at which point a vaccine potentially becomes ineffective and also potentially dangerous.

Besides, what use is a vaccine when the people are *starving* to death?

In a UK TV documentary in April 2014, scientists reported their findings after exhuming victims of the Great Plague in London where, during a period of weeks, six in every ten people died of the bubonic plague. Archaeologists found that it came after weather changes had made food scarce, and plague victims' bones showed they were suffering from severe malnutrition. Malnutrition causes epidemics; malnutrition enables viruses and bacterins to create harm. It was malnutrition that allowed bubonic plague to see over half the population of London off.

In another example, malnutrition was assessed in relation to whooping cough in the UK. Mathematical modelling showed that epidemics were driven by seasonal weather conditions and increases in wheat prices. These two factors predicted the force of infection and the number of people who died. The same authors found a correlation between malnutrition, population size, weather, and measles epidemics. [10,11]

Another paper states: "Infection and malnutrition have always been intricately linked. Malnutrition is the primary cause of immunodeficiency worldwide ... There is a strong relationship between malnutrition and infection and infant mortality, because poor nutrition leaves children underweight, weakened, and vulnerable to infections, primarily because of epithelial integrity and inflammation." Essentially, without proper nutrition, specifically vitamin A, the body's digestive and mucosal barriers are impaired, leading to inflammation and infection. [12]

A Cochrane review found that vitamin A megadoses lowered the number of deaths from measles in hospitalised children under the age of 2 years. A later Cochrane review found that vitamin A supplements actually reduced the incidence of measles in healthy children aged 6 months to 5 years. [13]

Another paper showed that zinc increases the competence of the immune system, producing a greatly enhanced response to infection. [14]

The risk of children suffering from flu can be reduced by 50% if they take vitamin D, doctors in Japan found. Vitamin D, which is naturally produced by the human body when exposed to direct sunlight, has no significant side effects, costs little and can be several times more effective than anti-viral drugs or vaccines. [15]

Another journal argues that it's possible that selenium deficiency may foster viral replication, possibly triggering outbreaks of Ebola, in this case, and perhaps even facilitating the emergence of more virulent viral strains. [16]

In 1968, the World Health Organization published "Interactions of Nutrition and Infection," which suggested that the relationship between infection and malnutrition was a synergistic one. [17] The Copenhagen Consensus project on hunger and malnutrition even suggested that "efforts to provide vitamin A, iron, iodine, and zinc generate higher returns than do trade liberalization or malaria, water, and sanitation programs." [18]

Farmer Dick Roper proved the nutrition point with his dairy herd, reported before the UK launched itself into a massive badger killing spree. For almost a decade, Mr Roper had been leaving cakes made from sugary molasses laced with supplements, including high doses of selenium, near the badgers' setts on his land as a way of keeping their immune systems in prime condition.

"Everything I read pointed to the trace element selenium being the solution," Roper said, "so I decided to make cakes of molasses with the highest dose of selenium permitted. I got Ministry permission and started leaving my cakes outside the setts in the woods. This has worked for nearly a decade in a TB hot spot but I can't understand why Defra has not done more research into my theory... I don't believe badgers have to be shot."

The Badger Trust and Soil Association also called for research. The Soil Association said: "We back Dick Roper's call for more research into the effects he has discovered. It is a health strategy which would be far preferable to culling." Defra declined to comment. [19]

See also references 20, 21 and 22.

There is also another way of looking at infections: having childhood infections is thought to *protect* from illnesses later [23].

Dr Viera Scheibner takes it further, asserting that childhood infections reduce the risk of developing serious diseases such as cancer and leukaemia in adulthood – these infections are protective [24].

This makes sense when you realise – on the simplest of levels – that cancers are associated with inflammation. Childhood infections mature the type 1 response, whereas vaccines tip us into type 2 responses. Type 2 responses are inflammatory responses, and cancer and inflammation are bedfellows.

A groundbreaking study published in *Nature* also challenges assumptions about viruses. The paper, "An enteric virus can replace the beneficial function of commensal bacteria," [25] asserts that despite the commonly held belief that viruses are vectors of morbidity and mortality that must be vaccinated against in order to save us from inevitable harm and death, a growing body of research shows that our own genome is 80% viral in origin. The new findings present evidence that viruses in the gastrointestinal tract can help maintain health and heal a damaged gut – and the gut houses 80% of the immune system. The authors conclude that viral infection of the gut may be helpful once antibiotic treatment has wiped out intestinal bacteria.

Ken Cadwell, PhD, stated: "Consistent with the 'hygiene hypothesis,' natural infections during childhood and onward, may prime our immune system and help to balance the Th1 (innate) and Th2 (adaptive) poles of immunity, producing a healthy immune system as a result. Vaccines, by disrupting this evolutionarily determined balance, may be contributing to widespread immune dysregulation, both suppressing innate immune mechanisms as well as over-stimulating the adaptive pole, contributing to widespread autoimmunity in exposed populations … we are left with a crucial question: is the present-day globally orchestrated vaccine agenda really improving health, or does it belie a hubris that shirks the scientific evidence in favor of an agenda that wishes to exert control over the human body due to economic and socio-political agendas?"

Similarly, AW Taylor-Robinson from the University of Leeds, wrote in *Allergy* [26]: "Multiple vaccinations shift this delicate balance [between Th1 and Th2], favoring the development of atopy [atopy is a syndrome characterised by a tendency to be "hyperallergic"] and, perhaps, autoimmunity through vaccine-induced polyclonal activation leading to autoantibody production. An increase in the incidence of childhood atopic diseases may be expected as a result of concurrent vaccination strategies that induce a Th2-biased immune response. What should be discussed is whether the prize of a reduction of common infectious diseases through a policy of mass vaccination from birth is worth the price of a higher prevalence of atopy."

Agricultural Development is one of the largest initiatives of the Bill and Melinda Gates Foundation. Their website says that to date, the charity has committed more than US$2 billion to agricultural development efforts, primarily in Sub-Saharan Africa and South Asia. The emphasis appears to be upon increasing farm productivity, using 'better' seeds and getting produce to market. I wondered if this meant GMOs, and it turns out that it does. News reports [27,28] confirm that the Gates Foundation has been criticised for getting into bed with Monsanto and agribusiness commodity giant Cargill. The foundation bought 500,000 Monsanto shares worth around $23 million:

Agra Watch – a project of the Community Alliance for Global Justice – was outraged. "Monsanto has a history of blatant disregard for the interests and wellbeing of small farmers around the world... [This] casts serious doubt on the foundation's heavy funding of agricultural development in Africa," it thundered.

"But it got worse. South Africa-based watchdog, African Centre for Biosafety, then found that the foundation was teaming up with Cargill in a $10m project to "develop the soya value chain" in Mozambique and elsewhere. Who knows what this corporate-speak really means, but in all probability it heralds the big time introduction of GM soya in southern Africa.

"The fact is that Cargill is a faceless agri-giant that controls most of the world's food commodities and Monsanto has been blundering around poor Asian countries for a decade giving itself and the US a lousy name for corporate bullying." [27]

Obviously, one of the richest men in the world is entitled to disagree with me, and may even know more than me, but it seems to me that spending $2 billion on 'improving' the food situation with GMOs is questionable and questioned, but he's spent a considerable amount on vaccines where malnutrition is rife. Malnutrition can make vaccines dangerous.

According to UNICEF [29] "More than 30 per cent of children in developing countries – about 600 million – live on less than US $1 a day. Every 3.6 seconds one person dies of starvation. Usually it is a child under the age of five. Some 300 million children go to bed hungry every day... More than 90 per cent are suffering long-term malnourishment and micronutrient deficiency.

"The best start in life is critical in a child's first few years, not only to survival but to her or his physical, intellectual and emotional development. So these deprivations greatly hamper children's ability to achieve their full potential, contributing to a society's cycle of endless poverty and hunger."

Maximising one's investments in the face of this, well, what can I say?

But it goes further. According to F William Engdahl, writing in the on-line GlobalResearch site, Gates has teamed up with such luminaries as the Rockefeller Foundation, Monsanto Corporation, Syngenta Foundation and the Government of Norway, among others, to invest tens of his millions in what is called the 'doomsday seed bank.' Engdahl concludes: "Time will tell whether, God Forbid, the Svalbard Doomsday Seed Bank of Bill Gates and the Rockefeller Foundation is part of another Final Solution, this involving the extinction of the Late, Great Planet Earth." [30]

Chapter 56
Oligarchy and philanthropy – or exploitation?

According to Global Health Watch [1] "For some, Microsoft is one of the great success stories of modern-day business and Bill Gates's subsequent philanthropy an exemplar of generosity and humanity.

"But there is a need to look at philanthropy more critically. The lack of examination of how wealth is created can perpetuate the myth that scarcity, rather than inequality, is at the root of much persisting social and economic problems and nurtures a culture of noblesse oblige for the wealthy and privileged to help the less fortunate. Neither does it help address the implications of conceding such power to the wealthy.

"Furthermore, in many countries, philanthropy is a way for the rich to avoid paying tax. In the US, it is estimated that 45 per cent of the $500 billion that foundations hold actually 'belongs to the American public' in the sense that this is money forgone by the state through tax exemptions (Dowie 2002). Similarly, corporate social responsibility programmes can distract public attention away from the lowering of corporate tax rates across the world and the avoidance of tax by the rich."

A 2009 *Lancet* article [2] looked into Gates Foundation spending: "The Gates Foundation funds a wide range of contributors to global health, extending from UN agencies to global health partnerships, the World Bank, universities, and non-profit and non-governmental organisations. All the key contributors to global health have an association with the Gates Foundation through some sort of funding arrangement. Coupled with the large amount of money involved, these relations give the foundation a great degree of influence over both the architecture and policy agenda of global health. Through its funding of non-governmental organisations and policy think tanks, the foundation also confers power and influence on a selected number of organisations and in doing so, establishes some leverage over the voice of civil society.

"These observations are pertinent because the Gates Foundation is not a passive donor. The foundation actively engages in policy making and agenda setting activities; it has representatives that sit on the governing structures of many global health partnerships; it is part of a self-appointed group of global health leaders known as the H8 (together with WHO, the World Bank, GAVI Alliance, the Global Fund, UNICEF, the United Nations

Population Fund [UNFPA], and UNAIDS); and has been involved in setting the health agenda for the G8. The Gates Foundation is also involved in setting the research agenda of several public health priorities, a role that was controversially criticised by the former head of WHO's malaria programme, who complained that the dominance of the Gates Foundation in malaria research risked stifling the diversity of views among scientists.

"The finding that one organisation, PATH, was awarded nearly $1 billion stands out and raises the question as to whether some organisations might be better characterised as agents of the foundation rather than as independent grantees.

"... most of the high child mortality in poor countries results from an underlying lack of access to basic needs such as food, housing, water, and safe employment. Thus, rather than viewing the hundreds of thousands of child deaths from rotavirus infection as a clinical problem that needs a vaccine solution, a better approach might be to view it as a public health problem that needs a social, economic, or political intervention to ensure universal access to clean water and sanitation.".

The article continues, "Research by Devi Sridhar at Oxford University warns that philanthropic interventions are 'radically skewing public health programmes towards issues of the greatest concern to wealthy donors'. 'Issues,' she writes, 'which are not necessarily top priority for people in the recipient country.'

"Parallels may be drawn between the inequalities of today and the Victorian era, when health provision for the poor depended on the largesse of the rich. Oscar Wilde observed of the philanthropists of that era: 'They seriously and very sentimentally set themselves to the task of remedying the evils that they see in poverty, but their remedies do not cure the disease: they merely prolong it.' Then and now, as Wilde said, 'the proper aim is to try and reconstruct society on such a basis that poverty will be impossible.'"

There have also been rumblings that the foundation's attempts to help poor farmers won't actually help them [3]. "Who ends up in control? Is it the farmer or some big agri-firm like Monsanto?" The Guardian [4] also asked, "The Bill and Melinda Gates Foundation's investments in Monsanto and Cargill have come under heavy criticism. Is it time for the foundation to come clean on its visions for agriculture in developing countries?"

But who is Gates actually trying to help? A 2012 article in *New Internationalist* [5] stated: "Microsoft lobbied vociferously for the World Trade Organization's TRIPS agreement (the agreement on trade-related aspects of intellectual property), which obliges member countries to defend patents for a minimum of 20 years after the filing date. As recently as 2007, Microsoft was lobbying the G8 to tighten global intellectual property (IP) protection, a move that would, Oxfam said, 'worsen the health crisis in developing countries'." This essentially means that Gates is accused of protecting the interests of Big Pharm above the health of the poor people his foundation states it is here to help.

Importantly, the Gates Foundation has been criticised for investing assets to exclusively maximise the return on investment. As a result, its investments include companies that have been criticised for worsening poverty in the same countries where the foundation is attempting to relieve poverty. [6, 7] In 2002, the Wall Street Journal informed us that the Bill and Melinda Gates Foundation had purchased shares in nine big pharmaceutical companies valued at nearly $205 million -- an investment likely to attract attention more for its symbolism than its size [8]

The 2007 *Los Angeles Times* investigation [9] found that the charity, via its trust, invests in "companies that contribute to the human suffering in health, housing and social welfare that the foundation is trying to alleviate". The foundation didn't challenge the thrust of the article, which included allegations that it invested in an oil company responsible for causing health problems by burning off its unwanted gas in an African country in which the foundation was active in trying to improve the population's health. But the charity decided after a brief review not to change its investment policy. Critics have suggested that Gates' approach to Global Health and Agriculture favours the interests of large pharmaceutical and agribusiness companies (in which Gates invests) over the interests of the people of developing countries.

The Lancet [2] stated, "The research funding of the Foundation is heavily weighted towards the development of new vaccines and drugs, much of it high risk and even if successful likely to take at least the 20 years which Gates has targeted for halving child mortality." This implies, at best, that the foundation seeks to develop better vaccines, in the meantime promoting the dangerous ones so they can be trialled or assessed in the bodies of an unsuspecting public.

Is the foundation using human beings as guinea pigs? There are commentators saying they are.

Global Research.ca [10] states: "Heavily invested in Big Pharma, the Gates Foundation is well positioned to facilitate pharmaceutical R&D strategies tailored to the realities of the developing world, where '[t]o speed the translation of scientific discovery into implementable solutions, we seek better ways to evaluate and refine potential interventions—such as vaccine candidates—before they enter costly and time-consuming clinical trials.' In plain language, BMGF promises to assist Big Pharma in its efforts to circumvent Western regulatory regimes by sponsoring cut-rate drug trials in the developing world.

"Africa soon experienced an "unprecedented increase in health research involving humans" who were typically "poverty-stricken and poorly educated"; the results were predictably lethal. In 2010 the Gates Foundation funded a Phase III trial of a malaria vaccine developed by GlaxoSmithKline (GSK), administering the experimental treatment to thousands of infants across seven African countries. Eager to secure the WHO approval necessary to license the vaccine for global distribution, GSK and BMGF declared the trials a smashing success, and the popular press uncritically reproduced the publicity. Few bothered to look closely at the study's fine print, which revealed that the trials resulted in 151 deaths and caused "serious adverse effects" (e.g., paralysis, seizures, febrile convulsions) in 1048 of 5949 children aged 5-17 months.

"Similar stories emerged in the wake of the Gates-funded MenAfriVac campaign in Chad, where unconfirmed reports alleged that 50 of 500 children forcibly vaccinated for meningitis later developed paralysis. Citing additional abuses, a South African newspaper declared: "We are guinea pigs for the drugmakers."

The implications for lower vaccine costs aren't positive, either: "The hope that GAVI's funding of vaccines would push down their prices has been belied. One review found that prices actually went up after GAVI funding, meaning that the higher costs are borne by poor nations when GAVI funding is withdrawn. Entering into advance commitments to market this vaccine in developing countries allows GAVI to divert Gates Foundation money to vaccine manufacturers, without providing commensurate benefits to the children it is supposed to help." [11]

According to the writer and activist Ruben Rosenberg Colorni [12]: "The Bill and Melinda Gates 'Foundation' is essentially a huge tax-avoidance scheme for enormously-wealthy capitalists who have made billions from exploiting the world's people. The Foundation invests, tax free, money from Gates and the 'donations' from others, in the very companies in which Gates owns millions in stocks, thus guaranteeing returns through both sales as well as intellectual-property rights."

You then have to ask whether this is philanthropy, or exploitation?

It seems that, since Oliver died, I have been living in the observation space between power and impotence, and I've concluded that the human race desperately needs to address the problems associated with too much power versus too little power.

'Scientists' often withhold information from the general public, possibly because they believe it's in our best interests. Yet in the absence of rigorous, independent, scientific information – and an informed public –

decision-making becomes an exercise in upholding the preferences of those in power. In most of the developed world, power has become increasingly concentrated in fewer hands – hands which are inevitably attached to personal wealth, big business, and the state. This is something we all need to be seriously concerned about.

People believe that they live in a democracy, but we are sailing fast towards oligarchy, which is a form of government in which all power is vested in a few people or in a dominant class or clique. This is becoming a government ruled by the rich rather than anyone we may have democratically voted for. This money enables individuals with whatever motivation to influence the lives of others; money with which to control people's lives and the way they behave. With the media increasingly reluctant to publish dissenting facts – truth – about vaccine damage or anything else that threatens to disrupt corporate profit, billionaires (who also tend to own the media) have the power to control what you even think.

But what if their motivation is to reduce the population – to kill off the weak and ill-educated? To kill off the troublesome poor? What if your child is an inconvenience; a blot on the statistics?

And what if they want to keep information from you so you do as you are told; and they want to spy on you and use their wealth to 'counteract' what they mistakenly assert to be untrue?

What if someone with billions of dollars thinks he's right when he's actually wrong, and has the power to open your front door and put his hand in your house, and change the whole landscape of your world?

And what if the billionaire's motivation is merely to make himself richer at the expense of others, or thinks your life is so inconsequential that you should be used in his experiments?

We cannot claim that we know the answers to any of the above questions. But we have a right to ask them, and we have a right to care about each other and our collective fate. I am personally not sure that one person, or an elite group, whose elitism is based upon how much money they have, has the right to dictate whether you live or die without including you in the decision-making process.

Just because someone is rich and therefore powerful, it doesn't give them the moral right to embark upon a programme that affects the lives of others without those others having a right to understand – fully, without censorship – what is being offered to them in the name of philanthropy. Nor does it give anyone the right to walk away from the carnage they have caused. Kill someone with a gun and you go to jail. Kill someone with a vaccine, and no-one seems to act or even care. They just seem to count the numbers and turn away.

Chapter 57
Another synchronous meeting

An email arrived in my inbox from an America travel firm that was putting on a cruise to the Caribbean for dog lovers. They wanted to know if I was interested in being a lecturer on the cruise, and offered to fly me and Rob to Florida and put us up in one of the luxury cabins on the ship. It sounded like a horrible job, but somebody had to do it (said with irony of course).

During one of my lectures on the ship, a couple were sitting in the audience and laughing so much that I actually stopped to ask them why. It turned out that they were Dr and Mrs William R La Rosa of the Hayward Foundation. I felt very honoured to meet this couple – the work they sponsored is of huge importance. I was even putting slides up about the research they sponsored, and they were thankfully laughing in agreement with me. What kismet that we should meet.

The Hayward Foundation wanted to know if vaccines caused autoimmune disease in humans, and since humans cannot allegedly be experimented upon (although the vaccine industry has a long history of testing their vaccines on ethnic minorities, the poor, the disabled, orphans and the military), they asked Purdue University to conduct the research on dogs.

The research showed that vaccinated dogs – but not non-vaccinated dogs – had developed autoantibodies to a large range of their own biochemicals. Long before I met William La Rosa I wanted to understand the implication of these autoantibodies, so I looked them up. This merely meant typing in the name of the antibody alongside the word 'function'. I subsequently wrote an article that was published in *Nexus* magazine, an extract of which appears below. This information, incidentally was published in *Journal of the American Holistic Veterinary Medical Association* (JAHVMA), Volume 46, Spring Issue, 2017, and made up a page of the article. When I asked its author, PJ Broadfoot DVM, why she hadn't credited my work, she replied: "If some form of that article ever gets published for the general public, I would be happy to acknowledge your contributions to the data!" You see, it's not the done thing to give credit to your work unless you're one of them.

A team at Purdue University School of Veterinary Medicine conducted several studies to determine if vaccines can cause changes in the immune system of dogs that might lead to life-threatening immune-mediated diseases. They obviously conducted this research because concern already existed. It was sponsored by the Haywood Foundation which itself was looking for evidence that such changes in the human immune system might also be vaccine induced. It found the evidence.

The vaccinated, but not the non-vaccinated, dogs in the Purdue studies developed autoantibodies to many of their own biochemicals, including fibronectin, laminin, DNA, albumin, cytochrome C, cardiolipin and collagen.

This means that the vaccinated dogs – but not the non-vaccinated dogs – were attacking their own fibronectin, which is involved in tissue repair, cell multiplication and growth, and differentiation between tissues and organs in a living organism.

The vaccinated Purdue dogs also developed autoantibodies to laminin, which is involved in many cellular activities including the adhesion, spreading, differentiation, proliferation and movement of cells. Vaccines thus appear to be capable of removing the natural intelligence of cells.

Autoantibodies to cardiolipin are frequently found in patients with the serious disease systemic lupus erythematosus and also in individuals with other autoimmune diseases. The presence of elevated anti-cardiolipin antibodies is significantly associated with clots within the heart or blood vessels, in poor blood clotting, haemorrhage, bleeding into the skin, foetal loss and neurological conditions.

The Purdue study also found that vaccinated dogs were developing autoantibodies to their own collagen. About one quarter of all the protein in the body is collagen. Collagen provides structure to our bodies, protecting and supporting the softer tissues and connecting them with the skeleton. It is no wonder that Canine Health Concern's 1997 study of 4,000 dogs showed a high number of dogs developing mobility problems shortly after they were vaccinated (noted in my 1997 book, *What Vets Don't Tell You About Vaccines*).

Perhaps most worryingly, the Purdue studies found that the vaccinated dogs had developed autoantibodies to their own DNA. Did the alarm bells sound? Did the scientific community call a halt to the vaccination program? No. Instead, they stuck their fingers in the air, saying more research is needed to ascertain whether vaccines can cause genetic damage. Meanwhile, the study dogs were found good homes, but no long-term follow-up has been conducted.

Before publishing the results of my research, I got in touch with Larry Glickman at Purdue University who had led the Hayward-funded study. Our initial emails were cordial, until I sent Glickman my conclusions in relation to the implications of the presence of autoantibodies. He basically went ape-shit on me, ranting about dog owners who choose not to vaccinate. I considered his final email to be extremely hostile, and was disappointed that he hadn't – as I had hoped – either endorsed my conclusions or given me the science to disprove them. I sighed and left it at that.

The article, named 'The Science of Vaccine Damage', soon circulated around the internet, attracting a great deal of attention.

Meanwhile, William R. La Rosa wrote 'A Possible Etiology of Autoimmune Diseases' [1], saying: "The vaccinated group developed significant levels of autoantibodies against: fibronectin, laminin, DNA, albumin, Cytochrome C, transferrin, cardiolipin, collagen. The responses varied among individual animals, probably reflecting genetic differences. The clinical significance of those autoantibodies remains to be determined, but speculation must be that something in the vaccines is one of the etiologies (in the genetically susceptible dog) of such diseases as Cardiomyopathy, Lupus Erythematosus, Glomerulonephritis., etc. …

"Autoimmune diseases in dogs are clinically similar to those in humans. We hope that Veterinary and Medical Schools will continue and expand these preliminary research studies. Our companion dogs are crashing all around us and maybe we are now finding one of the sources of the problems. It has been so easy to point fingers at breeders but they may not be entirely at fault. Let us continue this important research to help our future generations of dogs and possibly children. Yes, indiscriminate breeding can genetically predispose the dog but is the trigger mechanism indiscriminate vaccinations?"

Take a look at the Appendix for research relating to autoantibodies and autoimmunity. It's pretty clear that vaccine-induced autoantibodies are bad news.

Chapter 58
Annual Unnecessary Vaccination Month

During 2008, we became concerned that Intervet, supported by the PDSA animal charity, was plugging annual vaccines for dogs and cats through a high-profile TV and press marketing campaign. Vets in the UK became part of the sales force, and many of their promotional stories – talking about death and disease if people don't give their pets shots – appeared in local newspapers. I wondered if these stories were the result of a press release template provided to vets by Intervet, which would be standard public relations practice.

The promotion was a 'bogof' (buy one get one free), and the story was that if a dog or cat's shots had 'lapsed' by 18 months, then owners could get their friends a *full puppy or kitten series* for the price of a booster – which means that vets and the veterinary vaccine industry either don't understand the science, or don't care about the science.

There is no science to support giving adult dogs or cats a series of shots – you only need one, and only then if the animal hasn't already developed immunity. So the bogof was redundant, except that it made people think they were getting something their pets needed (but didn't need) for a bargain basement price. It also increases the risk.

Why do puppies and kittens get a series of shots? Because maternal immunity from mother's first milk destroys viruses, rendering vaccines ineffective. Vaccines only work when maternal immunity has waned, and since no-one knows when maternal immunity wanes in a particular puppy, a series is given in the hope that it might eventually have waned before the last puppy shot. None of this applies to adult animals.

There is of course the issue of the leptospirosis vaccine. Lepto is a bacterium with around two hundred strains or 'serovars' and protection from the vaccine is short-lived and incomplete. This means that if you want partial protection, then you need to boost annually or even more frequently. However, the WSAVA says that it is a 'non-core' or optional vaccine. This means it should only be used if a *significant* disease threat exists. Lepto is rare in most parts of the world, including the UK, and it's the vaccine most associated with severe adverse reactions. Frankly, many think it's a pretty bad vaccine looking for a market.

More recently, MSD (which now owns Intervet) has come up with a lepto vaccine containing four rather than two of the serovars, and vets are putting out local press stories to say that the old vaccine didn't work –

which they didn't think to tell us before the new one arrived. One on-line article (now taken down) quoted a vet saying that eight of the nine dogs in the area who got lepto had been vaccinated against it and dogs need to come in for the *new* shot due to 'epidemics' in the area. However, seeing what I have seen, I would actually query any alleged epidemic.

Ronald Schultz, arguably the world's most eminent independent expert, said:

"We have seen very few cases of leptospirosis at the University of Wisconsin Veterinary Medical Teaching Hospital during the past 10 years, even though the Midwest is an endemic area. The cases seen have been associated with serovars present in the vaccines as well as other serovars, and they occurred in dogs that had been vaccinated annually, and in some cases the most recent vaccinations had been given less than six months before disease.

"Because of the generally poor efficacy, routine use of leptospira bacterins cannot be recommended. To be protective for the two serovars present, a vaccine would need to be given every four to six months. However, this is not recommended because of concern of hypersensitivity (types I and III) reactions. This is clearly a product that needs to be improved before it should be recommended for routine use in all dogs."

The on-line *Merck Veterinary Manual* [1] states:

"Vaccination is not always an innocuous procedure; adverse effects can and do occur. Therefore, all vaccination must be governed by the principle of informed consent. The risks of vaccination must not exceed those caused by the disease itself."

Informed consent means that those receiving the vaccine, or paying or giving consent on behalf of someone else, must be informed of possible adverse reactions and agree to them. MSD (Merck) is not – I suspect – informing pet owners of the potential outcomes of their new four-way lepto vaccine. Further, vets and the vaccine industry are buying the line that lepto is endemic in the UK when no data has been presented to show that it is a *significant* risk exceeding the vaccine risk.

In fact after some national newspaper coverage generated by grieving owners of vaccine-damaged dogs, the British VMD reluctantly admitted that 120 dogs had been killed by MSD's lepto 4 vaccine, and some 2,000 had suffered adverse reactions. [2]

Then in 2017, the VMD issued a press statement [3] saying: "… the VMD has received fewer than two adverse reactions for L2, and fewer than seven for L4, for every 10,000 doses sold. This includes every suspected adverse event reported – even cases that were considered unclassifiable or were later found to be unrelated to the vaccine."

We are none the wiser. How many dogs have died? How many vaccines had been sold?

So … if seven in 10,000 dogs react to the L4 jab, and 3 million dogs are vaccinated against it in the UK, this means 2,100 adverse reactions. This is almost ten times higher than the number of dogs who allegedly contract leptospirosis in the UK according to MSD's own CICADA survey figures. The risk:benefit ratio just doesn't stand up. And why did the VMD release the figures as percentages? So we wouldn't work it out?

Type I reactions, which the WSAVA relates to lepto vaccines, involve acute anaphylactic shock, where the individual can die very swiftly. Type III hypersensitivity reactions, also associated with lepto shots, can lead to autoimmune conditions such as Lupus, arthritis, and pemphigus.

Why, you might ask, is Intervet (now MSD) free to promote biological products when they are arguably unnecessary and potentially harmful? How is it that they are allowed to place advertisements in the press and on TV, warning of dire consequences if their products aren't used annually? Where is the legislation to protect consumers from purchasing products that are unnecessary and associated with risk?

So in 2008, I sent a letter to the Advertising Standards Authority (ASA) explaining why the Intervet campaign, in our view, fell foul of the ASA Code of Practice. I also sent references and scientific papers to show that veterinary bodies around the world do not support annual shots for the core diseases, and that duration of immunity studies show they aren't necessary.

According to the ASA, advertisements should be legal, decent, honest and truthful. Their Code of Conduct states: "If there is a significant division of informed opinion about any claims made in a marketing communication they should not be portrayed as generally agreed.

"No marketing communication should cause fear or distress without good reason. Marketers should not use shocking claims or images merely to attract attention. Promoters should make all reasonable efforts to ensure that their promotions, including product samples, are safe and cause no harm to consumers or their property.

"Literature accompanying promotional items should give any necessary warnings and any appropriate safety advice. Marketing communications should not condone or encourage unsafe practices."

I felt certain that if the ASA were to read the information and science supplied with my letter, and if they were in a position to make decisions that were unbiased by politics or commerce, then they would have to rule that the Intervet advertising campaign fell foul of its code of conduct.

Before letting me have their ruling, the ASA contacted me to ask if we were planning any legal action. Why they might ask this is not clear.

The ASA did not uphold the CHC complaint. We received, instead, a letter saying:

"We have reviewed the advertisements but I should state from the outset that we will not be taking further action on this occasion.

"The advertisements state that advertisers are offering vaccination for those animals whose vaccinations have lapsed. We believe that most readers and viewers are likely to understand that there might be a risk of reduced protection from diseases if vaccinations have lapsed."

But the core vaccines hadn't 'lapsed'. Dogs simply don't just lose immunity to the core diseases at an arbitrary 18-month milestone. I had made this clear to the ASA – with references.

The ASA calls itself independent, but it is a body funded by the advertising industry, which benefits financially from major corporate clients such as MSD and the wealthy pharmaceutical industry in general.

The ASA stated: "I understand your concerns that the advertisement fails to warn consumers that there are risks associated with vaccinations. However, we consider that such information is not necessary to be included in the advertisements. We believe that most consumers are likely to understand that there are risks association with vaccinations because of what they are. As such, we consider that the omission of such information is unlikely to mislead consumers as to the dangers of vaccinations."

The ASA clearly wasn't referring to the sort of consumers who contact CHC with depressing regularity after their dogs become ill or die from unnecessary annual shots. Naturally, we were somewhat astonished by the ASA's response. Or am I being disingenuous? Was I really astonished? No, not really.

You see, we had already contacted most of the official bodies that are there to protect consumers and their dogs. We've had dealings with the VMD over the years, but their remit seems to be more about making multi-nationals richer and happier than protecting consumers and their pets. We've been in touch with veterinary colleges, but of course colleges frequently enjoy funding from pharmaceutical and pet food companies.

We've had correspondence with veterinary bodies in the UK – but for reasons we can only speculate about, they're still supporting annual jabs or doing a Pontius Pilate on the matter ("it is up to the veterinary surgeon to decide...").

We've written to many of the large animal charities, sharing the science about annual vaccination, and the potential adverse effects – but they were still putting out literature to persuade pet owners to vaccinate annually... and some of them even joined forces with Intervet to help them with their annual Unnecessary Vaccination Month. And the law, it seems, doesn't currently make it mandatory for charities to fess up to who is throwing money at them.

We've lobbied our MPs over the years, and asked for independence from the 'experts' our governments choose when setting policies. But governments, it seems, don't appear to think there's any problem that vaccine industry consultants, or people benefiting from research funding from the vaccine industry, should recommend annual vaccination whilst posing as independent experts.

I copied my MP in with all the correspondence between myself and the ASA. He replied that the situation sounded very disturbing, and passed my letter on to Hilary Benn, who passed the matter on to Jeff Rooker MP, Minister for Sustainable Farming and Food, and Animal Welfare.

Mr Rooker wrote back, saying that the Veterinary Medicines Directorate is responsible for ensuring the safety, quality and efficacy of veterinary medicines used in the United Kingdom, blah blah blah. All authorised dog and cat vaccines on the UK market have been manufactured to an acceptable quality, blah blah blah.

And then he pulled a diseased old rabbit from a dirty old hat, and referred to the VPC Working Group on Feline and Canine Vaccination. Perhaps you'll remember this? It's the guidelines written by two vaccine industry consultants/research funding recipients/shareholders and a member of a 'veterinary defence' organisation – which of course backed annual vaccination.

And so it is that it is still legal and acceptable for corporations and vets to take your money and promote products that aren't necessary or very effective, and which are potentially harmful. Simply because the people with the power and the wealth say it's OK – despite the science, and despite the morality of such actions.

Intervet subsequently scaled down the marketing of its annual sales binge; TV advertisements have disappeared for now. But the dragon is not dead: if you're a sucker or ill-informed, you can still be persuaded to pay to subject your adult dog to a full and unnecessary puppy series – risking their wellbeing and life at the same time.

In February 2015, I received a letter in the post from my vet, headed 'Vaccine Amnesty'. This offered my dogs a complete 'two shot' booster against parvovirus, parainfluenza, distemper, hepatitis and leptospirosis. I could get a second two weeks after the first, free of charge. Yet there is no science to support giving adult dogs a full cocktail booster or a second two weeks later because, once immunised against parvo, distemper and hepatitis, they remain immune for years or life. There is, however, science to suggest that it can be harmful to give this series. So my vets, and the vaccine company, either misunderstand the science or they are lying to me in order to gain financially from my potential ignorance.

I would add that the vaccine company behind this unnecessary vaccine campaign is Intervet/MSD – otherwise known as Merck, and the campaign appears to go against its own guidelines. This is the same Merck that has put, in its Veterinary Manual, "Vaccination is not always an innocuous procedure; adverse effects can and do occur. Therefore, all vaccination must be governed by the principle of informed consent. The risks of vaccination must not exceed those caused by the disease itself." [1]

Chapter 59
Dinners of misinformation

One day, about fourteen years into the CHC campaign to end over-vaccination, I received an email from the vet Patricia Jordan. She had seen my Science of Vaccine Damage article, published in *Nexus* magazine, and told me it had a profound effect on her. Patricia gets angry when people use the 'you're not a vet' card on me, saying I am a better scientist than most of them – which endears her to me greatly, of course.

We featured an interview with Patricia in our April 2009 CHC newsletter, heralding the arrival of her extensively-researched book on vaccination, *The Mark of the Beast*. Patricia Jordan has literally sacrificed her life and her career to help the animals and redeem the veterinary profession. Whilst at college, Patricia noticed that there were a lot of corporate sponsors.

"Coming through as wide-eyed senior students," she said, "the only book we ever got on nutrition was from Hills 'Science' and of course the teaching hospital was stocked with free inventory from Hills. Therefore all I learned about nutrition was the Hills propaganda. The college was also stocked with free vaccines. We got nothing but propaganda when you think of it."

Dr Jordan is particularly concerned with what she calls 'dinners of misinformation' – so-called continuing education for vets in practice. "Pure hogwash at the vaccine industry dinner I attended, pushing their latest feline vaccines and providing junk science that's really propaganda. I have attended plenty of them and can only say that I have documented with photos, tape recordings and video footage that these programs are about conflict information, propaganda and seducing veterinarians into pushing their drugs and vaccines.

"To see this on a much broader scale all you have to do is attend the national meetings, which I stopped after nine years of that nonsense. It is criminal that any professional can get credit for attending that dribble – and that propaganda is the only continuing education most professionals receive.

"Also, we would get scholarships, textbooks, equipment, free poison for our own pets, clothes, trips, prizes. When one calculates the heavy toll that propaganda has ... even the free publications that disguise themselves as legitimate research articles, it's a cycle of professional deception worse than the unrecognised and unacknowledged adverse effects of those wares."

Once in practice, Patricia became even more disillusioned. "By the time I had been in practice for seven years I knew that western medicine not only didn't work, but that it was responsible for making more disease and more death. I found it de-constructed health rather than built health.

"I had never associated the benefits of over administration of vaccines, so my patients did not have the serious amount of disease that I saw coming from practices that embraced the full potential of aggressive 'preventative health' measures based on western medicine.

"The practice I worked for in Massachusetts not only supported over vaccination, and with the most highly adverse vaccines available, but they verbally chastised me for spending any time talking to clients about their pets' diets, preferring instead to push whatever they'd overstocked. The experience was so traumatizing; it was my first experience with money doctors or business veterinarians that are so prevalent in our profession.

" My awakening came in 1989 when I saw with my own eyes, a veterinarian purposely causing disease with the use of vaccines and drugs. He had used a hormone therapy in a cat and then charged for working up the mammary problem it caused. I questioned him on this and he yelled at me. I finally witnessed him strangle a pet to death and through all of this, I realized that there was a very ugly truth in veterinary medicine.

"There were those who used these drugs and vaccines knowing that they would generate more and more money for them through the propagation of more medical problems. So I stopped working for that business vet and opened up my own practice. I didn't know how bad the problem had become until I found myself working once again for another business veterinarian. I am still traumatized.

"Sadly, I felt betrayed for, ironically, the veterinary profession is known as "the other family doctor" and "the compassionate profession". I suppose I aged a lifetime when I realised this. I also felt more alone than ever.

"When I saw animals that were aggressively over vaccinated yearly and saw their health destroyed by the time they were four or five, I knew it was the immune system's reaction to these yearly assaults that was the link to the diseases – autoimmune disease, cancer, so much chronic disease when they were aggressively administering vaccines, drugs, poisons and toxins.

"I realised that everything – the demodex we treat, the fungal infections we treat, the parasites, and most of the infectious diseases – all were in actuality coming from the adverse results of vaccinations.

"I mean, you vaccinate a puppy into immunosuppression and then they break out with disease. The T cells fall out from the vaccines and then you get demodex, parasites, fungal infections. Once I saw what was happening in those patients, it wasn't hard to track the road of pathology. Looking into the research, it's all there – cancer from vaccines is not exclusive to cats and fibrosarcoma. Vaccines are full of genetic mutators and carcinogens and protein sequences that are causing Lyme Disease Syndrome etc. Also, I could see, once the veil was removed, just how hard our profession works to "not see" any effect of what our very own hands have done.

"Once enlightened, I tracked down the research and I found it. I have almost 250GB of it, from not only veterinary research but also in human research papers. I now understand how much better humans are than dogs and cats at deflecting genetic transmutations and mutations (to a certain point).

"I realised the much greater assault on the animals undergoing yearly immune assaults from vaccines and then the poor quality of nutrition (which really is the foundation of good immunity). I then understood why the problems were so much more frequent in the animals."

Of her veterinary colleagues, Patricia says: "There is so much angst between conventional veterinarians and the truth. With truth comes responsibility and that's simply too much for most to bear. I mean, I have had conventional doctors tell me, "I am too old to learn anything new". I have heard them say, "I don't care, they can't make me stop," and the new vets, who are still under the delusion that there is only good intentions behind those who pushed their company's version of health into their faces, into their bank accounts, into their student loans, car payments, exalting their ego, and the list goes on and on and on … many can't see truth.

"I have to admit, I now have no tolerance for them, they can't face facts, and I can't stop finding the research that proves that medicine and vaccines and the poor foods are the bulk of the disease process. Once I realized that I was "working with the enemy", that they don't call it the medical mafia without reason, I even called the AVMA and they suggested that I find another job.

"I now see where health comes from. It comes from nutrition. It's probably no secret that veterinary and medical doctors get little to no nutrition training in school. I believe that this is because the pharmaceutical companies are set up for health de-construction, not health, and cause more disease. They change the face of disease but never treat the root of the disease. I was so surprised to find out that it was gene theory and certainly not germ theory that was the key to understanding health.

"I look for the day that, as Richard Pitcairn wrote in his paper, A Foolish Practice, that he predicted, 'in 50-100 years the idea of injecting disease to cure disease will be seen as dangerous as bloodletting and pure mercury administration'. In other words, the greatest medical assumption ever made will be looked back upon with shame and horror."

Chapter 60

Mind games

Some years after my Science of Vaccine Damage article went viral on the internet, in which I described the implications of autoantibodies discovered in vaccinated, but not unvaccinated dogs, someone wrote to Larry Glickman, the lead researcher of the group that found the antibodies, to ask for his comments on my conclusions (you may remember that I had asked him for his comments when I first wrote the article and he got mad at me but didn't discuss the science).

So years later, Larry wrote of me: "I think this is how some individuals deal with death or illness of a pet or child. They try to rationalize what happened by placing the blame on physicians or veterinarians rather than on the genetics or environmental factors. Many of Catherine O'Driscoll's conclusions make no sense to me, whether they relate to autoantibody production following vaccination of dogs or the need for Leptospirosis vaccination which she often challenges".

Once again, a scientist chose to get personal rather than engage in the science, and that's worrying because it obscures what is true.

Psychologically healthy people understand that it's impossible to truly know what another person is thinking or feeling unless you ask them. So let's pretend that Larry Glickman asked me about my thoughts and feelings and I told him what I thought and felt.

I would have told him something like this: It seems to me that it has to be wrong that dogs should die at the ages of four, five and six. I felt the need for reasons, which themselves would lead to solutions and prevent dogs, who are members of our families, from dying at unacceptably young ages in the future. Blame is a useless emotion. Reasons and solutions are more productive: they can lead to the end of suffering. Scientists seek answers to such questions – but I wouldn't call *every* scientist bitter, or infused with the need to blame.

Because Larry Glickman responded a few years after my article was written, in the absence of any scientific argument from him, I wondered if there was any more research available to provide clarification. If I'm wrong about something I'm more than willing to be corrected or, in the absence of help from the experts, to look for truth myself.

So I looked again. A quick internet search threw up a scholarly scientific book called *Autoantibodies* by Y Schoenfeld, ME Gershwin, and PL Meroni. [1] The authors wrote:

249

"Autoimmune diseases are characterized by the presence of auto-reactive lymphocytes in affected tissues and circulating autoantibodies, immunoglobulins reacting against self-antigens." In other words, the presence of autoantibodies is associated with autoimmune disease.

They added: "The mere detection of autoantibodies in an asymptomatic person or in an apparently healthy subject should not be neglected. It is now appreciated that autoantibodies may predict the eventual development of a full-blown autoimmunity, such as specific HLA, IgA and complement components deficiencies."

Another paper [2] explains how environmental cofactors can influence the expression of autoimmune disease.

The authors of *Autoantibodies* stated: "Involvement of autoantibodies in disease progression and complications, especially in the form of immunocomplexes, is widely accepted."

Therefore, if dogs in the Purdue study developed autoantibodies when they were vaccinated, but the non-vaccinated dogs didn't develop autoantibodies, it's clear that, given the 'right' cofactors, vaccines could trigger the progression of autoimmune disease. In other words, we are potentially injecting stealth disease.

The presence of thyroid autoantibodies before the onset of visible symptoms, for example, could predict the development of thyroid disease, according to Gershwin and Meroni.

A review article [3] in *In Practice*, Michael Day, senior lecturer in Veterinary Pathology at the University of Bristol, states that environmental influences are crucial to the expression of immune mediated disease and that the most important of these is likely to be exposure to microbial antigens following natural infection or *vaccination*. Mr Day divides immune mediated disease into four main groups – hypersensitivity diseases, autoimmune diseases, immune system neoplasia (the formation of tumours) and immunodeficiency diseases.

In a letter to *Veterinary Times* during July 1999, veterinarian Lyn Thomson responded, "This would indicate that veterinarians must consider and report the whole range of immune mediated diseases post vaccination, including flea allergy, atopic dermatitis, dietary hypersensitivity, contact hypersensitivity, asthma, autoimmune diseases, lymphoma, lymphoid leukaemia, multiple myeloma, plasmcytoma, histiiocytoma, thymoma [types of tumours], and immunodeficiency disease." The letter wasn't published, but it's worth thinking about!

It doesn't take long to find that scientists have asked the questions and found some answers relating to the presence of autoantibodies. Why did Glickman and his team not take the research to its important conclusion, or at least look up the many existing references to the presence of autoantibodies? Why did he get angry with me for highlighting the implications of vaccine-induced autoantibodies rather than discuss the science?

It's important to depersonalise it here. Larry Glickman is one of thousands of professors who conduct research within academic establishments, much of it funded by government and the pharmaceutical industry. As such, he's just following the accepted and normal pattern. But as he's crossed my path, it's worth treating Professor Glickman as a case study. With authority, after all, comes responsibility.

An on-line biography confirms that Larry Glickman has more than 300 published papers to his name. It is of course conceivable that I have got it wrong. I am not, after all, a trained scientist. But why would a trained scientist take the time to make personal remarks, rather than take the time to explain to me, scientifically, why I'm wrong – especially as he knows I'm out there sharing this information?

However, contrary to his comments about me, Glickman was quoted in DVM magazine [4] after a six-year study showed that rabies vaccines increase autoantibodies. The study monitored the effect of IMRAB-3, the most widely used rabies vaccine in the United States, on dogs.

"There's a whole host of autoimmune diseases out there," Glickman said. "Some think they're caused by environmental factors, maybe viruses. We think it's immunizations."

So whilst Larry was unable to agree with me directly, he was able to agree with me indirectly in a veterinary publication.

Scientists need research funding; without which they cannot progress their work. And research funding can be turned on and off like a tap by the governments and corporations that provide it, as well as the agenda-rich super-rich. Frankly, you'd have to be an idealist to bite the hands that feed you. Therefore scientists might agree with you, but it could be foolhardy to admit it. That's my conclusion, anyway. But, then, I am doing what I criticised Larry Glickman for doing: trying to guess his motivations.

According to Dr Marcia Angell in her book, *The Truth About Drug Companies* [5], "Over the past two decades the pharmaceutical industry has moved very far from its original high purpose of discovering and producing useful new drugs. Now primarily a marketing machine to sell drugs of dubious benefit, this industry uses its wealth and power to co-opt every institution that might stand in its way, including the US Congress, the FDA, academic medical centers, and the medical profession itself. (Most of its marketing efforts are focused on influencing doctors, since they must write the prescriptions.)"

And don't think that these tactics are limited to America – they are worldwide. Dr Angell continues:

"If prescription drugs were like ordinary consumer goods, all this might not matter very much. But drugs are different. People depend on them for their health and even their lives. People need to know that there are some checks and balances on this industry, so that its quest for profits doesn't push every other consideration aside. But there aren't such checks and balances."

In fact, the independent scientists and academics who we might have relied upon in the past to tell us the truth about pharma dangers are very unlikely to do so now.

Dr Angell explains: "Beginning in 1980, Congress enacted a series of laws designed to speed the translation of tax-supported basic research into useful new products – a process sometimes referred to as "technology transfer." The goal was also to improve the position of American-owned high-tech businesses in world markets.

"The Bayh-Dole law enabled universities and small businesses to patent discoveries emanating from research sponsored by the National Institutes of Health [an American government department], the major distributor of tax dollars for medical research, and then to grant exclusive licenses to drug companies. Until then, taxpayer-financed discoveries were in the public domain, available to any company that wanted to use them. But now universities, where most NIH-sponsored work is carried out, can patent and license their discoveries, and charge royalties. Similar legislation permitted the NIH itself to enter into deals with drug companies that would directly transfer NIH discoveries to industry.

"Bayh-Dole gave a tremendous boost to the nascent biotechnology industry, as well as to big pharma. Small biotech companies, many of them founded by university researchers to exploit their discoveries, proliferated rapidly. They now ring the major academic research institutions and often carry out the initial phases of drug development, hoping for lucrative deals with big drug companies that can market the new drugs. Usually both academic researchers and their institutions own equity in the biotechnology companies they are involved with. Thus, when a patent held by a university or a small biotech company is eventually licensed to a big drug company, all parties cash in on the public investment in research.

"These laws mean that drug companies no longer have to rely on their own research for new drugs, and few of the large ones do. Increasingly, they rely on academia, small biotech start-up companies, and the NIH for that. At least a third of drugs marketed by the major drug companies are now licensed from universities or small biotech companies, and these tend to be the most innovative ones. While Bayh-Dole was clearly a bonanza for big pharma and the biotech industry, whether its enactment was a net benefit to the public is arguable.

"The Reagan [and Thatcher] years and Bayh-Dole also transformed the ethos of medical schools and teaching hospitals. These non-profit institutions started to see themselves as "partners" of industry, and they became just as enthusiastic as any entrepreneur about the opportunities to parlay their discoveries into financial gain. Faculty researchers were encouraged to obtain patents on their work (which were assigned to their universities), and they shared in the royalties."

More worrying, perhaps, is the fact that there's a barely visible line between academia, industry, and regulators. Robert Califf, for example, was appointed FDA commissioner. According to EcoWatch [6], "Califf, formerly chancellor of clinical and translational research at Duke University, received money from 23 drug companies including Johnson & Johnson, Lilly, Merck, Schering Plough and GSK according to a disclosure statement on the website of Duke Clinical Research Institute."

Medscape, the medical website, disclosed that Califf "served as a director, officer, partner, employee, advisor, consultant or trustee for Genentech." Portola Pharmaceuticals says Califf served on its board of directors until leaving for the FDA.

In disclosure information for a 2013 article in *Circulation*, Califf also listed financial links to Gambro, Regeneron, Gilead, AstraZeneca, Roche and other companies and equity positions in four medical companies.

Califf has gone on record saying that collaboration between industry and regulators is a good thing. He told NPR, "Many of us consult with the pharmaceutical industry, which I think is a very good thing. They need ideas and then the decision about what they do is really up to the person who is funding the study." [7] What?

He is known for defending Vioxx which is reported to have caused at least 50,000 heart attacks and events before its withdrawal. (Merck is said to have known about Vioxx' cardio effects but marketed the blockbuster drug anyway).

Califf was instrumental in the Duke drug trial of the blood thinner Xarelto and a cheerleader of the drug despite medical experts' objections to its approval and 379 subsequent deaths. Duke, where Califf directed clinical research, is still recovering from a major research fraud scandal that resulted in terminated grants, retracted papers and a *60 Minutes* special. It is the least appropriate place from which to choose an FDA commissioner.

Many had high hopes for the FDA when Margaret Hamburg was confirmed as commissioner in 2009 because of her public health background.

But she swiftly moved to loosen conflict-of-interest rules governing those who can serve on FDA expert advisory committees and appointed Califf the FDA deputy commissioner for medical products and tobacco as she was leaving. Califf was also Obama's choice for FDA Commissioner.

This is not the first time the FDA has brought in a Big Pharma cheerleader to lead the agency that regulates Big Pharma.

In 2005, a 33-year-old Wall Street insider known for recommending hot medical stocks, Scott Gottlieb, was named FDA deputy commissioner for medical and scientific affairs. When a multiple sclerosis drug trial was stopped because three people lost blood platelets and one died, Gottlieb called it "an overreaction" because the disease, not the drug, might be to blame. [8] He rushed Chantix, Pfizer's stop-smoking drug, varenicline, to market, which was linked to a string of 2006 suicides and the violent death of Dallas musician Carter Albrecht. Gottlieb was forced to recuse himself from planning for a possible bird flu epidemic because of his financial ties to Roche and Sanofi-Aventis and had to bow out of work related to Eli Lilly, Proctor & Gamble and five other drug companies.

Even without a Pharma-funded FDA commissioner, many dangerous drugs approved by the agency have been withdrawn due to great harm. Who remembers Vioxx, Bextra, Baycol, Trovan, Meridia, Seldane, Hismanal, Darvon, Mylotarg, Lotronex, Propulsid, Raxar or Redux?

According to Ecowatch, Califf's confirmation amounted to a handover of the agency to Big Pharma. [9]

What we in fact have is an industry – intimately involved with both human and animal health and lives – in bed with governments and the academics who might have been counted on to protect us against fraudulent claims and dangerous drug side-effects. To add insult to literal injury, our taxes are spent on delivering drugs and vaccines that can cause harm, and which might barely be needed – just so the vaccine industry and Big Pharma can walk away with the profits, which they secrete in offshore bank accounts.

Chapter 61

There is no test to prove vaccine damage

Dear Catherine

I am so glad to have found your web site. I have two rough collies and one smooth; my rough, Storm, had her first injection the day before I picked her up. The day I picked her up she had very runny poo. I know prior to her jab her tummy and everything else was fine.

I took her back to my vet and after several false leads he concluded she had Giardia, but she had also developed a runny nose in one nostril. It was a creamy colour and occasionally green. The Giardia cleared up; however the nose problem kept reappearing whatever antibiotic was used, and after her second vaccination it seemed worse again. It eventually cleared up, but re-occurred on several occasions. When my puppy had her vaccinations Storm's nose started again, and again after the puppy's second vaccination.

Still not tying it in with the vaccination I had Storm's booster done, and her nose started again. The vet gave her a swab in the nostril, but nothing untoward showed up. I treated her with some homeopathic vaccination detox and she was clear for nine months but ten days ago I took her to meet my friend's Spitz puppy who had just had her jabs, and now Storm's nose has started again. It starts with an extremely runny nose in her left nostril but it is clear, and over a couple of days it becomes coloured and just runs like a tap, then it gets thicker and slows up a bit.

I am convinced it was her original vaccination that sparked all this off, and the vet thinks it may have been but of course won't commit himself. Any idea if it may have been?

Thanks

Barb Glover

An ocean of suffering, an ocean of harm. So a swab showed it wasn't an infection; it was something else. Once again I advised that there is a general principle that if a drug or vaccine appears to cause a problem when given once, and the problem occurs again if you give it a second time, then you can assume that the drug/vaccine is responsible.

Autoimmunity appears in Storm's scientific trail if anyone cares to follow it. I mentioned earlier that the book '*Autoantibodies*' states: "It is now appreciated that autoantibodies may predict the eventual development of a full-blown autoimmunity, such as specific HLA, IgA and complement components deficiencies."

Not being a trained scientist, I didn't know the implications of HLA and IgA complement component deficiencies, so I looked them up. I discovered that HLA class I deficiency is associated with skin ulcers, *sinusitis* and chronic lung disease [1]. So vaccines can cause autoimmune disease and this may involve sinusitis, or the discharge of gunk from the nose.

IgA is found in the saliva, mucous membranes, and intestinal secretions, where it may serve as the first line of defence against various *sinus*, respiratory, and gastrointestinal infections. Consequently, a deficiency of IgA heightens one's vulnerability to infections and inflammatory conditions. People with IgA deficiency are also more susceptible to autoimmune diseases such as rheumatoid arthritis, systemic lupus erythematosus, and chronic hepatitis; *respiratory allergies* and asthma; chronic diarrheal diseases; and some types of cancer.

There is currently no conventional cure for IgA deficiency, so treatment is aimed at easing symptoms and controlling associated diseases. Colostrum may help.

I told Barb that I thought her vet should report this as an adverse vaccine reaction to the VMD, quoting the references I gave her. If he won't, I said, then she can ask her vet for the form and do it herself.

I added that I would also ask her vet to rule out any autoimmune diseases, and I'd take my dog to a very good homeopathic vet. I finished with, "You might ask your vet to contact the vaccine manufacturer and see if they will pick up the tab."

Chapter 62

Dirty tricks

A year or so later, on the strength of Larry Glickman's comments to the effect that I am a pet owner looking for someone to blame, a TV producer, Jemima Harrison, went on Facebook on a number of occasions to say that, "Catherine O'Driscoll's work is not supported by science or the scientists she cites". Jemima, in true tabloid style, had taken a single individual – Larry Glickman – and transformed him into a group of people and, on the strength of this, she seemingly thought it appropriate to repeatedly libel me on the internet. I suggested that her opinion was top level and that she needed to go deeper.

Rachel Carson, author of *Silent Spring*, which exposed the dangers of agrichemicals, had urged everyone to ask who speaks, and why they speak. In this highly commercialised capitalist system, the need to do this has never been greater.

So this is a true story about a scientist appointed to monitor adverse reactions to veterinary drugs. It involves pharmaceutical companies, a PR firm, a government licensing body, 'activists', private investigators, a professor, and an American senator. It's about attempts to derail the career of a scientist who recommended a drug be taken off the market because it was harming too many dogs. It also demonstrates why so few people in a position to speak out actually do so – and why everyone in a position to speak out, who cares about life and truth, should – because they can't derail *everyone*.

So here's the true story: In 2005, American Senator Charles Grassley's Committee on Finance received allegations from Dr Victoria Hampshire that she was wrongfully removed from her post at the FDA. She believed that this was due to her work cataloguing an increasing level of adverse reactions to ProHeart 6, used to treat canine heartworm.

Reports initially involved allergic-type reactions. Other problems followed and the label was amended repeatedly to include further unwanted responses to the drug. Anaphylaxis and anaphylactic shock, depression, lethargy, hives, and fluid or swelling in the head and face were amongst the reported side effects. The label was amended again to include reactions involving the heart and lungs, and again to include 'rare' reports of death.

Dr Hampshire alerted her colleagues at the FDA, and called for action. She was ignored. Soon, consumer advocacy groups contacted the

FDA, lodging complaints about the drug. Over 5,500 adverse events had been reported, many involving young and formerly healthy dogs. Grieving pet owners generated over 20 national news stories. Finally Dr Hampshire's colleagues within the FDA began to listen to her, and it was agreed that ProHeart 6 should be removed from the market.

Senator Grassley stated in his report [1] that the pharmaceutical company Wyeth (the parent company of Fort Dodge Animal Health), made misleading statements about Dr Hampshire to the FDA in the hope of having its drug returned to the market.

Fort Dodge had contracted its PR firm to begin a "communications outreach plan to respond to the recall." This included contact with "veterinarians, veterinary medical associations and key contacts in the animal health community, members of Congress, and others believed to have influence at the FDA."

The PR firm investigated Hampshire, and forwarded information about her to Fort Dodge. Private investigators were also hired. The company alleged that Hampshire had a vendetta against the company and ProHeart 6, centring around the fact that she had a web site so that friends, family, and former clients could order veterinary products. It generated minimal income, and frequently no income at all. It was not designed to solicit internet clients. Fort Dodge, however, claimed that the site represented a conflict of interest.

Information on Dr Hampshire gathered by the PR firm and private investigators included personal property records for her home, business records relating to her web site, and taxation records. The aim was to show that Dr Hampshire favoured a competitive drug on her allegedly 'active internet veterinary pharmacy'.

Wyeth also alleged that Dr Hampshire had inappropriate contacts with anti-ProHeart 6 activists. Although several 'activists' did contact Hampshire, these were actually pet owners reporting adverse events, and her responses were within her job description. This itself horrifies me – that grieving pet owners should be labelled activists (someone involved in a campaign or social cause ... but meant pejoratively in this case). It also horrifies me that a pharmaceutical conglomerate should feel it inappropriate for the regulator to have contact with pet owners. The regulator is, conceivably, there to protect us and our pets?

Dr Hampshire then became the subject of a secret internal FDA investigation and got the cold shoulder from colleagues without knowing why. She was reassigned and no longer the lead reviewer of ProHeart 6. According to a May 2007 report in the *Los Angeles Times*, Senator Charles E Grassley, who had been investigating Hampshire's case, said Wyeth "tried to destroy a reputation." [2, 3] He added: "Her own agency sold her down the river."

However, even without the presence of Dr Hampshire, safety concerns based on serious adverse events later warranted the continued recall of ProHeart 6.

Dr Hampshire was in line for criminal prosecution, although charges were later dropped. In support of a conflict of interest accusation, for example, Fort Dodge falsely claimed that its agent had purchased competitive heartworm medication from her web site. They had not. They had tried, but were unable to do so.

Meanwhile, the FDA received a letter from a vet who was outraged at statements made by a Wyeth rep. He was told by the rep that Wyeth had Victoria Hampshire 'investigated by private detectives', that her 'financial interests had been verified', and that once Dr Hampshire was 'taken care of' the adverse event reports against ProHeart would drop off and the product would return to the market. No action was taken by the FDA in response to this complaint.

Ultimately, the case against Dr Hampshire was closed although she didn't get her job back. Her case is widely documented on the web, including interviews with Dr Hampshire.

Senator Grassley made several recommendations to the FDA to stop this sort of scenario happening again. Had Senator Grassley not got involved, what would have happened? Would we have ever known what goes on at the FDA?

Senator Grassley wrote to Commissioner Crawford at the FDA, stating: "it appears that there is a systemic problem with the pharmaceutical industry filing complaints against FDA employees and advisory panel members in an attempt to exclude those with dissenting views so that [the regulated companies] can obtain favorable results from [regulators]."

In a major address on the Senate floor, the Iowa senator went on to declare, "Brave whistleblowers have come forward to expose the too cozy relationship between the [FDA] and the drug industry. Hampshire's hard work and dedication to science and drug safety placed a bulls-eye on her reputation and career. The FDA cannot serve the American people and the interests of the drug industry at the same time."

Now, Jemima Harrison, please take note: Senator Grassley's investigation into Hampshire's case mentioned someone called Larry Glickman. Senator Grassley testified that a representative of the American Veterinary Medical Association forwarded an email from Larry Glickman, VMD, a professor at Purdue University, which discussed Dr Hampshire. The email asserted that Dr Hampshire's actions were important because they "reflect a deliberate attempt by Victoria Hampshire to exclude veterinarians in the decision making process".

Senator Grassley's report notes stated: "Dr Glickman was introduced by FDAH [Fort Dodge Animal Health] at the September 1, 2004, meeting as a consultant for FDAH. In addition, Dr Glickman presented FDAH's study data at the January 31, 2005, VMAC meeting. See VMAC January 31, 2005 Meeting Transcript (Att. 4) [4]. Dr Glickman had gathered data used by FDAH to support the position that Pro Heart 6 was safe. It is unknown whether Wyeth informed FDA that FDAH had these contacts." with Dr Larry Glickman, testifying at a hearing in favour of ProHeart 6, stated: "I disclose that I am not receiving financial compensation for my appearance today, nor am I currently affiliated with Pfizer Animal Health." (Pfizer had by this time bought Wyeth.) Please note the inclusion of the statement ... 'nor am I *currently* affiliated with Pfizer ...'

Pfizer, Fort Dodge, Wyeth, whoever ... they are all also vaccine manufacturers.

But Glickman was getting busy in terms of heartworm prevention. He's at an AAVP (American Association of Veterinary Parasitologists) conference, sponsored by, amongst others, Pfizer Animal Health – with a presentation from Larry about heartworm preventatives [5]. Here's a video from Nadler & Associates Inc (Custom Marketing Services) of Larry Glickman attesting to the wonders of ProHeart 6 on behalf of the marketing company's client Fort Dodge [6].

What we have is an academic exercising his legal right, like all academics, to take his clothes off and jump into bed with the pharmaceutical industry. Which calls into question academic impartiality. Summing up his testimony to the FDA [7], whilst not *currently* affiliated with Pfizer, Larry Glickman stated that in a study to analyse the electronic records of all dogs visiting any Banfield veterinary hospital between January, 2002, to August, 2004, the overall adverse reaction rate was remarkably similar for the dogs that received ProHeart -- 89.2 per 10,000 -- versus those that had received the most commonly used oral heartworm preventive -- 89.1 per 10,000.

"Similar rates for ProHeart 6 and the most commonly used oral heartworm preventive were also observed for allergic reactions," said Larry. "In fact, most of the allergic reactions that did occur could be explained by the dog having received the vaccine rather than by a dog having receiving a heartworm preventive drug.

"Our conclusion at the time was that the safety profile of ProHeart 6 and the most commonly used oral monthly heartworm preventive was similar.

"Based on these findings, we concluded there appears to be no scientific rationale for continued withdrawal of ProHeart 6 from the marketplace. And ... by the way, just to address an issue that was raised, or a question that was raised, this morning, we found that the allergic reaction rate for dogs that received either oral or injectable ProHeart was about 15 per 10,000 [1,500 reactions per million dogs receiving ProHeart], while the reaction rate for these same products when concurrently administered with a vaccine was about 45 per 10,000 [4,500 reactions per million dogs], so about a threefold increase."

According to a report in *JAVMA News* [8], on the basis of the number of reports judged to be possibly related, the FDA concluded that the number of deaths associated with ProHeart 6 was greater than with other heartworm preventives, relative to the market shares of the products. The FDA also believed that ProHeart 6 was associated with a greater number of certain organ system events and allergic reactions. Despite three label changes, the CVM continued to receive a large number of serious adverse drug event reports. The FDA expressed concern with the timing of reports coinciding with peak serum concentrations of the drug.

Considering that ProHeart 6 is used as a preventive and alternatives exist, the FDA asked Fort Dodge for the recall. The FDA was of the opinion that a higher standard for safety of preventive drugs should exist as compared with therapeutic drugs (vaccine hawkers take note).

ProHeart 6 was ultimately returned to the market, with – according to Senator Grassley – help from Larry, with the stipulation that veterinarians receive special training.

Glickman was also involved in a major Banfield study which looked into vaccine reactions in dogs. [9] The general conclusion was that vaccine reactions are rare – which is what pro-vaccinators love to quote. Mind you, the study did only look at records for three days post-vaccination which, in my humble opinion, is a study designed to hide adverse reactions rather than to find them. Remember, reactions can occur hours, days, weeks, months and even years post-vaccination.

However, what the study did find was that within only three days of vaccination, 4,678 adverse events were associated with administration of 3,439,576 doses of vaccine to 1,226,159 dogs. The rate decreased significantly as body weight increased. Risk was 27% to 38% greater for neutered versus sexually intact dogs and 35% to 64% greater for dogs approximately 1 to 3 years old versus 2 to 9 months old. The risk of a reaction is significantly increased as the number of vaccine doses administered per office visit increased; each additional vaccine significantly increased the risk of an adverse event by 27% in dogs who weighed less than 10kg (22 lb) and 12% in dogs above 10kg.

Conclusions and Clinical Relevance—Young adult small-breed neutered dogs that received multiple vaccines per office visit were at greatest risk of a reaction within 72 hours after vaccination. These factors should be considered in risk assessment and risk communication with clients regarding vaccination.

It also showed that the cumulative effect of yearly shots is bad news.

That's a shock – I thought, according to the 'rational' experts – vaccines were safe. Oh, and please tell me if a vet has ever told you, as he stands poised with the needle, that your small, neutered, 1-3 year old dog is at greatest risk from a vaccine.

In a documentary called *One More Girl* [10], a film concerning the Gardasil vaccine, former Pfizer vice president Peter Rost said:

"Universities, health organisations, everybody that I've encountered in my former career as a Pfizer executive, are out there with their hands out. Everybody's begging for money. Nobody has any money. The government doesn't have any money. Universities don't have any money. The only ones who have money are those big multinational corporations, and they have lots of money. And they use that money to basically buy influence.

"The way it's done is, number one, you give these organisations and institutions grants for various kinds of research; you develop research together with them; you establish friends; you make sure that they become beholden to you, and you also pay individual professors, doctors and researchers directly.

"You may pay them as speakers to travel around the country – a thousand, two thousand dollars per day, sometimes more. You give them money for programmes, educational programmes where they can make a profit, and then they put on these programmes as they're supposed to be third party, independent from the corporation, which is all fine, but as you and I can both imagine, if you have a promotional budget as a corporation, you're probably going to give that money to the universities that most support your drug.

"And the ones that don't, who are critical in any shape, way or form – they're not going to get anything.

"And everybody knows that this is how things work. And that means that even if you can officially claim that this is arm's length, we didn't have anything to do with it, we just gave them a grant, they can do whatever they want with it … the reality is they're not going to continue to get money unless they're saying what you want them to say. They know it, you know it – it's only maybe the public that doesn't know it.

"And that's how you influence the medical establishment. Simply, with money."

This means that commercialised science is terminally sick – unless its members go in and heal it, you can't trust a word they say.

Chapter 63
Horrendous vet bills

Andy Hancox emailed for my help after his 13-month-old Dogue de Bordeaux, Hooch, appeared to have a serious reaction to a vaccine. I asked for more information.

> Hi Catherine
> Thank you for your fast response, I will outline the details. On 17th December 2013, I bought my wife a Dogue de Bordeaux (Hooch). On 24 December, we took him to the vets for a check-up and primary vaccination of Nobivac DHP / Nobivac lepto2. Not being aware of the serious and life threatening reactions that could follow, on 7th January 2014 Hooch suffered severe cluster seizures. He was rushed to an emergency vet in Coventry where he spent the night and was transferred to the Willows animal hospital in Solihull where he spent a further two nights, and received MRI, ultra sound scans on liver/kidneys and also a spinal tap. He was shaved in various places, looking like a patchwork quilt, all costing in excess of £5,800 there. The diagnosis was epilepsy and we were advised that this means seizures due to unknown cause.
>
> He was put on anti-seizure drugs – phenobarb and Keppra. We arranged to pick Hooch up and bring him home. When we collected him he wasn't the same dog we took to the vets. He was erratic and howling, and totally confused. After getting back onto the Willows they took him off the phenobarb but he remained on the Keppra. Things improved slightly but we still had a dog that was lethargic, so after calling our own vet they and the Willows lowered the Keppra. We gradually got our pup back.
>
> On the 20th January 2014, he was due another vaccination and we took him for this again, not aware that this could be harmful. The next day he suffered more seizures. We administered rectal diazepam which prevented cluster seizures and visited the vets again where they started treating for epilepsy, altering drug dosage etc. During the next few months Hooch was having seizures approximately every eight weeks. They were single and not so violent, but I noticed that every time he was treated with Advocate flea and tick treatment he would seizure shortly afterwards.
>
> I pointed this out to the vet who agreed it could be a reaction to the Advocate and said that when he is due his next Advocate she would try something different. We went away thinking hopefully that was the cause of the seizures, not even linking the vaccinations.

We carried on treating our pup with Keppra and dealing with the seizures, and just being there to reassure Hooch. Then on the 15th January 2015, he was due his booster of Nobivac DHP/ Nobivac lepto2. We brought him home and all seemed fine.

I came home from work and the pup was in the window, tail wagging, getting excited. I got indoors and he jumped down off the chair to greet me, running and slipping on the wooden floor, yelping, not able to put pressure on his front paw. Thinking he had broken a leg we rang the vet and took him straight there. The vet said she wouldn't be able to x ray him because of his condition and that she didn't want to sedate him and he would need to go to the Willows. They told her to give him a pain killer and anti-inflammatory drug injection. Before she did, my wife expressed her concern about giving him more drugs so soon after his booster. She assured us it was ok and that the specialist at the Willows had advised it, and they would see Hooch at 8.30 the next morning.

After the injection we took Hooch home and within one hour he was cluster seizing again. This is when it clicked with me that the seizures are due to the drugs. I then started to investigate the Nobivac drugs and just couldn't believe that two different vet practices hadn't made this link.

I am convinced that these drugs are the cause of my pup's seizures. I just can't believe it has taken me so long to realise that I have been consenting to poisoning my much loved pup. What can I do to help get these chemicals out of his system? Is there anybody I can go to to get this investigated, or any vets that would look into this further for me?

Added a pic of our boy,
Many thanks, Andy

Hi Andy

Hooch is beautiful – thank you for sending me a photo of your boy.

I agree with you. The fact that Hooch had cluster seizures shortly after his puppy shots, and had them again after his booster, confirms that the vaccine caused the seizures. There is a scientific paper that establishes this:

'Stratton K, et al (1994) Adverse Events Associated with Childhood Vaccines: Evidence Bearing on Causality'.

Properly documented, the Institute of Medicine's Vaccine Safety Committee accepts the 'rechallenge' effect as evidence of causation. The hypothesis is that the disease should be more severe in those exposed twice if the disease were caused by the vaccine. Putting the above in plain English: if your dog has seizures after one vaccine, was stabilised, and then had seizures after another, you can be sure that the vaccine caused the seizures.

The *Merck Manual* also tells us that many different vaccines can cause encephalitis. This means inflammation of the brain, which can involve lesions throughout the brain and central nervous system. Epilepsy is confirmed on autopsy, with lesions showing in the brain. Also, epilepsy is known to be a symptom of encephalitis.

It is also accepted and acknowledged that vaccines can provoke delayed reactions – anything from minutes later, to days, weeks, months and even years later.

So your little boy is, without any doubt, vaccine damaged.

Having said that, the picture is complicated by other drugs. Advocate contains moxidectin, which is also the active ingredient of ProHeart 6, which has damaged thousands of dogs. Seizures are listed as one of the adverse reactions [1]. You'll see that, "ProHeart 6 [also known as moxidectin] should not be used in sick, debilitated or underweight animals. ProHeart 6 should be given with caution in dogs with pre-existing allergic disease, *including previous vaccine reactions*, food allergy, atopy, and flea allergy dermatitis."

Eventually ProHeart was put back on the market, but with the stipulation that vets in America must receive special training to prescribe it.

However, if your vets couldn't get their heads around the fact that Hooch had two previous vaccine reactions resulting in lethargy and epilepsy, they will administer moxidectin in a gung-ho fashion, not realising it's contra-indicated. (I personally wouldn't give my dogs moxidectin under any circumstances – but I've spent the last 25 years working in this field, so I am at an advantage.) Having said this, Advocate – which is also moxidectin – doesn't have seizures listed as an issue in its datasheet. I would suspect that this is a failing of the datasheet, for if moxidectin is associated with seizures or contra-indicated for dogs with seizures in relation to the datasheet for the brand name ProHeart 6, it should potentially be listed in relation to the brand name Advocate.

I would add that vets are not taught vaccinology. Their education on vaccination stops short of "do it" and "this is where you put the needle in". They are not taught about potential adverse reactions apart from anaphylactic shock, which is where an individual can die very quickly unless adrenaline or similar is administered.

You might also ask your vet to alert the VMD to the damage your dog has suffered as a direct and certain result of vaccination, compounded and made worse by Advocate. The manufacturers get away with it, claiming that adverse events are very rare. In reality, they are not rare at all – they are just rarely reported and therefore not added to the adverse event monitoring scheme.

I am angry on your behalf, and so, so sorry for poor wee Hooch. I am also sorry for the pain and expense you and your wife have been put through – and all because the system that licenses and prescribes these products is corrupt. Our pets are not protected by our government. Rather, the pharmaceutical industry is protected and supported by our government. Unfortunately Hooch is just another victim of this.

I am so sorry for what you have been through. Let me know where you are and I'll see if I can recommend a holistic vet near you.

With love,
Catherine

Oceans of suffering. Oceans of pain.

Chapter 64
Money, money, money

Academics conduct research. That research needs funding. The worry is that industry might only give funding to those academics who are amenable to control, which renders the system amenable to corruption. This means that you might be persuaded to buy drugs and biologics that are bad for you and your loved-ones because an academic who is being paid by the pharmaceutical industry told you to.

It is perfectly conceivable that academics take the decision that, for example, heartworm is a serious disease in dogs and that although heartworm drugs come with risks, there is a case for giving those drugs. They might also believe that canine viral disease can be deadly, and that vaccines to prevent them are mandatory, irrespective of known adverse effects. They could be making a risk-benefit analysis – which is their right to do.

I might add that it's also our right as pet owners to have access to truthful information that will enable us to conduct a risk-benefit analysis ourselves regarding the health of the souls we are responsible for. We don't need academics with potential research funding conflicts to arrogantly make those decisions for us. Well, actually … it would save a lot of time if we could take their word for it rather than need to seek the truth ourselves. In fact, what's the use of 'experts' if we can't trust them?

Because industry intrinsically funds academics, and industry might be biased towards profits and shareholder dividends, we should have the right to ask questions regarding scientifically presented 'facts' – just as we should have a right to question our governments without fear.

My concern is that academics are forced to go cap in hand to industry for research funding, and they are also for-hire to industry – which, in point of fact, is grossly unfair to the scientific community. If we value science, we should give scientists funding without commercial strings attached. The way things are, we absolutely must be cautious about even academic research, and the pronouncement of people with letters after their names. We must ask 'who speaks and why?'

If you ever wondered why the pharmaceutical industry, and questionable vaccines, have so much support from practically everyone, the answer is evident: the industry pays for it. It's not just idealism promoting vaccines and dangerous drugs, for if it were, then the provision of clean drinking water to the world – in order to reduce infection – would also have the active support of academics.

In their book, *Food is Better Medicine Than Drugs* [1], Patrick Holford and Jerome Burne outline where the pharmaceutical industry's marketing money goes, as John and I had done in 1994 when we first started Canine Health Concern:

- Industry pays for trials that test the safety and effectiveness of their drugs.
- They pay for medical journals through advertising and reprint fees. (I would add that, often, the people who own the medical journals might have financial interests in pharmaceutical companies.)
- They pay the academics. Clinical practice guidelines advise doctors on the drugs to use for various conditions. However, 80% of the academics who write them have financial links with the companies whose products they recommend.
- They pay for doctors' further education … fully 60% or more of that education is paid for by drug companies.

A Compass report [2] pointed out that the majority of drugs offering therapeutic advances have been funded by us via our governments, and not by the pharmaceutical industry. The authors complained about biased clinical trials, and the control (via its money) the industry has over which clinical trials get done. And they complained about excessive contact between the pharmaceutical industry and medical professionals. "While the Department of Health invests nearly £4.95 million in postgraduate education for doctors, the pharmaceutical industry spend over 300 times as much: £1.65 billion."

The authors were also concerned that the industry is increasingly seeking to exert influence through patient or advocacy groups in the UK. In a study of patient groups that disclosed financial information, 83% had received funding from the industry. This is, in fact, why my own organisation Canine Health Concern has difficulty being heard over the large animal charities which have done nothing to stop over-vaccination: we don't accept industry funding or control.

A Europe IFAH report [3] was cheery about the prospects for selling drugs into the veterinary market, and especially positive about high spending [aka extremely gullible] pet owners: "The opportunity to provide long-term care for ageing pets is an attractive one. The human-pet bond has a high economic ceiling, and both veterinarians and the animal health industry have recognised the potential of this market segment."

In other words, the industry cashes in on the love we have for our friends, and marketing money – sales propaganda – makes us spend more.

Despite the pharmaceutical industry being richer than your wildest dreams, *Drug Discovery Today,* a pro-industry journal [4], bemoaned the fact that new drug discovery is time-consuming and expensive, and a new model is required – one that rewards academic research contributions with funding, intellectual property ownership, and royalty share:

"Academia needs industry. Industry needs academia. It is clear what has to be done: industry, government and research charities need to consider effective strategies to fund and sustain the development of our academic drug discovery capabilities."

I am fully aware that the pharmaceutical industry and its employees believe that finding new drugs to treat disease is a good thing to do, and that people like me are being unfair when we criticise. But it looks as though the ties between big business, academia, charities, and governments are forming themselves into knots, and independent research – such as still exists – will disappear. The pharmaceutical industry has a history of burying unfavourable research and hiring academics to come out with research findings to generate sales, and they already have largely secretive partnerships with charities to help promote those sales.

But we also need to be cautious about government funding.

Larry Glickman's on-line CV [5] says he has raised over $10 million in grants and contracts from federal agencies alone, including the National Institutes of Health (NIH), the CDC, the FDA, the Department of Education, and the Department of Agriculture. He has also raised an unknown but probably significant amount of research funding from industry. One could say he's a mean, lean research funding machine. You'd fight to get him if you were a dean at a university.

Out of interest, he also got a $1.2 million grant from the CDC to develop a National Companion Animal Surveillance Program to detect acts of bioterrorism and emerging zoonotic infections. Biowarfare will feature later, and it's key to understanding why your vet encourages you to over-vaccinate, or why your doctor promotes vaccines for children when the scientific sense of doing so is not clear.

As an aside, a small voice in my head keeps quietly asking whether the insistence on some form of annual vaccination for pets, with vaccines that are dangerous or have dubious need, might have something to do with research into bioterrorism and 'emerging zoonotic infections'.

In defence of Glickman and his university, they are not alone in taking money from industry. It's the norm, albeit at the successful end of normal. Although this is the way it is and Larry hasn't broken any laws, I am questioning whether it should be acceptable if it's the truth we're seeking.

The pharmaceutical industry also gives money to government agencies, so funding from government can't be regarded as pure, either: governments also give money and products to industry, too. And as we shall see later, there is more to this than meets the eye.

For example, Pfizer on its website [6] proudly boasts of its contributions to such bodies as the American Public Health Association through its Public Health Fellowship in Government. This programme provides a 'unique public policy learning experience … for those who wish to spend a year in Washington DC, *working in a congressional office on legislative and policy issues* related to health, the environment, or other critical public health issues.'

What moral right has a pharmaceutical company got to put its minions into government agencies to help influence legislative and policy issues related to health?

Through the CDC-Hubert Global Health Fellowship, Pfizer-sponsored students are mentored by CDC staff and learn through hands-on experience while working on a public health project in a developing country. Surely this is the fox playing in the hen house, or at least the fox cosying up to the chickens?

Pfizer's NIH Medical Research Scholars Program facilitates "the most creative, research-oriented medical, osteopathic, dental, and veterinary students to the intramural campus of the NIH in Bethesda, MD". The NIH … an independent government agency? Do you think, if I won the lotto, the VMD would allow me to put informed dog lovers in their offices, or even holistic vets?

Pfizer's CDC Experience Applied Epidemiology Fellowship enables eight "medical students … to spend up to one full year at the CDC in Atlanta, Georgia."

So Pfizer offers a spider's web of grants which might help to ensure a cosy relationship between the American government, regulators, and itself. The UK also benefits from Pfizer handouts [7]. Other pharmaceutical giants get involved in the same sort of thing – and, as in the UK, the pharmaceutical industry contributes massively to the economy. Politicians who wish to stay in office might therefore be reluctant to upset these conglomerates.

In fact, I was shocked to hear former prime minister Tony Blair declare on TV's Question Time that governments come unstuck through messing with big business. So what's the point of voting, then, if you're an ordinary person trying to find your way through the minefield of staying alive? Who is there to vote for who doesn't put the wealthy elite and the corporate agenda ahead of us, or who can be counted on to curb corporate power? And if politicians with integrity and an understanding of the effects of over-abundant power actually do appear, such as Labour's Jeremy Corbyn, it makes absolute sense that the media, owned also by the elite, should seek to attack the movement.

It is speculated that Blair's wealth is in the multi-millions, although a spokesman in *The Telegraph*, January 2015 [8], said, "He is rather artfully putting his income into a partnership that has no requirement to file public accounts. You can never get to the bottom of what his income is because it always goes into an entity that has to file nowhere other than with HM Revenue & Customs."

I was speaking to an elderly man yesterday who told me he'd given up voting because they're all in it for the money. "Look at Blair," he said, rolling his fingers to count the bank notes.

Some of Blair's fortune comes from advising investment banks and governments, but in 2001, under Blair, the UK aligned itself on the side of the pharmaceutical industry in the battle over cheap drugs for developing countries, declaring that patents on medicines must be upheld even in poor countries where millions are dying of diseases such as tuberculosis and Aids.

The government's position, endorsed by Tony Blair and written by ministers together with the heads of the major drug companies in the UK, including GlaxoSmithKline and Merck, stated: "Intellectual property rights [patents] are the lifeblood of the innovative pharmaceutical industry."

Rather than allow poorer countries to produce cheaper drugs to fight conditions such as Aids, Blair acted to protect pharmaceutical industry profits. While UN agencies and charities welcomed the lowering of medicine prices in the developing world the UK government was publicly backing the position of the pharmaceutical giants.[9]

Pfizer's web site states that although there are laws with which Pfizer complies when it comes to throwing money at political candidates, or political lobbying, it makes donations though its Political Action Committee. [10] That's what you'd call a nice little loophole.

It's all legal and above-board, but is it right? Should multi-billion international companies be allowed to give money to doctors, veterinarians, academic institutions, charities, government bodies, 'independent' medical bodies, political parties, and individual politicians? On the face of it, there's nothing wrong with it – except that, as we have seen many times, such as in the case of Dr Victoria Hampshire, industry doesn't always play fair.

All of this calls democracy into question, since those of us on the fatal end when drugs and vaccines go wrong are bereft of billions or millions with which to butter the palms of academics, medical bodies, charities, government or politicians. We don't have lucrative consultancies to offer them, or overpaid jobs waiting for them when they leave office. We just have – in the case of humans – vaccine damage compensations schemes which limit the legal fallout for the vaccine industry.

Indeed, Pace Environmental Law Review, Vol 28 [11], states:

"Starting in 1988, no vaccine manufacturer was liable for a vaccine-related injury or death from one of the recommended vaccines 'if the injury or death resulted from side effects that were unavoidable even though the vaccine was properly prepared and was accompanied by proper directions and warnings'. This language stems from the Second Restatement of Torts.

"In addition to broad liability protection, the 1986 Law also provides another shield to manufacturers under federal law. *The 1986 Law permits them the right to not disclose known risks to parents or guardians of those being vaccinated.* Resting on the 'learned intermediary' doctrine, manufacturers bear no liability for giving, or failing to give, accurate or complete information to those vaccinated, and have only to provide relevant information to doctors, who must give patients CDC Vaccine Information Statements."

A lady only ever swears deliberately, so I'll leave you to turn the air blue at your own discretion. It's one rule for the rich and powerful, and another (go to jail) for the poor and powerless. We're just grieving parents, spouses, or pet owners. And if we object to our loved-ones being killed, we're called activists – and pharmaceutical companies, it seems, think we shouldn't even be allowed to talk to regulators.

CHC, the organisation I founded in 1994 to campaign against over-vaccination and to promote real food and alternatives to drugs and their unacceptable side-effects, has no marketing budget, and no lobbying budget. We consider ourselves lucky when we manage to get through a month without worrying too much about how we pay the overheads associated with living in a small rented cottage and keeping our work going. We don't have company cars, or expense accounts, or pension funds, or money to pay anyone off with. I'm not moaning, but stating a fact.

Contrast this with the money a top pharmaceutical boss can make. Whilst you may not think this relevant, we are in fact getting closer to the reason why companion animals are over-vaccinated, and why human children are given dubious vaccines with unacceptable side effects.

The Compass report [2] listed the top ten executive pay and remuneration packages in the pharmaceutical industry in 2008, in the middle of another global financial crisis caused by the increasingly deregulated capitalist system, when many of us were struggling to keep the roofs over our heads:

CEO	Pharmaceutical company	Pay ($m)	Pay (circa £m)
Miles White	Abbott	33.4	16.366
Fred Hassan	Schering-Plough	30.1	14.749
Bill Weldon	Johnson & Johnson	25.1	12.299
Bob Essner	Wyeth	24.1	11.809
Robert Parkinson	Baxter	17.6	8.624
Daniel Vasella	Novartis	15.5	7.595
Richard Clark	Merck	14.5	7.105
Frank Baldino	Cephalon	13.5	6.615
Sidney Taurel	Eli Lilly	13.0	6.370
Jeff Kindler	Pfizer	12.6	6.174

Just to spell this out, the CEO of Abbott was paid nearly thirty-three-and-a-half-million dollars for a year's work in 2008. That's nearly $3 million a month. The poorest of the listed CEOs only got a paltry twelve-and-a-half-million dollars for the year, or just over a million a month. What does a person have to be or do to justify that kind of money?

As I look around me during these years of austerity, I begin to be convinced that it's deliberate; that the movement of money away from the poor and towards the rich is somehow planned.

According to a 2013 report, issued during another time of recession and hardship by Americans for Tax Fairness [12], Merck's new CEO joined a corporate call for Social Security cuts in America, while enjoying his own gilded retirement benefits. Sitting on the steering committee of Fix the Debt, a corporate-funded campaign of more than a hundred CEOs, Kenneth Frazier and colleagues called for cuts to Social Security and Medicare, corporate tax cuts, and a new tax system that would allow corporate offshore profits to be forever US tax-free.

Frazier is also a member of the Business Roundtable, a powerful lobbying group of more than two hundred large company CEOs. It supports making targeted cuts to Medicare and raising the Social Security retirement age from 67 to 70.

Frazier's Merck retirement accounts were worth $14.4 million at the end of 2011, enough to generate an $81,772 monthly retirement check starting at age 65. That's 62 times more than the average US Social Security retiree.

What we are beginning to see is an apparently callous disregard for the economic security or physical wellbeing of the majority of the population – from the head of an alleged healthcare corporation.

The Americans for Tax Fairness report also examines Pfizer: "Pfizer knows the prescription for avoiding taxes and for staying in business despite a decades-long record of fraud, bribery, and illegal marketing of its products," they said.

"Pfizer's tax avoidance Rx: Hide all your profits offshore. Pfizer has 40% of its sales and 50% of its assets in the United States, the largest and most lucrative drug market in the world. And yet the firm claims to have not made a profit here since 2007. Pfizer reported more than $9 billion in losses in the United States from 2010 to 2012, while earning more than $43 billion in profits in the rest of the world. It received $2.2 billion in federal tax refunds over the three-year period."

The American government *gave* poor old Pfizer $2.2 billion from taxpayer money?

Like Merck's boss, Pfizer CEO Ian Read was also calling for corporate tax cuts and an increase in your retirement age from 67 to 70. Read's $49 million Pfizer retirement account would, in contrast, give him a splendid $275,000 a month from the age of 65. Many of us would love to own a home of our own, and one month of Read's retirement pay would set us up for life. And imagine how much clean water a month's salary would buy, and how many lives would be saved.

Americans for Tax Fairness adds that Pfizer spent $10.4 million lobbying Congress in 2012 and nearly $131 million since 1999.

In contrast to helping the poor, many of the world's richest individuals, the global one percent, hide billions in tax havens, as do the corporations many of them run. They profit from the healthcare system; they don't contribute to it via their taxes.

Global corporate fat cats hold $21-32 trillion in offshore havens, money hidden from government taxation that would benefit people around the world, according to findings by James S Henry, the former chief economist of the global management firm McKinsey & Company. The International Consortium of Investigative Journalists, in April 2013, revealed how widespread the buy-in was to these tax havens. [13]

The findings were damning: government officials in Canada, Russia, and other countries have embraced offshore accounts, and the world's top banks have worked to maintain them. Moving money offshore has implications that has ripped through the world economy. Part of Greece's economic collapse was due to these tax havens, for example. This hidden wealth is a huge black hole in the world economy that has never been measured, and which could generate income tax revenues between $190-280 billion a year.

According to ActionAid, tax dodging is a massive issue for people in the west and in developing countries, where it costs an estimated $160 billion a year – £12 billion of that applies to the UK.

The following fact is so important when considering infection and whether or not vaccines are the answer: *Developing countries lose three times more to tax dodging than they receive in aid every year.* If they don't care if people starve or drink out of dirty puddles, why should they care if they save them with vaccines? Could it be that they can make money from vaccines, but none from feeding the starving or giving them clean water? Or even playing fair with the countries they appear to be raping?

Corporate tax avoidance is unjust. It harms ordinary people around the world, increasing poverty and inequality. This, in turn, increases the likelihood that epidemics will ensue, simply because millions of people can't afford to eat well, or at all.

And here, for me, is the crux of the matter: while people starve and live in squalor, vaccines are lauded as some sort of philanthropic, socially acceptable, saviour. Yet if people are malnourished and lack basic sanitation, vaccination represents a danger – not a benefit. Without adequate nutrients, the immune system cannot respond to the stress of vaccination in a healthful way. Puppies starved of vitamin B5, for example, died when they were vaccinated. Another study showed that selenium and vitamin E deficiency in dogs resulted in depressed antibody titers in response to vaccination with distemper and hepatitis. [14]

Malnutrition renders vaccines potentially dangerous, and less likely to confer immunity. Neither can malnourished people fight viruses and bacteria in a healthy way. The pharmaceutical companies know this. Consider the wording in Intervet's vaccine datasheet, way back in the 90s: "Immunocompetence may be compromised by a variety of factors … including diet."

Those of us who now feed our dogs a raw, biologically appropriate diet have put this concept into practice – and we are seeing the benefits with our own eyes.

So how do you feel about this? Are you happy that multi-millionaire pharmaceutical bosses are pushing arguably dangerous and ineffective vaccines and drugs, trying to get you to work into your 70s, lay off staff in your country and ship jobs overseas, want to reduce your unemployment benefits and healthcare support, and seek to ensure that their corporations pay as little tax as possible whilst benefiting through government bodies from the tax you have paid?

As the newspaper proprietor Robert Maxwell once said when asked about his riches, "Making the first million is easy because you can spend it. When there is nothing left to buy you have to just want money". Perhaps hoarding money needs to be seen as a psychiatric disorder more dangerous to society than paranoid schizophrenia, and classified as such?

But don't forget your flu shot! It may not work, and it could kill or paralyse you, but who gives a damn?

Chapter 65
Heading for the hills

Rob and I were gearing ourselves up for Foundation in Canine Healthcare weekend workshops around the UK. We wondered if CHC members might help us get 'bums on seats'. After all, we had saved them a fortune in annual booster jabs, helped them avoid vet bills to treat vaccine-induced illness and malnutrition, and from watching their young dogs suffer or die.

I thought about our internet discussion group – hardly any of the people on this were members of CHC. With heavy heart, I realised that they were unlikely to want to help us get the news out there in face-to-face workshops. The internet is a fabulous resource, helping us to get important information out there; but it has also created a society that expects its information for free. Few seem to consider the cost of providing that information.

Rob and I talked about it. The discussion group took up a lot of my time: sometimes half of each day. We reasoned that we were going to be very busy if we were planning to travel around the UK, and I no longer had the time to keep this group going.

Instead, I invited everyone to become a paid-up member of CHC and join a new discussion group for CHC members only. Two lovely members – Julie Arnold and Jytte Smith – agreed to moderate it for me. This was to be a campaigning group, where everyone was committed to spreading the word about over-vaccination and natural feeding. It would have a purpose, and an intent to share the truth with dog lovers who only had their vets' outdated information to rely on. My aim was to defeat apathy and build an army.

Unfortunately, my call for support backfired when a CHC member, within the space of about two minutes, set up a rival discussion group and invited everyone to decamp to it 'for free'. The opinion soon got around that CHC was charging people to be on their discussion group, whereas I saw it as a perk for people who supported CHC's work by becoming members. I also saw it as a necessary development, because two people can only do so much against the multi-billion international pet food and vaccine industries. We really needed to form ourselves into a movement capable of effecting swift change.

But it's hard to get people to understand this. They don't appreciate the politics behind over-vaccination or the capitalist impetus that puts profits before life. Many are only concerned about their own dogs, and it takes an awakening to go beyond that.

So there followed a tirade of abuse from people who were disgusted at me for closing the group down. Insult after insult came through cyberspace. My sister Leslie said something to defend me and was called a 'dirty little scud' – a badge she wears with pride. One girl said that she was a member of CHC long before Catherine and John ever got involved (what?); another – after seeing all the negative comments – piped up to ask: "Who *is* Catherine?" Rob and I were by this time practically rolling on the floor with laughter – that's one of the many things I love about Rob: he laughs when others would get angry.

Then I shut the group down.

Over on the new discussion group for CHC members only, which – according to my plan – was for people who were committed to campaigning to end over-vaccination and promoting real food for dogs ... lots of people came up with wonderful ideas, chiefly involving what *I* could do next. It was suggested I could run a dog show, write to various bodies, stand on my head and recite the Koran, and do a sponsored head shave (I am being ironic). So I was still, to steal a name from a film, "Cinder-effing-rella".

Meanwhile, getting on the road meant that there was no legitimate reason to stay at Carsegray. The house was far too big, and unless we were running workshops there it would be time to move on. We put our intentions out to the Universe by selling furniture, knickknacks and clothing that we no longer needed, and had a bonfire.

We went to view cottages in Angus, but they were either tiny or there was nowhere to walk the dogs except in pesticide-drenched arable farmland. So I telephoned Carsegray's estate manager, Charles Gow, and told him that we were planning to move out, and asked if the estate had any cottages that we might decamp to. Charles had none, but suggested I contact a friend of his who managed another country estate near Perth. As luck would have it, he had a Georgian farmhouse available and we went to have a look.

Once again we drove up a long single-tracked tarmac drive bordered by rhododendrons. But this time the drive was slightly harrowing. To the left, there was a steep drop of about 40ft, which gave me the willies. Rob pointed out that cars don't usually veer off the road. I wondered, though, how we'd manage to get up or down the drive if there was snow or ice. But we reasoned that, working largely from home, there would be few occasions where it would matter much.

The house at the top of the hill was just what we were looking for – in fact, more than we could have hoped for. It had space for an office – CHC's HQ – plus a fairly large room if we wanted to hold workshops there.

Rob loved the place. It was clean and freshly painted, and had panoramic views across magnificent treetops and down to the Carse of Gowrie, an expansive valley with the river Tay gliding through it. We were once again surrounded by farmland; there was a tenant farmer who kept sheep on the surrounding hills. And we felt that we could just about manage the rent.

So we hired a van and took to lugging furniture about. Moving from Carsegray was like moving out of around six normal houses. In the middle of carrying another double mattress to the van, Rob announced that it was like wrestling jelly. We were so tired by this stage that hysteria was close by, and we both collapsed in the van, laughing hysterically and feeling unbelievably weak.

Much of our furniture was going to auction, which paid for the move, but we still had to load up the removal van and drive to the farmhouse and unload it six times, as there was a limit to the size of van Rob was legally able to drive. Then we cleaned Carsegray from top to bottom to leave it in a respectable condition, and strolled around the house with Hamish, Charles Gow and Ernie the estate overseer to make sure we hadn't pinched any of the antiques or trashed the place. Thankfully they were all very complimentary about the condition we left the house in.

Three days after moving into the farmhouse, we hosted our first weekend workshop. I met one of the ladies who attended it recently. She remarked that I appeared to be very tired!

Chapter 66

The Church of modern medicine

So let's return briefly to Larry Glickman, who continued his critique of my article with:

"My take is that there are impurities in animal vaccines that result in autoantibody production and allergic reactions following vaccination. Dog and cat vaccines are admittedly less pure than most human vaccines but the trade-off is a significantly lower cost. I suppose if pet owners were willing to pay $50 or more per dose of vaccine the situation might be improved, but on the other hand many less dogs and cats would ever be immunized. So all in all I think animal vaccine companies are doing a good job as are veterinarians in providing preventive health care. Are dog and cat vaccines safe? Yes, but we could do better."

With respect to the highly lucrative Larry Glickman, I am stunned by his reasoning. He is actually saying that dog vaccines are impure, but this is OK because pet owners won't want to pay more for purer vaccines. Vaccines are safe, but they could be safer. So what are they? Are they safe or not? He appears to be saying that we are happy to put our dogs at risk of autoimmunity, allergies, brain damage, cancer and death – so long as we can save some money.

But let's not depersonalise the effects of 'less pure' vaccines. The effects are, in fact, the deaths of people – dogs and other animals who are loved and cherished: people who don't deserve to suffer whilst being told 'it's good for you'.

It's my understanding that pet owners pay to vaccinate their dogs because they love and care for them, and because we are constantly being told – falsely – that boosters are needed every year and they're safe. We want to protect our dogs, and to honour their lives with our care. We don't want to put them at risk of terminal diseases at the same time. Were we to understand that we are injecting sub-standard products – with impurities – into our dogs, that will cause autoimmune disease and allergies, we probably wouldn't inject them. We certainly wouldn't inject them every year knowing that our pets were already immune.

Stepping into Larry's mind and making a stab at his reasoning, bearing in mind that we never know what anyone thinks unless we ask them and they're willing to tell us, he probably believes in vaccines as the saviours of the universe and chooses to work towards making vaccines safer. Personally, I'd prefer he came back to me when his job is done – at which point I might decide to use the *safe* vaccines.

I would also point out that the veterinary vaccine industry is a multi-billion, international, highly profitable, blossoming, growing, business. Is it too much to ask that the products they sell us might be free from contaminants? Would we buy food knowing that it's ridden with deadly bacteria, excusing the manufacturer because at least the food was cheap?

In fact, vaccine contamination is a real problem if you want to be able to take your dog for a jab in the sure knowledge that he isn't going to die as a result of it. And lest Glickman's words comfort you with the belief that human vaccines don't contain contaminants, you'd be wrong to be complacent, because they frequently do. Many adjuvants are arguably contaminants that shouldn't be injected into anyone's body: peanut oils which lead to nut allergies, for example.

Meanwhile, I received an email from another scientist who had read my Science of Vaccine Damage article. Andrew Maniotis, PhD, Visiting Associate Professor of bioengineering: program of tumour mechanics and tissue regeneration, University of Illinois at Chicago wrote:

"I don't think it is coincidental that two of the molecules that the vets find (especially the tissue-controlling two molecules laminin and fibronectin) that are deregulated in vaccine-induced, cancer-harbouring animals, are the same ones we have found reverse, kill, or promote tumours [in humans].

"It is logical that these two tissue constructing molecules in the correct or incorrect amounts induce tumour dormancy or killing as we have found, and at different amounts (as when a vaccine disturbs a tissue and fibronectin is produced in abundance while laminin is suppressed) they can, when not in proper amounts, induce tumour growth and metastasis.

"I estimate that, if thousands of cats each year develop tumours at the site(s) of their vaccinations as these vet organisations now claim, and nobody knows how many dogs do, although other studies show they also develop a variety of cancers, accompanied by the production of anti-fibronectin, anti-laminin, anti-collagen, anti-cardiolipin, and anti-DNA antibodies associated with immediate onset arthritis, autoimmune diseases of all kinds, demyelination syndromes, haematological pathologies, etc., that perhaps The Church of Modern Human Medicine someday will become concerned regarding the 1:160 autism rate, rates of diabetes, asthma, and also, just maybe, the escalating cancer rates in our children and other humans following the mass vaccine crusades of the past 40 years."

Chapter 67
Only healthy dogs should be vaccinated

Dear Catherine

I am the owner of Ted, a 10 year old Labrador. I have been alarmed by information that I have learnt in the past few days around vaccinations, particularly so in respect of Ted's recent struggles. He went to the vet for routine annual jabs and a check up on his front paw; he had been limping for a couple of days; his chronic arthritis was referenced, and he was diagnosed with an ear infection as well as an infection in his foot for which he was given antibiotics. He also had his annual vaccinations.

On his return home he ate his dinner. However he became lethargic and off colour as the evening wore on. He refused his bedtime antibiotic and even the piece of meat in which it was disguised and took himself off to bed. In the morning he was surrounded by diarrhoea and vomit. He was very listless and was immediately taken to the vet. He was put on a fluid drip, given steroids and antibiotics, and stayed at the hospital for five days. He continued to have blood in his diarrhoea, continued vomiting and we were told that he had haemogenic gastroenteritis and that he was 'very poorly'.

Gradually he began to take small amounts of food and we were sent home with a light diet and an array of antibiotics and probiotics.

Further tests have identified campylobacter and a 415 enzyme level indicating pancreatitis, both of which combined, the vet says, caused his illness. My understanding is that these are difficult diseases but it is the timing and severity that confuses me. There is no doubt that the tests have indicated these issues but apart from his limp he had displayed no symptoms of either. Everything was normal as far as I knew. He has been fit and well with a good appetite, exercised daily and a normal weight. For all these things to manifest so quickly and in such a short space of time has left me very concerned that it was his vaccination that caused it all. But according to the vet the timing is pure coincidence.

This has led me to begin reading all the information that I can find around side effects of vaccinations and this is how I have come across your writings.

I am very frustrated and annoyed at what I have been reading. What is more there is absolutely no acknowledgement from the vet that it was anything else but pure coincidence and misfortune.

I am now asking if he should have been given the jabs at his age, alongside his foot infection, his arthritis – and did he need them at all for 'protection?'

Could the jabs have compromised his immunity so that the campylobacter became significant? I understand that the dog could have been a carrier of this with no symptoms. [Yes – around 49 per cent of dogs carry it.] Could the steroids have altered the enzyme levels to give the pancreatitis?

I know that you will have lots of questions from concerned pet owners on this subject. I am looking for a steer as to whether to pursue this further with the practice. I have an appointment with the practice head next week and would welcome an indication from you as to whether you feel that this could be a direct link with Ted's vaccinations.

Jackie Hurley

Oceans of pain. Oceans of sorrow. Vaccines are licensed for use in healthy animals only. A dog with an infection requiring antibiotics can hardly be considered healthy. In fact, I really don't think antibiotics and vaccines are good bedfellows, and particularly bacterial vaccines. Vaccines are also known to cause inflammatory 'itis' conditions. Within hours of being vaccinated, Ted developed pancreatitis. Almost half of dogs carry campylobacter without overt problems; its effects are mostly experienced by puppies whose immune systems are not yet developed – not by adult dogs. Vaccines cause immunosuppression, which left Ted open to opportunistic infection. Ted was also ten years old and didn't need a vaccine.

Despite all this, his vet said that his vaccine-induced illness was coincidental.

Chapter 68

How to wield power in the modern world

As 2010 rolled in, Rob and I decided it would be a great idea to waste several months on a fruitless exercise, although we didn't realise it would be fruitless when we had the brilliant idea.

So ... the World Small Animal Veterinary Association, the American Veterinary Medical Association, the American Animal Hospital Association, and the Australian Veterinary Association had now made public pronouncements to say that immunity to the core canine and feline diseases persists for many years and probably for life, and we should vaccinate no more frequently than every three years. And vaccines are not harmless.

A number of veterinary vaccine manufacturers responded by getting three-year vaccines on the market. There's nothing to say that three-year vaccines are any more efficacious than one-year vaccines, by the way, or that they are even any different. If they'd applied for ten- or seven-year vaccines, they would probably still have been the same vaccines. After all, it was the 'old' yearly-boosting vaccines that Ron Schultz discovered didn't need boosting every year!

Vets in the UK are largely self-regulating. Judging by the discontented pet owners who have sought justice against what they perceive to be veterinary malpractice, to have a vet reprimanded for malpractice by the veterinary boys' club in the UK – the RCVS – would appear to require him to rape your grandmother, or conduct some similar act. If he's coercing you into over-vaccinating your pet and taking money by deceiving you – well, no-one is going to care.

Unfortunately, in my humble opinion, the wording used by veterinary bodies such as the WSAVA – that vaccines should be administered 'no more frequently than every three years' – is open to misinterpretation. Those who make money from vaccines only hear the 'every three years' part of the sentence.

However, we reasoned, three-year vaccines now meant that one-year vaccines were redundant. And if we could have one-year vaccines taken off the market, then we would at least put a stop to annual vaccination. So we turned to the regulator.

We wrote to Steve Dean, then head of the VMD, asking the VMD to withdraw redundant one-year core vaccines for dogs and cats. According to its website and literature, "The vision of the VMD is the responsible, safe and effective use of veterinary medicinal products. In working towards achieving this vision the VMD aims to protect public health, animal health, the environment and promote animal welfare by assuring the safety, quality and efficacy of veterinary medicines."

In my view, the VMD fails on every count. In fact, I've become used to bodies such as this telling us they're exact opposite of who they are.

Steve Dean replied to us with a 'position paper' which, apart from extolling the virtues of the smallpox vaccine (?), merely reflected what already happens. It didn't address the request to withdraw redundant vaccines from the market.

So we replied to the VMD with a lengthy two-part document. This was carried, along with all of the correspondence, on the VMD's website, but has now been removed – although we have kept it on the Pet Welfare Alliance site [1]. Letters from the VMD are on file.

In part one of our response to the VMD's response, we presented the science to show how vaccines can destroy our dogs' immune systems, setting them up for diseases like cancer, leukaemia, autoimmune haemolytic anaemia, and many other names which boil down to a slow, agonising and painful death. Further scientific papers were presented to show that the more you vaccinate, the more you increase the risk.

Steve Dean replied at length, but let this extract impart his general view and tone:

> Critically reviewing Canine Health Concern's (CHC) letter, attached papers and references totalling over 380 pages will take some considerable time and, therefore, this response may be supplemented by further comment or questions in due course. It is clear that the contents are largely opinion based upon a considerable amount of anecdotal comment from dog owners, various third party opinions and quotes (some adequately referenced and some not) and, at least in those areas where VMD is directly involved, the information provided is often selective, misinterpreted, misunderstood or quoted out of context. The principle thrust of CHC's response appears to be challenging the safety of canine and feline vaccines both in terms of their authorisation and their use by the veterinary profession in the UK. The over-riding impression is of a CHC position based on an eclectic mix of published 'extracts', utilising poor scientific rigour and anecdotes to justify an anti-vaccination stance. As a science-based regulatory agency such poorly substantiated, selective arguments rarely gain much credence although we will try to extract the relevant points you make and address them.

Steve hadn't had time to 'critically review' our submission, but he was nevertheless able to conclude that it was crap! We need to be aware of lethal double standards: he clearly missed the irony that he was defending annual vaccines when no science has ever existed to support annual vaccination against the core viral diseases. How's that for scientific rigour or bias?

I also thought he was taking unfair advantage of my lack of scientific training; that I was just a pet owner. Had scientists been doing what scientists should be expected to do, I wouldn't have had to get involved. And – believe me – I wish it hadn't been necessary. Nor do I think it appropriate for a regulator to shower scorn on a member of the public who is seeking to alleviate suffering.

In response to Steve's assertion that my submission was based upon anecdote, and to help educate the regulator, I assembled the hundreds of scientific references I had previously submitted and sent them to him as a block. It was another case of government agents making out that something was the opposite of what it actually was, and if the VMD could convince over-vaccinating vets that our science was dodgy, it would be music to their ears.

In his defence, and in defence of the VMD, Steve claimed that the work of the VMD and its decisions are based on established and recognised science. Well, change the established and recognised science, then! It's highly flawed, and causing harm! I'd add that the AVMA has made it clear that "...the one-year revaccination frequency recommendation found on many vaccine labels is based on historical precedent, not scientific data."

To me it's pretty simple. We don't need to vaccinate our dogs every year, subjecting them to the known potential dangers. But frustratingly, it doesn't matter how you say it, or how rigorously you substantiate what you're saying, if the other fella wants to hold onto his views – for whatever reason, and you are invited to ask yourself what the reason might be – then nothing is going to persuade him otherwise.

Backwards and forwards the correspondence went. Ultimately, Steve said the VMD would not withdraw unnecessary annual core vaccines "because the risk of an adverse reaction doesn't exceed the benefits". Since the VMD's Suspected Adverse Reaction Reporting Scheme (SARRS) doesn't show that many dogs have adverse reactions to their shots, then the 'legislation' will not allow them to withdraw one-year vaccines.

Steve ignored the fact that by withdrawing one-year core vaccines, which can be legitimately replaced in every case by 3-4 year vaccines, we are safely reducing the frequency of revaccination, which also reduces the risk of adverse events. It is my contention that *any* adverse reaction to a biological product that isn't needed is unacceptable. And where is the *logic* behind injecting biological products which are known to decimate the immune system (autoimmunity, allergies, cancer, brain damage …) if the individual is already immune? The only logic must be related to boosting sales, rather than boosting immunity.

In both human and veterinary medicine, it is estimated that only around one percent of adverse drug reactions ever get reported. Yet Steve reckoned the VMD's passive and voluntary reporting scheme is great. I can personally confirm that vast numbers of pet owners in the UK have suspected adverse reactions but their concerns were dismissed by their vets, and no report was filed.

I'll just repeat something John suggested in the 90s: if veterinary practices were given inexpensive software to log illnesses and drugs and vaccines given, we could do away with the passive reporting scheme and get the actual facts. But the veterinary pharmaceutical industry and the VMD vetoed John's suggestion. I'll add that unless the VMD makes such a system available, they are wilfully guilty of poor scientific rigour (touché!).

In part two of our paper to the VMD, we looked at the 'system' which keeps annual vaccination in place. This includes pet charities which take money from veterinary pharmaceutical companies and promote over-vaccination, with no legislation to get them to declare those donations; vets who are inadequately trained and rely upon booster income; pet owners who may not question the advice they're given; veterinary teaching establishments which rely upon pharmaceutical industry funding; and governments which need big business to employ people, pay taxes, and give MPs a sideline or jobs when out of office. It also includes the VMD.

I went to London to meet up with Oliver Letwin MP, thanks to CHC member Gabbie Slade who arranged the meeting as one of his constituents. Oliver Letwin co-authored the poll tax which ended Margaret Thatcher's career and caused huge public outrage – so I was speaking to a stalwart of the Establishment.

In 2005, Mr Letwin was appointed Shadow Secretary of State for Defra, of which the VMD is a part. It was reported that he'd requested a role less onerous than his former treasury brief so that he would have time to pursue his career in the City. As I shook his hand within the dark halls of the House of Commons, I looked at Mr Letwin and saw images of his country pile, and I was right: when the MPs' expenses scandal broke, Mr Letwin reportedly agreed to repay a bill for £2,145 for replacing a leaking pipe under the tennis court at his constituency home. How the devil did he imagine his tennis court or pipework were reclaimable parliamentary expenses?

His parliamentary voting record is interesting. He voted very strongly against paying higher benefits over longer periods for those unable to work due to illness or disability, and very strongly against raising welfare benefits at least in line with prices. Ironically, he was a member of the Conservative disability group, although clearly he wasn't a champion of the under-privileged.

Mr Letwin ushered us through the murky back rooms of Parliament and onto the terrace overlooking the Thames. He insisted I answer his questions, which I did – although *my* chief question concerned how it might be possible to influence the VMD to remove one-year vaccines from the market. "Ah," he said, "you are trying to beat the Establishment. This is not something you can do."

I live in hopeful optimism, however. There are precedents to help that optimism along, such as the fact that slavery is no longer legal, and women have the vote.

Oliver Letwin informed me that the Secretary of State for Defra, who is a Minister appointed by the Prime Minister, must follow the advice of the VMD. Stop for a moment and consider that last sentence. Our democratically elected government is unable to interfere with the decisions of the VMD which, many suspect, is an arm of the pharmaceutical industry.

This is how democracy works in the UK: If you wrote to your MP, as many of our members did, and said you didn't think it right that the VMD keeps one-year vaccines on the market, which means that pets are being over-vaccinated and experiencing harm, your MP will write to the Minister who will write to the VMD, and *the VMD will write a response* which the Minister will send to your MP, and your MP will send it back to you. In short, you may as well miss out the middle men and write directly to the pharmaceutical industry/VMD. Either way, you'll get told to sod off.

Later, I suggested to Oliver Letwin by email that it would appear that we are wasting our time seeking democratic representation if government is incapable of influencing the decisions of the VMD. He replied:

"I am afraid that the Veterinary Medicines Directorate is an independent body and the Government cannot overrule it." Which means that we are governed by faceless civil servants we didn't vote for. Who, then, is telling the civil service what to do – the Shadow Government which conspiracy theorists talk about?

In an article in the *Boston Globe*, October 19th 2014, we are told to vote all we want, but the secret government won't change [2].

"The Obama version of national security looks almost indistinguishable from the one he inherited. Critics tend to focus on Obama himself, but Tufts University political scientist Michael J Glennon has a more pessimistic answer: Obama couldn't have changed policies much even if he tried. Our government no longer works that way.

"In a new book, *National Security and Double Government* [3], he catalogs the ways that the defence and national security apparatus is effectively self-governing, with virtually no accountability, transparency, or checks and balances of any kind. He uses the term 'double government': There's the one we elect, and then there's the one behind it, steering huge swaths of policy almost unchecked."

Nothing, though, is impossible Mr Letwin. I think you'll find that many of us are becoming self-determined and have stopped listening to government 'regulators' – which are not regulators at all, but industry sales agents.

We invited the VMD to change our perception by demonstrating its independence from the pharmaceutical industry by withdrawing redundant one-year licenses, and by re-drafting its advice to pet owners which, in our opinion, is openly dishonest when it claims that vaccine reactions are only mild. They have not acted on either of these suggestions. The VMD says on its website [4]:

What about 'side effects', 'adverse events' and the reported dangers from over vaccinating?

It is extremely rare for any serious side effects to follow vaccinations. Mild reactions such as animals being a little quiet or off their food for a day or so are possible but are short lived. Any adverse effect is generally far outweighed by the benefit of protection against serious disease [says who?]. The independent [they're having a laugh] Veterinary Products Committee (VPC) reviewed all UK authorised dog and cat vaccines between 1999 and 2002. They concluded: "Vaccination plays a very valuable role in the prevention and control of major infectious diseases in cats and dogs". Although adverse events occasionally follow vaccination, including the suspected failure to work well, the VPC concluded that the 'overall risk/benefit analysis strongly supports their continued use.

This appears to me to be a pharmaceutical industry sales pitch from a government department, playing down the carnage. Notice they didn't quote the 'independent' VPC vaccine review when it stated that dogs need annual core vaccines.

Now, accepting that I'm not a trained scientist and this book might be, according to Steve, potentially, "... largely opinion based upon a considerable amount of anecdotal comment from dog owners, various third party opinions and quotes (some adequately referenced and some not)…" you just can't get around the fact that vaccines can cause harm. The VMD overtly lies and tells us on its website that vaccine damage is restricted to your beloved dog being off his food, or the vaccine failing to work well. The VMD issues statements in defence of vaccines which do not appear to be supported by the science. Why would they do that, do you think?

In our initial letter to the VMD, we asserted that they had failed to take action to ensure that veterinary vaccines are administered no more frequently than is necessary, or to warn and protect the pet owning public from spurious claims on the part of veterinary vaccine manufacturers and veterinary surgeons. We referenced independent duration of immunity studies and asked the VMD to make it clear that core MLV vaccines do not need to be 'boosted' annually. We also called for clarification on optional non-core vaccines.

We referred the VMD specifically to Intervet's 'National Vaccination Month' (which we had previously asked the ASA to adjudicate on). Steve claimed that Intervet was doing nothing wrong.

Whilst refusing to withdraw redundant one-year vaccines from the market and accusing me of presenting biased and shoddy information, the VMD also replied that vets should vaccinate every three years whilst claiming that this was in line with WSAVA guidelines. It is here that semantics matter: 'every three years' is poles apart from *no more than* every three years' – when immunity is known to last for years and probably for life. The VMD also dissed the titre testing option – where owners can ascertain whether their pets have circulating antibodies to the core disease, which means they are immune and do not need revaccinating.

At around this time, Tony Blair's chief of staff Jonathan Powell wrote his memoires. The book was called *The New Machiavelli; How to Wield Power in the Modern World*. A *Sunday Times* review revealed that Powell entered politics motivated by power:

"The self-confessedly power-hungry new Machiavelli finds, once he enters 10 Downing Street with Blair in 1997, that what he wants isn't there. It comes as a blow to him to discover that the power of the British prime minister is 'illusory … like the crock of gold at the end of the rainbow'. Civil service mandarins and newspaper proprietors seem to be wielding real power, to the envious consternation of the occupants of No.10."

So when your baby or your pet suffers a vaccine reaction, they are demonstrating – whether you know it or not – that our elected representatives are powerless in the face of civil servants who appear to make the decisions, the pharma industry whose main ambition is to increase profits, and the media whose owners have an interest in manipulating how you think.

This is scientific fraud on a massive scale, supported and endorsed, it seems, by government – government which has, under successive leaderships, given the VMD carte blanche to do as it pleases. The British government set the VMD up with the clear brief to make life easier for corporations, and successive governments have appointed the staff. And although "the VMD is an independent body and the government cannot overrule it," it is still part of government – an unelected and ungoverned part of government.

A government is a group of people with the authority to govern a country or state. Our veterinary products regulator is, by definition, governing – with our elected government unable to interfere.

Can we trust the medicines that are licensed for your pets? Did you vote for this?

Chapter 69

Do we know what we're doing?

At around the same time, in 2010, researchers in Scotland and Japan isolated a feline retrovirus in dog and cat vaccines. [1, 2]

This study is important for two reasons. The first is that your dog may be injected with a retrovirus which might cause cancer or leukaemia so that, rather than preventing disease, you are paying to potentially kill him; the second is that the government regulator doesn't seem to care. The study authors stated:

> In this study, we isolated a feline infectious ERV (RD-114) in a proportion of live attenuated vaccines for pets. Overall, it is possible that our data under-represent the number of vaccines from which RD-114 can be isolated....
>
> Collectively, our data show unequivocally that RD-114 is present in live attenuated vaccines commonly used in dogs and cats from different continents and produced by three different manufacturers... the large-scale exposure to RD-114, particularly of the dog population, may have effects that are impossible to predict even if successful RD-114 transmission was an extremely rare event.
>
> Millions of puppies are vaccinated annually worldwide, and they may be more susceptible to RD-114 infection than cats as the dog genome does not harbor RD-114. ... it is impossible to rule out chronic effects, especially as we were able to grow RD-114 very efficiently in dog cell lines, confirming older published studies....

Retroviruses can cause cancer and leukaemia. Several (unidentified) brands of vaccines for cats and dogs in the UK and Japan have been found to contain a cat retrovirus. This contamination probably came when manufacturers developed their vaccines on cat kidneys which were infected with the retrovirus. It's likely to be seed stock, since several brands from different manufacturers were involved. Cancer and leukaemia won't show up immediately after the jab, but would take around five years – by which time you won't know a vaccine killed your friend.

The study concluded that:

• Future studies will be necessary to determine whether RD-114 has any negative impact in cats or dogs....

- A recently identified novel human retrovirus (xenotropic murine leukemia virus-related retrovirus [XMRV]) has been found in some forms of prostate cancers and chronic fatigue syndrome in humans [murine relates to mice and rodents]
- sensitive PCR-based RT assays [as used in this study] are not required for veterinary vaccines

This is a policy. The reason pet vaccines are not tested using PCR-based RT assays is a policy: a plan has been agreed.

The paper stated: "The risks of infection by ERVs from xenospecies through vaccination have been ignored," and concluded: "As long as feline cells are used to produce vaccines, there is a risk that infectious RD-114 virus contaminates live attenuated vaccines. Because RD-114 virus productively infects cells from cats and dogs, the virus can infect these animals in vivo [in a living animal]. Since certain ERVs infect new host species and induce diseases, the potential risks of infection by ERVs in humans and animals should be reconsidered."

Writing in US *Dog World*, March, 1995, W Jean Dodds offered clarification on the implication of retrovirus contamination in dog vaccines:

"Immune–suppressant viruses of the *retrovirus* and parvovirus classes have recently been implicated as causes of bone marrow failure, immune-mediated blood diseases, haematologic malignancies (lymphoma and leukaemia), dysregulation of humoral and cell-mediated immunity, organ failure (liver, kidney) and autoimmune endocrine disorders – especially of the thyroid gland (thyroiditis), adrenal gland (Addison's disease) and pancreas (diabetes). Viral disease and recent vaccination with single or combination modified live virus vaccines, especially those containing distemper, adenovirus 1 or 2 and parvovirus, are increasingly recognised contributors to immune-mediated blood diseases, bone marrow failure and organ dysfunction."

A feline retrovirus in vaccines could cause serious problems for our dogs – but at least we get 'cheap' vaccines! According to Kennel Club research, one in four dogs in the UK can be expected to die of cancer. Retroviruses are implicated in this scenario.

Retroviruses were first associated with malignant disease in animals more than a hundred years ago. In 1908 the Danish veterinarians Ellerman and Bang [3] observed that erythroleukaemia is infectiously transmissible in chickens. Then in 1911, Rous in the USA and in 1914, Fujinami in Japan showed that some avian sarcomas could be transmitted by inoculation of cell-free filtrates [4,5]. Filtrates, by the way, are liquids that have been passed through a filter.

In the 1960s, Howard Temin, a virologist at the University of Wisconsin, suggested that an RNA tumour virus could give rise to a DNA copy, which would then insert itself into the genetic material of a cell. Temin's theory was dismissed, like most fundamental departures from conventional wisdom. But he never wavered. Finally, in 1970, he and David Baltimore at the Massachusetts Institute of Technology simultaneously discovered reverse transcriptase, the special enzyme that can do exactly what Temin predicted: make DNA from RNA.

The discovery has had a profound impact on modern medicine. It not only explained how cancer can be caused by a virus but provided researchers with the tools they needed to understand the origins and natural progression of diseases like AIDS. It also created a new field, retrovirology, and, more than that, it began to erase the tenuous borders between viruses and genes.

Retroviruses cause cancers in chickens, sheep, mice, and other animals, but their effect on humans became clear only in the late 1970s, with the identification of two viruses that cause forms of leukaemia. Retroviral proteins are particularly abundant in certain kinds of tumour cells, and scientists wondered to what degree they might be a cause of cancer. Working with mice in 2005, Thierry Heidmann found that endogenous retroviruses were present in large quantities in tumour cells. Similar viruses have been associated with many cancers (and other diseases). [6]

After Canine Health Concern alerted the VMD to the presence of RD-114 in various unidentified brands of canine and feline vaccines in the UK, they called a meeting at European level. Their subsequent report stated: "The benefits of vaccination against cat and dog diseases clearly outweigh the potential risk that is linked to the presence of replicative retrovirus RD114 in vaccines. The threat represented by retrovirus RD114 is currently theoretical. No prompt regulatory action is warranted, although corrective actions need to be undertaken." [7,8]

I was advised by a microbiologist that a lack of 'prompt action' is unlikely to be because it's difficult to screen identified retroviruses out of a vaccine. It's more likely because it takes years to re-license clean products, and manufacturers with dirty vaccines would be without vaccine revenue until the uncontaminated licenses arrive. Meanwhile, every time you have your dog or cat vaccinated, you could be injecting-in a contaminant that might kill them slowly. My microbiologist friend (who is afraid to be identified) estimated that it will take around five years for cancer or leukaemia to arrive – and by then you can't pin anything on anyone.

Meanwhile, the Japanese researchers continued with their work. They concluded in 2014, [9] that:

Quite importantly, RD-114 virus grew efficiently in cells of dogs which are vaccinees. ... Even if RD-114 virus does not proliferate in dogs after experimental infection, we cannot dismiss the risk of infection with RD-114 virus in dogs completely. Canine attenuated vaccines are inoculated in several million dogs per year around the world, and RD-114 virus may mutate and acquire more infectivity/productivity in dogs. Therefore, although the risks posed by RD-114 virus are still unclear at present, it is desirable to develop the means to produce RD-114 virus-free vaccines.

Parvovirus – a killer disease in dogs – was almost definitely caused by contaminated vaccines, once again implicating the use of cat parts in vaccine manufacture.

Ian Tizard wrote: [10]:

"Prior to 1978, few parvoviruses had been isolated from dogs, and none were considered pathogenic ... in the spring of 1978, severe disease attributable to a parvovirus was recognised almost simultaneously in dogs in the United States, Canada, Australia, New Zealand, South Africa and Europe ... selective pressure and subsequent mutation more likely occurred in a tissue culture environment than through dog-to-dog passage. Thus it is speculated that CPV might have arisen through rapid accidental passage of FPV or mink enteritis virus in a canine cell culture line. Cells infected with the new mutant may then have been transmitted globally through a contaminated biological product such as a vaccine ... it is interesting to speculate on the consequences of this host range extension had it involved human beings instead of dogs."

It's also interesting to see what Tizard had to say about the adenovirus (hepatitis) vaccine in dogs: "Canine adenovirus 1 vaccine strains ... can multiply in the renal tubular cells of dogs and cause subclinical kidney infection. As a result, virus may be shed in the urine of vaccinated dogs and may spread to other animals."

Tizard finishes his critique – in 1990 – with the following words: "The best way to ensure that such hazards do not develop in the future is to seek alternatives to modified-live products. Modified-live vaccines have served us well, but their time is past. We can no longer afford them."

For a more in-depth analysis of "The Emerging Risks of Live Virus and Virus Vectored Vaccines: Vaccine Strain Virus Infection, Shedding and Transmission" by the NVIC, see [11] This report concludes:

"Live vaccine virus shedding is a possible source of transmission of vaccine-strain viral infection but how frequently that occurs is unknown. There is no active surveillance of live virus vaccine shedding and most vaccine strain virus infections likely remain unidentified, untested and unreported.

"The impact of vaccine-strain virus shedding infection and transmission on individual and public health is a question that deserves to be asked and more thoroughly examined by the scientific community. The fact that children and adults given live virus vaccines have the potential to pose a health risk to both unvaccinated and vaccinated close contacts should be part of the public conversation about vaccination."

This is particularly interesting in relation to the Disneyland measles outbreak during 2015, since the MMR vaccine is a MLV vaccine [12,13]. The CDC put the outbreak down to people not being vaccinated, whereas greenmedinfo.com says: "Just a few months ago, a study published in PLoS titled, 'Difficulties in eliminating measles and controlling rubella and mumps: a cross-sectional study of a first measles and rubella vaccination and a second measles, mumps, and rubella vaccination,' brought to light the glaring ineffectiveness of two measles vaccines (measles–rubella (MR) or measles–mumps–rubella (MMR)) in fulfilling their widely claimed promise of preventing outbreaks in highly vaccine compliant populations. We dove deeply into the implications of this study in our article titled, "Why Is China Having Measles Outbreaks When 99% Are Vaccinated?"

Decades after Tizard's concerns were aired, MLV vaccines are still in use, and there's no sign of their replacement. It also appears that rather than needing to be concerned for the health of vaccinated people from unvaccinated individuals, the reverse is probably more likely. We need to stay away from people who submit to the needle.

Drugs and vaccines aren't harmless. They all come with side-effects. Some of those side-effects are life-threatening. But not all drugs and vaccines deliver what they promise. Yet – if the VMD is anything to go by – governments appear to collude with the pharmaceutical industry to get drugs and biologics to market and keep them there, and hide adverse effects, which include infecting non-vaccinates. How much of this is about human and animal health, and how much is about money or even genocide?

When my dogs died and I asked why, I discovered that our pets are a political issue. The Hampton Review [14, 15] made it clear that the VMD is primarily there to fast-track drugs and biologics to market. Its key 'stakeholders' are industry – not the animals or the animal owners.

The VMD was established following the publication, in February 1988, of the Review of Animal Medicines Licensing by Mr P.W. Cunliffe CBE, former Chairman of ICI Pharmaceuticals Division [16].

Can you believe this? The VMD was established in line with the ideas, thoughts and recommendations of a top man from the pharmaceutical industry! The regulated set the regulator's agenda. My horror is based upon the fact that I am looking from the viewpoint of an individual who is sickened by unnecessary deaths as a direct result of products licensed and approved by the VMD.

Since its establishment, the VMD has succeeded in meeting its full cost recovery targets from industry; that is, industry money funds the VMD, the regulator. Further, whilst part of the European Union, if the VMD won't license a product, corporations can go to any other European country and give their license fee to them. Therefore the VMD's income is won in competition with others, contingent upon the VMD granting licenses. This means that it's in the VMD's financial interests to view license applications favourably. The same applies to other European countries, which seems to place the pharmaceutical industry in an enviable position.

The VMD's mission statement is to assure the safety, quality and efficacy of veterinary medicines, but this is the exact opposite of what it does. Rather, it ensures that its 'customers' (the pharmaceutical industry) receive excellent service.

As a dog owner whose primary goal is to secure the health and wellbeing of my dogs, it seems to me that the VMD has lost its stated direction, which was to ensure "the responsible, safe and effective use of veterinary medical products." Rather, the VMD appears to act as a government body concerned with the need to fast-track veterinary products to market.

The VMD appears to be unconcerned with the safety of the pet population. How can it be when it facilitates the sale and use of yearly vaccines that are not required, refusing to withdraw them from the market; under-plays or appears to wish to hide adverse reaction rates; dismisses alternatives such as titer testing, and promotes industry marketing material – such as the POOCH survey – in defence of unnecessary vaccination?

The Veterinary Medicines Directorate is conflicted. Our pets and other animals seem merely to be the cash cows, offered up in sacrifice.

Chapter 70

Keep on keeping on

Rob and I spent the next few years on the road, delivering the Foundation in Canine Healthcare, and Animal Communication and EFT, workshops. I loved it – it was wonderful to see so many deeply happy and satisfied people leaving at the end of the weekend. I am proud to say that many of our delegates returned again and again to benefit from the experience and the loving, safe, environment we provided.

I think that, if someone were to ask me what gives me the most fulfilment, I would have to say it is the look on the faces of delegates who arrive at workshops in a state of anxiety and distress, and who leave – after being empowered with knowledge and an EFT session – with glowing smiles on their faces.

Rob and I had great fun, too, staying in cheap hotels and having a right old laugh. There were many economy hotels and B&Bs where our feet stuck to the carpet; where the fire escape led directly through our room; where you could hear every word or groan in adjoining rooms and, less appealingly, you could hear everything from adjoining bathrooms. But rather than moan and look on the bleak side, we laughed about it. Frankly, staying in dives with a sense of humour is much more fun than staying in five star establishments (which, in the glory days before I ditched the money in favour of life, I had actually done).

Then Rob asked me to marry him and we began to excitedly plan a wedding. We set our sights on a magical day with clowns and jesters and men on stilts, and fire eaters, and elephants and magicians, and a big multi-coloured circus tent.

And then we got real and invited a small selection of friends and close family to join us for an on-the-cheap civil ceremony in our garden.

That year in Scotland was unusually sunny and warm – we were blessed. On the day, my sister-in-law Angela climbed to the moors above the house and picked purple heather which she fashioned into a head band for me. Our dear friends Rod and Gerry created casseroles for our evening guests, and Gladys, Rob's mum, bought flowers. My friend Elaine Clifford made a wonderful wedding cake for us, fashioned as the 'Yes' logo. And the local farmer dropped off a gift of trays of raspberries and strawberries. Rob and I walked through our garden to a makeshift altar to the sound of 'Nous Sommes du Soleil', the Yes song we both put at the top of our Desert Island Discs list.

As part of our vow, we made a promise to one-another; it's a promise that we have also made to ourselves as we live our lives:

"I promise to honour our union by always speaking the simple truth. I will place truth ahead of wanting to be right. I will place truth ahead of fear. I will place truth ahead of convenience. I will speak the simple truth clearly, kindly, directly and with love."

Everyone was blubbing, but Edward, a selection of sheep, and Rob provided the entertainment. As we made our vows, Edward interrupted with loud barks, enticing *anyone* to play with him, so Leslie stepped in, and sheep from the neighbouring field bleated and baahed in significant places. (Will you, Robert *Bah* Ellis …). Then Rob got his guitar and amp out and performed many of my favourite songs.

Later, Rod and Gerry officiated over a Native American ceremony in our garden, where we bowed to the four directions while our non-believing guests had a good laugh at our expense. Did we mind the laughter – heck no.

Gifts of money paid for a honeymoon in Ireland, and Gladys stayed to take care of Edward, Daniel and Gwinnie.

It was a wedding on the cheap, but it was the most beautiful day of my life.

Once the festivities were over and things settled down, we began to realise that you cannot stay on the road indefinitely. Rob in particular was finding it increasingly difficult to keep up with work back at the office, and he was tired. I, too, felt in need of a break. We were hosting a weekend workshop once every two weeks, which meant that we were left with only three days in the office most weeks, making it difficult to keep up with normal CHC work.

So we had the brilliant idea of putting the workshops on-line. We spent months filming the lectures, and months researching web hosting and associated technicalities, and months publicising them … and they were a resounding flop. Suddenly there was no money coming in from workshops – which wasn't good news.

However, now that we weren't travelling all the time, we had time for other things. One project took centre stage; it was initiated by a wonderful dog-lover in London called Brian Cleghorn. Brian absolutely loves the dogs and is an avid CHC supporter. Like many of our wonderful members, Brian accosts dog owners in the park and hands out CHC leaflets, desperate to help end over-vaccination and extol the benefits of real food for dogs. He is so passionate that many of his fellow-dog walkers hide from him behind bushes, unwilling to be swayed – which is a laudable accolade on Brian's part. It takes a lot to be shunned and to still keep going.

Brian also paid to place advertisements in relevant London and TV/film journals, looking for a production company that would do a follow-up to the *World in Action* documentary. One day he telephoned me with an idea: "Why don't we start a fund to produce a film ourselves?" he said. "I'll definitely contribute."

"I don't see much point," I replied, knowing that members hadn't responded too favourably to our fund-raising efforts in the past. But Brian was so keen that I promised him I would raise the issue in our next newsletter.

Blow me down, but our members donated a total of £18,000 to get the project off the ground. Brian cashed in his PEP insurance and gave us £7,000 of the total. Gavin and Val Thomson donated £2,000, passing on a legacy from Gavin's late mother. Other members gave what they could, anywhere between £5 and a few hundred pounds. I know that, however much people gave, they collectively donated enough to make a highly professional film – and I'm in awe of them and will never be able to thank them adequately.

I telephone Brian James, the producer of the World in Action documentary, and he put a crew together. We were on our way.

We interviewed homeopathic vets Chris Day and Richard Allport for the film, asking their views on the vaccine issue. The vet Michael Fox, who lives in America, was in England while we filmed, so we went to meet him at his mother's home and filmed his views on the pet food recall scandal that had recently taken place in North America.

Gary Smith also featured – he's a systems analyst and cancer researcher who made a groundbreaking scientific discovery about the modes of inflammation. Gary asserts that inflammation is behind cancer and other immune-mediated conditions, and that, amongst other things, vaccines cause inflammation. Ironically and rather interestingly, Gary's wife Allison is a direct descendant of Edward Jenner who pioneered the smallpox vaccine.

We also went up to Yorkshire to interview Keith Dickinson, a dog trainer who had attended one of our EFT workshops. Whilst at the workshop, EFT had cured his longstanding shoulder and arm problem, and he was very interested in information about vaccines and the natural diet. He has subsequently started a successful raw meat business – he is one of many dog lovers who have established their own businesses as a result of the information we have worked hard to share. He proved to be an excellent advocate of the raw diet, and very supportive of us and our work.

The delightful Chrissie and Jens Diron, who had hosted a workshop for us in Canada the previous year, also gathered a group of their friends and associates who had changed to raw and stopped over-vaccinating since the workshop. They filmed a fabulous segment for the documentary. The lovely Patti Vesalo, who we had met on the Caribbean cruise, also got some friends together and sent a Skype message in support of the 'crusade' from America.

The film was shaping up well.

Chapter 71
John checks out

Behind the scenes, we had discovered a problem with John. He was still using an email account that had been created while we were together; Rob had to clear it via the web from time to time, otherwise our mailboxes would over-fill and we couldn't use them.

One day Rob turned to me in the office and said, "John isn't using his email account." Now this wasn't a particularly informative statement, but it had an immediate effect on me. I fell apart, feeling that something was dreadfully wrong. John had made it clear that he didn't want contact with me, so I emailed his friend Simon to ask if John was alright. Simon emailed back, suggesting I phone him. The news was devastating: John had cancer.

As details unfolded, the picture became dire. He had moved to a new town and was unable to register with the local medical practice as it was full. Instead, he was assigned to a pool system. He'd consulted a random doctor to be told, incorrectly, that he had haemorrhoids. But he was gradually feeling worse and worse. Eventually they organised a cancer test but nobody got back to him with the results. Months later he was feeling really sick and was finally told that he had colon cancer. By this time, it had advanced too far.

I got in touch with him and asked if I could visit. He was in hospital recovering from a colectomy. When I told him how upset I was for him, he grasped my hands like a drowning man gasping for air. He was on his own. His wish to find love hadn't materialised, and he was living in a flat with no-one to care for him.

I took to visiting him as often as I could, brought shopping, and organised MacMillan nursing care, and I contacted some of our mutual friends so that they could offer their support.

But John was angry with me, so in some ways the visits were difficult. He had a history of cutting people off and leaving them behind. When we first met, for example, he decided that he wanted nothing more to do with his daughters; he had physically attacked me when I urged him to stay in touch with them. But now things were different – he was dying – and I asked if he would like me to tell his daughters. He was adamant that they weren't to be informed. Now I, too, had been cut off; my presence was merely tolerated.

Then one night I heard him cry out while I was sleeping: "I'm dying." The next day I discovered that he had been transferred from his flat to a hospice and arranged to visit. He told me, "I nearly died last night," but of course I already knew.

John was comfortable and pain-free in the hospice, and seemingly at peace, and I visited him as often as I could between filming, and I took Edward along to cheer him up. Following John's instructions, Rob went to his flat and finalised his accounts and sent them off to Company's House. John was touchingly pleased to have his affairs in order.

Fairly soon the cancer spread through his body, including his lungs, and he was unable to speak. Impetuously, I took hold of his hand as I was leaving the hospice one day and said: "I'm so sorry to see you like this John. I love you very much and wouldn't wish this on anyone." Once again he grasped my hands like a man gasping for air.

The next day when I visited, John summoned his strength and spoke his last words: "Thank you for coming." Those words meant a lot to me. It took a lot of effort to say that, and I took it as a gesture of tenderness and reconciliation.

And finally, on my last visit, I walked into his room to find him unconscious and saw that his breathing was laboured. He was dying. He would have died alone in the hospice had I not arrived.

Charlotte, Joanna and Julia – the three girls from the village in Northamptonshire whose childhood we had been honoured to share – had sent him a card. They told him how much we had meant to them as children, and that we had taught them a lot. I read their words out to John as he lay there unconscious, hoping that his spirit would be able to hear.

And then I did EFT to help him with his passing. He let out one last breath, and was gone. I drove home with the tears streaming down my face.

Much to my regret I was unable to attend John's funeral because we had some fifty CHC members arriving in the Midlands to be filmed for the CHC documentary on the day Simon had chosen. As I was John's ex, Simon made it clear that I was surplus to requirements.

Simon told me that John's funeral was a sorry affair, with a few stray neighbours attending. Simon made an address about John's sorry life. I was upset about this – because it wasn't all sorry. We had shared some great times together, and John had had friends who thought the world of him.

Years down the line I had an insight about this tragic man's life and took the opportunity to ask a psychologist acquaintance if she might be willing to answer my questions about this. She agreed to do so. I told her:

"My late ex-husband was a lovely man in many ways but he was tortured as a child. His father used to lock him in a room and torture him for hours on end, including putting his face in a bucket of water and holding a wet sponge to his face. This is from being a tiny toddler. So he was pretty damaged.

"Every now and then, out of the blue, he would turn into a crazy violent person. I found the best thing to do was to hold eye contact with him, but I noticed that he wasn't inside. Also, he genuinely seemed to have no knowledge or memory of his violent outbursts.

"So my question is, does someone with multiple personality disorder not know or remember who or what they have been when they slip into another personality state?"

"What you describe is something I work with every day in some of my patients who have been severely traumatised," Katherine replied.

"You are describing what I would describe as a dissociative defence. These defences protect the sense of 'I am' (whatever theoretical model we use to explain this) from experiences that are too overwhelming to be digested, learned from, and included in the evolving sense of self – experiences that are genuinely traumatic. These defences indeed come into play in multiple personality disorder, as well as other diagnostic categories. Your ex-husband would have had to seek help in order for a definitive diagnosis to be made. Reading between the lines, his story is a tragic one. I am so sorry.

"The traumatised part of the mind becomes a law unto itself and is compelled to re-enact the trauma because it knows nothing else... And yes, indeed, when a person's psyche has had to split in this way, the different states of being do not know one another and must never know one another because the threat of the two coming together is greater than that of physical death. Untreated, people are at risk of suicide – which, when the issues are understood, can be understood as a form of self-protection.

"This is all dreadfully upsetting for those who love the person, the trauma resonates and goes on resonating until the scream that could not be screamed in the past is heard in the present (that is my way of putting it).

"I hope these thoughts are helpful to you. Please ask anything further that you want to."

John taught me something invaluable, and this is that we cannot judge one-another, because we are all programmed by our childhoods, our experiences and education, and our subconscious thoughts and fears. I personally think that this is a BIG one to know, and it changes the way you live your life and treat others.

I find it helpful, useful and life-enhancing to seek to avoid hatred and any need for revenge or even reparation. Instead, I look for something to love in everyone whilst working to change the system for the better.

We are all human beings, doing the best we can with the knowledge we have available. We cannot possibly judge another human being. Rather, it would be better to iron out our own myriad faults and get ourselves out of the prison of the mind, which no-one else can do for us.

I told my sister Leslie that a psychologist had confirmed that John may have had a multiple personality disorder, and Leslie was terribly upset for him. "But the other John was lovely," she said. "It's just a pity that so few people got to see that John."

Every now and again on Facebook, someone will put a poster up along the lines of 'you are responsible for your actions', but I know that this isn't always true. Deeply traumatised children become traumatised adults, and they're not always in control of their behaviour. They are psychologically incapable of controlling what they do, let alone, in some cases, even knowing what they do. Human brains are programmed by their experiences.

Knowing this, I feel horror at my own government when it drops bombs on children in foreign countries. They are creating terrorised people who may themselves become terrorists. The cycle of harm and enmity will never end while our governments make human sacrifices – "collateral damage" – of this kind.

We all know that these wars are waged for the benefit of the wealthy elite. Iraq for its oil, Afghanistan and Syria so that oil and gas pipelines could be laid; always so that wealthy corporations and billionaires in the shadows can dish out the spoils. However he met his end, David Kelly, the expert who was vocal about the non-existent weapons of mass destruction, laid down his life for the truth that affects us all.

I hope that in some way John's scream has finally been heard by sharing this with you. He did so much to help the dogs, however much his personality may have offended others.

Analysing my own life as best as anyone can from such close quarters, I believe that I developed unusually deep relationships with my dogs *because* the relationship I had with my husband was difficult and isolated me from others who were unable to accept him. My dogs gave me people to love and, I am convinced, they loved me. Because of them I was able to choose love rather than hate.

I'm very grateful that I was with John when he died. I had and still have a great deal of love and compassion for him, and even gratitude. He had a brilliant mind but he was very damaged.

Without John, I would never have started Canine Health Concern or even kept it going; neither would I have written books and articles to help my fellow dog lovers raise healthy, long-lived, dogs. I firmly believe that God uses our faults for good if we let Him, and that John's life was not ultimately a sorry one. In terms of the effect he had on the lives of dogs and dog-loving strangers, his life was a triumph – whether people know it or not.

Christ said: 'Forgive them Lord, they know not what they do,' and I feel sure that John will be on the other side, rested, and at peace.

Chapter 72

People power

On the day of John's funeral, fifty or so CHC members assembled in the centre of the UK, and traipsed up and down a field with their vibrantly healthy dogs. Then they sat individually in front of camera, attesting to their joy now that they had healthy dogs – with no or minimum vaccines, and lots of raw fresh meaty bones to eat.

When Rob and I watched the final cut we got overly emotional and cheered and clapped. It was a spectacular group achievement. Our DVD was named, *In Search of the Truth About Dogs, a guide to natural canine healthcare*. Rob's beautiful music provided the background themes, and we were delighted with the job Brian James, Nick and Andrew had done. The next task was to get it out there.

In time, we had many letters from members who told us they had been badgering their friends and neighbours about vaccines and pet food for years to no avail, but once they could be persuaded to sit down and watch the film, they saw the light.

Some criticised us because it wasn't in depth enough, but its intention was to break through the minds of those who were unwilling to look at the natural rearing message at all. The idea was that they sit down for half an hour in front of the TV and the film would do the work – and it appeared to be doing it very well.

One morning Rob came into the kitchen where I was making breakfast. "I've had an email from Sally Morris," he said. "Her dog's got CDRM."

We had a chat about it.

"Also," he said, "Beth Owen wants ten copies of *What Vets* for her puppy pack."

"That's good," I replied.

"Oh, and we've won an award."

"What?" I asked.

"The Dog Writer's Association of America – we won the Best DVD of 2008 Award. Apparently it's called a Maxwell."

"What?" I repeated with a big smile on my face. "We've won an *award*, and you come in here and casually chat about dogs and books, and then you think to add that we've actually won an award?"

I went straight into the office to see what it was all about. Turns out that, according to the Dog Writer's Association of America, a Maxwell is the dog-world equivalent of an Oscar. I couldn't wait to tell our members and Brian James – because although I received the award as the writer of the DVD, the credit has to go to our members who forked out enough money to pay for a professional TV-ready film and, of course, to the producer of that film and his team.

Chapter 73

If you can name something, it ceases to have power over you

The question remains: Why do the government and the vaccine industry promote annual pet vaccination when it's unnecessary? If you can understand why something happens, then generally you can do something about it. Diagnosis is key – if you know what's causing an itch, chances are you can resolve the itch.

I've always veered away from the suggestion that vets over-vaccinate because booster income accounts for the veterinary practice's profitability, irrespective of the harm caused. My impulse is always to look for the good in people, rather than sink to the lowest possible conclusion. Although superficial evidence doesn't necessarily support the view that humans always do the best they can with the knowledge they have available, I think that if you look below the surface, it's generally the case.

But doing the 'best they can' is a complex decision. Vets, as an example, have to do the best for themselves and their families, for their staff, for their businesses, and also for their clients and patients. Sometimes the interests of one don't coincide with the interests of others. There are also powerful influences that seek to manipulate the profession.

Vaccine company executives and government agents may also know that a particular product is causing harm, but they also have to make complex decisions about their jobs, families, companies, and even the state. And because roles are compartmentalised in corporations, I believe that few employees actually understand the harm their products cause.

Whichever way you look at it, vaccines are big business – so the profit motive has to be behind at least some of the decision-making process.

According to marketsandmarkets.com, the animal vaccines market will be worth $8.6 Billion by 2018 [1].

However, when you look at the animal vaccine market and seek to understand it, you also need to look at the larger vaccine market, which encompasses human vaccines. Both, at their roots, are the same industry. According to Statista, 'the statistical portal' [2], these were the Top 10 biotech and pharmaceutical companies worldwide based on market value in 2014 (in billions of US dollars):

Johnson & Johnson – 277.8 billion
Roche – 258.5 billion

Novartis – 229.8 billion
Pfizer – 205.4 billion
Merck – 166.9 billion
Sanofi – 138.1 billion
GlaxoSmithKline – 128.9 billion
Gilead Science – 109 billion
Novo Nordisk – 100.8 billion
Amgen – 93.1 billion

By contrast, depending on whose figures you look at and when they were prepared, the UK's national debt (how much Britain owes) is over a trillion pounds. Wikipedia stated on the day I looked, "Due to the Government's significant budget deficit, the national debt is increasing by approximately £73.5 billion per annum, or around £1.4 billion each week.." The American government owes about $18.2 trillion at time of writing. [3]

The pharmaceutical industry is in the black, whereas governments tend to operate in the red. If money is power, who – then – is more powerful?

Bloomberg reported that Merck's sales of "Gardasil, a vaccine to help prevent certain diseases caused by four types of human papillomavirus (HPV), were $665 million, an increase of 15 percent for the *quarter*. The increase was partially offset by lower sales in Japan due to the government's decision to suspend proactive recommendation of HPV vaccines in the country." This report is now only available to professional service subscribers.

Despite being a lucrative vaccine, Gardasil is nevertheless throwing up many adverse reaction reports. The family support group thetruthaboutgardasil.com, asserts that they are not telling you that thousands of girls are having adverse reactions to it. The group states, "Since Gardasil's introduction in 2006, the Vaccine Adverse Event Reporting System (VAERS) has received more than 20,000 reports of adverse side effects reportedly related to Gardasil. These reports include serious adverse side effects including Guillain Barre, lupus, seizures, rheumatoid arthritis, and multiple sclerosis, among others. There also have been 92 reported deaths among girls who received the Gardasil vaccine."

Others are having seizures, strokes, dizziness, fatigue, weakness, headaches, stomach pains, vomiting, muscle pain and weakness, joint pain, autoimmune problems, chest pains, hair loss, personality changes, insomnia, tremors, heart problems, paralysis, rashes, nerve pain, fainting, and vision and hearing loss. There is no known treatment, no insurance cover, and no effective medical help.

Even the *British Medical Journal* has reported on the carnage [5]: "The human papilloma virus (HPV) vaccine Gardasil®24, sublicensed to Merck, is believed to cause adverse side effects including seizures, blood clots, paralysis and even death in some young women. It is also thought to induce premature ovarian failure—sterility—in some cases."

A CBS News item in 2009 reported that one of the lead researchers for Gardasil was speaking out about its risks, benefits and aggressive marketing [6]. Diane Harper said young girls and their parents should receive more complete warnings before receiving the vaccine to prevent cervical cancer. Harper helped design and carry out the Phase II and III safety and effectiveness studies to get Gardasil approved, and authored many of the published papers about it. She has been a paid speaker and consultant to Merck. It's highly unusual for a researcher to publicly criticise a medicine or vaccine she helped get approved.

Harper said that there is no data showing that it remains effective beyond five years. This raises questions about the CDC's recommendation that the series of shots be given to girls as young as 11-years old. "If we vaccinate 11 year olds and the protection doesn't last... we've put them at harm from side effects, small but real, for no benefit. The benefit to public health is nothing, there is no reduction in cervical cancers, they are just postponed, unless the protection lasts for at least 15 years, and over 70% of all sexually active females of all ages are vaccinated."

Harper also said that enough serious side effects have been reported after Gardasil use that the vaccine could prove riskier than the cervical cancer it purports to prevent. Cervical cancer is usually entirely curable when detected early through normal screenings.

On the other hand, Wikipedia asserts: "The Food and Drug Administration (FDA) and the Centers for Disease Control and Prevention (CDC) consider the vaccine to be safe." [7]

And on yet another hand, in an interview in the April 2014 issue of French *Principes de Santé,* former Gardasil doctor and Merck employee Dr Bernard Dalbergue, said, "The full extent of the Gardasil scandal needs to be assessed: everyone knew when this vaccine was released on the American market that it would prove to be worthless.

"Diane Harper, a major opinion leader in the United States, was one of the first to blow the whistle, pointing out the fraud and scam of it all.

"I predict that Gardasil will become the greatest medical scandal of all time because at some point in time, the evidence will add up to prove that this vaccine, technical and scientific feat that it may be, has absolutely no effect on cervical cancer and that all the very many adverse effects which destroy lives and even kill, serve no other purpose than to generate profit for the manufacturers.

"Gardasil is useless and costs a fortune! In addition, decision-makers at all levels are aware of it! Cases of Guillain-Barré syndrome, paralysis of the lower limbs, vaccine-induced MS and vaccine-induced encephalitis can be found, whatever the vaccine."

I assume you get the picture: Pharmaceutical companies are richer than governments, and victims of vaccines are generally out on their own. And they continue to push a questionable vaccine despite safety concerns, and we're told it's actually safe. Tie this dichotomy of information in with other information, such as Wikipedia refusing to carry studies showing the effectiveness of homeopathy and EFT, then you have to ask what Wikipedia's financial backers are up to.

The advice you are given about vaccination by medical doctors and veterinarians is as much to do with politics and big business profits as it is to do with the laudable aim of halting disease.

But who actually developed the HPV vaccines? We're led to believe that they're products developed by Merck and GSK, but it turns out that the underlying technology originated in American government laboratories – the NIH [8]. Does this mean that the American government gets royalties each time these vaccines are injected? And does this explain why the Japanese, as you shall see in a moment, directly mention pressure put upon governments in relation to trade negotiations with superpowers?

Another link credits a GAVI scientist, Ian Frazer, with the HPV vaccine's invention [9]. So let's see if we can follow the money.

The following extract is from *FierceBiotech*, the Biotech industry's daily monitor, July 2009:

In times of crisis, Big Pharma turns to vaccines

Long being regarded as an unattractive market, vaccines have re-emerged as a successful growth driver for Big Pharma. The launch and rapid uptake of novel, high-price products such as Wyeth's Prevnar or Merck & Co's Gardasil, along with the emergence of novel vaccine technologies and favourable legislation have brought vaccines back into the main focus of pharmaceutical and biotech companies.

This report has more meaning when you realise that the time is up on many of the world's most lucrative pharmaceutical money spinners – the 'blockbuster drugs'. Their patents have run out or are running out, and the manufacturers stand to lose billions in income. They're failing in the search for new useful drugs, and are looking for something else to drive profits – and that something else is vaccines.

And then Australian vaccine researcher Elizabeth Hart sent me a paper from the Indian *Journal of Medical Ethics* [10] which didn't pull its punches on HPV vaccines or the commercialisation of healthcare.

The paper, 'Lessons learnt in Japan from adverse reactions to the HPV vaccine: a medical ethics perspective', is so frank, I'm going to sound a drum roll for its authors: Hirokuni Beppu, Masumi Minaguchi, Kiyoshi Uchide, Kunihiko Kumamoto, Masato Sekiguchi, Yukari Yaju. Thank you for your honesty and integrity. Let's work together to ensure that people learn the truth, and that this paper isn't just another in a long line assigned to a dusty shelf where it doesn't see the light of day.

The authors wrote: "HPV vaccines were approved later in Japan than in the western countries (October 2009 for Cervarix, and July 2011 for Gardasil). The vaccination rate was initially low. However, after a campaign for the promotion of the vaccine, which led to government subsidisation of the cost of the vaccine in November 2010, the vaccination rate increased exponentially. This was followed by an unexpected increase in reports of adverse events (AEs). Importantly, these vaccines gave rise to *a large number of serious AEs.*

"Other key features of the ADRs [adverse drug reactions] reported with HPV vaccines are the diversity of the symptoms and their development in a multi-layered manner over an extended period of time.

"The ADRs include complex, multi-system symptoms, such as seizures; disturbance of consciousness; systemic pain, including headache, myalgia, arthralgia, back pain and other pain; motor dysfunction, such as paralysis, muscular weakness, exhaustion and involuntary movements; numbness and sensory disturbances; autonomic symptoms, including dizziness, hypotension, tachycardia, nausea, vomiting and diarrhoea; respiratory dysfunction, including dyspnoea and asthma; endocrine disorders, such as menstrual disorder and hypermenorrhoea; hypersensitivity to light and sound; psychological symptoms, such as anxiety, frustration, hallucinations and overeating; higher brain dysfunction and cognitive impairments, including memory impairment, disorientation and loss of concentration; and sleep disorders, including hypersomnia and sudden sleep attacks. In some cases, these symptoms impair learning and result in extreme fatigue and decreased motivation, having a negative impact on everyday life. The situation in Japan is similar to that in other countries which have also reported a specific cluster of serious and complex symptoms that develop across multiple body systems over an extended period of time.

"On January 20, 2014, the expert advisory committee established by the MHLW presented the view that the diverse pain and motor dysfunctions experienced by many individuals after HPV vaccination comprised psychosomatic reactions to anxiety or stimulatory pain caused by needle injection [viz, it's all in the mind], and were not due to any components of the vaccine itself. However, doctors and researchers who examined patients with post-vaccination symptoms arrived at a completely different conclusion, highlighting both the characteristic symptoms and course, which are difficult to explain as psychosomatic reactions.

"Thus, the safety of the HPV vaccine remains far from certain in Japan, justifying the public's strong distrust. Recognising the potentially negative influence of these events on public opinion in other countries, *pharmaceutical companies initiated a counter-intervention strategy through public and private organisations, such as the World Health Organisation (WHO). The Global Advisory Committee on Vaccine Safety (GACVS),* one of the WHO's advisory committees, claimed it had "not found any safety issue that would alter its recommendations for the use of the vaccine" and criticised the MHLW's decision to withdraw active recommendation.

"Regarding Japan, the GACVS statement says that 'review of clinical data by the national expert committee led to a conclusion that symptoms were not related to the vaccine'. However, there are major problems with the expert committee's investigation.

"The most serious problem is that very few members of the committee actually examined patients with post-vaccination symptoms. The committee's investigation focused exclusively on pain and motor dysfunction, and ignored many other diverse symptoms that have been observed. Further, cases in which adverse events occurred more than a month after vaccination were excluded from consideration on the ground that most adverse effects of vaccines occur within one month of vaccination. However, subsequent studies have clarified that symptoms commonly appear even after a considerable period of time has elapsed since vaccination.

"The methods used for determining psychosomatic reactions to be the cause of symptoms are also open to question.

"Further, as *11 of the 15 members of the expert advisory committee have conflicts of interest with vaccine manufacturers,* the public is justified in requesting that a more diverse range of scientists reviews the relevant data. Thus, the safety of the HPV vaccine remains far from certain in Japan, justifying the public's strong concerns. Outside Japan, Jefferson et al and Gõtzsche et al also expressed concern about the nature and quality of regulation of the HPV vaccine by the European Medicines Agency.

"The proponents of the HPV vaccines claim that they are 98% – 100% effective in preventing cervical cancer. In reality, however, the absolute risk reduction (ARR) provided by HPV vaccines is, at most, 0.1% – 0.7%, on the basis of calculations using the existing data. Further, this indicates only the reduction in the risk of developing pre-cancerous lesions, while the risk of developing cervical cancer remains unknown.

"In the previous sections, we discussed various issues regarding the safety and effectiveness of the HPV vaccine. It is now appropriate to ask how such questionable vaccines have come into widespread use. The answer, at least with respect to Japan, can be found in a structural flaw, combined specifically with the following factors: (i) aggressive promotion by the pharmaceutical industry, *(ii) trade negotiations by economic superpowers,* and (iii) contemporary medicine, which is characterised by overconfidence in technology and a lack of humility with respect to listening to patients' complaints.

"According to information obtained by Medwatcher Japan under the Transparency Guideline for the Relation between Corporate Activities and Medical Institutions of the Japan Pharmaceutical Manufacturers Association, the funds received by the Expert Board from vaccine manufacturers amounted to ¥73,500,000 (¥35,000,000 in 2012 and ¥38,500,000 in 2013) [¥73,500,000 is over £500,000]. In addition, the *secretary of the Expert Board was found to have been working at GlaxoSmithKline Co.* as the Director of Marketing for vaccines for up to eight months prior to the launch of Cervarix. These facts strongly suggest that the activity of the Expert Board was not altruistic, but was actually disguised promotion.

"*The promotion of the HPV vaccine during Japan–US trade negotiations has also created pressure on Japan to adopt the vaccine.* For many years, the promotion of vaccination has been one of the most pressing requirements in trade negotiations with the US, Japan's most important trading partner. The Center for Strategic and International Studies, a civilian think tank that is part of the US military–industrial complex, criticised the indecisiveness of Japan's government in reports issued in May 2014 and April 2015, reflecting the irritation of US industries.

"Basic defects inherent in the medical community underlie the issue of the HPV vaccine. In 2004, Sheldon Krimsky pointed out the increasing influence of commercialism in academic science and biomedical research in his book, *Science in the private interest.* He wrote, '...the mix of science and commerce continues to erode the ethical standards of research and diminish public confidence in its results'.

"Science is now misused to protect the interests of the pharmaceutical industry, and has been used to deny the causal relationship between the drug and its adverse reactions. Many researchers and experts are attempting to exclude inconvenient truths from consideration.

"This historical background has created a situation in which the mass media and regulators cannot easily ignore the victims' complaints about the side-effects of new vaccines. It is here that we may find a clue on how to solve this problem. It is necessary to enhance transparency at every step of the approval process for pharmaceutical products, from new-drug development to post-marketing surveillance. At the same time, it is crucial to strengthen the management of conflicts of interest, and develop a system by which citizens can participate directly and have a voice in the planning of public health policy."

Frankly, if we made everyone sit down and read this paper, they would lose their vaccine-induced rose-tinted spectacles and get real to what is happening. But, then, how do you *make* people open their eyes?

Chapter 74
Can you dance the fiasco?

When I ask why the British government won't put an end to unnecessary vaccines for animals, I'm also drawn to ask why governments around the world fund vaccines that don't work, but which deliver harm.

In 2009, for example, the world was herded into a panic over an allegedly looming swine flu pandemic. As a result, shares of the world's largest flu vaccine makers rallied the day after WHO declared its first official flu pandemic, for the H1N1 virus, since 1968 [1].

Shares of GSK, AstraZeneca, Novartis and Baxter all advanced at least 4%. Novartis was gearing up to fast-track H1N1 vaccines, culturing batches of the virus which it received from the CDC.

A *Kalorama* report [2] predicted more than a doubling of vaccine sales by 2013. "2008 was another 'stellar year' for the world vaccine market", they chirped, "with sales growing by nearly a quarter in the year".

Baxter filed a swine flu vaccine process patent a year ahead of the 'pandemic', and Novavax saw its stock soar 75 percent after the company announced it would be working with the NIH to evaluate its first batch of H1N1 vaccine.

Ninety million doses of the swine flu vaccine had been ordered by the UK government.

Meanwhile, *Pulse*, a newspaper intended for 'health professionals only' reported that GPs were accusing the government of ratcheting up fear over swine flu; that the chief medical officer, Sir Liam Donaldson at the Department of Health, was scaremongering and plunging the nation into fear – without any evidence that the virus was in any way worse than normal winter flu. [3]

Newspapers reported that new vaccines involve years of clinical trials, but the new swine flu vaccine was to be approved by regulators in just five days. This meant that the public could be counted on to line up as experimental guinea pigs.

One problem, of course, is that governments around the world have also set up vaccine damage compensation schemes which protect vaccine manufacturers from expensive claims. There's a limit on any compensation you might, if you're lucky, get from your government – and even then you have to prove that your life has been substantially ruined before you'll get anything. That's if you're still alive to fight for it.

A UK government website [4] states: "If you're severely disabled as a result of a vaccination against certain diseases, you could get a one-off tax-free payment of £120,000. This is called a Vaccine Damage Payment…" The site goes on to state that it can affect other benefits and entitlements like working tax credit, child tax credit, pension credit, and housing benefit. Jeez.

Through the 1970s and 1980s, the number of lawsuits brought against vaccine manufacturers increased dramatically, and manufacturers made large payouts to individuals and families injured by vaccines. In this environment of increasing litigation, mounting legal fees, and large jury rewards, many pharmaceutical companies left the vaccine business. By the end of 1984, only one US company still manufactured the DTP vaccine, and other vaccines were losing manufacturers as well. So governments stepped in. [5,6]

Under the US National Vaccine Injury Compensation Program (NVICP) [7], those claiming a vaccine injury from a covered vaccine can't sue a vaccine manufacturer without first filing a claim with the US Court of Federal Claims. Certain medical events are presumed to be side effects of vaccination as long as no other cause is found. The claim filer is reimbursed according to a formula, provided that all the medical records meet NCVIA standards and that review by the US Department of Justice determines that all legal standards have been met. If a claim is denied, or if the claim is approved and the claimant rejects the compensation, only then may the claimant file a civil lawsuit.

The US Vaccine Injury Table shows how hard it is to make a claim. Only if your vaccine reaction fits its limited list within a very limited timeframe will it be presumed that the vaccine was the cause of the injury or condition unless another cause is found. For example, if you received the tetanus vaccines and had a severe allergic reaction (anaphylaxis) *within 4 hours* after receiving the vaccine, then it is presumed that the tetanus vaccine caused the injury if no other cause is found. So if you're accepting a shot, you'd better hope you die in time to get up to $250,000!

Don't you think it's interesting that vaccines, touted as 'safe', merit a whole damage limitation category of their own? Think about this. And if manufacturers didn't think it financially safe to carry on selling the DTP vaccine, why would you want to inject it into your child?

Moving forward to May 20th, 2009, *Bloomberg* reported that the man who helped to develop the Tamiflu anti-viral drug believed that the swine flu 'epidemic' had been caused by human error in a laboratory [8]. *Bloomberg* mentioned that, "earlier this year the avian flu virus made its way into a consignment of seasonal flu vaccines, which were destined for around 18 countries in Europe. Some scientists also suspect that the

Russian flu outbreak of 1977 was started when a virus was accidentally released from a laboratory."

Baxter flu vaccines contaminated with H5N1 (the human form of avian flu) were received by labs in the Czech Republic, Germany and Slovenia. The contamination incident came to light when the subcontractor in the Czech Republic inoculated ferrets with the product and they died [9]. Ferrets shouldn't die from exposure to human H3N2 flu viruses. But whilst H5N1 doesn't easily infect people, H3N2 viruses do. If someone exposed to a mixture of the two had been simultaneously infected with both strains, he or she could have served as an incubator for a hybrid virus able to transmit easily to people.

That mixing process, called reassortment, is one of two ways pandemic viruses are created.

Initially, Baxter refused to reveal how the vaccines were contaminated with H5N1, saying it was a "trade secret." After increased pressure, they claimed that pure H5N1 batches were sent by accident.

According to fiercevaccines.com (an industry journal) [10], the fact that Baxter mixed the deadly H5N1 virus with a mix of H3N2 seasonal flu viruses is hard to understand. "Baxter International has confirmed that vaccine shipments sent to subcontractors in Czech Republic, Slovenia and Germany were contaminated with live H5N1 avian flu viruses. The contaminated product, which Baxter calls 'experimental virus material,' was a mix of H3N2 seasonal flu viruses and H5N1 viruses produced at the company's research facility in Orth-Donau. The problem was discovered when ferrets inoculated with the experimental mix died. Baxter was notified on February 6, but has kept quiet about the details surrounding the mix-up, the Canadian Press reports."

The H5N1 virus on its own has killed hundreds of people, but it becomes more airborne when combined with flu viruses. The effect could have been a potent, airborne, deadly biological weapon.

And then ... drum roll ... Baxter secured more lucrative government contracts to produce swine flu vaccines. Makes you wonder. Baxter wasn't reprimanded – it was apparently rewarded after making a mistake that could have killed millions of people.

But the 2009 so-called swine flu epidemic, like the avian flu before it, proved to be no different to regular seasonal flu. Meanwhile, governments handed billions over to the pharmaceutical industry in a sort of reverse tax bonus. The *Independent* reported that the no-show pandemic cost the UK government £1.2 billion [11].

Swiftly, reports of vaccine reactions started to circulate.

In Canada, after 6.6 million doses of H1N1 vaccine had been

distributed there were reports of mild adverse events in 598 people including nausea, dizziness, headache, fever, vomiting, and swelling or soreness at the injection site. There were also reports of tingling lips or tongue, difficulty breathing, hives, and skin rashes. Thirty six people had serious reactions, including anaphylaxis and convulsions. Meanwhile, GlaxoSmithKline recalled a batch of vaccines in Canada. [12]

According to many press reports, hundreds of thousands of swine flu shots for children were recalled because the vaccines had 'lost strength'. The shots, made by Sanofi-Pasteur, were for children between the ages of six months and three years. Despite the recall, parents were told not to worry, and not to bother doing anything if their children had received the defective shot. "The vaccine is safe and effective," said CDC experts. In February, Novartis recalled five lots of seasonal flu vaccine under similar circumstances. [13]

In the USA 46 million doses had been distributed and 3,182 adverse events were reported. The CDC stated that the "vast majority" were mild, with about one serious adverse event in 260,000 doses. Of the 3,182 reports, 177 (6%) involved serious health events (defined as life threatening or resulting in death, major disability, abnormal conditions at birth, hospitalization, or extension of an existing hospitalization). [14]

In Japan around 15 million people had been vaccinated and 1,900 cases of side effects and 104 cases of death were reported. The health ministry announced that it would conduct epidemiologic investigations. [15]

In France, around five million people had been vaccinated by 30 December 2009. 2,657 cases of side effects, eight cases of intrauterine death and five cases of miscarriages were reported [16]. Fewer people were vaccinated in France than in America, but the adverse event rate was proportionally much higher – which means they either had different vaccines, or the adverse event reporting system was better in France.

In 2010, The Swedish Medical Products Agency and the Finnish National Institute for Health and Welfare received reports of narcolepsy as suspected adverse reactions following GlaxoSmithKline's Pandemrix flu vaccine. Narcolepsy is a rare disorder which causes people to fall asleep suddenly. The reports concerned children aged 12–16 years occurring one to two months after vaccination. It was concluded by Finnish authorities that there was a clear connection between the Pandemrix vaccination campaign of 2009 and 2010 and a narcolepsy epidemic in Finland. [17]

At the end of March 2011, an MPA press release stated: "Results from a Swedish registry based cohort study indicate a 4-fold increased risk of narcolepsy in children and adolescents below the age of 20 vaccinated with Pandemrix, compared to children of the same age that were not vaccinated." Narcolepsy is a life sentence.

Other agencies, such as the NIH in the US and WHO played the side-effects down. [18,19] Apparently, "No substantial differences between H1N1 and seasonal influenza vaccines were noted in the proportion or types of serious adverse events reported." – which is worrying as it indicates that normal seasonal influenza vaccines can destroy people's lives, too. However, in October 2014, the British government bizarrely introduced a programme to give flu shots to children between the ages of two and 16, starting with the youngest [20].

By March 2014, *International Business Times* was reporting that the Pandemrix vaccine – for a pandemic that never materialised – had caused narcolepsy and cataplexy in hundreds of children across Europe, with news that it could do this in one in every 16,000 people receiving the vaccine. [21]

Narcolepsy affects a person's sleeping cycle, leaving them unable to sleep for more than 90 minutes at a time, and causing them to fall unconscious during the day. The condition damages mental function and memory, and can lead to hallucinations and mental illness. Cataplexy causes a person to lose consciousness when they are experiencing heightened emotion, including when they are laughing.

The Pandemrix vaccine was manufactured by pharmaceuticals giant GlaxoSmithKline, which refused to supply governments unless it was indemnified against any claim for damage caused. [22] The company will pay the bill, and claim the money back from the government.

Of course you'll find many sites on the internet from bods claiming that these claims aren't true, and that the vaccine was really safe. In which case, why did the British government require GSK to pay out £60 million to brain damaged people who received the vaccine?

"There's no doubt in my mind whatsoever that Pandemrix increased the occurrence of narcolepsy onset in children in some countries – and probably in most countries," Emmanuelle Mignot, a specialist in sleep disorder at Stanford University in the United States told Reuters. The paper was originally published in the journal *Science Translational Medicine* in December 2013. It was later retracted. Mignot had been paid by GSK to research the effects of the drug, and GSK continued to support him after the retraction according to Reuters on August 7th 2014 [23].

Among those allegedly affected were NHS medical staff, many of whom are now unable to do their jobs because of the symptoms. They were planning to sue the government for millions in lost earnings. However, the vast majority of patients allegedly affected – around 80% – were children.

Despite a 2011 warning from the European Medicines Agency against using the vaccine on those under 20 and a study indicating a 13-

fold heightened risk of narcolepsy in vaccinated children, GSK refused to acknowledge a link [24]

Luisa Dillner, writing in *The Guardian* [25], said: "I asked Tom Jefferson, the lead author of the Cochrane Review on Vaccines for Preventing Influenza in Healthy Children, which looked at findings from 75 studies, if I should give my four-and-a-half-year-old the nasal [flu] vaccine spray.

"No," he says, because the trials show a reporting bias on the harms of the live attenuated influenza vaccine (the form of vaccine delivered nasally). "Influenza vaccines are about marketing and not science," he says. "We have few trials, and masses of very poor quality observational evidence. We have presented evidence of considerable reporting bias, which governments continue to ignore. The science is missing and so making an informed decision is very difficult."

The people who take it upon themselves to make decisions about whether or not you or your children or pets should have vaccines deal in numbers and statistics. They don't deal with the personal impact of their decisions. Vaccines are safe, and reactions are rare, blah blah blah. But this is not true for the people whose lives have been ruined by a vaccine the populace was frightened into submitting to – for a pandemic that didn't materialise.

Ann Ridyard runs a raw feeding business in the Wirral and is an active CHC supporter. Ann hosted an evening talk for me, and her mum and dad gave me a real Wirral welcome and invited me to stay in their lovely home. Ann's mum Lilian Derbyshire developed Guillain-Barre syndrome a few weeks after a flu shot and her life remains in danger over six years later. Statistics released in March, 2014 by the US Department of Health and Human Services revealed that the flu vaccine remains the top vaccine to cause injuries which are being compensated through the vaccine court, and that Guillain-Barré Syndrome, a crippling disease, remains the top injury being awarded compensation due to the seasonal flu vaccine. [26,27]

This year Lilian was back in hospital, with Ann posting the family's trauma on Facebook. Bear in mind that Lilian has never been well since she contracted GBS:

"Update on Mum: It's an incredible story for anybody who has followed it, but we appear to have made it through the woods and out the other side. We are now in a muddy place. They told us she wouldn't make the first 24 hours (sepsis, pneumonia, kidney trauma, very low oxygen) . . . she did . . .they told us she wouldn't make the next 24 hours . . . she did . . . they told us every day for nearly the first two weeks that we would lose her . . . we didn't. She had a heart attack, the pneumonia returned, they told us that we would lose her . . . we didn't. They brought her round, she promptly pulled out her feeding tube, refused another and demanded food. They told us she would never breathe again unaided, they told us that the kind of support she needed could only be given in a hospital or specialised setting, they had a no resuscitation note on her file. We were given the 'turning off machine' chat more times than I care to remember, she was given her last rights!! Twice!! . . . Every time she defied them. Again my wonderful Mother proves them wrong . . . SHE BREATHES unaided!

"We are six weeks in, my Mum no longer has tubes, monitors, lines and bags attached to her. So now they are talking about letting her out. Mum still has a lot going on and they say we will have home carers. This is new territory for all of us, but apparently it's support for her in the home as she still has the Gillian-Barre issues. So our dream of having her home for Christmas may still happen . . . Still praying, but also worried how we will cope."

A week later, Lilian was out of hospital with a team of carers on board, then three weeks later she was rushed back into hospital. Ann wrote:

"3am and mum's been admitted back into hospital. Breathing is not too good. She has infection and pneumonia back again so back on oxygen and, for some bizarre reason, they have told her that they will not be able to resuscitate should she have a heart attack – why haven't they told us? Feel so stressed it is unreal."

The family is unaware whether Lilian's plight has been registered as a vaccine adverse event. Let's be clear about Guillain-Barre syndrome, which happens to real people: It begins with tingling and weakness starting in your feet and legs and spreading to your upper body and arms. As it progresses, muscle weakness can evolve into paralysis. Signs and symptoms may include prickling, pins and needles in your fingers, toes, ankles or wrists; weakness in your legs that spreads to your upper body; unsteady walking or inability to walk or climb stairs; difficulty with eye or facial movements, including speaking, chewing or swallowing; severe pain; difficulty with bladder control or bowel function; rapid heart rate; low or high blood pressure; difficulty breathing; and choking on your own saliva.

About 80% of patients have a complete recovery within a few months to a year, although minor findings may persist, such as areflexia (an absence of reflexes). About 5–10% recover with severe disability, with most cases involving severe proximal motor and sensory axonal damage with inability of axonal regeneration (neurological and central nervous system diseases). Despite improvements in treatment and supportive care, the death rate is still about 2–3%, even in the best intensive care units. Worldwide, the death rate runs slightly higher at 4%, mostly from a lack of availability of life-support equipment during the lengthy plateau lasting four to six weeks, and in some cases up to one year, when a ventilator is needed in the worst cases. About 5–10% of patients have one or more late relapses, in which case they are then classified as having chronic inflammatory demyelinating polyneuropathy (caused by damage to the myelin sheath, the fatty covering that wraps around and protects nerve fibres) of the peripheral nerves.

So, would you rather take your chances with the flu and suffer for a week or two, or would you prefer to run the risk of the above? Are you up for a numbers game; for Russian roulette? Your government probably thinks you should be up for the gamble, and its agents will tell you that vaccines are safe... before they walk away to wash their hands.

Chapter 75

Marketing a pandemic

So many people are encouraged by their doctors to get their flu shots each year, but it turns out there's no proof that they work, although they do represent a health risk. So once again we need to ask if flu shots are about profits or health?

To determine the *value* of flu vaccines for children, Tom Jefferson, MD, and colleagues at the respected Cochrane Collaboration looked at over a thousand studies. The results were reported in *The Lancet*. Here's the conclusion: "We recorded no convincing evidence that vaccines can reduce mortality, hospital admissions, serious complications, and community transmission of influenza. [1] Doctors read the Lancet, so they must know this.

"Though the US Centers for Disease Control (CDC) and Prevention advises flu vaccines for babies 6-23 months because they tend to suffer more complications once they get the flu, no evidence supports the recommendation."

Lone Simonsen, PhD, and colleagues at the National Institute of Allergy and Infectious Diseases conducted a review of 33 consecutive flu seasons, from 1968 to 2001. Simonsen and colleagues found that the number of flu-related deaths among elderly Americans increased steadily during the 33-year-period, despite the fact that their acceptance of flu vaccinations also steadily increased.

Another study showed that the flu vaccine does not appear to be effective in preventing influenza-related hospitalisations in children, especially children with asthma. In fact, children who get flu vaccine are three times more at risk for hospitalisation than their peers who do not get the vaccine.

Of 48 reports involving more than 66,000 adults, "Vaccination of healthy adults only reduced risk of influenza by 6% and reduced the number of missed work days by less than one day. It did not change the number of people needing to go to hospital or take time off work." [2,3]

I'm just a dog owner with no scientific training. If I can read a report and see that flu vaccines provide little or no benefit but do pose risks, why can't governments, which pay out billions for these virtually useless shots? It's difficult to understand why the flu vaccine, with such poor performance and poor evidence of efficacy, could become such a worldwide phenomenon. And it's even more difficult to understand why the UK government should instigate a nationwide flu vaccine programme for children in 2014, after the publication of the Cochrane Review.

I got in touch with Tom Jefferson from the Cochrane Collaboration and asked him this very question: why?

"I would have thought that the motivation for canine vaccines is very much the same as the motivation for human vaccines," he said. "It's a very complex issue. I think it would be wrong to assume that everyone who supports vaccines is on the payroll of the pharmaceutical industry. That's not the case. They believe in it. They're believers."

It would, it seems, be safer to believe in fairies or, indeed, archangels.

In 2009, according to the *Telegraph*, the UK government was preparing to offload millions of unwanted swine flu vaccines as officials predicted there would be no third wave of the 'pandemic'. Fewer than 5,000 people in Britain were thought to have contracted swine flu by January 9th [4].

Ministers had signed contracts worth £100 million to deliver 90 million vaccines to Britain. The government was considering exercising a break clause in its contract with Baxter, which supplied vaccines used by the NHS. There was no such clause in the GSK contract but ministers were in discussions with the company about future supplies.

David Salisbury, the Department of Health's director of immunisation, admitted that this still left the problem of vaccines which had already been delivered, but added that the government would keep a stock in case the virus returned. A number of other countries also announced plans to sell off their surplus vaccines. Who to? Who in their right mind would want them?

India was luckily in the midst of an alleged H1N1 pandemic by February 2015. Maybe they were persuaded to buy the unwanted vaccines? [5] According to the *Toronto Star*, more than 11,000 cases had been reported since mid-December. However, a report the next day by the *Times of India* [6] stated that the number of H1N1 positive cases touched 241 on Sunday, 22 February. That's a big discrepancy, and not very scientific, making me wonder whether the tabloid media has a reason to inflate the numbers.

An Indian friend told me: "A few years back there was this scare of bird flu and millions of birds were culled and a warning was given to take Tamiflu in case anyone contracted bird flu symptoms. So they are at it again and since they failed miserably with bird flu, the scare of swine flu has appeared and we are seeing daily news of people dying of swine flu. They have got wiser this time hence the deaths being reported. I asked at a lab if people were coming for testing for swine flu and the reply was negligible. This is very wise marketing as our country is a fertile field for selling any drugs or medicines."

Meanwhile the vaccine manufacturers did quite well out of inaccurate pandemic predictions for the fourth quarter of 2009. GSK made $1.7 billion, Novartis got $700 million, and Sanofi-Aventis pocketed a cool $500 million. Apparently you have more chance of being struck by lightning than winning the lotto, but it seems investing in vaccines offers better odds, no matter how dodgy they are.

According to *Pharma News*, the Parliamentary Assembly of the Council of Europe (PACE) planned to hold an emergency debate and inquiry into the influence exerted by drug makers on WHO's global H1N1 flu campaign. The text of the PACE resolution [7] approved by the Assembly stated:

"In order to promote their patented drugs and vaccines against flu, pharmaceutical companies influenced scientists and official agencies responsible for public health standards to alarm governments worldwide and make them squander tight health resources for inefficient vaccine strategies, and needlessly expose millions of healthy people to the risk of an unknown amount of side-effects of insufficiently tested vaccines."

The WHO's "false pandemic" flu campaign was "one of the greatest medicine scandals of the century," according to Wolfgang Wodarg, chairman of the PACE Health Committee, who introduced the parliamentary motion. "The definition of an alarming pandemic must not be under the influence of drug-sellers," he said.

In June 2010, Fiona Godlee, editor-in-chief of the *British Medical Journal*, published an editorial [8] which criticised WHO, saying that an investigation had disclosed that (here we go again) some of the experts advising WHO on the pandemic had financial ties with drug companies which were producing antivirals and vaccines.

For goodness sake – when are they going to get the people with financial ties to the pharmaceutical industry off government committees? And until they do, why should we trust a word they say?

Margaret Chan, Director-General of the WHO, replied stating, "Without question, the BMJ feature and editorial will leave many readers with the impression that WHO's decision to declare a pandemic was at least partially influenced by a desire to boost the profits of the pharmaceutical industry. The bottom line, however, is that decisions to raise the level of pandemic alert were based on clearly defined virological and epidemiological criteria. It is hard to bend these criteria, no matter what the motive".

Nevertheless, the criteria were wrong, and many people paid for it with their lives; the rest of us paid via our taxes. Once again, we pay for this and they give us that.

In August 2010, the *Daily Mail* [9] stated that "a third of the experts advising the World Health Organisation about the swine flu pandemic had ties to drugs firms" and that of the 20 members of the Scientific Advisory Group for Emergencies, which advised the British Government on swine flu, 11 had done work for the pharmaceutical industry or were linked to it through their universities.

Fast forward to June 2013, and here's an article by epidemiologist Tom Jefferson of the Cochrane Collaboration. [10] Entitled, 'Of influenza, flu, potions and key opinion leaders', Jefferson explains that bugs and flu are not necessarily influenza. They are caused by a variety of viruses, but the surest way to create a market is to ramp up an existing problem or manufacture a brand new one. "The finishing touch for creating our market is to get academia, public health agencies and the media so involved in the issue that they are unable (and, in some cases, unwilling) to look critically at what is going on, to think outside the box. An even better move is to get decision makers to make policy and police it. This guarantees unsolvable conflicts and a passport to no change of policy, even in the absence of any valid data to support it."

In the July 2009 Canine Health Concern newsletter, we looked into the advisability, in the face of a potentially deadly flu epidemic, of grasping for the Tamiflu drug, finding – even then – that there was little to support its use, and plenty to be concerned about.

Newspaper and internet reports were telling us that Tamiflu wasn't terribly effective, and it could make some people's condition worse – some patients with influenza are at a higher risk for secondary bacterial infections when on Tamiflu.

Also, Tamiflu wasn't very well tested in the field. Authorities in Japan were expressing concern as some people who took the drug were 'falling from windows and balconies or running into traffic'. According to Roche, two people under the age of 21 died from brain infection, and seven deaths from neuropsychiatric symptoms had also been attributed to use of Tamiflu by adults.

In 2014, Tom Jefferson revealed that the makers of Tamiflu had buried unfavourable reports on the drug, leading to a misleading review by the Cochrane Collaboration. By this time, Tamiflu had generated sales in excess of $18 billion. When, eventually, the Cochrane research team managed to wrestle unfavourable Tamiflu studies from the arms of Roche, the Cochrane team concluded that the benefits of Tamiflu didn't outweigh its harms.

"Worryingly, the welfare of patients seems a secondary consideration for all stakeholders," wrote Jefferson. "The crux of the saga remains the ability of independent analysts to quickly access the full clinical data on any product or device. Initiatives supported by regulators and the industry are being introduced to try to prevent future scandals, but data on existing drugs remain hidden. Everything for me is marketing and publicity, unless proven otherwise. Companies, regulators, politicians, and researchers might consider the lessons of Tamiflu and put patients first and making a nice little earner a distant second." [11]

A *Guardian* article concerning the Cochrane Collaboration's experience over Roche's Tamiflu stated: "Since percentages are hard to visualise, we can make those numbers more tangible by taking the figures from the Cochrane review, and applying them. For example, if a million people take Tamiflu in a pandemic, 45,000 will experience vomiting, 31,000 will experience headache and 11,000 will have psychiatric side-effects. Remember, though, that those figures all assume we are only giving Tamiflu to a million people: if things kick off, we have stockpiled enough for 80% of the population. That's quite a lot of vomit."

It's also a lot of young people going mad and jumping out of windows to their deaths.

Chapter 76

Wresting the truth from the British government

In my unremitting quest to find the answer to why the VMD would continue to license one-year core vaccines when three-year core vaccines can legitimately replace them, and why governments buy and promote vaccines that offer no benefit but measurable harm, let's take a look at a paper that appeared in March 2011.

Lucija Tomljenovic PhD of the University of British Columbia published a paper in the journal for the *British Society of Ecological Medicine* [1] following a Freedom of Information Act request to the British government. It was entitled, 'The Health Hazards of Disease Prevention'.

Tomljenovic discovered that British government officials had deliberately concealed information from doctors and patients to get them to comply with vaccination schedules. She called this an ethical violation. Documents obtained from the UK Department of Health (DH) and the Joint Committee on Vaccination and Immunisation (JCVI) revealed that the British health authorities have been hiding the human carnage for the last 30 years.

Documents showed that the JCVI withheld and skewed critical data on severe adverse reactions, including childhood vaccines causing encephalitis, meningitis, cot deaths, convulsions, anaphylaxis, brain damage, fits, cessation of development, and death.

Tomljenovic asserted that the JCVI and DH may have violated International Guidelines for Medical Ethics, including the Helsinki Declaration and their own Code of Practice.

Transcripts of JCVI meetings show that some of the committee members had extensive ties to pharmaceutical companies and that the JCVI frequently co-operated with vaccine manufacturers on strategies aimed at boosting vaccine uptake.

Rather than reacting appropriately when safety concerns over specific vaccines arose, the JCVI either remained inactive, skewed or removed data, and made intensive efforts to reassure the public and authorities on vaccine safety. In addition, the Committee persistently relied on dubious studies while dismissing independent research, promoted vaccine policies, and actively discouraged research on vaccine safety.

By mid to the late 1980s, the JCVI had become increasingly concerned about publicly associating the terms "death" and/or "brain damage" with the word "vaccine", due to the negative repercussions they perceived this would have on vaccination policy. Concerns were exacerbated by the increasing burden of litigation surrounding pertussis vaccine-suspected injuries, and the possibility that vaccination could be linked to some cases of Sudden Infant Death Syndrome.

Tomljenovic wrote: "In 1989, 10 years prior to the controversial Lancet report by Wakefield et al., the JCVI appeared to have been fully aware of the outcomes of the investigation carried out by the National Institute for Biological Standards and Control, which unequivocally established a link between the mumps component of the MMR vaccine (the Urabe-9 strain) and cases of vaccine-induced meningitis/encephalitis. In response to this, the JCVI appeared to have actively engaged in skewing and censoring data available to the public, continued to use Urabe-9 containing MMR vaccines, and made intensive efforts to reassure both the public and the authorities of the safety of all MMR vaccines. According to the transcript of a JCVI meeting in 1989, the causal agent of vaccine-induced meningitis/encephalitis was unequivocally identified."

The JCVI's solution appeared to be to give doctors little information about MMR vaccine safety issues. At other meetings, Committee members discussed the problem of limiting litigation, although "*it was difficult to protect manufacturers against such heavy compensation claims*". So your child's brain has been fried, and she sits screaming on the floor all day, rocking backwards and forwards, and *all they appear to be concerned about is how to protect vaccine manufacturers from costly claims.*

In government committees where members have a conflict of interest (i.e., they're taking money from the companies selling the product in question), they are supposed to declare their interests and leave the room. Tomljenovic discovered from the minutes of a meeting concerning the new conjugate Group C meningococcal vaccine that this ethical measure did not take place.

At the beginning of the meeting, Professor Hull, the Chairman, asked members to declare their interests. Professor Cartwright was involved in manufacturers' studies on the vaccines, including health trials. Dr Goldblatt was involved in a company-sponsored study and had provided a clinical expert report to the MCA for one manufacturer. Dr Jones was involved in trials for two of the companies involved. Dr Schild said that NIBSC was evaluating the vaccines. In spite of these substantial conflicts of interests: "There were no objections to these members continuing to take part in the meeting and it was agreed that they would be able to provide a valuable input to the discussion in common interest."

It is worth noting that the Professor Hull, who allowed those with financial ties to the vaccine industry to remain in the meeting, and downplayed vaccine adverse effects, is the same Professor Sir David Hull who contacted the dean of the Royal Free Medical School to ask the dean to 'bring to bear whatever pressure he could' to stop Dr Andrew Wakefield from acting as an expert witness on behalf of vaccine-damaged children [2]. It's interesting that people like David Hull get knighthoods, the Establishment's top award.

Dr Tomljenovic commented: "The apparent close ties between the pharmaceutical industry, JCVI and the DH perhaps explain why DH funded studies were not adequately designed to detect long-term vaccine-related adverse outcomes…"

In terms of government bodies seeking to reassure the general public and educate health professionals with regards to the alleged safety of vaccines, Tomljenovic's report is as scary as any horror film. Health professionals were 'educated' using highly censored information. Safety concerns were simply dismissed by the JCVI. *How* information was to be imparted was also considered important.

Tomljenovic concluded: "By apparently prioritizing vaccination policy over vaccine safety, the JCVI, the DH and the Committee on Safety of Medicines (CSM) may have shown a disregard for the safety of children. Through selective data reporting, the JCVI in conjunction with the DH, has promulgated information relating to vaccine safety that may be inaccurate and potentially misleading, thereby making it impossible for the parents to make a fully informed consent regarding vaccination."

It makes me think of a car whose manufacturers discover has faulty brakes. Do they keep the model on the market, accepting that a percentage of drivers might lose their lives in head-on collisions?

"Furthermore, by apparently misleading patients about the true risks of adverse reactions so as to gain their consent for the administration of the treatment and seemingly siding with vaccine manufacturers rather than public health interests," Tomljenovic continued, "the JCVI and the CSM appear to have signally failed their fiduciary duty to protect individuals from vaccines of questionable safety. If these provisional conclusions are indeed correct, then the information presented here may help us in understanding the UK government's and the JCVI's official position on vaccine damage – that is, one of persistent denial."

If we join the pieces of the puzzle together, we might perhaps draw conclusions as to why Andrew Wakefield was vilified, and why scientists distanced themselves from him and any favourable reporting of his work, for fear of government reprisals [4].

We might also remember the lawyer Sally Clark whose two beautiful sons died after they were vaccinated, before she was blamed and sent to jail, and who died years before her time – in part at least because her medical advisors would not stand up and tell the truth for fear of government reprisal. Consider, also, that government 'experts' sat on their hands and allowed her and other parents and their children to suffer, despite wide media coverage of her case. Presumably they considered the odd death of a baby and allegedly 'rare' cases of autism and other forms of brain damage to be insignificant. And maybe they reasoned that putting an innocent, grieving, mother behind bars was for the 'greater good'?

Why didn't Dr Tomljenovic's report make it into the mainstream media? British citizens have been misled, with serious repercussions such as unnecessary deaths and ruined lives. I would have thought that this was news.

Professor Andrew Pollard became the new Chair of the JCVI. Professor Pollard is also a Director of the Oxford Vaccine Group [4] which undertakes studies of vaccine products. The Oxford Vaccine Group has enrolled over 10,000 children and young people into clinical trials in the Thames Valley since 2001. Professor Pollard has also been involved in the development of the meningitis B vaccine. These are clearly – to me anyway – serious conflicts of interest, especially when it comes to adding vaccine products, such as meningitis B, to vaccine schedules in the UK.

Meanwhile, alternet.org stated that the US FDA officially belonged to Big Pharma following the appointment of Robert Califf as its commissioner [5,6].

"Califf, chancellor of clinical and translational research at Duke University until recently, received money from 23 drug companies including the giants like Johnson & Johnson, Lilly, Merck, Schering Plough and GSK according to a disclosure statement on the website of Duke Clinical Research Institute.

"Not merely receiving research funds, Califf also served as a high level Pharma officer, say press reports. Medscape, the medical website, discloses that Califf "served as a director, officer, partner, employee, advisor, consultant or trustee for Genentech." Portola Pharmaceuticals says Califf served on its board of directors until leaving for the FDA.

"In disclosure information for a 2013 article in *Circulation*, Califf also lists financial links to Gambro, Regeneron, Gilead, AstraZeneca, Roche and other companies and equity positions in four medical companies. Gilead is the maker of the $1000-a-pill hepatitis C drug AlterNet recently wrote about. This is FDA commissioner material?

"Califf has gone on record that collaboration between industry and regulators is a good thing. He told NPR, "Many of us consult with the pharmaceutical industry, which I think is a very good thing. They need ideas and then the decision about what they do is really up to the person who is funding the study." What?

"He is known for defending Vioxx which is reported to have caused at least 50,000 heart attacks and events before its withdrawal. (Merck is said to have known about Vioxx' cardio effects but marketed the blockbuster drug anyway.)

"Califf was instrumental in the Duke drug trial of the blood thinner Xarelto and a cheerleader of the drug despite medical experts' objections to its approval and 379 subsequent deaths. Xarelto's serious and foreseeable risks were back in the news this week.

"Duke, where Califf directed clinical research, is still recovering from a major research fraud scandal that resulted in terminated grants, retracted papers and a "60 Minutes" special. It is the least appropriate place from which to choose an FDA commissioner."

However, if you're a member of the Pharma Mafia, it's a great move. Unfortunately, it doesn't seem as though the public safety is of particular importance here.

Chapter 77

Loss and public relations

Those of us who sit on all of this information and seek to help others with it also live ordinary lives. For the first few years of living in our rented farmhouse in Perthshire, Rob and I and our family of three dogs were very happy. Scotland is a wonderful place to live if you have dogs, because we are given the right to roam and there is so much open countryside that you generally have the world to yourself.

During this time Rob wrote and recorded a wonderful album about our life together and each of the dogs, which was happy and upbeat and full of love. I can honestly say that we were blessed.

But writing long reports to the VMD, mounting press and social media campaigns, and answering people's emails and phone calls about their dogs' illnesses and deaths is work that goes unpaid. Financially, once again, things were getting very tricky for us. We were having difficulty in keeping the house heated during the long Scottish winters, and Rob was in a state of constant anxiety, trying to juggle the accounts. For myself, I was utterly fed up that there was no money available to buy *anything*.

Gwinnie by now was an old girl of 15, and Edward and Daniel were into their teens. I was so proud of my 'children'. Gwinnie was years between vet visits; she was a lovely old girl, content and loving. Edward was an impeccable dog, beyond reproach of any kind. Ted, who used to doggie sit for us, said he was the perfect dog – happy to play if you wanted to play, happy to lie quietly if you were busy, and happy to walk with you if you wanted to walk. He was always so upbeat, full of it, and on the ball.

And Dannie was, like Edward, still charging about the countryside in a macho sort of way, full of life and vigour.

We asked our vet to print off their veterinary records and saw that they had cost us an average of £10 per year in veterinary bills. With no vaccines to decimate their immune systems, and with healthy real food, our dogs were ambassadors for the message we worked hard to impart. But then, along with our finances, everything started to dissolve around us.

My sweet Gwinnie was the first to go. She was fifteen years and eight months old. Only the day before, she had come walkies with us, down to the bottom field. She refused to stay home. Spirited, wilful. "How dare you go on walkies without me!" She would not let us. She made us laugh with love. Only the day before, she had danced across the garden, sparks of joy flying from her eyes. Only the week before, she had walked into my office and stood next to me, and told me she loved me. Only a few days before, she had paddled in the puddle. Only the night before, she had followed me for left-overs. I honestly thought we had more time.

But neither time, nor the events we all have to face in our lives, let up. We have no choice but to keep moving forward. Our hearts break time and time again, and yet we all continue because we have no choice. But death from old age – well at least there is some justice in it. We buried our darling girl in the garden and put flowers on her grave.

Around this time I wrote an article for *Dogs Today* [1] about a young dog called Spangler whose skin started splitting after he was vaccinated. Although the vaccine manufacturer denied any link, some of Spangler's dead and dying skin was sent by his vet to an independent laboratory which could "neither confirm nor deny" that his cellulitis (inflammation of the soft tissues of the body) was a result of bacteria entering Spangler's body at the time of vaccination.

However, the Merck Manual tells us that serum (used in vaccines) can cause Type III hypersensitivity reactions, including a highly inflammatory skin condition involving painful local lesions leading to tissue necrosis (skin death); as well as widespread vascular injury.

Devastatingly for his owner, and the dog himself, Spangler eventually had to be euthanised. You can read the full article on the CHC website.

In response to the article, Intervet put their PR consultants Blue Zebra onto the case. They wrote to *Dogs Today* asking for the right to emphasise the benefits of vaccines, specifically in relation to the 'leptospirosis outbreaks' that were appearing around the UK. *Dogs Today* contacted me for a comment, so I engaged the services of CHC members and we rang round veterinary practices to see if we could pin these alleged lepto outbreaks down. There were none we could find.

Beverley Cuddy, the editor, didn't allow Intervet to place its own story but put an independent journalist, Hsin-Yi Cohen, onto the case [2].

The journalist reported that, "Dr Ronald Schultz, one of the world's leading authorities on veterinary vaccines, says, "I find there's still a fairly high percentage of dogs that do not respond to the Leptospirosis vaccine. In addition, of all the bacterin vaccines, Leptospirosis causes the most adverse reactions."

The article continued: "Given that its effectiveness has been questioned and the risks highlighted, was this really a vaccine worth having, we wondered?

"Intervet's PR company seemed keen to provide some answers. Unfortunately, when the response finally arrived, not all our questions were addressed. In particular, Intervet did not substantiate its claims regarding the Leptospirosis outbreaks, instead citing just one anecdotal account of an unvaccinated working Labrador that had died from the disease...

"Because it is a zoonotic disease – one that can be transferred to humans – the threat of leptospirosis cannot be underestimated. However, this does not mean that vaccination is necessarily the answer. Not only is this the vaccine most commonly associated with serious adverse reactions, especially fatal canine anaphylaxis, but it also seems to give poor protection from the disease. If the vaccine were potentially dangerous and not very effective, why would you want to give it to your dog, unless there was a serious threat of exposure to the disease? Just how prevalent is the disease?"

Intervet was unable to give any figures and, despite lepto being a zoonotic disease, the journalist could find no record of human leptospirosis infection: "I find it astounding that there is currently not even a rudimentary system to record incidence of Leptospirosis. Surely if this disease is meant to be so deadly to our dogs and so dangerous to humans, there would be some kind of recording system in place? How can pharmaceutical companies fighting something that is supposedly so serious, rely purely on anecdotal reporting? Unfortunately, unless there is a formal reporting scheme for infectious disease in dogs, which provides independent data (free from both pro- and anti-vaccine bias) about the incidence of cases, we will never really know how common a disease Leptospirosis is...

"Despite the evidence from studies that show a link between vaccines and illnesses like autoimmune haemolytic anaemia, [Intervet's] Chris Bradley is sceptical of any real risk from vaccines."

Chris Bradley was quoted: "I don't discount that there are cases of haemolytic anaemia or injection site cancers, but there is no clear evidence that it is definitely caused by the vaccine. For example, with the injection site cancers, the scruff of the neck – where the tumour is detected – is also the place for a lot of other procedures, such as steroid and antibiotic injections and topical flea applications. In an animal that is genetically susceptible, any of these causes could lead to the formation of a tumour – it is not necessarily the vaccine. Yes, there is the odd case that may have a possible link to vaccines but the incidence is so low, it's not considered significant. Our pharmacovigilance database has had no recorded incidence of anaphylactic shock in dogs from our vaccine and very little record of other reactions.

"Obviously, if certain dogs were particularly susceptible – like certain humans with bee stings – then the vets would warn the client and perhaps recommend a different vaccination schedule. But I firmly believe that, in the majority of cases, the benefits of vaccination far outweigh the risks."

The article continued: "Catherine O'Driscoll, however, has a different perspective. "The 'monitoring' is at present the SARRS scheme. It calls for vets to voluntarily report suspected reactions. The words, 'voluntarily' and 'suspected' are key.

"Time after time we are contacted by dog owners whose dogs suffered epilepsy, brain damage, skin problems, allergies, etc., immediately after vaccination, and the vet denies there is any vaccine link. Therefore, no adverse reaction report is filed. If a report is filed, then a committee sticks its finger in the air and makes a subjective decision – and many of the 'experts' at the VMD (Veterinary Medicines Directorate) and the VPC (Veterinary Products Committee) are paid consultants for vaccine companies.

"Further, vets are not trained in college to look for such reactions. They are only trained to look for anaphylaxis. They are also unaware of latest research. For example, one lady who contacted Canine Health Concern – her dog had vaccine-site cancer but the vet said it's only seen in cats so must therefore have another cause. Yet in August 2003, the *Journal of Veterinary Medicine* published a report to say that vaccines also cause vaccine-site cancer in dogs!"

The article concluded that there are two sides and that the best we can hope for is informed consent from vets (which I don't think is likely any time soon).

"Meanwhile, the sceptics, like Catherine O'Driscoll, cynically believe in more financial motives, saying, "The fact that the leptospirosis vaccine is dangerous and practically useless, and fighting a disease that is barely a problem, doesn't much matter to them."

I wish I had been a fly on the wall during meetings between Intervet and Blue Zebra PR, and wonder how long the relationship might have lasted after this PR disaster. But I shan't be too worried for them, since Zebra's 'past and present' clients include NOAH (the veterinary pharma trade association), Hill's pet 'food', and the BSAVA. I find it interesting that the British Small Animal Veterinary Association shares a PR firm with the veterinary pharmaceutical industry and a processed pet food giant. Cosy.

In the end, Intervet wrote to Beverley Cuddy to say they were withdrawing any potential advertising revenue, demonstrating the power they like to wield with their cash. Good ol' Beverley published that letter, too. Here's another lady who cannot be bought.

More recently, data on the incidence of leptospirosis in dogs seems to have cropped up. For example, during 2012 the Animal Health and Veterinary Laboratories Agency (AHVLA) tested 8,203 serum samples from a range of species for diagnostic, monitoring and export purposes [3]. Only a few samples were examined for the full range of serovars. "These data only indicate serological evidence of exposure *and/or vaccination* (which is widely practiced in cattle and dogs) and not clinical disease."

In dogs, there were 346 indications of L. Canicola, 152 of *L.* Icterohaemorrhagiae, 33 for *L.* Bratislava, and 26 for *L.* Pomona. L. Copenhageni was seen in one case, and others showed at zero. The two with highest incidence involved strains for which a vaccine for dogs is available, which might indicate that the fact that the dogs had been vaccinated accounted for the high numbers.

Now unless something really drastic has happened in the intervening couple of years (which is not likely), the veterinary vaccine industry appears to be misleading us in order to make sales.

Even during 2014, when floods caused a big problem in the UK, another government report [4] said that there were no lepto positives relating to flooding (which is supposed to increase the risk of lepto).

Another government report [5], first published in July 2013, says "Leptospirosis is more common in tropical areas of the world and is still uncommon in the UK."

Yet despite all the independent evidence, the VMD and the vaccine industry, aided by vets, are telling us that lepto is 'endemic' in the UK and every dog should be vaccinated against it every year. Despite the adverse effects.

Chapter 78
My joy-filled master dog

One day, while I was sitting alone at the kitchen table, Dannie walked into the room and laid down on the floor next to me, projecting sorrow into me with such strength that I was immediately overwhelmed with it. I looked sharply down at him. He was telling me that the cancer we had detected had gone too far. We sat there together for a while in the silence while the news sank in.

I absolutely hate death. It's the one thing in this world that we are ultimately powerless to defeat. Death is the ultimate slap in the face; a reminder that we are not God, and that we are essentially limited.

Normally when one of my dogs has died, I've sat down and written about them so that I can connect with them, remember them, and celebrate their life. It seems to me that, when faced with any form of destruction or loss, the only way out is through creativity.

But I couldn't sit down and write about Dannie. I couldn't even speak about him. I didn't want to let anyone into the dark sanctuary of grief we shared together. I would have done anything in my power, and I did do everything in my power, to stop my little Dan from dying. So whilst I could not make Dannie live, I was unable and unwilling to let him go. If I didn't speak about him out loud, or allow anyone inside, I could hold him within me for ever.

I have difficulty getting my head around the fact that one day your beloved is there, and the next day he's not, and there's nothing you can do about it. Even though dogs can't verbalise what they think, their minds and their bodies can surely communicate with us; their presence is very real. And I find it astounding and disturbing that a person should simply cease to exist.

For weeks after Dannie died, I was distressed when I walked into a room and he wasn't there. I resented very much that he was no longer with me, no longer cracking jokes and acting the clown; no longer smiling at me and giving me beautiful butterfly kisses; no longer stalking us in the Highlands, staying close enough to know where we were, but far enough away to revel in the freedom of the hills. I wanted to see his tail on the skyline again. I wanted him to be here now, picking up his enormous teddy bear and dancing down the hall, looking so adorable that my heart nearly burst.

I was so cross about Dannie's death. It's really unfair that we are rewarded for loving someone by having them taken away.

Two weeks after Dannie died his ashes were ready for us to collect from the vets, so Rob and I walked up the hill behind our house, onto the moors, and set Dannie free. We scattered his ashes to the four winds, and remembered him running free, hunting for rabbits, his muscles rippling and his mind focused. And in setting Daniel free, the dark clouds lifted and the light came back into my body and my heart.

And I was free to remember the happiness of Daniel O'Driscoll, Laughter Dog, Shimmering, Sparkling, Joy-filled Master Dog.

I am so very, very thankful that Dannie came into my life. I gave up wailing at God, and gratitude took its place. When I look back over the years, I see Dan the Man as a puppy – so adorable and huggable. He smelt so good. I can see him growing into a young man, thinking it hilarious when the cows below our garden ran away when he crept up and barked at them through the fence. I see him watching Edward intently, wanting Edward's bone and Edward's toy, distracting him so he could run in and pinch the treasured prize. Then I see him prancing like a pony with the treasure in his mouth.

I see Dannie lying under the sheet – he loved me to cover his head and poke him through the cloth. I see him rolling in the fields, and rolling even harder if I laughed. I remember he was hopeless at catching balls or titbits. He tried, really he did – but he must have been at the end of the queue when the coordination was handed out. He was a canine Bennie Hill, tongue lolling out for his comedy catching showcase. He was also useless at hunting. He tried so much harder than Edward – but whereas rabbits seemed to leap into Edward's mouth without him even trying, Dannie would hunt with total attention and rarely managed to catch a thing.

In life, I know that Daniel was ever mindful of me. I absolutely know he loved me, and he knew I loved him. Dogs are like that, aren't they? If you take a dog into your heart, he's always on your side, forever rooting for you. Dogs want the best for their humans, they really do. Daniel's life mission was to make me laugh, and it was my job to repay him by laughing heartily at every joke he cracked. The more I would laugh, the more he would do what I was laughing at; and the more he would shimmer and shine and sparkle and do it all again.

Oh Dannie. Thank you so much.

Another part of Daniel's personality lay in his vulnerability. Daniel made my heart ache with maternal love. I wanted to protect him and cosset him and put his complex mind at ease. Like all legendary comedians, Dannie was very vulnerable. The thing is, if all was not calm and well in our world, Dannie felt the need to turn things around. He would take on his loved-ones' pain and carry it for them, whilst at the same time trying to cheer everyone up. Dogs do this, don't they.

I personally believe that the spirit can never die, that the essence of who we are simply discards its worn-out body and moves on to the next adventure, passing through a place of profound peace, and meeting up with others who have gone before. I know that my little Dan Man is with Chappie, Sophie, Prudence, Oliver, Samson and dear, sweet, Gwinnie. I also know that Dannie's essence will always be with me and Rob. My faith is lashed very tightly to the flag of hope – that we will all meet our loved-ones again one day.

So here I am, but Daniel is not here.

Except, when I wrote: "I was free to remember the happiness of Daniel O'Driscoll, Laughter Dog, Shimmering, Sparkling, Joy-filled Master Dog", Daniel was actually here with me in the room, over the moon at the description I had found for him. He was so happy and excited, just as he used to be in life, that he lit up every cell in my body. Have you ever had that feeling, when you're so full of joy and spirit is close, that your whole body tingles?

Isn't it interesting that our dogs never seem to judge us, and that Christ, the King of Love and Forgiveness, also asked us not to judge one-another? And isn't it interesting that death and loss offer us the ultimate lesson in acceptance of what is?

And so I thank our Dannie for the love he gave and received, and for the knowledge that our love has deepened and intensified across the veil of death. Daniel is no longer on the outside of me, wagging his tail. He is inside me, in my heart, where he will always stay.

Dannie lived a good long life, for this I am thankful. For despite being vaccine-free, and despite never having 'scientifically formulated' processed food touch his lips, my boy remained strong and lived a healthy, long, life.

Chapter 79

We welcome a damaged soul into our home

Edward took Dannie and Gwinnie's deaths very badly. We worried for him and surrounded him with love, but his heart was breaking. Rob and I discussed Edward's grief and thought about getting another friend to cheer him up.

We couldn't afford to buy another Golden Retriever so we thought about getting a rescue dog. A year or so earlier, we had been invited to put on a weekend workshop for a UK-based Papillon breed club, and many of the delegates had brought their little dogs with them. We were very impressed with this breed – they were small and dainty, yet incredibly intelligent and biddable. Their owners told us that Papillons are as easy to train as the famously accomplished Collie breed. And unless you knew it, you'd never guess that a Papillon was a toy Spaniel – a gun dog breed. I had the idea of phoning Debs Gornall who runs a Papillon rescue group.

"Oh Catherine," she said, "I have the perfect dog for you. He's called Georgie. He really needs you. He doesn't like men, and he bites!"

"That's the dog for us," we said.

So we drove from Scotland to the north of England to collect George. Deborah showed us into her sitting room and brought him in. We were shaken to discover that he was more of a wild animal than a dog. He paced the room anxiously and span in angry circles, growling and snarling. To be honest, I was frightened by his behaviour; it was shocking. The only thing we could do was herd him into a small crate and hurry him home.

A few hours later we introduced Georgie to Edward who, we were delighted to see, was overjoyed to see him. When he went into a spin by Edward's leg, Edward simply held his ground and calmly waited until he stopped. I was so impressed with my boy.

Rob and I were not quite so sanguine. Every time we looked at George, he growled at us. He would stand in doorways growling, so I didn't know whether to go through. I ask you – this tiny little thing was truly intimidating me, although I also knew that he was frightened and some of my apprehension concerned how I could make him understand that I meant him no harm.

Georgie wouldn't let anyone touch him. Trying to do so had him spinning and snarling and biting his tail, or our hands if we weren't quick enough. If we accidentally walked near him, he would attack our feet and we had to keep our shoes on or wear a firm pair of slippers. He had a ferocious temper.

Nor could we get a collar or lead on him unless we resorted to trickery. I had to stand outside the garden gate with a treat, with Rob inside the gate with a slip lead, slipping the lead quickly over his head when George went for the treat. Getting the lead off was another matter. We had to put a towel over him to protect our hands while we took it off. He would snarl and lunge for us, his eyes red with rage.

A few days into living together, Rob held out his hand for Georgie to sniff, and Georgie went into another spin. "That's not behavioural," I said to Rob. "That looks like neurological damage."

There is a form of epilepsy in dogs which involves spinning. Called 'complex partial seizure', it can be difficult to recognise but includes lip snapping, snapping the air, aggression, spinning, and obsessive behaviour. Georgie fitted the pattern: he fixated on flies, bird song, and light reflections, and sometimes he will obsessively lick the carpet for hours (unless we give him a homeopathic remedy which stops this, or put him under light therapy). He'll even be lying asleep and suddenly jump up and spin – you can see the electricity being discharged.

How do you groom a dog who won't allow you to touch him? How do you ensure that he's in good health? How do you inspect his teeth or his ears? How do you get the grass, burrs and knots out of his coat? What do you do if he growls at you every time you look at him?

Two weeks into sharing our home with this little fiend, Rob and I sat with heavy hearts. "What have we taken on?" we asked. "How can we look after him if we can't touch him?" But we knew we couldn't take him back to the rescue. "If we can't help him, then who can?" Rejecting the little fella would probably be signing his death warrant.

Not long after he came to live with us, we took Edward and George to visit our friends Rod and Geraldine and we walked together around their beautiful garden. Then we went inside for coffee. So we're sitting there chatting and suddenly Rod started howling and screaming. We all looked at him and wondered if he'd gone mad. Then it transpired that Georgie had hold of Rod's big toe in his teeth. He had inadvertently knocked into George, and George was exacting his revenge. Luckily Rod is a kind and gentle soul who refrained from kicking the little dog off.

I telephoned a friend who is a gifted medical intuitive. "He's vaccine damaged," was her immediate response. "It's like epilepsy." She suggested a number of homeopathic remedies for us to try – all for the unwanted effects of vaccines.

Sometimes it's difficult to know which came first – the chicken or the egg. I feel sure that some of his problems come from unsympathetic handling in the past, but endorsement of our belief that George might be vaccine damaged came when we found Dieter Harsch and Iris Parizek in Germany who run a CHC equivalent over there. Dieter is a Bioenergetic therapist. He offered to take a look at Georgie's hair sample for us – and came back with the diagnosis of vaccine damage. Dieter sent more homeopathic remedies to treat this.

We have adopted a non-confrontational approach with this little man – and thank goodness he isn't a large dog or this option just wouldn't exist. He would have been called a dangerous dog and euthanised.

Although there have been times, especially in the early days, when Rob and I were heavy-hearted, wondering why we had allowed ourselves to be 'suckered' into taking Georgie on, we have grown to love him with such a depth that he has totally won our hearts over. We just adore him. Small improvements are big events in our house. And he is such a loving, loyal little dog. It's years since he's bitten.

I used to see him looking at me and knew he longed to be cuddled, but he understands that he's not like other dogs, and that he can't be. However, being himself is more than enough. When I broke my leg a few years ago, it was George who insisted upon looking after me and sleeping with me in my downstairs isolation. It's Georgie who wants to ensure we are all together. And it's Georgie who has charmed his way into our hearts.

What strikes me about George is that he had many behaviours that correlate to the behaviours of autistic children, including:

- avoidance of eye contact
- hypersensitivity to light, noise, touch, smells, tastes
- peculiarities of hearing (like autistic children, Georgie goes mad for some sounds such as bird song, motorbikes and flies, but is oblivious to other sounds, such as thunder)
- lack of interest in play
- obsessive behaviours
- aggression towards self or others
- distressed if routine is disrupted

Temple Grandin has autism and has written a number of books, including *Animals in Translation*, *Thinking in Pictures*, and *Emergence*. She also invented devices that eliminate some of the cruelty to animals in slaughterhouses.

Temple reveals that the child with autism often wants a hug, even craves it, but has to pull away because touch is painful. She calls it sensory overload. Loud noises are unbearable. She writes, "I had a fixation on spinning objects, a preference to be alone, destructive behavior, and an intense interest in odors. Spinning was another favorite. I'd sit on the floor and twirl around. This self-stimulatory behavior made me feel powerful, in control."

We asked Debs, the rescue coordinator, to make enquiries about Georgie. Had he been vaccinated every year? His previous owner replied that, yes, he had – and volunteered that his behaviour got worse every year. This tiny dog, who is smaller than most cats, received the same dose of vaccine every year as a Great Dane or Pyrenean Mountain Dog.

Meanwhile, Teresa Binstock, a research scientist who has Asperger's, provides some interesting references in relation to aluminium and its presence in vaccines. Note that myelin surrounds nerves; it is our nerve insulation:

"Anti-myelin antibodies," she writes, "have been described in autism. In at least some such children, might injected aluminum have been an etiologically significant factor amid processes leading to anti-myelin antibodies, especially for individuals with aluminum hypersensitivity and/ or weak alleles which participate in aluminum detoxification (clearance)?"

Aluminum is a known neurotoxin, and according to Christopher Exley of Keele University, aluminum-containing products are likely fuelling the rise in Alzheimer's disease.[1-14] In an article published in the journal *Frontiers in Neurology*, he writes:

"We are all accumulating a known neurotoxin in our brain from our conception to our death. The presence of aluminium in the human brain should be a red flag alerting us all to the potential dangers of the aluminium age. How do we know that Alzheimer's disease is not the manifestation of chronic aluminium toxicity in humans?"

People with aluminum toxicity display many of the same symptoms as those with dementia, Parkinson's, ADHD, autism, and other neurological diseases, and mounting evidence suggests aluminum may play a significant role in the development of those (and other) diseases.

Other toxins to beware of include fluoride and glyphosate. They are toxic in their own right, but research suggests they may be even more hazardous in combination. But of course aluminium, and mercury, are just two potential causes of autism. The live viruses themselves are potentially capable of causing inflammation and damage to the brain, and serum – which is contained in vaccines – as well as the foreign proteins vaccines are cultivated on, could also trigger damaging inflammatory responses.

But there is good news: after being treated for vaccine damage, George's behaviour improved. When we gave him CBD oil from the cannabis plant, Georgie changed. We can now stroke him, he doesn't obsess about flies or lights, and we can brush against him without getting a devil dog response.

Chapter 80

Joy and sorrow

Barbara Storey, a long-time friend and CHC member, phoned me. "Catherine," she said, "I was going to leave it as a surprise but when I heard you were looking for a rescue, I thought I had better get in touch now. I've set up a fund with Patsy Cullen and Pam Graham so you can get your Golden Retriever puppies. It's not right. You do so much for us and the dogs, and it's wrong that you can't afford your own puppies."

I was overwhelmed and very moved. When Gwinnie and Dannie died, Gabriel had told me that they were going to reincarnate and come back to us. He said to expect them to arrive in a litter in the spring. I had told Barbara, but added that I couldn't see how this might happen since we couldn't afford two Golden Retriever pups at £800 each. This must have been when I told Barbara our plans to get a rescue. She was hoping to tell me before we had done it – but she was too late.

Barbara, Patsy and Pam had contacted some CHC members and supporters. Although I was embarrassed about it, they – a group of 58 amazing people – responded generously with enough money to buy two puppies, a crate, and some puppy accessories.

Meanwhile, our own finances were getting worse and worse, and Rob was in a state of high anxiety. It didn't help that we were grieving for Gwinnie and Dannie, either, or that Georgie was proving to be more of a handful than we had expected. Rob had grave misgivings about getting two puppies. "We're just not in the place for it," he said. "Life is stressful enough."

But if Dannie and Gwinnie were coming back to us, I couldn't say no to Barbara, Patsy and Pam's initiative, which was fuelled by love and friendship. I overruled Rob and he, being such a kind and thoughtful man, acquiesced.

I got in touch with another CHC member, Christine Rogers, who bred naturally reared Golden Retrievers. She was expecting a litter in the spring, and we put our names down for two of them. I was shattered when she telephoned to say that there had only been five pups and we couldn't have our two.

So I telephoned Sue Hawkins who had bred Edward and Daniel, hoping for good news. "Sorry, Catherine," she said, "but I haven't bred a litter for years." She put me in touch with Golden Retriever breeders who might be able to help. It was now June and time was running out to find a litter that had arrived in the spring as Gabriel had predicted. I was panicking but, on the other hand, knew that if Dannie and Gwinnie were meant to come back to us, then somehow they would.

I found a couple who had a spring litter – with two puppies yet to find homes. We went to see them and put our names down for them: a boy with the temporary name of 'Laid Back', and a girl who they called 'Stripy Tail' to distinguish her from others in the litter.

But Rob was right: it was definitely the wrong time to bring two puppies into our home. Finances were dire and morale was low. It was therefore somewhat ironic to receive an email from a woman in America who hated my book, *Shock to the System*, so much that she felt it necessary to write and spew out her hatred. She sent the email to Rob; he was so upset by it that he didn't know whether to share it with me. Apparently I was – yet again – a money-grabbing deceiver, living a life of luxury in a castle in Scotland on the back of my deceitful books. She was, she said, a freelance journalist and she was going to make sure I was vilified in every dog paper in the land.

Well, I clearly wasn't very good at my life of crime.

I hoped that the puppies would cheer us up and give Edward renewed vigour. We worried, though, about Georgie as we knew he would bite them if they invaded his personal space. Years ago I had reasoned that I would never keep an aggressive or violent dog. It's utter madness to live with a dog who causes chaos in a home, who can't be trusted, and who reigns with terror. But we all judge other people until we find ourselves in the same situation and our good counsel for others goes out of the window; at which point we perhaps move from judgment to understanding.

So Georgie stayed because we love him and he deserved a chance, and these two little puppies eventually came home with us – and Georgie trained them well.

But Edward didn't seem to like the pups. He barked at them ferociously and resented very much that they were getting five meals a day when he had only two. It was distressing to see my darling Edward so upset. He had always been the perfect dog – calm and sensible and full of fun. We had made a terrible mistake bringing the puppies home.

Edward was slowing down by now and one day he turned back from his walk and asked to go home. My heart sank as I let him back in the house and kissed him, and rushed back to help with George and the puppies. Edward had been to the vet's a few times lately and we had been told he had arthritis. I had started looking for remedies and supplements to help him.

The next day we all went into the garden to take in the sun. Rob had built a play pen for the puppies which Ruby immediately escaped from – escapology being one of Gwinnie's chief traits, of course.

I put a blanket out for Edward to lie on and he pootled around in the bushes. It broke my heart to see him resenting the puppies so much, and to realise that my once vibrant boy – the Robert Redford of Dogs – was getting old.

The next morning I awoke at five o'clock, hearing Edward panting along the corridor. I went to see him, knowing that something was seriously wrong. I put him in the car and took him to see Gavin, our vet, leaving Rob to look after the puppies. Unfortunately Gavin wasn't on that day so I saw another young man. I'm sorry to say that I was worried that this was another young lad fresh out of veterinary college, and said something tentatively to that effect, hoping to get Edward seen by a more experienced vet. Why is it that our dogs always get ill at weekends? There was nobody else available and, besides, the young man had actually been qualified for six years!

He listened to Edward's heart and felt his stomach, and told me that Edward was in heart failure. He wanted to do an exploratory op but warned me that our beloved boy might not survive the anaesthetic. I told him I would need to speak to Rob and left Edward while he conducted some tests, then telephoned Rob to explain what was happening. Then I drove home to pick him up. We agreed that it would be unfair to put Edward through an operation that he might not survive, and wondered how it would do any good anyway. Stunned, we got into the car and drove back to the vet's to see him.

For the last time, we gave Edward some raw chicken wings – the wings he dearly loved – and took him for a gentle walk and told him how much we loved him. And then we took him back to the surgery so he could be put to sleep.

Rob kissed and hugged our boy and told him how much he loved him, and I went to do the same, but Edward turned his head away from me as the vet put the needle in. I was so taken aback.

Rob was beside himself with grief. He and Edward had a very special bond; he absolutely adored that dog. For good reason: think of Edward and you would see bright, sparkling, joyous light. But my own grieving process was halted. Rob was inconsolable, and I was deeply troubled.

For a few years, I had been an assessor for James French's ACT – Animal Communications Training. James and his partner Shelley are building a quality standard for animal communications, and his students must achieve at least 90 percent accuracy when communicating with animals. As a result, I often have students communicating with my dogs so that I and other assessors can confirm that they are indeed communicating with our pets.

After Edward had gone, I asked three trainee ACT communicators to talk to him. The first two reported that he seemed very listless and depressed and that he didn't even lift his head to speak to them. I knew that something was dreadfully wrong, because my Edward was famous for his energy and vigour. He was the life and soul of every party, barking on command with utmost joy, and always up for fun.

I was grieving and lost – what was wrong with my boy? So I sat down and communicated with him myself and apologised for bringing the puppies in. I assured him that I loved him – he was the most perfect and special of dogs. I would never have wanted to hurt him. I adored him.

The next time I had the opportunity to ask one of James French's students to talk to Edward, he came in bringing a litter of Golden Retriever puppies, barking and smiling and wagging his tail. He explained that he didn't resent the puppies at all, but that he was heartbroken that he could no longer run and jump and do all the things with us that he had once done. He told me that he was coming back to us, and that he would be one of the puppies he had brought with him for the communicator to see.

I told the animal communicator that I didn't know how this would happen. Rob was unlikely to want us to have another dog, especially just yet, and we are getting older. This is one of the reasons we got little Georgie – it's not easy to pick up an elderly Golden Retriever whose back end has gone when you're an old age pensioner. If a Golden Retriever were to live to the age of, say, 15, I would be in my 70s.

"Don't worry about that," Edward said. "Next time I come I'll be looking after you."

How strange life is. I don't want to be looked after. Does this mean I'm going to be crippled or immobile, and that I have to wait until then before I see my darling Edward again?

If I have a trained assistance dog, does this mean he's going to have to be vaccinated into a diseased state before I can have him? And will the charity he comes through insist I vaccinate him every year, even when he doesn't need those vaccines? Will they stipulate the food he must eat, and project their delusions about crap in a bag onto the dog who has come to be my friend and helper? Does Edward have to suffer from malnutrition and vaccine-associated disease in order to be with me again?

But, yet, I long to have Edward back with me, whatever the reason for his coming. And no – he won't come to me if it means I have to bow down to the outdated and harmful practices of a charity that insists upon procedures that cause harm.

In this small way at least, I *will* beat the Establishment. I know a lot of people!

Chapter 81

Seeking shelter

We realised that we'd have to downsize if we were to keep CHC going rather than capitulate and go out and find proper jobs. I still had my vow to fulfil and Rob was doing the work he came here to do.

We looked around Perthshire for a smaller, cheaper, cottage. But another recession was on its way, caused by a vastly unregulated banking system, and the competition was steep for rented property. I looked on the internet and found several to let three hours away in the Scottish Borders, so we arranged to view them. One was a rather ugly looking place that, I noticed, had stayed on the market for months. The rent was even lowered as I continued to keep an eye on it. We added it to the viewing list, simply because we were in the area anyway.

We liked the first place we viewed. It had outhouses which, with a little hard work, could be turned into a habitable office. But we were pipped at the post when a man whipped out his wallet and put a deposit down straight away. The second house was in the middle of a concrete farmyard. The garden was tiny, and tractors and other heavy farm equipment would be in use throughout the day, which didn't feel safe for the dogs. Besides which, the farmer told us that if he decided to take on another farm hand, we'd have to move out to make room for him.

The third, the ugly little place, had been empty for a year and, as a result, felt cold and unwelcoming, and its window frames were rotting. But it was in the middle of a cattle farm and surrounded by beauty. I stood in the garden and took in the view. Ahead of me were beautiful green pastures heading down to a river lined by a red sandstone cliff and an abundance of trees. To my right was a ruggedly beautiful iron-age fort. And to my left and behind me there were ancient woodlands.

As I stood and gazed at the views, the wild flowers, grasses and trees began to pulsate and shimmer, their colours taking on a significant intensity. "Stay here," they said.

"This is the place," I said to Rob, and he agreed.

The landlord's letting agents asked to see our accounts, which was a frightening request. Our finances weren't in good shape and we began to wonder if we'd end up homeless. After examining them, they reported that we could only afford £74 per month in rent, which was of course considerably lower than required. The agent had made allowances in our expenditure for things we had learnt not to spend money on.

Thank God, but the manager of the farmhouse wrote a glowing reference for us and our new landlord gave us shelter.

Once again we were moving to a smaller home, so I sold off most of our furniture and went along to a few car boot sales with our bits and pieces. I was pleased to note that I didn't mourn my *things*, but that I enjoyed selling them and meeting the people who were delighted to have them. The proceeds went towards a tractor mower fund, because our new tiny cottage had a large garden which would need it if we were to keep the grass in order.

We hired a van, loaded it up, and did the same thing over and over again, until eventually we had squeezed into our little cottage. Our neighbours at the farmhouse, Campbell and Lorna, knocked on the door and offered their help, which we were touchingly grateful for. They stayed with us way past midnight lugging furniture and boxes about.

Rob's mum had also decided to move to a retirement apartment in Somerset. With utmost generosity, she gave us some cash which paid for our move. Meanwhile my sister Mollie and her husband John insisted upon replacing the worn-out linoleum in the kitchen; my sister Leslie and Glenn bought a dresser for us so we had room for out pots; and my stepmother Sandra paid for a shed to house the dogs' freezer as there was no room for it in the house.

We stayed happily in the cottage for six years, until we more than outgrew the space; now we're in a rented bungalow in woodland, waiting for the spring to arrive so we can see the flowers and trees burst into life. We dream of building our own eco-friendly home, so when the system collapses – as it may – we at least have an infrastructure to keep us warm. But the likelihood of this happening is about as high as winning the lottery – yet the world still turns and we still live, and we can be happy without such possessions. Relationship with another living being – *this* is what we cannot do without, and which money cannot buy.

One beautiful summer day, I was sitting in the garden with the puppy Freddie by my side, and I looked down at him and he'd transformed into a hologram of pulsating pink and green stripes. Pink and green are the colours of the heart chakra, and Freddie was showing me that he was a being of love, and nothing but love. Sometimes, as he walks across a field, I see Dannie, my macho man.

Rob and I have fallen in love with Freddie, Ruby and George. We have so much to be grateful for. Although Freddie and Ruby's beginning was stressful, and although we feared we'd done the wrong thing by bringing them into our home, we were wrong. We shouldn't have feared. They are where they should be and need to be. The plan is unfolding as it should.

We haven't vaccinated in over twenty five years. Our dogs are healthy and vibrant and rarely need to see a vet – except for Freddie, who came with a heart murmur, thyroid disease, and food sensitivities! But even with these inherited disabilities, he is strong, fit and healthy. We trust that by feeding raw and avoiding vaccines and other toxins, he will live a long and healthy life.

Chapter 82

Politics, bias and broken promises

As Crufts drew to a close in March 2013, we were contacted by dog breeders who were appalled at the advice offered by the Kennel Club's Assured Breeder Scheme (ABS) on its re-vamped website. Membership of the Scheme allows breeders to use the KC's literature and logo to promote their puppies, lending an air of authority and respectability. However, informed breeders were being invited to issue inaccurate and misleading vaccine guidelines to new puppy owners through its on-line puppy vaccine template. My heart sank, because CHC is a campaigning group and it falls within our remit to challenge such advice from powerful sources. However, I've been doing this for long enough to know that we're bashing our already bruised foreheads against a brick wall. So I sighed and took action.

By calling for 'routine immunisation', the Kennel Club was undoing all the work that had been done to legitimately and safely reduce vaccine frequency in dogs – as called for by the WSAVA at the beginning of the Century.

Kennel Club guidance seemed likely to promote over-vaccination, advising puppy owners to follow their ill-educated vet's advice regarding vaccine schedules. There was no mention that the core vaccines provide immunity for years or life, and no mention of the titer testing option. Instead, there was a threat to vets that unless they follow the SPC (commonly known as the datasheet), they would metaphorically have their heads chopped off – the same threat issued by the VMD as it refused to withdraw one-year core vaccines.

Although the Kennel Club vaccination advice had been developed 'in conjunction' with the WSAVA Vaccine Guidelines Group, there were material differences between Kennel Club and WSAVA advice.

Steve Dean had become the chairman of the Kennel Club. He was formerly head of the VMD which does what it can to speed drugs and biologics to market. The KC's puppy vaccine template read like a missive from the VMD.

The Pet Welfare Alliance, an organisation we had formed to unite pet health advocates from around the world, issued a press release calling for the Kennel Club to produce guidance for breeders and puppy owners that reflects current scientific knowledge.

Bill Lambert was driving home from Crufts when news of the release got to him, and he and his team hastily reacted to the cannon ball shot across his bows. Bill is in charge of the Kennel Club's Assured Breeder Scheme, although it transpires that he needs clearance from about two thousand committees before he can blow his nose.

Bill wrote to express annoyance that we had issued a press release rather than contact him direct – but our experience of the Kennel Club over the years has been one of disinterest and, despite its claims that it wants to promote canine health, its template seemed to show otherwise. I could see no point in writing to them. I have an entire library of unanswered letters, after all.

However, Bill promised in his letter to me that if I drafted a new puppy vaccine template and got WSAVA approval, he would make it available to ABS members. As I read his offer, I had an instinct that he was issuing me with a challenge that he didn't expect me to meet.

I had emailed Ron Schultz and Michael Day of the WSAVA vaccine guidelines group, asking them if the existing Kennel Club vaccine template was indeed approved by the WSAVA. Michael Day replied that it was, and pointed out that a link to the full WSAVA guidelines had been provided by the KC, and that individual countries make up their own minds. I replied to Michael Day and Ron Schultz with an impassioned reprimand – I can't believe I did that:

"With utmost respect Professor Day, the following principles are not being covered in Kennel Club 'advice': the WSAVA VGG advises against annual vaccination for the core diseases and even states that puppy shots, if given around 16 weeks, are likely to provide lifelong immunity against the core diseases; is not keen on promoting indiscriminate use of the non-core vaccines; promotes titer testing as an alternative to indiscriminate vaccination; and informs vets that it is acceptable to stray from the SPC with informed consent.

"On the basis of what you say, the WSAVA is failing to provide clear guidance. To say that your recommendations related to current core vaccination for puppies and boosters for adult dogs were incorporated is (with respect) not true. How does, "dogs must be routinely vaccinated" cover WSAVA guidelines? Knowing that vets around the world continue to over-vaccinate against all the canine diseases, how can the WSAVA be comfortable with advice that pet owners should follow their vets' advice WITHOUT clarifying the actual science?

"Knowing that few vets around the world do titer tests instead of one- or three-year boosters, and the Kennel Club has left titer testing out of the picture … how can the KC possibly be doing ANYTHING in line with WSAVA guidance? Surely the WSAVA VGG is there to REDUCE vaccine load on companion animals, not to support faulty, incorrect and damaging advice?

"Please understand, I have immense gratitude to WSAVA members who have done a tremendous job in promoting the science surrounding over-vaccination, but it seems these days that the message is being watered down so that nothing will change in the long term. The WSAVA is in an incredibly important position. It MUST give better clarity.

"'National requirements' do NOT alter the science.

"I don't expect you to answer this email, which is a pity. In my experience, scientists always back out of the debate when – I suspect – political considerations are involved. I hope you prove me wrong."

With many thanks

Catherine

There had been no reply. Would Ron Schultz and Michael Day even speak to me now? Ever the nervous optimist, I drafted new guidelines for the Kennel Club's ABS puppy pack template and contacted Professors Schultz and Day. Much to my relief, they replied graciously and, with a few tweaks, a template was agreed. It was essentially a summary of the much longer and more involved WSAVA vaccine guidelines document. Bill and Ron liked it so much they even made it available through the WSAVA VGG website. Sadly, it was taken down around the same time as *The Telegraph* did a piece on the lepto vaccine killing dogs [1] and NOAH attempted damage limitation. I emailed Ron to ask if the WSAVA had been got at, but he didn't reply.

If you look at the WSAVA puppy guidelines, still on our Pet Welfare Alliance site [2], you'll see that although I don't vaccinate my dogs, I respect the rights of others who may choose the WSAVA's minimal vaccine schedule. In reality, I long for the day when vaccines are seen for what they are.

Joyously, I sent the new WSAVA-approved puppy vaccine guidelines off to Bill Lambert at the Kennel Club, and waited. And waited. And waited, and waited some more. More than four years later, I am still waiting for the ABS to give new puppy owners the WSAVA-approved template that Bill Lambert promised to make available to them. This would be a new template that would ensure that millions of puppies won't be over-vaccinated and risk vaccine-induced death and disease.

During Crufts 2014, television viewers were treated to an interview with the TV presenter Clare Balding and Nick Blaney, 'veterinary advisor to the Kennel Club'. Nick also became president of the British Veterinary Association in 2007. I bet the veterinary vaccine industry loves him.

Eileen Lane, who recorded and transcribed the interview advised me: "You may like to have some Rescue Remedy and count to ten before you read this although I guess after 20 years you have developed broad shoulders and have had to learn to cope with so very much of this, or your blood pressure would permanently be through the roof!"

Clare – ... from a question sent in by email, could the vet please explain why dogs need vaccinations every year but in humans they last a lifetime? I meet quite a few dog owners out walking who say annual vaccination damages the dog, it's rather confusing.

Nick – well yes, it is rather confusing but in fact we don't vaccinate against every disease every year. The success of a vaccine rather depends on the nature of the organism that you're trying to create a vaccine out of so what's true about one virus might not be true of a different bacterium and we have a package of different components that are used according to the requirements, some years, not other years, and as far as vaccination causing disease this is nothing more than an internet myth. There is not one shred of evidence and if we go down that path we'll have in dogs the same as that dreadful MMR vaccine story which was based on nothing more than misinformation.

Clare – ... there are veterinary stalls, in every hall there is more than one but there's a lot of herbal supplements, there's all sorts of stuff you can give your dog whether you're looking to improve its breath or the quality of its coat or indeed you're looking to try and make sure it doesn't get one of the diseases.

Nick – well, I suppose I take a rigid scientific view of these things and I want to know that there's proof that these things work and for a lot of it quite frankly there's no proof at all and all I'd say is that as an owner of a dog you have a responsibility to look after the health of the animal. If you choose to take some wacky remedy yourself that's up to you, but feeding it to your dog, that is another matter.

Clare – thank you Nick, I shall not discuss herbal remedies with you again at all.

Um, so as a vet who takes a rigid scientific view, why isn't he proclaiming to the rooftops that we've been administering vaccines to a schedule that, according to Colorado State University, is so unscientific that "we may as well vaccinate every full moon"? And to say that there isn't a shred of evidence that vaccines come with adverse effects is *misleading or misguided.*

These people come on the TV and parade themselves as scientists, but for some reason they don't like the science. They downgrade the truth to internet myth. And dog owners suck it up because this fallacious advice comes from an 'expert' who carries the full authority of the Kennel Club, which loves dogs – doesn't it?

No wonder Bill Lambert's buttocks appeared to tighten every time I emailed him to ask when the Kennel Club was going to, as promised, make my WSAVA-approved puppy vaccine template available. No wonder he stopped even replying to me.

The wording on the Kennel Club puppy template included dross that's very similar to the dross on the VMD website, and possibly written by the same person. Adverse reactions were downplayed, the question of vaccine frequency was not answered (an analysis of the overall benefits and risks strongly supports the continued use of vaccination"), and "It is important for veterinary surgeons to understand that, when departing from the SPC, they do so under their own responsibility". They also include:

> "Some lobby groups have accused the veterinary profession of over-vaccinating – perhaps using vaccine yearly when there may well be a longer lasting immunity to disease. To challenge this view would involve further testing beyond the scientific evaluations already undertaken by the manufacturer to determine the duration of immunity as specified in the SPC."

The lying gits. Thousands of puppies, if their owners take the Kennel Club's advice, would be over-vaccinated, with the potential of unnecessary harm. What an utter betrayal of the love and trust we receive from our dogs.

As for the Assured Breeder's Scheme's advice on diet, compiled with the aid of one of the KC's main sponsors – the Pet Food Manufacturers Association – raw (aka real) food is just too difficult for you to get right. Perhaps our IQs have dropped significantly since our grannies used to give their dogs bones and table scraps.

It's such a shame – shame being the operative word – because the Kennel Club has it within its power to revolutionise canine health for the better. However, being an optimist, I know change is always possible. In 2017, Junior Hudson actually got the KC to incorporate titer testing information on its link, and many of the more misleading claims were removed!

Chapter 83

Let's hear it for the brain damaged

Dear Catherine

I am taking my English Bulldog Rooney in to be neutered on Monday. I am giving him St John's Wort for his aggression, which started after receiving his rabies shot and his DHLPP all at once. I contacted a homeopathic vet and we tried several different treatments. Nothing seemed to work. I am now trying St John's Wort although I am led to believe that if discontinued he will return to his aggressiveness. Now I am trying neutering and if he must continue forever on the St John's Wort, so be it. My husband and I love him so we will continue to try to resolve his aggression.

Bernadette Kurtz

With alarming frequency, news stories appear in the UK of yet another dog savaging a child. Anyone who knows dogs knows that dogs don't do this sort of thing without reason. It was time to smash my bloodied brains against another brick wall, so I wrote to the editor of *Veterinary Times*:

Dear Sir

There seems to be a constant stream of media stories surrounding dog attacks on both adults and children in the UK. Some of these will no doubt be due to the way in which the dogs are treated by humans: a lack of training and socialisation, poor diet, cruelty, and so on. However, we are concerned that one potential cause is being overlooked.

Vaccines are known to cause neurological effects. Are veterinarians aware of this, and are they examining the vaccination records of dogs exhibiting sudden unprovoked aggression?

The WSAVA has repeatedly called for vets to reduce the antigenic load, and to stop annual vaccination so as to minimise unwanted sequelae. Neurological effects may be thought to be uncommon (although they are likely to be vastly under-reported), but any reaction which leads to the maiming or killing of a human being and the destruction of the dog is surely unacceptable – especially when the vaccine was not needed.

The veterinary profession must respond to the science, and

stop over-vaccinating. The consequences are too awful to allow the profession to continue to ignore expert advice. This is a link to the WSAVA puppy vaccine summary:

http://www.wsava.org/sites/default/files/New%20Puppy%20
Owner%20Vaccination%20Guidelines%20May%202013_0.pdf

The above link was taken down shortly after the UK's veterinary vaccine industry got upset about media coverage of the four-way lepto vaccine. It's still on our Pet Welfare Alliance website, though.

The summary clarifies with regard to vaccine frequency: "The WSAVA states that we should vaccinate against the core diseases no more frequently than every three years. This is often taken to mean that we should vaccinate *every* three years – but this is not the case. If the dog is already immune to these three core diseases, re-vaccinating will not add any extra immunity."

Kennel cough and leptospirosis vaccines are deemed 'non-core' or 'optional', and the world experts say that they should only be used if there is a known disease threat in the area. Yet it seems that UK vets believe that the leptospirosis vaccine, with its short-term efficacy, is an annual necessity. This vaccine is known to stimulate the most severe side-effects.

One must weigh the risks and benefits: how prevalent is leptospirosis in the UK? No-one seems to know. Industry sales data is not a reliable source. Where are the official statistics for this zoonotic disease? Think: if leptospirosis and Weill's Disease were that common, an official database would exist somewhere, and yet it didn't for years – until I started questioning this vaccine. Do the potential unwanted effects of the leptospirosis vaccine – which can include brain damage – justify the vaccine's use where no or little disease threat exists?

Canine Health Concern, through its international initiative The Pet Welfare Alliance, sent thousands of letters to local authorities, kennel and cattery owners, boarding establishments, breeders, dog clubs, breed clubs, breed rescue organisations, charity/rescue, and pet insurers to inform them of:

• Potential lifetime immunity to the core viral diseases
• The optional nature of non-core vaccines
• Potential vaccine adverse effects

- The availability of inexpensive in-house titre testing kits that will negate the need to revaccinate already immune dogs and cats
- That the presence of antibody for the core diseases confirms that the animal is immune and does not need revaccinating

We wrote to every veterinary practice in the UK with the above facts, plus vaccine adverse effects references. We negotiated a discount for veterinary practices against VacciCheck, the in-house titre testing kit. Titre testing can mitigate vaccine booster loss.

Vets need to be aware that vaccinating is not the same as immunising, which is why vaccinated dogs succumb to viral and bacterial disease. Only the presence of circulating antibody can confirm immunity, and only the absence of circulating antibody can justify revaccination.

We have so much to thank the veterinary profession for. By updating vaccination policy, we will have much more to thank them for. First do no harm.

Yours faithfully
Catherine O'Driscoll

The editor left the references out, remarking that anyone who was interested could apply, which of course most wouldn't. I wanted the evidence to be right in front of vets. For scientists, published references are important. Without them, my letter could be viewed as opinion rather than scientific fact. So I'm including references here.

Out of interest, the government and the industry have recently tried to cobble together data concerning the prevalence of lepto in the UK – which isn't very much! 250 dogs out of 8.5 million. And bearing in mind that you get false positives with lepto, it's probably even fewer.

Vaccine-induced brain damage – references

1. Grene, CE, ed, Appel MJ, Encephalitis has been shown to appear in dogs after vaccination. *Canine Distemper in Infectious Diseases of the Dog and Cat,* 2nd edition, Philadelphia: WB Saunders, 1998: 9-22.
2. AIP McCandlish et al: "Post-vaccinal encephalitis is a recognised complication of the administration of certain strains of live attenuated canine distemper vaccine (Hartley 1974, Bestetti and others 1978,

Cornwell and others 1988)". *Veterinary Record* 1992 (130, 27-30),

3. *Braund's Clinical Neurology in Small Animals: Localisation, Diagnosis and Treatment*: "Post vaccinal canine distemper encephalitis occurs in young animals, especially those less than six months of age. It has been recognised as a disease entity for a number of years, and is believed to be association with vaccination using live virus. The pathogenesis of this disease is unclear, but may result from insufficient attenuation of the vaccine virus which causes subsequent infections of the CNS; the triggering of a latent distemper infection by vaccination; other vaccine components; or an enhanced susceptibility of the animal (e.g., animals that are immunosuppressed)."

4. G. Bestetti1, et al, Encephalitis following vaccination against distemper and infectious hepatitis in the dog. "A 4-months-old, male, healthy dog developed CNS-symptoms 10 days after the second vaccination with live, attenuated distemper and canine hepatitis virus." *Acta Neuropathologica* Volume 43, Numbers 1-2 / 69-75 -- 1/1/1978

5. Wilson RB, Holladay JA, Cave JS: A Neurologic Syndrome Associated with Use of a Canine Coronavirus-Parvovirus Vaccine in a Dog. *Compend Contin Educ Pract Vet.* February 1986; 8[(2)]:117-124.

6. Protein glutamate is added to vaccines to preserve the virus in vaccines. Meat, fish eggs, milk and cheese tend to be high in protein glutamate. High levels of glutamic acid have been shown in animal studies to cause damage to parts of the brain unprotected by the blood-brain barrier, leading to a variety of chronic diseases http://www.ncbi.nlm.nih.gov/pubmed/15167034

7. Shiina T, et al, Jpn J, "Experimental studies on paralysis after antirabies vaccination. I. Histological studies on acute demyelinating encephalomyelitis in guinea pigs." *Microbiol;* 2[(2)]:187-96. -- 4/1/1958

8. T Hemachudha, et al, Myelin basic protein as an encephalitogen in encephalomyelitis and polyneuritis following rabies vaccination: "Encephalitis and polyneuritis occurring after rabies vaccination are believed to be immunologically mediated. We studied antibody responses to neural antigens in 36 patients with major neurologic complications, 25 with minor complications, and 39 with no complications after immunization with a brain-derived, Semple rabies vaccine." *New England Journal of Medicine* Volume 316:369-374 , Number 7 -- 2/12/1987

9. R K Garg, Acute disseminated encephalomyelitis: "T cell mediated autoimmune response to myelin basic protein, triggered by an

infection or vaccination, underlies its pathogenesis " *Postgraduate Medical Journal*; 79:11-17 -- 1/1/2003

10. Bale JF Jr, Neurologic complications of immunization. "Individual vaccines can produce systemic or neurologic reactions ranging from minor events, such as pain and erythema at the injection site, to major complications, such as seizures, shock, encephalopathy, or death." *J Child Neurol.*; 19[(6)]: 405-12. -- 6/1/2004

11. *Merck*: "In acute disseminated encephalomyelitis (post infectious encephalitis), demyelination can occur spontaneously, but usually follows a viral infection or inoculation (or very rarely a bacterial vaccine), suggesting an immunologic cause."

12. Olsen D, et al, "Expression and characterization of a low molecular weight recombinant human gelatin: development of a substitute for animal-derived gelatin with superior features." "Gelatin is used as a stabilizer in several vaccines. Allergic reactions to gelatins have been reported, including anaphylaxis. These gelatins are derived from animal tissues and thus represent a potential source of contaminants that cause transmissible spongiform encephalopathies." *Protein Expr Purif.*; 40[(2)]:346-57 -- 4/1/2005

13. Ballerini, Rico B et al., Neurological Complications of Vaccination With Special Reference to Epileptic Syndrome *Review Neurol*, Jul-Aug 1973; 43: 254-258.

14. Wisniewski, H.M.; Sturman, J.A.; Shek, J.W. Chronic model of neurofibrillary changes induced in mature rabbits by metallic aluminum. *Neurobiol Aging.* 1982, *3*[(1)], 11-22.

15. Pendlebury, W.W.; Beal, M.F.; Kowall, N.W.; Solomon, P.R. Neuropathologic, neurochemical and immunocytochemical characteristics of aluminium. *Neurology.* 2008 May 6; 70[(19)]:1672-7.

16. Petit, T.L.; Biederman, G.B.; McMullen, P.A. Neurofibrillary degeneration, dendritic dying back, and learning-memory deficits after aluminium administration: implications for brain aging. *Exp Neurol.* 1980, *67*[(1)], 152-162.

17. Petrik, M.S.; Wong, M.C.; Tabata, R.C.; Garry, R.F.; Shaw, C.A. Aluminum adjuvant linked to Gulf War illness induces motor neuron death in mice. *Neuromolecular Med.* 2007, *9*[(1)], 83-100.

18. Gherardi, R.K.; Coquet, M.; Cherin, P.; Belec, L.; Moretto, P.; Dreyfus, P.A.; Pellissier, J.F.; Chariot, P.; Authier, F.J. Macrophagic myofasciitis lesions assess long-term persistence of vaccine-derived aluminium hydroxide in muscle. *Brain.* 2001, 124(Pt 9), 1821-1831.

19. Shaw, C.A.; Petrik, M.S. Aluminum hydroxide injections lead to motor deficits and motor neuron degeneration. *J Inorg Biochem.*

2009, *103*[11], 1555-1562.

20. Golub, M.S.; Gershwin, M.E.; Donald, J.M.; Negri, S.; Keen, C.L. Maternal and developmental toxicity of chronic aluminum exposure in mice. *Fundam Appl Toxicol.* 1987, *8*[3], 346-357.

21. Redhead, K.; Quinlan, G.J.; Das, R.G.; Gutteridge, J.M. Aluminium adjuvanted vaccines transiently increase aluminium levels in murine brain tissue. *Pharmacol Toxicol.* 1992, *70*[4], 278-280.

22. Struys-Ponsar, C.; Guillard, O.; van den Bosch de Aguilar, P. Effects of aluminum exposure on glutamate metabolism: a possible explanation for its toxicity. *Exp Neurol.* 2000, *163*[1], 157-164.

23. Cohly, H.H.; Panja, A. Immunological findings in autism. *Int Rev Neurobiol.*2005, *71*, 317-341.

24. Banks, W.A.; Kastin, A.J. Aluminum-induced neurotoxicity: alterations in membrane function at the blood-brain barrier. *Neurosci Biobehav Rev.* 1989, *13*[1], 47-53.

25. L. Tomljenovic, and C.A. Shaw, Aluminum Vaccine Adjuvants: Are they Safe*? Current Medicinal Chemistry, 2011, 18,* 2630-2637 "Aluminium presented in this form carries a risk for autoimmunity, long-term brain inflammation and associated neurological complications and may thus have profound and widespread adverse health consequences."

26. Department of Paediatrics, Tokyo Medical University, Japan, found the measles virus in patients with inflammatory bowel disease and autism. (*Dig Dis Sci,* 2000, Apri; 45[4] 723-9) . The sequences obtained from the patients with ulcerative colitis and children with autism were consistent with vaccine strains.

27. Karen L. Roos, et al, "The Smallpox Vaccine and Postvaccinal Encephalitis" "Before we become complacent with the idea that we will respond to a bioterrorism attack with a mass immunization program for smallpox, it is important to be reminded of the risk and clinical manifestations of postvaccinal encephalitis... The first case of postvaccinal encephalitis as a complication of the Jennerian cowpox inoculation was observed in 1905. A century later, there is no effective therapy." *Semin Neurol* 22: 095-098 --1/1/2002

28. Klemm D, et al, "The management of meningoencephalitis following rabies vaccination" *Med Klin*;63[34]:1354. -- 8/1/1968

29. Yahr MD and Lobo-Antunes,"Relapsing encephalomyelitis following the use of influenza vaccine" *J, Arch Neurol.* 27[2]:182-3. -- 8/1/1972

30. Levine,S et al, "Hyperacute Allergic Encephalomyelitis: A localised form produced by passive transfer and pertussis vaccine." "Blockade of histamine H1 receptors may reduce mortality in pertussis

immunisation-induced encephalopathy in mice." *American Journal of Pathology*; 73:247-260 -- 1/1/1973

31. L. Steinman, et al, Murine model for pertussis vaccine encephalopathy: linkage to H−2, "Local, systemic and neurological complications have been observed following pertussis (whooping cough) vaccination in children. These often occur soon after primary or secondary immunization. The neurological syndrome ranges from minor irritability to convulsions, coma, and on rare occasions death." *Nature* 299, 738 – 740 -- 10/21/1982

32. Graus F, et al, Acute necrotic myelopathy associated with influenza vaccination. *Lancet*; 1(8545):1311-2. -- 6/1/1987

33. Yoshiomi Okuno,Incidence of Subacute Sclerosing Panencephalitis Following Measles and Measles Vaccination in Japan "The Japanese Committee for the National Registry of Subacute Sclerosing Panencephalitis (SSPE) confirmed that 215 cases of SSPE occurred", *International Journal of Epidemiology* Volume 18, Number 3 Pp. 684-689 -- 10/1/1988

34. Saito H, et al, Tohoku, Acute cerebellar ataxia after influenza vaccination with recurrence and marked cerebellar atrophy. "A 5-year-old, previously healthy girl developed symptoms and signs of acute cerebellar ataxia (ACA) 8 days after having received an influenza vaccination." *J Exp Med*; 158[1]: 95-103. -- 5/1/1989

35. D'Cruz OF, et al, Acute inflammatory demyelinating polyradiculoneuropathy (Guillain-Barre syndrome) after immunization with Haemophilus influenzae type b conjugate vaccine. *J Pediatr*; 115(5 Pt 1):743-6. -- 11/1/1989

36. Dodick DW, et al, Department of Neurology, Mayo Clinic. Acute disseminated encephalomyelitis, an inflammatory demyelinating disease of the central nervous system, can occur after viral infections or vaccinations. *Mayo Clin Proc.* 73[12]:1193-5. -- 12/1/1998

37. Piyasirisilp, Sucheep a; Hemachudha, Thiravat b, Neurological adverse events associated with vaccination, *Neurology* 15[3]:333-338 -- 6/1/2002

38. Robert Ball, et al, Development of case definitions for acute encephalopathy, encephalitis, and multiple sclerosis reports to the Vaccine Adverse Event Reporting System, *Journal of Clinical Epidemiology* Volume 55, Issue 8, Pages 819-824 -- 8/1/2002

39. Claude Vital, et al, Postvaccinal inflammatory neuropathy: peripheral nerve biopsy in 3 cases. "Autoimmune inflammatory polyneuropathy (PN) can be triggered by vaccination. *Journal of the Peripheral Nervous System* Volume 7 Page 163 -- 9/1/2002

40. Bale JF Jr, Neurologic complications of immunization. "Individual vaccines can produce systemic or neurologic reactions ranging from minor events, such as pain and erythema at the injection site, to major complications, such as seizures, shock, encephalopathy, or death." J Child Neurol.; 19[6]: 405-12. -- 6/1/2004

Chapter 84
I don't vaccinate – and here's why

Our dogs are in the midst of an epidemic. It's not an epidemic of viral disease, but of chronic ill health. They're besieged with itchy, pus-laden, scabby skin; vomit and diarrhoea are the norm. One in every hundred dogs suffers from epilepsy, and an even higher number lives with painful arthritis. Allergies and autoimmune diseases are also reaching epidemic proportions: dogs are becoming allergic to life.

We also seem to have a tremendous number of dogs with behavioural problems, largely due to over-vaccination and processed pet food. Vaccines are known to cause inflammation of the brain, as well as lesions throughout the brain and central nervous system. Cancer is also a potential vaccine consequence.

Years ago, I was the typical 'responsible' dog owner. My four Golden Retrievers were vaccinated every year, and they were fed a 'complete and balanced' pet food, recommended by my vet. The red carpet was metaphorically rolled out once a fortnight, each time I visited with a dog suffering from chronic disease. Eventually the problems became more serious: my dogs started to die years before their time.

Over the years, I've collected research documents to help me make decisions about my dogs' husbandry, and to share what I've learnt with other dog lovers. I also hoped that vets would take notice of the research and stop over-vaccinating. All medical interventions come with a risk – even the humble aspirin can be deadly. So you have to do a risk/benefit analysis whenever you consider medications

So imagine my dilemma years ago, when Edward and Daniel came into my home. Having already seen my vaccinated dogs suffer with chronic illnesses, and dying from cancer and leukaemia – knowing that vaccines may have caused these illnesses – what was I to do? I concluded that I would rather risk viral disease with my dogs than have them suffer from the epidemic of chronic and fatal illness that is gripping the canine population. I appreciate that some will consider me irresponsible. But what actually are we running from when we vaccinate?

OK, so distemper is so rare that most vets in the UK haven't seen it in at least ten years. Also, according to the top researchers, and stated by the American Veterinary Medical Association, once immune to viral disease, dogs are immune for years or life. So why are vets and vaccine manufacturers still trying to get us to vaccinate against viral disease every year, or even three-yearly – especially when you consider the risk?

According to the WSVA, once a dog is immune to distemper, parvo and hepatitis, they are immune for years or life. So why keep vaccinating against them? Kennel cough is easily treated in most cases, and the vaccine isn't very effective. So what's the point? Leptospirosis is rare (my vet told me he hadn't seen it in ten years), and the vaccine is associated with some of the worst adverse reactions. Isn't this vaccine an unacceptable risk, then?

In my view, you get a healthy adult dog by not vaccinating at all. Vaccines derange the immune system, leading to all sorts of chronic illness. From all I've seen and read, vaccines do *not* set your dog up for good health. They have the potential to make your dogs itchy, scratchy, vomiting, diarrhoea-filled, sickly, sub-normal shadows of their former selves – ready and waiting for the more serious killers like cancer to arrive.

Does this mean I've left my beloved dogs open and unprotected against viral disease? No. Puppies are given the homoeopathic nosode, a safer vaccine alternative. They are also fed naturally, providing vital nutrients to boost their immune systems, and they're exercised well (which also boosts the immune system). I also give my puppies concentrated colostrum (mother's milk) to support their immune system. Have they ever suffered from recurrent hot spots, allergies, digestive upsets, eye and ear infections, or any other chronic illnesses? No. Did they die of cancer at the age of five, or leukaemia at the age of six, or paralysis at the age of four – as my vaccinated dogs did? No. In fact, they're *probably* very well equipped, and healthy enough, to withstand the diseases I might otherwise have vaccinated against.

Is probably good enough? Well – it's the best anyone is going to get. Because even vaccines cannot guarantee immunity.

So am I taking the high risk option? I don't think so. It seems to me that good health is a God-given natural right. It's only man who messes it up. The natural order is wiser than any of us, and those of us who don't vaccinate our dogs are proving natural law to be right.

With regard to the thorny homeopathic nosode issue, there are a number of studies attesting to the fact that they actually work. These studies are few, but they exist. Steve Dean jibed in relation to nosodes that, 'if there is no disease threat then even water will work' – well, here's the thing, Steve: water won't give your dog allergies, autoimmune diseases, brain damage or cancer, either.

Studies attesting to the efficacy of nosodes are carried on the CHC website.

Chapter 85

Misleading us again

As stated earlier, in April 2014, in response to the new WSAVA puppy summary and possibly my letter in *Veterinary Times*, the veterinary vaccine industry issued a statement via its trade association, NOAH [1].

NOAH claimed that the WSAVA puppy summary, on the WSAVA website for around four years, contained discrepancies regarding the protocols veterinary practices had adopted and the advice contained in the SPCs (the document approved by the industry-loving VMD). The veterinary vaccine industry wasn't happy about the clarification given for non-core vaccines; nor were the vaccine vendors happy about the promotion of titre testing in place of unnecessary shots – quoting one out-of-date and biased research paper in support of their assertion.

NOAH went on at length about the licensing procedure and rigorous assessments they are subjected to, and asserted that the veterinary surgeon is best-placed to tell the client to [over] vaccinate. So, they say, is the veterinary surgeon best-placed to make a risk assessment about leptospirosis vaccination, claiming that the majority in the profession consider lepto a core vaccine (although the WSAVA calls it non-core). Any decision not to include lepto in the programme would, in NOAH's opinion, require clinical justification and informed consent from the client. The decision regarding kennel cough vaccination should also, according to NOAH, come from the vet who should offer informed consent to the client.

The problem here, of course, is that vets are not educated in vaccinology and are being encouraged by NOAH and the VMD to make more of lepto and kennel cough than informed pet owners might do, chiefly because we don't want to inject brain damage, allergies or autoimmunity into our dogs without good cause.

NOAH expressed concern that the WSAVA is continuing to educate the public and claimed there was a lack of evidence for the association between vaccination and the onset of diseases such as epilepsy and arthritis.

Dr Jean Dodds, God bless her, responded directly to NOAH:

Dear Colleagues:
    I read with interest the "NOAH Statement on canine vaccination" dated April 14, 2014, but feel that several points need to be clarified in response. Specifically:
    The statement , *"We are not aware of any evidence that*

suggests that leptospirosis vaccines are associated with any increased risk of adverse reactions or that toy breeds of dogs require any additional precautions when receiving vaccinations against leptospirosis", flies directly in the face of the known adverse hypersensitivity reactions to leptospirosis vaccines.

As listed in the 2011 AAHA Canine Vaccination Guidelines (1; p. 15): Non-infectious vaccines, like leptospirosis, can induce –

- Acute adverse reactions (e.g., hypersensitivities) include: anaphylaxis, injection site pain, angioedema (facial edema), injection site granulomas, local inflammation abscesses, lameness, reactivation of immune-mediated diseases in predisposed dogs.
- Delayed adverse reactions (e.g., hypersensitivities) Ischemic vasculitis (skin), increase in severity of type I atopic disease, reactivation of immune-mediated diseases (e.g., IMHA, IMTP, RA, etc.), and other hypersensitivity disorders possible in predisposed dogs (rarely occurs).

Inactivated (killed) vaccines can be associated with a higher incidence of adverse events when administered as a polyvalent combination product, especially in small breed dogs [1]. Further, vaccine reactions are under-reported in veterinary and human medicine.

The paragraph stating: *"Serology is a useful diagnostic test with regards to assessing humoral responses but can have limitations for determining vaccination status in individual animals. Results are not always easy to interpret (Burr, 2006), take no account of cell mediated immunity, and for the owner may set false expectations. This may result in difficult decisions when the results reveal an indeterminate level as well as additional cost of sampling and significant delays whilst awaiting results"*, **is misleading** as modified live virus (MLV) vaccines are effective because they provide the same immunity (cellular, humoral, systemic, and local) produced by natural exposure [1,2]. Properly immunized animals have sterilizing immunity that not only prevents clinical disease but the presence of antibody also prevents infection. Furthermore, the animal doesn't need and should not be revaccinated since the vaccine could elicit an adverse reaction (hypersensitivity disorder). It is best to avoid vaccinating animals that are already protected [1-4].

Serologic tests for measuring and monitoring the presence of immunity to the "core" vaccines of dogs and cats (feline panleukopenia virus) have been documented for many years to provide a reliable and accurate indication not only of circulating humoral immunity but also of cellular, systemic and mucosal immunity [1-9]. Published challenge studies have documented long lived protection from CDV, canine parvovirus (CPV-2) and canine hepatitis (adenovirus) (CAV-2), for at least 9 years and likely a lifetime, even in the absence of viral exposure or revaccination [2]. Memory B and T cells should provide an anamnestic (secondary) humoral- and cell-mediated immune response that limits virus replication and prevents disease. Immune responses to the MLV "core" vaccines, CDV, (CPV-2 and CAV-2, always stimulate both humoral – and cell-mediated immunity [2].

Lastly, the statement: *"but are concerned that oversimplification of potential linked adverse events such as epilepsy and arthritis do need qualification, given the lack of evidence for the association between vaccination and the onset of these diseases. Such statements are open to misinterpretation and owners may unjustifiably assume spontaneous disease is a result of a vaccine, putting the attending veterinary surgeon in a difficult position"*, is misleading because adverse vaccine reactions to canine distemper, rabies and potentially other vaccines are known to produce seizures or encephalitic reactions, especially in susceptible dogs [3,4,10].

Further, the infectious MLV canine distemper virus (CDV) vaccines are capable of reverting to virulence, especially if these vaccines contain the potent Rockborn strain of CDV (10, 11) They also are known to produce post-vaccinal encephalitis (PVE) [1,2]. The Onderstepoort or recombinant CDV vaccines do not produce PVE [1,2].

References

1. Link V. Welborn, DVM, DABVP (Chairperson), Members of the American Animal Hospital Association (AAHA) Canine Vaccination Task Force: 2011 AAHA Canine Vaccination Guidelines J Am An Hosp Assoc 2011: 47[5]: 1-42.
2. Schultz RD, Thiel B, Mukhtar E et al. Age and long-term protective immunity in dogs and cats. J Comp Pathol 2010;
3. Dodds WJ. Vaccination protocols for dogs predisposed to

vaccine reactions. J Am An Hosp Assoc 2001; 38: 1-4.

4. Dodds WJ. More bumps on the vaccine road. Adv Vet Med 1999;41:715-732.

5. Tizard I, Ni Y. Use of serologic testing to assess immune status of companion animals. J Am Vet Med Assoc 1998; 213: 54-60.

6. Twark L, Dodds WJ. Clinical use of serum parvovirus and distemper virus antibody titers for determining revaccination strategies in healthy dogs. J Am Vet Med Assoc 2000; 217[(7)]:1021–4.

7. Schultz RD. Duration of immunity for canine and feline vaccines: a review. Vet Microbiol 2006;117[(1)]:75–9.

8. Taguchi M, Namikawa K, Maruo T et al Booster effect of canine distemper, canine parvovirus infection and infectious canine hepatitis combination vaccine in domesticated adult dogs. Microbiol Immunol 2012; 56:579-582.

9. Ford RB. Vital vaccination series: Antibody titers versus vaccination. Today's Vet Pract 2013; 3[(3)]: 35-38.

10. Martella V, Blixenkrone-Moller M, Elia G et al. Lights and shades on an historical vaccine canine distemper virus, the Rockborn strain. Vaccine 2011; 29:1222-1227.

11. Demeter Z, Palade EA, Hornyák A et al. Controversial results of the genetic analysis of a canine distemper vaccine strain. Vet Microbiol 2010; 142: 420-426.

Jean Dodds is very polite, which I admire greatly. However, she didn't hear a word from NOAH in response to her concerns, and now NOAH has taken the statement off its website, leaving only a press release about it. I try to be polite, but sometimes I find it hard when corporations seek to obfuscate the truth. Their products are, after all, capable of killing our dogs. Please note that 'we are not aware of …' doesn't mean that there isn't any evidence. See also [(2)] relating to human vaccines for lepto being too dangerous for *humans*.

If you are persuaded by the science that once your dog is immune to parvovirus, distemper and hepatitis/adenovirus, he remains immune, there's a good chance that you won't be subjecting your dog to the cumulative annual vaccine risk.

But if the industry can persuade you that leptospirosis and kennel cough should be boosted annually – even if they don't tell you that these vaccines are associated with higher risk and/or aren't all that useful – then you're still going to be subjecting your dogs to the vaccine risk every year. This way, nothing is lost by the industry or vets, but good health is potentially lost by the animals they purport to serve.

In its position paper on authorised vaccination schedules for dogs, quoted by NOAH, the VMD stated: "Cases of canine leptospirosis in the previous 12 months were reported in 14.61% of UK veterinary practices surveyed in a recent study (Ball et al., 2014) (13 practices out of 89 which returned questionnaires). The authors note that all but one of the cases occurred in non-vaccinated dogs, highlighting the importance for dogs in the UK to maintain a current vaccination. Over 60% (8/13) of the cases resulted in fatality."

Let's try to make sense of the above figures. We'll start by saying that 13 out of 89 practices can't statistically represent the approximate four or five thousand vet practices in the UK in any meaningful statistical way. However, 14.61% of 4,000 practices – if the 89 respondents were anything to go by – would represent 584 cases of canine lepto in the UK in a year.

According to the Pet Food Manufacturers' Association, there were 8.5 million dogs in the UK in 2013. This would, then, mean that according to the VMD, one dog in every 7,272 got leptospirosis, whether or not they were vaccinated (since one vaccinated dog in the survey got it). If you take the vaccinated dog out of the picture, it would be one dog in every 15,000 non-vaccinated dogs getting leptospirosis. Do you see what difference only one dog makes in such a small survey?

However, the 'Cicada survey' by MSD Animal Health (part of Merck), which is featured on this website [3], shows a map of the UK with alleged cases of lepto reported by vets in the UK, although 'due to legal requirements' you can't look at anything unless you register and give them your identity and email address. You also only get to look at a map of colours if you're not a vet – they're censoring information for the general public. But one vet, Vicky Payne, an holistic vet who advocates for the lepto vaccine, was in correspondence with a CHC member and she told us that there were 250 cases of lepto a year. She said she got this figure from the makers of Nobivac (Intervet/MSD). Vicky put this figure on her practice website.

So somewhere along the line, the incidence of lepto extrapolated from the VMD/NOAH figures is vastly different from the incidence according to one vaccine manufacturer. 250 cases out of 8.5 million dogs is one in every 34,000 dogs, which is a very low risk in contrast to a vaccine noted for its severe side-effects.

Just to illustrate how meaningless statistics can be if the study isn't done properly, or if it's biased, I decided to do a Pop Survey on Facebook.

LEPTOSPIROSIS POP SURVEY – INTERIM RESULTS.
I asked my Facebook friends to answer two questions:

1. During 2012, did any of your dogs get leptospirosis?
2. Was the dog vaccinated against leptospirosis?

The questions were asked of 6,851 people. Of these, 423 people responded.

Please note that, like the survey quoted by NOAH, this is a 'self-selecting' survey. This means that only the vet practices which chose to answer answered, and only the Facebook friends who chose to answer answered. Therefore both surveys are potentially flawed and open to bias. (Making a point here about the reliability of any survey, whether pro- or anti-vaccine.) Where people had multiple dogs, their answer was counted as one.

- 315 people (74.46%) said they did not vaccinate against leptospirosis in 2012, and none of their dogs got lepto.
- 103 (24.35%) people said they vaccinated against lepto and their dogs did not get lepto.
- 4 dogs (3.74%) in the survey were vaccinated against lepto (up to date), and contracted lepto. Two of these dogs died of lepto.
- 1 dog was vaccinated against lepto and had unconfirmed lepto.

Conclusion: Vaccinating against Leptospirosis is counter-productive. 100% of dogs in our survey with Leptospirosis were vaccinated against it within the previous 12 months, some within weeks of contracting the disease.

This finding, interestingly, supports the 1996/7 CHC survey involving 3,000 dogs, in which 100% of dogs with Lepto in the survey contracted it within 3 months of being vaccinated.

Now then, in May 2014, Christopher Ball from the University of Liverpool presented a PhD thesis about leptospirosis in dogs. Maybe I should also be given a PhD for my Pop Survey so MSD can cherry pick from it? Mr Ball thanked "MSD Animal Health for funding the project, without which none of this work would be possible".

Mr Ball's MSD-funded thesis, which may be found through a web search or, should that fail, through Canine Health Concern, appears to provide MSD with its data on leptospirosis incidence in the UK for its CICADA website. However, the thesis (which resulted in Mr Ball being awarded his PhD) also states:

- Due to the perceived low rates of infection in the UK, the canine leptospirosis vaccine is also not currently considered a 'core' vaccine in the UK (unlike the vaccines for parvovirus, para-influenza virus, canine distemper and infectious hepatitis).
- In the UK, the human vaccine is not routinely administered due to the low incidence of cases (between 50-60 a year) (HPA, 2012).
- Climate plays a role in Leptospira infection rates, with temperate climates not having extreme weather situations that may contribute to infection rates. According to the Köppen climate classification, the UK has a rating of Cfb, meaning cooler summers but also milder winters. The classification reflects the milder climate changes between seasons which reduce the likelihood of leptospirosis.

Mr Ball sent out a questionnaire to veterinary practices in the UK for his thesis. Of the 472 questionnaires he sent out, only 89 were returned. Of these, by far the largest response came from vet practices which had seen no lepto cases in the previous twelve months. Only 13 practices reported a case within the last twelve months, of which only five had lepto confirmed by a laboratory test. A further 29 practices reported having seen a case within the last 15 years. No practice in the study reported seeing two or more suspected (or confirmed) cases in the 12 previous months. Does this make leptospirosis in dogs 'endemic' or a problem large enough to risk this vaccine? I think not.

Very similar extrapolated figures were presented by MSD on its website for the 'CICADA' survey, which is being used to justify annual vaccination against leptospirosis. Yet, to anyone unwilling to subject their dogs to unnecessary vaccines, these figures highlight a product desperately looking for a market, and not a validation for Lepto4.

Topically, I received this ping-back from one of my articles carried on the *Dogs Naturally* site:

> We have two pups who had life-threatening reactions when they went in for their second set of puppy boosters and also received the lepto vaccine (with our consent – although the vet did not warn us of side-effects, or mention that they really didn't need this) and the kennel cough vaccine (without our knowledge or consent).
>
> One became very ill immediately – lethargic, shaking, diarrhoea, not eating or drinking – and we discovered a few days

later that she had gone into liver and kidney failure and showed signs very similar to leptospirosis. The emergency care cost us approximately $8000. Just when we thought she had pulled through and we were starting to breathe a sigh of relief the other puppy became very ill. After numerous tests (including a spinal tap), she was confirmed to have polyarthritis, an autoimmune disease typically found in very old dogs. Her bills came in at $7000.

We believe both reactions were the direct results of the vaccines but the drug manufacturer claims that we could not prove it was the result of the vaccine (even though one became ill immediately after receiving it). The vet at the drug company claimed their illness could have been the result of anything, even "a disease doctor's haven't discovered yet". If that's not a load of crap, I don't know what is.

We now have a vet who understand our needs and concerns. If you're a pet owner who hasn't had a similar issue but is considering your options, you are truly blessed. We didn't start doing our homework until after the damage was done and our puppies were the victims of our ignorance.

Fast forward to January 2015, and vets around the UK were pushing a new four-way leptospirosis vaccine from MSD. This carries four of over 200 leptospirosis serovars.

The on-line Somerset Guardian carried a story about lepto in dogs. Sadly the link has now been taken down, but I did copy its content:

> A veterinary group is warning dog owners to be vigilant as it has seen a number of cases of Leptospirosis at its surgeries in Somerset and Bristol during December.
>
> Highcroft veterinary service says the condition, also known as Weil's disease, is a serious bacterial infection that affects dogs and can be fatal if not treated promptly.
>
> It is also possible for humans to contract Leptospirosis, particularly children and people who have poor immune systems.
>
> Symptoms in dogs include vomiting, diarrhoea, lethargy, high temperature and jaundice. *Eight out of the nine cases seen have been in vaccinated dogs* and vets suspect a new strain of Leptospirosis bacteria is emerging in this area, one that the classical vaccination does not protect against.
>
> Vet Catherine Bovens said: 'The disease originates from rats and can be contracted by wildlife and dogs, but is almost unheard

of in cats. It is spread through urine and tends to hang around in stagnant water. As rats are everywhere around us, we believe that all dogs in the Bristol, Bath and surrounding areas are at risk."

OK, so lepto rates reflected in Mr Ball's thesis were very low for each practice, and suddenly there's a new vaccine out and the numbers have risen in one practice (according to a bit of public relations). Let's analyse this. Shortly after MSD comes up with a four-way vaccine, a vet group is telling us that the old two-way vaccine was, in fact, rubbish – and that a massive eight of the nine cases were in dogs who had the old two-way vaccine. Before the introduction of the four-way, no-one thought to tell us how ineffective the old one was. But, seriously, how come lepto has risen so exponentially that this practice has experienced nine cases …. when other practices say they saw only 'a' case within the last 15 years?

One must question how, with all the rigorous testing which we are informed takes place for vaccines, did no-one pick up that the two-way lepto vaccines were ineffective? Will they refund all the injections given for the vaccines we are now told were of no use? For if we apply the sale of goods act, they were not of merchantable quality.

I bumped into a vet at a conference recently. He said, "I didn't tell you this; leave my name out of it – but I find it strange that there are suddenly lots of lepto cases just after a new four-way vaccine comes out. Coincidence?"

In an article in *Dogs Naturally* magazine [4], Dana Scott quotes Dr Patricia Jordan: "Based on serologic data, the main lepto serovars causing disease in dogs include L. pomona, L. grippotyphosa, occasionally L. autumnalis and L.bratislava, and rarely, L. canicola, L. hardjo, and L. icterohaemorrhagiae. What most people don't know is that the lepto vaccine only protects dogs against the main two serovars for about two weeks, if at all. [5] Stephen Barr of Cornell University states: "most [vaccines] claim year efficacy except those subunit vaccines covering L. pomona and L. grippotyphosa (protect for 2 to 2½ weeks post-booster)"

"This means that your dog has to be vaccinated twice for the lepto vaccine to protect against the primary two serovars and that protection only lasts for about two weeks. To be truly and fully protected against lepto for a one year period, this would require up to 26 vaccinations. Is this a risk worth taking?"

In another *Dogs Naturally* article [6], Dr Jordan states: "Vaccination with leptospira is fraught with problems. Of major concern is the fact that leptospira vaccines do not protect the dog from infection with leptospira or of renal colonization. Leptospira vaccines have little effect on the maintenance and transmission of the disease in the animal populations in which they are applied. The ineffectiveness of the vaccine is due in part to the many leptospirosis serovars and variability of pathogenic strains which are not addressed with vaccines.

"Of serious concern is that veterinarians are actively marketing [selling] for the drug companies. I have seen misinformation published not only in the local newspapers but also on the web. The advice of our professional medical experts is seriously compromised and devalued when they don't perform due diligence before advocating this marketing material. Where is truth in advertising?

"Drug companies create a market for their product even though the risk for the disease is practically non-existent and the vaccine is highly dangerous for animals. Human medicine is not exempt from this travesty with the GSK Hepatitis B vaccine, the Merck Gardasil vaccine, and the Bird Flu and the Swine flu vaccines – all resulting in calls for investigation and criminal charges to be brought against the WHO. WHO Vaccine Advisor, Juhane Eskola made over 6 million Euros researching vaccines for the recent swine flu "pandemic". Similarly, the CDC Childhood Vaccine Advisor, Dr Paul Offit made so much money with Merck making a rotavirus vaccine that he said 'it was like winning the lottery'."

Meanwhile adverse reactions to the new four-way lepto vaccine are raising their ugly heads: Nicola Tyson wrote:

"My puppy had the lepto vaccine at seven weeks old after being checked over thoroughly by my vet. Within four days she was lethargic, no appetite, high temperature and needed to be hospitalised on IV's. Her kidneys were found to be enlarged and she also had a heart murmur which hadn't been heard at her check-up. Gracie's is now eight months old and has been off medication for four weeks and is still under vet supervision. She had to go to a specialist vets clinic and was at one point hospitalised for over a week. We didn't think she would pull through. As I said she is still under vet supervision but well in herself at the moment.

"It had been suggested that the damage to Gracie's kidneys and other problems could have been due to the vaccine but it would be nigh on impossible to prove. My vet bills are up to £6,000 (not insured) and I am sure it was triggered by the vaccine, but when my vet rang the vaccine manufacturer they told her there had been no negative reports on other dogs reacting this way.

"Gracie was bred by myself and all her brothers are fit and well and had no reactions to their vaccines, which where through different vet practices and none were given the lepto."

Linda Hern wrote: "My six year old GSD bitch had the new lepto vaccine just after it came out, before I realised the dangers. She developed an angry red rash over her tummy and insides of her legs, and her bits. Vets prescribed antibiotics and steroids but it came back. That's when I started looking into why. I took her to a homeopathic vet and she did say that reports were coming in about reactions to it. My other dogs didn't have it or any of their boosters either."

Jan Cobden wrote: "I lost my healthiest bitch last year after a lepto vaccination. She was poorly overnight, and fitted the next morning. The vaccine people said it was too early after the vaccine to be the cause of her fitting!! She fitted on a fortnightly basis up to Christmas then had a strange session of looking like she had hiccups, you could almost see the electrical impulses going to her brain but she didn't fit. After that she fitted on a monthly basis. I was hoping that maybe she was getting over them but in late Feb she fitted eight times in one day. By the time I got to see my vet she wasn't getting over one fit before the next. He gave her some valium but before that had time to work she fitted so badly and didn't recover that I had to make the decision to have her put to sleep. I am still devastated about her nearly a year on."

Another lady emailed with more disturbing news:

"I am compelled to write about my Beautiful Dachshund Rupert who passed away on 8th March 2017. He had been suffering from AIHA, since 27th December. He was given Lepto4 on the 8th December 2016 as a booster. On the 18th December he was vomiting blood and had bloody stools. This went on until the 28th December when we had to rush him into the vet hospital. They did various blood tests which confirmed autoimmune haemolytic anaemia. He was on steroids and seemed to be doing well, then a massive heart attack on the 8th March. He was only 17 months old and it has broken my heart, I knew nothing about Lepto4 until it was too late, and now I am frightened to have any new puppies I may have inoculated. Thank you for reading this."

Elizabeth Tattersdale wrote: "My German shepherd Lexxie never had any problems until last year. We gave her an annual booster with lepto and she had a major flare-up of SLO (systemic lupoid onychodystrophy). She had this booster then her temperature went up. She was sick and within hours her nails were inflamed and started to loosen. She lost all her nails. It was horrendous – so much so I'm at a loss as to what to do about my pups' vaccines. They need it but their mum had that reaction. She didn't eat for days, just kept being sick. Her nails are now deformed. She hasn't had this year's booster and no SLO flare ups, either. Could be coincidence but I don't think it is. She is normally fit and active. This has ruined her nails and now they're brittle."

It's worth noting that aluminium, used in lepto vaccines, is particularly implicated in what is termed ASIA syndrome: 'Autoimmune (Auto-inflammatory) Syndrome induced by Adjuvants'.

A paper entitled, 'Mechanisms of aluminum adjuvant toxicity and autoimmunity in pediatric populations' [7] states: "Immune challenges during early development, including those vaccine-induced, can lead to permanent detrimental alterations of the brain and immune function. Experimental evidence also shows that simultaneous administration of as little as two to three immune adjuvants can overcome genetic resistance to autoimmunity … it is now clearly established that there is a bidirectional neuro-immune cross-talk that plays crucial roles in immunoregulation as well as brain function. In turn, perturbations of the neuro-immune axis have been demonstrated in many autoimmune diseases encompassed in "ASIA" and are thought to be driven by a hyperactive immune response; and the same components of the neuro-immune axis that play key roles in brain development and immune function are heavily targeted by Al adjuvants." See also further references listed for this chapter.

I'd like to make a clear point here: *you don't need to be genetically pre-disposed to develop autoimmunity post-vaccination.*

Again recently, a journalist from *The Telegraph* telephoned me. He was working on a story relating to the Lepto 4 vaccine. He told me that the VMD seemed reluctant to speak to him (that's no surprise), but that they did grudgingly admit that 120 dogs had died, and over 2,000 had suffered adverse reactions. The response was to leave it on the market and see what else happens.

The VMD then offered reassurance over vaccine concerns, which was published in *Veterinary Times* on March 20, 2017, with the sub-heading, "The VMD has moved to reassure vets following concerns raised in media reports of serious adverse events in dogs given the vaccine containing four strains of Leptospira bacteria". The VMD stated in the report: "We would like to reassure vets – and through them, dog owners – we are constantly reviewing adverse event report data to ensure the benefits of each UK licensed veterinary medicine product outweighs the risk posed by their potential side effects."

The VMD's press statement [8], now hidden on the web if it's still there, said: "… the VMD has received fewer than two adverse reactions for L2, and fewer than seven for L4, for every 10,000 doses sold. This includes every suspected adverse event reported – even cases that were considered unclassifiable or were later found to be unrelated to the vaccine."

So … if seven in 10,000 dogs react to the L4 jab, and, say, three million dogs are vaccinated against it in the UK, this means 2,100 adverse reactions. This is almost ten times higher than the number of dogs who allegedly contract leptospirosis in the UK according to MSD's own CICADA survey figures (they could only manage to cobble together/ extrapolate 250 cases of lepto in the UK).

The risk:benefit ratio just doesn't stand up. And why did the VMD release the figures as percentages? So we wouldn't work it out?

Chapter 86

Confused? Maybe that's the idea!

Again asking why we are told to vaccinate our dogs when we don't need to, let's take another look at the human vaccine market so we can seek to understand what's happening.

Beginning in summer 2014, the media started reporting on an Ebola virus outbreak in West Africa. Listening to the news here in England, it seemed we were all going to die again. This was the first Ebola outbreak to reach epidemic proportions. Extreme poverty, a dysfunctional healthcare system, a mistrust of government officials after years of armed conflict, and the delay in responding to the outbreak were all said to have contributed to the early failure to control the epidemic.

The NIH has been trialling Ebola vaccines for some time. A 2003–04 study [1], published in 2006, showed its vaccine to be less than safe, although it was touted as safe. Two subjects experienced "serious adverse events"; over 90 per cent had local injection site reactions; and recorded systemic symptoms included malaise, muscle pain, nausea and fever.

The *Federal Register*, the daily journal of the United States government, listed that the NIH was contemplating – back in March 2014 – granting an exclusive license to Exxell BIO Inc for a new vaccine covering Ebola – just in time for the Ebola panic that raised its head five months later. [2]

And here's where my investigations sent me off in an interesting direction.

Exxell BIO Inc appears to be a private company founded in 2011. The only information I could find is that its CEO is Leonard P Ruiz Jr, PhD – who is also the President of the International Medica Foundation.

"Dr Ruiz has 30 years of domestic and international experience in business development, technology transfer, and strategic partnering in the biotechnology, biopharmaceutical, and food and feed industries. During his career Dr Ruiz has commercialized over 50 products with total sales in excess of hundreds of millions of dollars."

The non-profit Medica Foundation also owns the rights to the RRV-TV vaccine for rotavirus. Ruiz was featured in the *American Journal of Epidemiology* slagging off research into age-dependent intussusception following the use of the rotavirus vaccine. [3]

Intussusception is a condition where the bowel telescopes in on itself. This causes the bowel walls to press on one another, blocking the bowel.

An operation to remove parts of the bowel can follow. It can be deadly.

But what is rotavirus, and how serious is it? According to the UK NHS website [4], rotavirus causes gastroenteritis and is a common condition where the stomach and bowel become inflamed. The two main symptoms of gastroenteritis are diarrhoea and vomiting which, they say, usually clear up in around five to seven days without treatment. It is prevented primarily by following good hygiene.

In contrast, according to a different government body, the UK Department of Health [5]: "In September 2013, the [rotavirus] vaccine will be offered to all children in the UK, aged between two and three months, and it is expected to halve the cases of severe infection and reduce the number of children admitted to hospital because of the infection by 70 percent."

So which government advice should parents follow? Does rotavirus threaten a self-limiting case of the squits, rarely requiring doctor intervention, and avoided with hygiene, or is rotavirus so serious that all children between two and three months in the UK need the vaccine, risking intussusception?

In other words, is it a ruse for vaccine manufacturers?

Two currently used rhesus (monkey) rotavirus vaccines are Rotarix by GSK, and Merck's RotaTeq. In 2010, the detection of DNA from pig circovirus within both vaccines prompted the FDA to suspend their use. This might indicate that both companies used the same seed stock, possibly from the same company or government body.

The suspension was swiftly revoked, with regulators deciding that health risks involved with the vaccine didn't offset the benefits. Although this contamination with a pig virus was thought to be benign, vaccines are supposed to be sterile. In some countries, like Spain, the vaccine is still off the market. I wonder, though, if parents were given the choice of maintaining good hygiene or subjecting their children to a pig virus and possible intussusception, which would they choose?

According to the greenmediainfo website [6], human cell lines can be infected with pig circovirus:

"Given these findings, if the FDA's 'scientific' justification for allowing millions of infants and children to be exposed to PCV1 and PCV2 DNA and possibly live viruses is that 'they cannot infect humans,' they are now compelled to correct their mistake or be found guilty of both risking the health and well-being of our children, as well as violating the medical ethical principle of informed consent."

I wondered whether the vaccine would be back on the market if it hadn't been developed, perhaps, by the people who regulate it? Oh here we go: here's a study conducted on potentially unsuspecting children in Ghana by Leonard P Ruiz and others, including Albert Kapikian from the NIH – an American government body. Their experiment found that the vaccine in question was *less harmful* to younger babies. [7].

Another paper [8] explains how, "Originally, [a new] human-bovine reassortant rotavirus vaccine was intended as a second-generation rotavirus vaccine. It was developed alongside the human-rhesus reassortant vaccine, RotaShield, an earlier invention of Dr Kapikian that was commercialized by Wyeth following US Food and Drug Administration approval in 1998. RotaShield was voluntarily removed from the market in 1999 after the vaccine was suspected of being linked to an increased risk for intussusception in children."

The newer cow-based NIH rotavirus vaccine was further developed through collaboration with Wyeth Pharmaceuticals.

And then there's Paul Offit. TruthWiki states:

"Dr Paul Offit may be the most widely quoted promoter, defender and apologist for the vaccine industry today. Known for his "RotaTeq" rotavirus vaccine (and its patent) and his knowledge about immune response, Offit was honored with award by the National Foundation for Infectious Diseases and recognized by the illustrious Bill Gates during one of Gates' global health projects to vaccinate the whole world. The CDC recommends Offit's rotavirus vaccine (for infants); however, auspiciously, Offit is also a founding advisory board member of the Autism Science Foundation. Autism has been linked to the MMR (measles/mumps/rubella) vaccine by Whistleblower vaccine scientist from the CDC, Dr William Thompson himself in a stunning confession. Paul Offit is also the author of a sketchy medical narrative: "Autism's False Prophets."

"In 2008, the program "Every Child by Two" Dr Paul Offit received hundreds of thousands of dollars in funding from pharmaceutical companies that manufacture vaccines. They claim this has no influence on their vaccine "safety" stance, but this has been exposed otherwise by reliable journalists. There is missing information on just how much Offit profited from the sale of his invention of a Rotavirus vaccine (that's never even been proven to work), but estimates are between $30 and $55 million of the 150 million dollar deal that was struck.

"According to an investigation by Age of Autism, Dr Paul Offit of the Children's Hospital of Philadelphia (CHOP is now their nickname), took home a fortune from the sale of CHOP, which had worldwide royalty interest in the Merck RotaTeq vaccine. Offit's former position on the CDC's Advisory Committee on Immunization Practices then comes into question, as his job description entailed creating the market for rotavirus vaccine; basically "voting himself rich" in the process. This is the same shill and vaccine promotor/orator who says he could get 10,000 vaccines at once and be fine."

There is a connection in all of this. Dr William Thompson's admission of scientific fraud at the CDC that led to African American boys under age three getting autism from MMR II vaccine was also recently revealed, but the mass media refused to cover it.

"In a single vote, the ACIP, or Advisory Committee on Immunization Practices, can create a commercial market for a new vaccine worth hundreds of millions. This is not possible with most patented products, but then again, vaccines are not like "most" products. For example, after the ACIP approved Offit's and Merck's RotaTeq vaccine to the official "childhood vaccination schedule," Merck's RotaTeq revenue rose from nothing to over $650 million within a couple of years (2006 – 2008) (Dial it back to 1998 until 2003 and Offit was a "member" of ACIP). Since three doses of RotaTeq cost about $200 and about four million infants and children are "mandated" to get it each year, do the math. To this day Offit still refuses to confirm how much money he made and to bury this conflict of interest and continue to only say he is a pediatrician in interviews represents ethics breaches right and left. It completely discredits the medical papers he writes about immune response and vaccine safety."

It's all getting a bit complicated. It appears that an American government department, the NIH, developed a vaccine that turned out to cause intussusception, and a non-profit foundation called Medica, of which Leonard P Ruiz is president, might own the rights, and then was it commercialised by Wyeth? And then another American government department regulates it. And Paul Offit also has the apparent ability to cash in on the vaccine.

Then another rotavirus vaccine crops up [9]. This time the star is Roger I Glass of the Fogarty International Center, which is part of the NIH. Glass was at a WHO conference when he had a discussion with an Indian doctor who noticed that rotavirus infected neonates (babies less than four weeks old) didn't develop diarrhoea. They wondered if these infections could protect older children.

Vaccine manufacturers joined in, and the Gates Foundation and program at PATH jumped on board. "By 2011," Glass stated, "we were finally ready to launch a trial with 6,800 infants at three sites in India conducted by an NGO, the Society for Applied Studies, that grew out of the need for larger field trials. Thankfully, the results have been positive. We hope the vaccine will be licensed so that it can be introduced in several sites in India. We're confident this will make a huge impact and go a long way to preventing the 100,000 rotavirus deaths that currently occur in that country every year."

And then Glass said something really important: "As we studied the epidemiology of rotavirus in India, we discovered *vast differences in the epidemiology of disease between low- and high-income settings.*"

Of course! Rotavirus is about poor hygiene – which is exacerbated by poor living conditions. It's another disease of poverty! And if you resolve the poverty problem, and teach basic hygiene, the vaccine wouldn't be needed.

However, the NIH trial record [10] states that intussusception has been designated as a safety issue. I could find no information as to how those 6,800 experimental children fared, and whether or not any of them had intussusception or died as a result of being part of a vaccine experiment. The trial began in 2011 and was estimated to finish in 2014, but as at May 2017, no study results had been posted.

I find Leonard P Ruiz interesting – not because I think he's done anything illegal, but because he has 'commercialized over 50 products with total sales in excess of hundreds of millions of dollars' and licensed a vaccine against Ebola just before scare stories about Ebola appeared in the media.

Just to put the Ebola outbreak into context, at time of writing just over 8,000 people have been infected with Ebola, whereas 800,000 people die every year from malaria, and every 3.6 seconds one person dies of starvation. There are 31,536,000 seconds in a year. If the figures are correct, it means that over 10,500 million people die of starvation each year. But how can you cash in on death by starvation if the people can't afford to even buy food?

Mr Ruiz is also a consultant/advisor to Inventprise, a "biotechnology company utilizing innovative technologies to improve existing vaccines". [11]

According to this website, Leonard Ruiz is also currently a working group member of the US Pediatric Formulations Initiative at the National Institute of Child Health and Human Development (NICHD), National Institutes of Health (NIH). He's a bio-businessman with strong government ties. It looks to me like he's a deal broker for the NIH which is developing vaccines using American tax dollars.

Ruiz has had leadership roles in for-profit businesses and non-profit foundations. He was CEO of the vaccine company Altravax, Inc. He was the former President of the business development fund, Global Genomics Capital, Inc. and had a leadership role in merging GGC into CytRx Corp which had a portfolio of vaccine adjuvant. He was one of the founders of Prolacta Bioscience, Inc., and was the CEO of The SOTA TEC Fund, a non-profit business development fund which invested in projects with business development potential at the Mayo Clinic and the University of Minnesota. He has also been the CEO of several biotechnology companies and has led the development of a successful animal biologics business targeting diarrheal diseases.

His international experiences includes projects in New Zealand, Malaysia (World Bank), Pakistan (USAID) and Africa. He holds a PhD in Organic Chemistry and has completed postgraduate studies in marketing, business development and patent law, and he's even been a MENSA member.

I find it interesting that this one man, who is probably one of many such men, manages to dip between government and industry roles with ease.

I also find it interesting that washing your hands can do as much as a vaccine in preventing bacterial infection in babies.

But I haven't quite got my head around the fact that governments are developing vaccines and then handing them over to the pharmaceutical industry to profit from. What's this all about?

Chapter 87

How can you ethically be the regulator for your own assets?

So returning to Ebola, an on-line piece in *Science* [1], stated that no experimental vaccine had ever been on a faster track toward widespread use. "It's absolutely unprecedented," said Marie-Paule Kieny, an assistant director-general at WHO.

On 5 September 2014, more than 200 technical experts convened by WHO recommended bypassing the usual regulatory pathways for potential Ebola vaccines and therapies. No one expected a vaccine would slow the epidemic directly, yet they thought it could help keep and attract workers leading containment efforts. Does this mean they thought health workers might contract Ebola despite the vaccine, but at least they were lulled into a false sense of security?

Pharmaceutical giant GSK, which was developing a vaccine in collaboration with NIH's National Institute of Allergy and Infectious Diseases, said it may produce as many as 10,000 doses by the end of the year. A second Ebola vaccine starting human tests that month was initially engineered by the Public Health Agency of Canada, another government body, and was being developed by NewLink Genetics of Iowa.

Both vaccines had protected monkeys and smaller animals in lab experiments, the article stated. Health care workers would be the first to get the vaccines, they said. Typically, vaccines that pass phase I safety trials move into expanded phase II and phase III trials to determine whether they actually work and should go to market. "Ebola vaccine developers have long contended that traditional efficacy trials could not be done because *past outbreaks have ended quickly with the help of standard infection control procedures.*" [My emphasis.]

Researchers planned to take advantage of the Animal Rule at the FDA, which says when efficacy studies "are not ethical or feasible," FDA will license vaccines for diseases if they work in two animal models and if large-scale phase II studies conducted in humans prove they are safe and trigger immune responses that mirror those in protected animals. So essentially, the outbreak offered a great chance to test new vaccines.

"Now, the push is to vaccinate people at high risk and try to gain interpretable data," said Adrian Hill, director of the Jenner Institute at the University of Oxford.

However, researchers might have trouble working out if the vaccine worked if a vaccine offers only partial protection, NIAID's Mascola said. "If there's a 50% mortality with Ebola and you use the vaccine and it's 40% protective, what does that mean?" he asked.

The WHO coven weren't sure which experimental vaccine to deploy …they talked about which vaccine is best. But even though one, the VSV, is weakened, *safety concerns remain about the possibility that it could cause neurological disease, as it has in some animal studies, or infect livestock.*

"We've been fooled by trying to translate monkey findings to humans before," said Fauci, who noted that *an AIDS vaccine worked well in monkeys and actually increased HIV infection rates when tested in humans.* Have a think about this: at least one Aids vaccine was responsible for increasing Aids.

Gary Nabel, who headed NIAID's VRC before leaving to join drug firm Sanofi, said manufacturers should massively scale up production before trial results are in. "If it were me personally, I'd err on the side of caution, and I'd think carefully about stockpiling doses. If it isn't safe, you throw away those lots. *In the worst case you've wasted some money.*

"If the virus spreads even farther and one of these vaccines does prove safe and effective but is not available, I think there'll be a lot of finger-pointing," he said.

I find it interesting that a former American government official, now an industry man, should think that you only waste money if a vaccine isn't safe. There seems to be no consideration of the lives an unsafe vaccine might destroy. Of course, to be fair, they may also be *thinking* about the lives a vaccine might save, despite failing to state that.

I also find it interesting that an Ebola vaccine was trialled by America's NIH back in September 2006. I've spent the last 23 years of my life asking my government to properly regulate the veterinary vaccine industry – but now it looks as though governments are part of the industry [2].

By September 2014, NaturalNews was reporting that the American government was awarded a patent on Ebola in 2010 – patent number is CA2741523A1. The patent was lodged by the American CDC [3]. This presumably means that the American government can demand royalties on all Ebola vaccines. In fact, if you do the research, you find that – again and again – vaccines are coming out of government laboratories. Isn't that a racket, considering governments claim to be there for the good of the people? How can you ethically be the regulator for your own assets, assets from which you profit?

Dave Hodges of The *Common Sense Show* [4], had this insight: "I want to be clear on this point, Ebola was invented, a vaccine for Ebola has existed for 8-10 years, some government sponsored institutions as well as some of the global elite have positioned themselves to profit enormously from the spread of the virus and the development of and dissemination of mandatory Ebola vaccines and the imposition of total martial law in the process.

"... the CDC owns 'the' patent on Ebola and all future strains. The summary of the invention also clearly claims that the U.S. government is claiming 'ownership' over all Ebola viruses that share as little as 70% similarity with the Ebola it 'invented'.

"Why would a government organization claim to have 'invented' this infectious disease and then claim a monopoly over its exploitation for commercial use? It is clear that the CDC plans to claim royalties on Ebola vaccines. This certainly increases the likelihood that the vaccines will become mandatory, thus increasing the profit potential for the patent holders.

"Another interesting fact is that Zika virus (ATCC® VR-84™), another pathogen we must now be scared about, was patented in 1947 by the Rockefeller Foundation! So if you're a conspiracy theorist, you'll believe that the Rockefellers are above governments."

Adding all the snippets of information together, I began to wonder if the Ebola outbreak had anything to do with money, bioterrorism and messing about with viruses in labs, and the fact that the world is over-populated?

A stunning book which came out in the 90s by Harvard graduate Len Horowitz came to mind. I went to my library and dug it out.

Called *Emerging Viruses: AIDS & Ebola: Nature, Accident or Intentional?* (Horowitz, Leonard G., DMD) [5], Dr Horowitz fell on the side of intentional, suggesting that concerns regarding world over-population alongside the cold war had caused the American government to develop a massive armoury of bioweapons. At the very least, he suggested, viruses are getting mixed with one-another in government labs around the world, with the risk of even more deadly viruses escaping and creating mayhem. As the title of his book suggests, he also questioned whether Ebola was part of the bio-warfare tool box. He was asking this question decades ago.

This brings parvovirus to mind. As with Aids, parvovirus appears to be a vaccine-induced plague. Parvo emerged suddenly across several different continents in the 70s, killing thousands of dogs. Several verifiable sources point to the theory that vaccine manufacturers cultivated the distemper vaccine on infected cats' kidneys and this was shipped around the world in vials, ready to be injected into our dogs. It was pretty much nailed as a vaccine-induced plague in the *Journal of the American Veterinary Medical*

Association [6,7,8]. In his paper, Ian Tizard outlined the consequences of vaccine contamination. He also commented at the potential horror of such an 'accident' occurring in human vaccines:

"One hypothesis regarding the origin of CPV [parvo]," he wrote, "suggests that this selective pressure and subsequent mutation more likely occurred in a tissue culture environment than through dog-to-dog passage. Thus, it is speculated that CPV might have arisen through rapid accidental passage of FPV (feline panleukopenia virus) or mink enteritis virus in a canine cell culture line. Cells infected with the new mutant may then have been transmitted globally through a contaminated biological product such as a vaccine."

Translation: parvo was created by a vaccine manufacturer and shipped round the world, ready to be injected into our dogs.

Tizard commented: " … it is clear that modified-live vaccines are intrinsically more hazardous than inactivated products. The hazards of residual virulence and contamination are obvious. More important, however, is the ability of new infective agents to develop through the use and dissemination of these vaccines. These agents are major threats to animal populations, wild and domesticated. The best way to ensure that such hazards do not develop in the future is to seek alternatives to modified live products. We must begin to replace modified live vaccines with inactivated products. Modified-live vaccines have served us well, but their time is past. We can no longer afford them."

Nothing has changed, though – we still have MLV vaccines. And parvo appears to be a vaccine-induced plague.

Ebola is a new disease; it first occurred in humans in 1976, in the Sudan, and later in Zaire. It was identified as a Marburg type virus, which itself was first described during small epidemics in the German cities of Marburg, Frankfurt, and Belgrade in the 1960s. Workers were accidentally exposed to tissues of infected African green monkeys whilst working for vaccine manufacturer Hoechst, today CSL Behring. Marburg is a Select Agent, WHO Risk Group 4 Pathogen, NIH/National Institute of Allergy and Infectious Diseases Category A Priority Pathogen, and a CDC Prevention Category A Bioterrorism Agent.

Ebola virus is also a zoonosis, meaning it's an animal infection transmissible to humans. It abides endemically in the forests of equatorial Africa, and has the potential to be weaponised for use in biological warfare. Ebola was investigated by Biopreparat for such use [9,10,11].

The 2015 West Africa epidemic involved a species of Ebola virus previously known only from outbreaks in the Democratic Republic of the Congo and its close neighbours. Also worth considering is that rainforests in the Congo Basin are being cleared at an alarming rate amidst global demand for mineral, energy and wood resources. Pressures on the 200 million hectare forests – though not has high-profile as those in the Brazilian Amazon or Indonesia – are enormous. Scientists have been warning for decades that deforestation of rainforests on this scale will release viruses and bacteria that we have not had to deal with before.

A *New York Times* article in 2012 [(12)] stated: "most epidemics — AIDS, Ebola, West Nile, SARS, Lyme disease and hundreds more that have occurred over the last several decades — don't just happen. They are a result of things people do to nature.

"Disease, it turns out, is largely an environmental issue. Sixty percent of emerging infectious diseases that affect humans are zoonotic — they originate in animals. And more than two-thirds of those originate in wildlife.

"In the Amazon, for example, one study showed an increase in deforestation by some 4 percent increased the incidence of malaria by nearly 50 percent, because mosquitoes, which transmit the disease, thrive in the right mix of sunlight and water in recently deforested areas. Developing the forest in the wrong way can be like opening Pandora's box."

Researchers are watching the interface where deadly viruses are known to exist and where people are breaking open the forests. By mapping encroachment into the forest you can predict where the next disease could emerge. So once again we have the capitalist quest for money destroying lives.

A puzzling fact about the West Africa epidemic is that it involved a species of Ebola virus previously known only from outbreaks in the Congo – in central Africa – and its close neighbours.

African natives became suspicious of the more recent outbreak, alongside fears that Western governments were deliberately causing disease on the continent. According to the Aid Worker Security Database [(13)] 87 health workers were killed by African villagers in 2003, rising to 155 in 2013. In September 2014, eight aid workers were killed in Guinea. Many villagers accused aid workers of spreading Ebola themselves.

The Disease Daily [(14)] reported that:

> On February 8th, 2013, at least nine young women working on
> a polio vaccination campaign were targeted and killed by gunmen
> in two separate incidents in Kano, the regional capital of Northern
> Nigeria. The two neighbourhoods where the attacks took place have
> seen previous actions by a Muslim extremist group known as Boko
> Haram, a Hausa term meaning "Western education is forbidden".

These attacks are not the first attacks against health workers in Nigeria. Two security officers guarding immunizers were killed by gunmen in October. Unfortunately, Nigeria is the second place where polio vaccination workers have been targeted and killed. Sixteen health workers – primarily women – were killed by Taliban gunmen in Pakistan in two incidents in December and January.

Boko Haram and the Taliban are not new to their respective areas, but the violence directed specifically at polio workers has drawn speculation. Some are concerned that conspiracy theories are spreading in the region that the vaccinations are harmful. Similar rumours led to a regional boycott of polio vaccination programs in 2003, a public health disaster that set back polio eradication efforts significantly. Others argue this is may be a copycat attack of those in Pakistan, meant as blowback from a CIA attempt to use a vaccination program as a ruse to gather intelligence on Osama Bin Laden. Such unfortunate consequences were predicted when the CIA program came to light in 2011.

This has led some critics to call for a public US government ban on CIA operations involving childhood vaccines. While this may help, it is unlikely to go far enough. Re-starting the vaccination campaign in Nigeria in 2003 required nullifying the prevailing rumors and conspiracy theories floating around in northern Nigeria. The key was regaining trust of both the local people and religious leaders.

Bill Gates wrote about polio eradication in his annual letter in January, focusing on how mapping, organization and statistical record-keeping were key challenges to ensuring vaccination programs covered everyone in Northern Nigeria. Such a rational approach is laudable, but unlikely to succeed without stepping up sociocultural outreach in both regions coupled with a government ban on covert CIA programs mimicking vaccination programs. Such a holistic approach may help quell recent violence and keep polio eradication in the region on track.

The report overlooks the fact that over 47,500 cases of non-polio acute flaccid paralysis have been linked to the oral polio vaccine given in India recently, which may itself have set back vaccination campaigns.

Earlier, in 2007, the *New York Times* [15] reported that five nurses, who had received death sentences, had been repatriated to Bulgaria after eight years' imprisonment on charges of intentionally infecting hundreds of Libyan children with HIV.

A guilty verdict saw a $426 million payout to families of infected children. Although WHO maintains that the re-use of syringes without sterilization accounts for only 2.5 percent of new HIV infections in Africa, a 2003 study in *The International Journal of STD and AIDS* found that as many as 40 percent of HIV infections in Africa are caused by contaminated needles during medical treatment. Even the conservative WHO estimate translates to tens of thousands of cases.

"Several esteemed science journals, including *Nature*, have suggested that the Libyan children were infected in just this manner, through the re-use of incompletely cleaned medical instruments, long before the Bulgarian nurses arrived in Libya. If this is the case, then the Libyan accusations of iatrogenic, or healer-transmitted, infection are true. The acts may not have been intentional, but given the history of Western medicine in Africa, accusations that they were done consciously are far from paranoid."

Most of the TV news reports I had heard on the subject of murdered aid and health workers tended to mention things like witch doctors and superstition. But knowing, as I do, the vaccine's ability to cause severe harm, I also knew that it would be foolish to belittle a whole continent and dismiss African concerns as unsophisticated folklore. This stinks of media collusion.

It also makes me wonder about the 'war on terror'. Maybe that's just a way to make nations submit to vaccine programmes and other corporate offerings the people don't want? Maybe the terrorists, rather than threatening *us*, are more likely to threaten the corporate agenda? Boko Haram means, 'western medicine is forbidden'? I wonder why. Maybe for the same reasons I – a westerner – don't use them?

According to the documents Horowitz unearthed via WHO *Chronicle* articles, WHO has exerted a powerful influence on the quality control of biological weapons since its inception in 1948. The coordinating body for this work was the WHO secretariat which worked with laboratories in other countries, most notably the Statens Seruminstitut in Copenhagen, the National Institute for Medical Research in London, and the Central Veterinary Laboratory in Weybridge, England. WHO, according to Horowitz, set the standards for the development, distribution and administration of all pharmaceuticals used throughout the world.

WHO was backed by powerful people like Kissinger and successive governments coming out of World War II, looking for ways to wage war other than through the use of the atom bomb. Viruses, and especially slow viruses (which prevent people from pinning the blame on, say, a vaccine because the damage occurs slowly) was where the money was going.

Government agencies, including the American NIH, the National

Cancer Institute, the CDC, the Department of Defence, the US Public Health Service, the Pasteur Institute in France, Porton Down in England, the Ivanofsky Institute in Russia, the International Agency for Research on Cancer, and others ... scientists around the world in government departments, and within pharmaceutical companies, were messing about with viruses in labs, splicing different viruses together from different species and immortalising them – creating super-viruses in the guise of preventative healthcare whilst also delivering powerful biological weapons. And *sharing* them with one-another! [16]

By the late 1960s, the WHO's and NCI's viral and cancer research centres in Denmark and Switzerland had served as authorised technical advisers and suppliers of 'prototype virus strains, diagnostic and reference reagents (antibodies), antigens and cell cultures' to 592 virus laboratories. Over 2,514 strains of viruses had been distributed. So rather than, say, leaving he rainforests alone and avoiding the release of previously hidden pathogens, they took viruses like Ebola, weaponised them, and developed potentially lucrative vaccines.

In 1994 a US Senate report documented the transfer to *Iraq* of the ingredients of *biological weapons*: botulism developed in Maryland, licensed by the Commerce Department and approved by the State Department. Anthrax was also supplied to Saddam's Iraq by the Porton Down laboratories in Britain, a government establishment. So any protestation that our governments want to protect humanity from infectious disease is somewhat disingenuous – they're selling biological agents to those who might attack us and their own citizens. During the 1980-90 Iran-Iraq war, America and Britain even sold armaments to both sides. [17]

Horowitz believes that, "HIV and its progenitors more likely evolved from simian (monkey) viruses altered by the deliberate or inadvertent insertion of cancer-causing viral particles from other animal species. We hypothesize these man-made mutants crossed over to infect the human population via contaminated vaccine experiments and vaccine programs. Such experiments and outcomes were commonplace in cancer virus research laboratories during the 1970s, at a time when collaborative vaccine developmental programs were ongoing, and before the initial outbreak of AIDS."

Horowitz thought it plausible that the Ebola virus also originated in NCI laboratories [18].

He unearthed a book by Norman M Covert called *Cutting Edge, a history of Fort Detrick* [19] – it's still available via Amazon. In it, the aptly named Covert, chief public relations officer for Fort Detrick, states (p. 17):

"From the moment of its birth in the highest levels of government, the fledgling biological warfare effort was kept to an inner circle of knowledgeable persons. George W Merck was a key member of the panel advising President Franklin D Roosevelt and was charged with putting such an effort together. Merck owned the pharmaceutical firm that still bears his name."

In fact, much medical research is funded by grants from government bodies such as the UK Medical Research Council (MRC) and the US NIH. When the basic research looks promising, the compound is sold, often to a biotechnology firm. For example, the UK's MRC holds patent no. WO 1986004242 A1 for "Improvements relating to influenza vaccine" [20].

In September 2014, NaturalNews reported that the CDC was awarded Ebola virus patent no. CA 2741523 A1 in 2010, and that the NIH owns patents on Ebola vaccines [21]. The Ebola virus was deposited with the CDC in 2007 [22]. I presume that these government agencies can demand royalties on Ebola vaccines. Isn't this corruption, seeing that these agencies exist for the good of the people? How can they ethically be regulators of their own assets from which they profit?

Vaccine safety proponent Robert F. Kennedy, Jr, notes: "The CDC is a very troubled agency, and it's not just me saying that. There have been four separate, intensive federal investigations by the United States Congress—a three year investigation, 2001, 2002, 2003, by the United States Senate, Tom Coburn's committee, by the Inspector General of HHS in 2008, by the Office Integrity in 2014. All of them have painted the CDC as a cesspool of corruption, of an agency that has become an absolute subsidiary of the pharmaceutical industry, and that has become a sock puppet, a spokesperson, a shill for the industry.

"CDC is not an independent agency. It is a vaccine company. CDC owns over twenty vaccine patents. It sells about $4.6 billion of vaccines every year." [23]

In fact, eugenics, biological warfare, and the transference of money from the poor to the rich under the guise of 'healthcare' were beginning to look like issues that tied governments, industry and the military *together*. It's called the Industrial Military Complex.

Our regulators, it seems *are part* of the pharmaceutical industry. Or to put it another way, the pharmaceutical industry is the part of government that siphons off the profits, taking our tax money to develop drugs and vaccines then offering them up to pharmaceutical companies. Then they stand by, refusing to ethically legislate, while corporations use loopholes to secrete taxes they might be expected to pay back to the nations in which their profits are generated – sending it overseas and out of reach. And if a vaccine harms you or a loved-one, our governments seem reluctant to stop them, and even promotes them.

I had found the Holy Grail, and I was as depressed as hell: Our regulators are not independent regulators at all. They walk like regulators, talk like regulators, even look like regulators – but they're not. Government itself is *involved* in the study and use of viruses and bacteria for warfare, with government bodies such as the NIH developing vaccines and handing them over to the pharmaceutical industry. No wonder the Veterinary Medicines Directorate, or at least Steve Dean, treat me as the enemy.

I questioned the collaboration between government and the vaccine industry when a 2007 foot-and-mouth-disease outbreak in the UK was traced to a shared government–industry research facility called The Pirbright Institute. The virus was used by three parties at Pirbright: the government-funded Institute for Animal Health, Merial Animal Health Ltd and Stabilitech Ltd. [24] My naïve question back then was: why would our government want to share a facility with the vaccine industry? I also asked the "why" question during the previous UK foot-and-mouth outbreak in 2001.

In a Trevor McDonald TV documentary it was asserted that the government department Defra was telephoning wood yards to ask about burning materials two weeks ahead of the announcement of any foot-and-mouth epidemic. In fact, a CHC member who ran a wood yard had already telephoned me to tell me the same thing. Why did Defra wait two weeks while this highly infectious disease took hold? The conspiracy theory was that the outbreak had started at the government's Porton Down biological warfare facility and that the government was trying to cover up the leak.[25]

The official advice was to stack the dead bodies of cattle and sheep out in the open air – even though foot-and-mouth is an airborne disease and stacking bodies in the open would likely spread it. My own vet even suggested that something fishy was going on [26].

So here is the answer I've been looking for: the VMD won't take redundant, one-year, core vaccines off the market because it looks like government and industry are one. Is this why the VMD parrots out industry sales data in defence of harmful vaccines? Is this why they won't put realistic and accurate adverse event reporting systems in place? Is it why the VMD doesn't appear to want us to use simple blood tests to confirm immunity rather than blindly revaccinating? And is it why they, as well as government bodies overseeing human vaccines, seem to hide and minimise vaccine adverse effects?

None of this is conspiracy theory. You don't need to be a conspiracy theorist to see and experience these facts.

Back in July 29, 1969, Horowitz revealed, the US House Republican research committee task force on earth resources and population, chaired by George Bush, cited the urgent need for population control activities to fend off a growing Third World crisis. Included in the briefing was information from the evangelical organisation Bill Gates had been trained to revere: Planned Parenthood.

A few years later, shortly after George Bush's retirement as CIA director, the State Department issued a series of three publications entitled, 'World Population: The Silent Explosion'. The publications issued a conflicted message – on the one hand talking about giving more food aid and vaccines to developing countries, but on the other hand implying that if the starving masses died, there would be less of a problem [27]

The Kissinger Report [28] states (p. 14):

"...There is an alternative view which holds that a growing number of experts believe that the population situation is already more serious and less amenable to solution through voluntary measures than is generally accepted. It holds that, to prevent even more widespread food shortage and other demographic catastrophes than are generally anticipated, even stronger measures are required and some fundamental, very difficult moral issues need to be addressed. These include...our own consumption patterns, mandatory programs, tight control of our food resources...

"...Implementing the actions discussed above...will require a significant expansion in AID funds for population/family planning. A number of major actions in the area of creating conditions for fertility decline can be funded from resources available to the sectors in question (e.g., education, agriculture). Other actions, including family planning services, research and *experimental activities on factors effecting* [sic] *fertility*, come under population funds..." (Emphasis added.)

The World Bank also got in on the act. In her book, *Reproductive Rights and Wrongs: The Global Politics of Population Control and Contraceptive Choice* [29], Betsy Hartmann noted that the World Bank's key device for administering population policy was, 'leverage over other forms of development finance'. This means that wealthier nations lend money to poorer nations in the knowledge that loans cannot be repaid. She noted that governments often burdened by massive foreign debt are persuaded to 'devalue their currency, privatise their industries, open their doors to foreign investment, freeze wages, raise food prices, slash social services and implement Bank sanctioned population programmes'.

In other words, the American-sponsored World Bank appears to be bankrupting foreign governments in order to advance the American Corporate Empire and its agenda, and impoverishing their citizens. Included in this agenda is what appears to be a plan to *reduce* the population.

Meanwhile, a BBC documentary about the Ebola outbreak, broadcast in June 2015, made it known that WHO dragged its feet for ten months after the Ebola outbreak first started. It did nothing, leaving Médecins Sans Frontières workers to deal with the spread and with woefully inadequate resources. Makes me wonder if WHO was keen to give it time so that vaccines could be advanced.

Chapter 88

Conspiracy theory, or cock-up theory?

So a foot and mouth outbreak in the UK was traced back to a water leak from a shared government/industry research facility called Pirbright – a research facility involving deadly viruses. [1] My question back then was: "Why would governments want to share a facility with the vaccine industry to research deadly viruses?"

Why did they wait two weeks while this highly infectious disease took hold? The conspiracy theory was that the outbreak started at another government biological warfare facility: Porton Down, and that the government was trying to cover up the leak. [2]

The official advice was to stack the dead bodies of cattle and sheep out in the open air – even though foot and mouth is an airborne disease, and stacking bodies in the open would likely spread it [3].

In December 2014, the *Guardian* reported that high-security labs that handle the most dangerous viruses and bacteria had more than a hundred accidents or near-misses in the previous five years [4].

Prof Richard Ebright, a US biosafety expert at Rutgers University in New Jersey, who reviewed government reports for the *Guardian*, said that, taken together, they revealed failures in procedures, infrastructure, training and safety culture at some British labs. Alarmed at a run of incidents at facilities that work on animal diseases, Ebright asked: "Does British agriculture have a death wish?"

The figures amounted to one investigation every three weeks at secure laboratories designed to carry out research on pathogens that can cause serious illness and spread into the community. Some of the organisms are lethal and have no vaccines or treatments. One blunder led to live anthrax being sent from a government facility to unsuspecting labs across the UK, a mistake that exposed other scientists to the disease. Another caused the failure of an air handling system that helped contain foot and mouth disease at a large animal lab.

Ebright, who testified to the House committee over the CDC anthrax incident, was struck by the similar failings at labs in the UK and the US. "The incidents at the AHVLA should really not occur. They involved not one error, but a whole chain of errors, and they are all essentially unforgiveable," he said. "They reflect the most elementary lapses and they are potentially very serious. To see them happening like that suggests there is a deep problem."

Scientists are also messing about with viruses in academic labs. In July 2014, for example, the *Wisconsin State Journal* questioned the safety of a scientist experimenting with deadly viruses and making them more deadly. [5,6] Colleagues expressed public alarm, fearing a leak that could start a pandemic. Stunningly, American regulators allowed the scientist to reduce his bio-safety rating.

And then in February 2017, Bill Gates announced that he foresees a new deadly strain of a lab-engineered virus emerging as a new threat that could wipe out tens of millions or even hundreds of millions. Since Gates is investing in experimental vaccines and presumably knows what happens in labs which stock deadly viruses, and has large shareholdings in the field in addition to worrying about world over-population, it's hard to know whether he was issuing a warning or a threat. [7]

But why is it so important for countries to champion bio research and run these risks? Maybe the following statement unearthed by Len Horowitz will provide insight?

In 1948, after WW II, US strategic planner George Kennan said [8]: "We [America] have 50 per cent of the world's wealth but only 6.3 per cent of its population. In this situation, our real job in the coming period ... is to maintain this position of disparity. To do so, we have to dispense with all sentimentality ... we should cease thinking about human rights, the raising of living standards and democratisation."

America no longer has 50 per cent of the world's wealth. In a 2017 interview, one of the world's leading intellects, Dr Noam Chomsky, stated in relation to who owns the economy: "Increasingly during the period of Neo-Liberal globalisation ... corporate wealth is becoming a more realistic measure of global power than national wealth. In virtually every economic sector, US corporations are well in the lead of the global economy." This would mean that the world is being governed by unelected organisations, outside democracy. Further, those corporations are charged with the task of maximising profits above all else. We don't matter anymore.

"The greater sham is the 'war on terrorism itself", said award-winning journalist John Pilger [9]. "The American goal is, and always was, the control, through vassals, of former Soviet Central Asia, a region rich in oil and minerals and of great strategic importance to competing powers, Russia and China. 'America will have a continuing interest and presence in Central Asia of a kind that we could not have dreamed of before [September 11]', said Secretary of State Colin Powell. 'This is just the beginning. The ultimate goal is a far wider American conquest, military and economic, which was planned during the Second World War and which, as Vice-President Cheney says, 'may not end in our lifetimes', or until the United

States has positioned itself as gatekeeper of the world's remaining oil and gas.'"

Should I submit myself and my loved-ones to vaccines that aren't needed and which may cause harm to support the military-industrial complex and the American Empire? I might add that the British have not relinquished their hold on empire, either.

In fact the UK is a premier base for the bio industry, also known as 'life sciences'. Steve Bates, CEO of the UK BioIndustry Association (BIA), said: "The UK is a great place for life sciences: a globally competitive tax and fiscal environment, a collaborative and thriving ecosystem as well as prominence on the government agenda are all key ingredients for success [10]."

Personally, I'd prefer if we all got rid of all the bombs and bio-weapons, and I believe that the majority of the population might agree with me if they knew that *we* were the ones leading the charge towards human destruction. The message is that we in the West are educated, liberal, decent, honest and true, and that the less powerful countries are full of terrorists and despotic tyrants who curb the free press, keep their people in poverty, and abuse human rights.

The actual truth is that we don't have a free press (try to get the truth about vaccines out there via the mainstream media, for a start!). And our Western governments promote and facilitate biological warfare, which appears to be a nice little earner. Above all, we have the power and we want to keep it – at the expense of everyone else.

Chapter 89

Where are the ethics; where is the compassion?

In the 21st century, there is no excuse for human beings to be without good nutrition and access to clean water – the two proven, safe, ways by which infection can be reduced. Unpaid taxes from corporations and the wealthy elite could eradicate this problem with ease.

Diseases from unsafe water and lack of basic sanitation kill more people every year than all forms of violence, including war. Children are especially vulnerable as their bodies aren't strong enough to fight diarrhoea, dysentery and other illnesses against which vaccines represent fools' gold – delivering potential, but not guaranteed, immunity in exchange for underlying health. Did you know, for example, that infant mortality dropped by 50 percent when America started chlorinating its water to kill harmful pathogens? [1]

You'll see from the following graph, from sanitation engineers Cutler and Miller [2], that major infectious diseases dropped away long before vaccines were introduced, and long before vaccines took the credit for halting epidemics. The numbers relate to shares of total mortality (viz., the percentage of overall deaths from all causes.) I've added the right-hand column to detail when vaccines were first introduced.

Cause of death	1900	1936	Vaccines
Major infectious disease	39.3	17.9	Too broad for a vaccine
Tuberculosis	11.1	5.3	Mass vaccination after WWII (post 1945)
Pneumonia	9.6	9.3	First vaccine 1977. The germs that can cause pneumonia are usually breathed in.
Diarrhoea and enteritis	7.0	n/a	Rotavirus vaccine not introduced until 1998 (but withdrawn due to safety concerns)
Typhoid fever	2.4	0.1	No vaccine
Meningitis	2.4	0.3	No vaccine until 1969

Malaria	1.2	0.1	Vaccine still in development; a new one is on the cards
Smallpox	0.7	0.0	The earliest vaccine – see Jayne Donegan below
Influenza	0.7	1.3	Vaccine introduced in 1935. Figures had increased! (flu is not water-borne)
Childhood Infectious diseases	4.2	0.5	Broad category (no vaccine)
Measles	0.7	0	First measles vaccine 1954
Scarlet fever	0.5	0.1	No vaccine
Whooping cough	0.6	0.2	Vaccine developed 1940s
Diphtheria and Croup	2.3	0.1	Vaccine fraught with problems before mid-1900s

Dr Jayne Donegan stated (relying upon government figures): "Even the success story of smallpox vaccination was not what it seemed: the enforcement of the compulsory smallpox vaccination law in 1867, when the death rate was already falling, was accompanied by an increase in the deaths from 100 to 400 deaths per million population".

Let us ask our governments to stop investing in deadly viruses and vaccine research, and honour everyone's basic human right to clean water and proper nutrition instead.

According to the World Economic Forum, ninety percent of the 30,000 deaths that occur every week from unsafe water and unhygienic living conditions [3] are in children under five years old – which puts the Ebola outbreak into perspective: 30,000 children die every week from poverty. The WHO reports that over 3.6% of the global disease burden can be prevented simply by improving water supply, sanitation, and hygiene.

They say this, and then push vaccines on us. An estimated 1.1 billion human beings lack access to clean water while a staggering 2.6 billion lack basic sanitation. This results in some 2.2 million deaths each year, mostly among children — deaths that can easily be prevented through proven, cost-effective measures. Action Against Hunger.co.uk states that every day 4,000 children die from diseases caused by dirty water.

Yet the combined wealth of the richest one per cent will overtake that of the remaining 99 per cent by 2016 unless the current trend of rising inequality is checked, Oxfam warned in January 2015 [4]. The human race has within its power the means to prevent most infections, simply by providing basic living conditions.

The type of inequality that currently characterises the world's economies is unlike anything seen in recent years, Oxfam's report stated. Using data from *Forbes* magazine's list of billionaires, it said those with interests in pharmaceutical and health care industries saw their net worth jump by 47 percent. Oxfam credited those individuals' rapidly growing fortunes in part to multimillion-dollar lobbying campaigns to protect and enhance their interests.

In a guest post for the *Financial Times* Mark Goldring of Oxfam stated, "Our report, out this week, sets out how two powerful forces – market fundamentalism and the capture of politics by elites – are driving this rapid rise in inequality." [5]

If Bill Gates were to cash in all of his wealth, and spend $1m every single day, it would take him 218 years to spend it all, Oxfam said. In reality though, he would never run out of money: even a modest return of just under two percent would make him $4.2 million each day in interest alone.

Isn't this crazy? If Bill Gates invested his philanthropic dollars in delivering clean water and food, I submit, he could save many more lives – without needing to unleash the 'rare' adverse effects caused by vaccines.

Oxfam has calculated that a tax of just 1.5 percent on the wealth of the world's billionaires, if implemented directly after the financial crisis, could have saved 23 million lives in the poorest 49 countries by providing them with money to invest in healthcare.

The continued rise of economic inequality around the world today is not inevitable – it is the result of deliberate policy choices, Oxfam claimed. Governments can start to reduce inequality by rejecting market fundamentalism, opposing the special interests of powerful elites, changing the rules and systems that have led to today's inequality explosion, and taking action to level the playing field by implementing policies that redistribute money and power.

Tax systems in developing countries tend to be the most regressive and the furthest from meeting their revenue-raising potential. Oxfam estimates that if low- and middle-income countries – excluding China – closed half of their tax revenue gap they would gain almost $1 trillion. But due to the disproportionate influence of rich corporations and individuals, and an intentional lack of global coordination and transparency in tax matters, tax systems are failing to tackle poverty and inequality.

But the vested interests opposing reform are very powerful, Oxfam asserted. There is a real risk that the gaps in global tax governance will not be closed, leaving the richest companies and individuals free to continue exploiting loopholes to avoid paying their fair share.

The Guardian commented [6]: "the combined worth of the world's *top five drug companies is twice the combined GNP of all sub-Saharan Africa* and their influence on the rules of world trade is many times stronger because they can bring their wealth to bear directly on the levers of western power."

But they're not stopping at that. Apart from exploiting the developing world's natural resources and refraining from contributing with their tax dollars, drug companies are also taking advantage of underdeveloped countries to perform clinical trials.

Wired.com [7] reported that India is becoming a very attractive place for drug companies to run clinical trials and test out new drugs, saving as much as 60 percent of the cost. "India has been the focus of medical research since the time when sunburned men with pith helmets and degrees from prestigious European medical schools came to catalogue tropical illnesses.

"The days of the Raj are long gone, but multinational corporations are riding high on the trend toward globalization by taking advantage of India's educated work force and deep poverty to turn South Asia into the world's largest clinical-testing petri dish.

"The sudden influx of drug companies to India resembles the gold rush frontier, according to Sean Philpott, managing editor of *The American Journal of Bioethics*."

Philpott revealed to Wired.com that such practices may be unfair, as "individuals who participate in Indian clinical trials usually won't be educated. Offering \$100 may be undue enticement; they may not even realize that they are being coerced."

The *Independent* reported on the problem in 2011 [8]:

> Western pharmaceutical companies have seized on India over the past five years as a testing ground for drugs – making the most of a huge population and loose regulations which help dramatically cut research costs for lucrative products to be sold in the West. The relationship is so exploitative that some believe it represents a new colonialism.
>
> Between 2007 and 2010, at least 1,730 people died in India while, or after, participating in such trials.
>
> (One such study included) the recruitment of hundreds of tribal girls without parental consent for an immunisation study sponsored by the Bill and Melinda Gates Foundation on the nod of

the warden of their government hostel. Several girls subsequently died. The study was halted by the federal authorities.

All of this flies in the face of the Helsinki Declaration [9]: "It is the duty of the physician to promote and safeguard the health, well-being and rights of patients, including those who are involved in medical research. The physician's knowledge and conscience are dedicated to the fulfilment of this duty."

Vaccine researchers constantly cross the line – the line of basic human decency, treating human beings as lab rats in pursuit of an ideal. And at least in some cases, in pursuit of money.

A WHO slide presentation [10] showed that Merck's RotaTeq made $284 million in sales in the first half of 2012. GSK's Rotarix made $266 million. Both of these vaccines are for rotavirus – which you will remember can be avoided by washing your hands, maintaining good hygiene, and living in conditions which make proper hygiene possible.

Pfizer's Prevnar 13 clocked up a whopping $1.847 billion, and Sanofi's PENTAct-HIB brought in $672 million in the first half of 2012. Merck's Gardasil sucked in a respectable $608 million.

Meanwhile, as stated previously, girls around the world had developed horrendous side-effects from the Gardasil vaccine. Multiple-sclerosis-like symptoms and neurological effects, including seizures, paralysis and speech problems, are reported by increasing numbers of girls and women.

In August 2009, the *Journal of the America Medical Association* reported that three medical associations helped to promote the use of Gardasil using funds from its manufacturer, Merck [11]. The American College Health Association, the American Society for Colposcopy and Cervical Pathology, and the Society of Gynecologic Oncologists used a promotion strategy similar to the one used by the drug company in its marketing campaign for the vaccine. The three associations received $199,000, $300,000 and $250,000 from Merck respectively in what's being described as an example of 'marketing and medical education [being] blurred'.

This would be tantamount to Canine Health Concern taking money from veterinary vaccine manufacturers and then going quiet on you. This book, for a start, would not exist if we were in that game. We'd be retiring to a sunnier clime and counting our money, leaving you, your dogs and your children to fend for yourselves.

Judicial Watch [12] received documents from the US Department of Health and Human Services revealing that its National Vaccine Injury Compensation Program (VICP) had awarded $5,877,710 dollars to 49 victims in claims made against the highly controversial HPV vaccines. Two hundred claims had been filed with VICP, with less than half adjudicated.

The Health Resources and Services Administration provided Judicial Watch with documents revealing that Merck's Gardasil brought in $608 million in one six-month period, whereas 49 of 200 people whose lives had been severely affected or terminated by this vaccine had received only $120,000 each for their suffering. The majority of those whose cases have been 'adjudicated' – 59 – were told to sod off. And the vaccine is questioned in terms of value or use.

In August 2013, *Mail India Online* [13] reported that the Indian Council of Medical Research (ICMR) had allegedly played hand in glove with the US non-government organisation, PATH, to promote the commercial interests of cervical cancer vaccine manufacturers, which they say were linked to the deaths of young Indian girls.

The Mail stated that the Indian Parliamentary panel had found the ICMR guilty of lending its platform to PATH, in an "improper and unlawful manner." The day the Mail's article was published, an extremely damning document was released by the Indian Parliament. The Parliamentary report stated that the committee had found the Indian Council of Medical Research guilty of helping PATH facilitate studies relating to the cervical cancer vaccine on young girls, endangering their lives.

The report stated that PATH's presence in India had been illegal. The project was reportedly funded by the Bill and Melinda Gates Foundation. The committee stated that approval and facilitation of the trials was against all laws of the land and international ethics, and a misuse of government funds. The committee was extremely scathing of PATH's activities, stating that it was their belief that in trying to get the HPV vaccination included into universal immunization programmes, PATH had resorted to an element of subterfuge calling the clinical trials by several different names

The trial conducted by PATH with HPV vaccines on 24,000 girls in Andhra Pradesh and Gujarat has been termed a "sordid incident" by the Parliamentary Standing Committee for Health and Family Welfare that found the entire matter "very intriguing and fishy". This trial has left in its trail at least 1,200 girls in the two states with chronic health problems.

Beyond these 24,000 girls, they said, other consumers of the two vaccines Gardasil and Cervarix are also at risk because the two companies have not bothered to update their product information to include serious side effects as they are emerging and being included in the inserts of other countries. [14,15]

PATH rejected claims in a press release, stating: "In particular, the report ignores the now voluminous evidence on the safety (225 KB PDF)

and efficacy (176 KB PDF) of HPV vaccines and falsely suggests that deaths may be causally linked to the vaccines. This is not only inaccurate, but may have tragic consequences for delivering these and other lifesaving vaccines to those who need them most." [16]

The WHO slideshow mentioned previously also highlighted the following issues:

- The vaccine market currently benefits from a spectacular growth rate : 10 – 15% per year versus 5-7% for Pharmaceuticals, and the US has a quarter share of that market.
- The global vaccine market is projected to rise to $100 billion by 2025.
- 5 large multi-national corporations make up 80% of the global market.
- Major focus is on new vaccine development for industrialised country markets [where the big money is].
- Organisations such as UNICEF and PAHO RF (Pan American Health Organization Revolving Fund) buy up 7.5% of world vaccines.

However, a 2012 Reuters report highlights another problem [17] – that of supposedly independent yet massively influential state bodies taking money from the companies that cause ill health in the first place: WHO's regional office (the Pan American Health Organization) was taking money – hundreds and thousands of dollars – from the food and beverage industry. This is the industry which plays a role in another epidemic, one of obesity and chronic disease.

Accepting industry funding goes against WHO's worldwide policies; it's prohibited. "If such conflicts of interest were perceived to exist, or actually existed, this would jeopardize WHO's ability to set globally recognized and respected standards and guidelines," said spokesman Gregory Härtl.

But the Pan American office – known as PAHO, had different standards allowing the business donations.

Reuters found: $50,000 from Coca-Cola, the world's largest beverage company; $150,000 from Nestle, the world's largest food company (against whose baby milk concerned mothers campaign, since it is often mixed with contaminated water); and $150,000 from Unilever, a British-Dutch food conglomerate.

The infusion of corporate cash is a most pointed example of how WHO is approaching its battle against chronic disease. Increasingly, it's relying on what it calls "partnerships" with industry, opting to enter into alliances with companies rather than maintain strict neutrality.

I can't help remembering commentary to suggest that all civilisations have fallen when their morality has also fallen.

Food and beverage companies now dominate policymaking in Washington and in cities and states across America. In Washington, the companies doubled their lobbying expenditures to $175 million during the first three years of the Obama administration, and defeated "soda tax" proposals in 24 states. As part of the National School Lunch Program, Congress even declared pizza a vegetable!

The Reuters report includes an interesting fact: the World Health Organisation's entire budget is about half of what Coca-Cola spends on marketing alone.

And here's PAHO – part of WHO – dangling carrots to wealthy conglomerates, helping them to avoid regulation and to influence regulatory environments. And a pizza is a vegetable. We all know that. Just as we all know that vaccines are perfectly safe.

Chapter 90

The truth about vaccine investment

Civilised society has enshrined in law the fundamental principle that no-one has the right to play God on anyone else's behalf. But governments appear to override these fundamental rights. Who has the right to decide whether or not you are allowed to make a choice, based upon available (uncensored) information, assessing the risks and benefits of the procedures you submit yourself or your loved-ones to? Someone like Bill Gates because he has a lot of money? Is that qualification any greater than mine or yours? Does having a lot of money qualify anyone to make decisions about *your* healthcare that could end up killing you or significantly destroying *your* quality of life?

And does a vet, whose education on vaccination stops at anaphylaxis, have the right to stipulate that you must vaccinate to their dictates? Insurance companies think your vet is qualified to force (over) vaccination – but who are the insurance companies owned by? Super-rich, and getting richer, vaccine company shareholders?

The issue was highlighted in the *New York Times* during March 2014: *Billionaires With Big Ideas Are Privatizing American Science*:

"American science, long a source of national power and pride, is increasingly becoming a private enterprise. In Washington, budget cuts have left the nation's research complex reeling. Labs are closing. Scientists are being laid off. Projects are being put on the shelf, especially in the risky, freewheeling realm of basic research. Yet from Silicon Valley to Wall Street, science philanthropy is hot, as many of the richest Americans seek to reinvent themselves as patrons of social progress through science research.

"This is philanthropy in the age of the new economy — financed with its outsize riches, practiced according to its individualistic, entrepreneurial creed. Yet that personal setting of priorities is precisely what troubles some in the science establishment. Many of the patrons, they say, are ignoring basic research — the kind that investigates the riddles of nature and has produced centuries of breakthroughs, even whole industries — for a jumble of popular, feel-good fields."

Hmmm … democracy? And they're actually missing the point. A lot of this research is funded with an aim in mind: that of making even more money. The real fear is that super rich individuals with questionable morals and more power, it seems, than governments, might not give a fig about our lives.

In 2006, the journal of *Clinical and Vaccine Immunology* [1] gave us a mini review of vaccine development issues presented during the GTCBIO Third Annual Conference on Vaccines – and it takes us right to the causes of the problem.

The paper, called "All Things Considered", provided an overview of concerns for "vaccine developers and the vaccine industry ... relevant to individuals in academia, industry, regulatory agencies, implementation, military, government, and physicians".

And us, of course. I would say it's relevant to us. Especially since the author stated that there are significant 'roadblocks' to developing and licensing new vaccines due to the "difficulty in preparing 100% safe and effective products, and the almost unavoidable (no matter how frequent or minor) adverse event". That would be us suffering those pesky roadblocks with our lives – if we open our arms to their needle, that is. The report said:

"...In addition, vaccines are administered to healthy individuals, and any side effects, even if unrelated to the vaccine, make the manufacturer a target for lawsuits ... Although vaccine development is motivated by its benefit to mankind, the *primary drive remains profit*, since vaccines are usually made by pharmaceutical companies..."

The author reported that although there are many diseases they could target with vaccines, the lack of a commercial market for them (i.e. people who can afford to pay for them) means that charitable or government funds would be required. "Recently, government funding of vaccine development has been driven by fear: fear of bioterrorism, fear of being blamed for inaction, and concern over lost revenue due to absence due to illness."

It has nothing to do with caring about us and whether we live or die, then?

The vaccine programme is not driven by a desire to ensure that people are living disease-free and happy lives. "Fear of the threat of bioterrorism elevates infectious diseases to the status of a military weapon and changes the definition of a vaccine program into a military deterrent."

Vaccines are about warfare. That's the long and the short of it. If your child or your dog or cat or horse suffers a life-threatening adverse reaction, well done. You've kept the nation safe. But also, don't forget that your taxes pay for vaccine programmes, which is an excellent ruse for sending even more money to our corporate controllers.

The report goes on to state:

"Project Bioshield was the answer that the US government came up with to create, fund, and activate vaccine development to control bioterror agents. Frank Rapoport (a lawyer with McKenna, Long and Aldridge LLP) and Monique K. Mansoura (a scientist with the Office of Research and Development Coordination) of the US government described the goals of Project Bioshield, which are to accelerate the research, development, purchase, and availability of priority medical countermeasures to protect the US population from the effects of chemical, biological, radiological, and nuclear threat agents. Basically, this program will create vaccines for the strategic national stockpile that can be distributed upon need."

But the US government has been driving bio-warfare for decades! This seems, to me, to be one of the examples of the bio industry representing itself as the opposite of what it actually is. The US is the world's biggest aggressor.

I just don't get why 'protecting the population' should mean governments have to hide the adverse effects of vaccines, support and promote vaccines that aren't effective or which are unsafe, condone and support the use of unnecessary vaccines, place vaccines ahead of nutrition and sanitation, put scientists out of business for telling the truth, and avoid expensive compensation claims from those whose lives have been ruined. Surely none of this is protecting the nation?

Truth protects the nation, especially its citizens, because it means you know what you're dealing with and can, armed with truth, make sensible choices.

The report stated: "Since 2004, contracts for over 80 million doses of anthrax vaccine have been awarded, and contracts for botulinum antitoxin and a next-generation smallpox vaccine are in progress. The estimated cost of smallpox vaccines for 2004 to 2012 is $1.9 billion. Project Bioshield will spend over $5.6 billion to stockpile vaccines for anthrax, smallpox, botulinum, Ebola fever, and plague."

I wonder how much clean drinking water that sort of money would deliver? And if they can no longer afford to pay us the pensions we've paid for, without choice, all our working lives, how can they afford this?

The 2006 report continued: "… Redefinition of vaccine development as a deterrent to biowarfare with the establishment of Project Bioshield has enticed the military defense industry to get involved in vaccines. For example, Lockheed, an aerospace, military defense company, bought Dyneport, a vaccine company. The extensive experience in lobbying Congress for funding by the military defense complex may change the nature of future vaccine development."

It's worth noting that in 2014, an online petition via SumOfUs. org sought to stop Lockheed Martin from taking over huge chunks of the UK National Health Service [2]. The petition organisers warned that, if successful, "the world's biggest weapons manufacturer could be in your GP's office, handling your records and scheduling your appointments. ... The NHS has been delivering these services to GPs for decades, but the NHS has been banned from meetings about its own future and isn't even allowed to bid.

"If this were really about saving the government money, bidding would be open to organisations that have already proven they can do the job. What's really happening is another step in selling off the NHS to the highest bidder."

I think they missed a point: Lockheed is into biological warfare. This could be our government seeking to put the agents of biological warfare where they're needed: right next to your arm with a needle – which the 'experts' will tell you are safe. The privatisation of the NHS is also potentially putting the corporations that make vaccines and drugs (or the super-rich who own the corporations) in position to award themselves contracts for those vaccines and drugs which may, or may not, work, or which contain weaponised viruses in this over-populated world. Why was the government stopping others from bidding, and why did it appear to be handing over more money than necessary?

It's also worth remembering that America is currently enacting laws to force people to be vaccinated against their wishes. Consider the implications of this in light of biowarfare organisations involving themselves in 'healthcare'. You'll be relieved to hear that Lockheed withdrew.

The journal of *Clinical and Vaccine Immunology* paper continued:

> The ogre for the vaccine industry of the 21st century will continue to be liability and lawsuits. Vaccines are a unique clinical intervention because they are administered to healthy individuals to elicit immune responses that in some individuals are unpredictable, and there is zero tolerance for side effects. Side effects and unknown outcomes are the basis for lawsuits. Fear and the cost of lawsuits have reduced the numbers of companies that make vaccines and caused the price of vaccines to rise enormously. [This is no longer the case – they're gearing up, not gearing down.]
> ...James Wood (Reed Smith), a lawyer who has been defending the vaccine and drug industry against litigation, described vaccines and the vaccine industry as a natural target for litigators with a defined pathway into the courts. There are ongoing lawsuits based on the use of thimerosal in vaccines and side effects of the DTP and measles vaccines. He mentioned an interesting

approach to legal action that is being pursued, an approach based on the potential consequences of the possible acquisition of simian virus 40 (SV40) in recipients of the early polio vaccines. SV40 can cause tumors in rodents but has no known association with human cancer. Wood suggested that a solution could be for Congress to enact a federal vaccine act that would create an efficient method of providing adequate compensation for vaccine-injured persons but also protect vaccine producers from punitive damages as long as the company showed compliance with FDA and Public Health Service rules. Such an action would reduce the legal costs for the development and marketing of vaccines and encourage new vaccine programs.

John Pilger, respected investigative journalist, writes: "Global economy is a modern Orwellian term. On the surface, it is instant financial trading, mobile phones, McDonald's, Starbucks, holidays booked on the net. Beneath this gloss, it is the globalisation of poverty, a world where most human beings never make a phone call and live on less than two dollars a day, where 6,000 children die every day from diarrhoea because most have no access to clean water.

"In this world, unseen by most of us in the global north, a sophisticated system of plunder has forced more than ninety countries into 'structural adjustment' programmes since the eighties, widening the divide between rich and poor as never before. This is known as 'nation building' and 'good governance' by the 'quad' dominating the World Trade Organisation (the United States, Europe, Canada and Japan), and the Washington triumvirate (the World Bank, the IMF and the US Treasury) that controls even minute aspects of government policy in developing countries. Their power derives largely from an unrepayable debt that forces the poorest countries to pay $100 million to western creditors every day.

"Promoting this are the transnational media corporations, American and European, that own or manage the world's principal sources of news and information."

Pilger describes how governments and transnational American corporations first destabilise governments and then go in and plunder their countries' resources. The war on terror, he explains, is merely a distraction which helps push forward the globalisation agenda. He also describes the sweatshops that exploit overseas workers who are forced to live in squalor on as little as 67p, or a dollar a day. British firms, and the British government, are not innocent, either. Tony Blair, for example, was known as Bush's Poodle.

It's also worth considering the assertions made by Carroll Quigley, a renowned professor of history at the School of Foreign Service at Georgetown University, and a lecturer at Princeton and Harvard.

Quigley's book, *The Anglo American Establishment*, tells how British Imperialists such as Cecil Rhodes, William Stead, Lord Esher, Lords Rothschild, Salisbury, Rosebery and Milner, drew up a plan for a secret society that aimed to renew the bond between Great Britain and the United States and bring all habitable portions of the world under their influence and control.

In another book, *Tragedy and Hope: A History of the World in Our Time*, Quigley explains that Money Power – controlled by international investment bankers – dominates business and government. In short, controlling and owning the money, bankers covertly control and own the world: governments, corporations, and you.

I personally think that ordinary workers in the West are being manipulated into the same position as those in the developing world. We have a minimum wage no-one can live on, minimum hours contracts, increasingly privatised healthcare, a welfare state that is being dismantled, and a bloodied and bowed trade union movement unable to champion workers' rights. Interestingly, even Mothercare, a shop for people with babies, has problems with reducing profit. Perhaps because parents can't afford new clothes for their babies anymore, which is the major flaw in neoliberalism.

At time of writing, a new wave of trade deals is being negotiated which threatens democracy, public services and the environment worldwide. If agreed, these secretive deals will give big business unprecedented new powers. Most controversially, they aim to set up special courts in which companies can sue governments over decisions they believe might harm their profits. The deals will remove regulation designed to protect people and the planet, and will encourage the privatisation of services like healthcare and education.

The Transnational Trade and Investment Partnership (TTIP) between the EU and US is one of the biggest of these deals – and the UK government is one of its major backers. Countries including Bolivia, Ecuador, Venezuela, South Africa and Indonesia, which have already been sued over decisions made for the benefit of their populations, are beginning to question, or even rip up, trade agreements with the EU.

A growing movement of people is opposing secretive corporate trade deals, demanding that governments be accountable to people rather than to big business.

One thing I know for sure: if my government had acted on the science rather than backing the pharmaceutical industry, my dogs would not have died of vaccine-induced diseases; nor would millions of dogs and children around the world have died – had their governments acted upon the science.

Chapter 91
The Great Transformer

Around the world, thousands of idealistic, dedicated, scientists join together with the common aim of developing safer vaccines to help rid the world of viral and bacterial disease. Who could say that this is anything other than a noble aim?

To make the point clearer, here is a photograph of a poor soul suffering from smallpox:

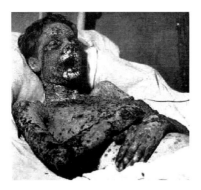

The concept of saving lives is what fuels vaccine research and delivery. Vaccines work, sometimes. I know, from studying the work of Ronald Schultz, that vaccines stimulate antibodies in most dogs against distemper, parvovirus and adenovirus and that, once they have antibodies, it's practically impossible for them to succumb to these diseases. Having said that, all of the non-vaccinated puppies in CHC Branch VacciCheck clinics have immunity (antibodies) to the core viral diseases as well. Yes – protection without vaccination.

Which is not to say that all vaccines are effective. There are many, many accounts of vaccination programmes failing, where, say, 95% of the population with a disease has been vaccinated against it.

But what fuels the anger between pro- and anti-vaccinators is that one side of the debate believes that the risks of vaccination outweigh the benefits, and the other side believes they do not.

I came into the debate when I realised that we are over-vaccinating our dogs, and that vaccines can cause harm. I didn't expect to spend over two decades of my life trying to influence people so that we'd reduce the vaccine load for dogs. I honestly thought that if I explained the myriad harms caused by vaccines (i.e., gave the reason why we should vaccinate less frequently), and let it be known that, once immune, dogs remain immune for years or life – then we would stop over-vaccinating and that would be that.

Nor was I expecting to be faced with so very much anger, or so much misinformation – or the startling fact that the scientific world works to a paradigm that accepts the sacrifice of some for the 'greater good'.

But perhaps the most stunning realisation of all – for a person who was an idealist and who believed in the goodness of human beings – is that vaccines appear to me now to be more to do with world over-population, money, profit, greed and biowarfare than they are to do with saving anyone's life.

Education – like history – is frequently a mobilisation of bias. I might even tentatively and timidly suggest that a lack of education leaves us more open to valid information that may have been schooled-out of others. Education might also remove the ability to be shocked when a 'minority' are sacrificed.

But let's face it: no-one wants to die of smallpox; it's a truly horrible disease. It was the first disease claimed to be defeated by vaccine science. Although, as already stated, Dr Jayne Donegan found (relying upon government figures): "Even the success story of smallpox vaccination was not what it seemed: the enforcement of the compulsory smallpox vaccination law in 1867, when the death rate was already falling, was accompanied by an increase in the deaths from 100 to 400 deaths per million population".

In its position paper, the VMD's Steve Dean, wrote: "The gold standard is provided by the example of small pox in humans. The last case in man was recorded in 1977 and in 1980 the WHO officially announced smallpox had been eradicated from the world."

I cannot criticise Steve Dean, or anyone else, for their belief in the benefits of vaccination. But it seems to me that Steve had been blinded.

George Dick was one of the UK's most eminent and highly decorated *pro-vaccine* scientists. The following is taken from his obituary in the Guardian:

> Professor George Dick, the immunologist who died aged 82, waged a long war against the vaccination of children for smallpox, which he blamed for killing more victims than the disease.
> By the 1950s smallpox was so rare in Britain that mass vaccination, even with its small risk of mortality, was killing more

children than would have died without it. In 1962 Dick spoke out at the British Medical Association annual meeting against the smallpox vaccination programme enjoined by the Minister of Health, Mr Enoch Powell. "He is asking for a sacrifice of at least 20 babies a year," Dick said.

Dick's conclusion was that, for smallpox, "we should now give up routine infant vaccination and depend on epidemiological control". To cheers from his fellow doctors, Dick advised Mr Powell to spend "more effort on devising a plan to reduce the risk of importation of smallpox into Britain."

But it was not until 1971 that Sir Keith Joseph, as Secretary of State for Social Services, announced in a letter to all GPs that the government-backed programme encouraging vaccination for children was to be dropped. Dick had made known his opposition to childhood smallpox immunisation to the committee that advised Joseph to drop the programme.

Since then the disease has become extinct, not only in Britain but also, according to the World Health Organisation, throughout the world.

In fact, there have been dissenters and anti-vaccination campaigners since vaccines were invented. This is because all vaccines present a risk. I can only include a small selection of examples in this already-too-long book, but open your eyes and you will see very much more. These relate to the smallpox vaccine, and come from *How to Predict Epidemics* by Andrew Maniotis, Ph.D., Program Director in the Cell and Developmental Biology of Cancer, Department of Pathology, Anatomy and Cell Biology, and Bioengineering, University of Illinois at Chicago [1].

A letter appeared in *The Lancet* on July 7th, 1860, signed a "Military Surgeon". It discussed the high number of amputations of the arm, and deaths, amongst soldiers following vaccination.

In 1867, non-payment of fines for refusing smallpox vaccination in the UK resulted in harsher penalties. Thousands left Britain rather than submit their children to the practice.

In 1868 the Anti-Compulsory Vaccination League was formed in Britain.

Smallpox vaccination in America led to an alarming spread in leprosy, according to successive reports to the Board of Health in 1868. This pattern was repeated following smallpox vaccination programmes in 1873 and 1881.

In 1868, Joseph Jones MD, Professor of Physiology and Pathology, University of Nashville, wrote that federal prisoners at Camp Sumpter, Georgia, were vaccinated and large gangrenous ulcers appeared at the vaccination point. This caused extensive destruction of tissues, exposing arteries, nerves and bones, and necessitating amputation in more than one instance. One-third of prisoners perished in less than seven months.

In 1870, despite the smallpox vaccine programme, an outbreak of smallpox occurred all over Europe.

During 1871, the Vaccinator-General of Trinidad gave evidence before the Select Parliamentary Committee that those who were not vaccinated experienced a rare incidence of leprosy, whereas soldiers who were subjected to mandatory military vaccines experienced high levels of leprosy.

In 1879 Mr PA Taylor wrote in The Lancet that he had seen scores of people who honestly believed that their children had died from vaccination. They took perfectly healthy children to be vaccinated, and in a few days a sore appeared on the arm, which spread all over the body, and finally the children died in agony.

Mr JT Hibbert, MP, Parliamentary Secretary to the Local Government Department, wrote: "The Return shows an increase of deaths from syphilis of infants under one year which, in my opinion, is one of the most unsatisfactory features in connection with vaccination, and one which leads me to support the proposed modification of the Vaccination Law now before the House of Commons." (*Lancet,* July 17th.)

Between 1886 and 1892 in Australia, when children died as a result of smallpox vaccinations, the government abolished compulsory vaccination and smallpox then declined to vanishing point. Australia had only three cases of smallpox in 15 years as compared with Japan's record of 165,774 cases and 28,979 deaths in only seven years under compulsory vaccination and re-vaccination.

In the *Occidental Medical Times*, April, 1892, Dr Sidney Bourne Swift wrote: "It must not be forgotten that leprosy was first discernible at the points of inoculation. Nor can it be considered remarkable, knowing how the disease had been propagated by the vaccination lancet. In one instance an entire school in Hawaii was swept away, with the exception of a single survivor, by this means."

Hawaiian Legislature, June 25, 1892. David Dayton, President, Board of Health wrote: "An effort is being made in the Legislature to repeal or amend the law relating to vaccination; the object being to leave vaccination optional with parents and individuals. The chief objection raised against the present compulsory system appears to be the belief that leprosy, and other diseases, have been propagated by means of vaccination."

Final report of the Royal Commission on vaccination, 1896: The commission could not ignore the evidence against vaccination so they recommended that mandatory vaccination should be stopped.

And on and on it goes – if you look.

Amidst all of the information swimming around in this book, and much that has had to be left out, one incident strikes me very heavily. It was included in Chapter 41.

From 1987 to 1989, scientists set up a centre near 30 remote villages in Senegal to research the effects of two high titer measles vaccines. Children who received the high titer measles vaccine were significantly more likely to die at 41 months than children who had a lower titer measles vaccine. But they weren't dying from measles – most of the deaths were from other common childhood diseases. They had lowered immunity, making them more susceptible to diarrhoea, dysentery, malaria, malnutrition, respiratory illness, and other infectious diseases.

Children who received the high-titer Edmonston-Zagreb vaccine died of other diseases at a rate of 80% higher than children who received the standard vaccine. There were 75 deaths for every thousand babies vaccinated. One in every six babies given this vaccine died within three years.

And then, to see if African American boys might also have similar adverse effects, they decided to try the vaccine on children in New York. Documents from the CDC show that in 2003, a staggering 340% increase in autism in African American boys related to the MMR vaccine. This data was hidden due to pressure from senior officials. CDC researchers recalculated their results by removing an age group to get the desired results.

These three paragraphs illustrate what it is that vaccine dissenters are saying: vaccines do not prevent disease, they *transform* disease. And not necessarily in a good way. On top of this, scientists appear to have no moral scruples when it comes to vaccinating children alongside a high possibility that they might die as a result. All I can do is stand here with my mouth open, in shock.

These high titer measles vaccines illustrate the point very powerfully. Those of us who choose not to use vaccines believe – having studied the available evidence – that vaccines, even the less overtly damaging ones, derange the immune system in innumerable ways, setting us up for other diseases. These other diseases can be mild, perhaps requiring a lifetime of medication as in the case of inflammatory conditions, or they can be severe, as in the case of autoimmunity, brain damage, cancer and death. Vaccines represent – amongst many, many other things – the shift from Th1 to Th2 responsiveness. We are exchanging viral and bacterial disease for chronic long-lasting conditions (which benefits the pharmaceutical industry), and acute life-threatening conditions. Yet the scientists on the spot don't seem to care about the pesky casualties.

Vaccines don't just prevent disease – they *transform* one potential disease into other diseases. Look at those Senegalese children: one in every six babies given this vaccine died within three years!

Every vaccine delivers this result along a spectrum, starting at mild and moving on to severe. And it isn't even pot luck in terms of who suffers most – it's a mix of the vaccine itself, alongside the individual's existing health status, his genes, nutritional status, sanitation, alongside poverty or wealth.

Those of us who don't vaccinate – well, we are choosing another way. This means preventative healthcare within a different paradigm: good food, attention to our spiritual and emotional wellbeing, less damaging healthcare alternatives .. and taking responsibility for the wellbeing of our physical bodies, with all this entails.

We also believe that a mix of idealism, tunnel vision, denial, outright lies, financial influences, and a quest for power and world dominance serve as a blindfold to the truth – the truth as we see it, anyway.

I'd love to see a day when those who are submitting themselves, their children or their animals to the vaccine needle are given full and truthful informed consent. We may decide, after all, that the threat of a particular disease is worth taking the risk for. But we don't appreciate being lied to about vaccine risks.

Chapter 92

Compassion

Have you noticed that so much that is wrong with our society is becoming visible now? For many of us these are scary times. But this is the first step in healing: we're noticing problems that were at one time hidden, and we're getting a diagnosis and taking steps to heal the nightmare we've created. Essentially this means a correction of the mind.

When societies become too large, people become anonymous. Anonymity enables people to hurt others, with no conscience and no comeback. This is what globalisation – the Capitalist Empire – appears to be achieving. There's so much happening now, and it involves so many people we do not know. It's hard to keep track.

But if a neighbour in your small village opens his bedroom window and shoots his gun at children in the street, you know his name and you know where he lives. The community will close in around him; people can protect one-another in small neighbourhoods.

There are too many faceless names in our society. There is too little accountability. There is too much power invested in the hands of too few. Globalisation is not serving us.

From what I can see, states and industry seem to conspire with one-another to limit the legal fallout from products they collectively create, approve, recommend, mandate, regulate, and profit from. Far from being concerned with preventative healthcare, the government-sponsored vaccine industry appears to be concerned with wealth, power, and warfare. This is against a backdrop of world over-population, earth changes, and a threatened scarcity of resources.

Accepting that there are good scientists with noble aims, governments and the vaccine industry nevertheless makes noises about ridding the world of viral and bacterial disease whilst ignoring the obvious solutions, such as giving money *away* to help those who have no clean water to drink or food to eat, and no roof over their heads. Instead we have 'Austerity', a programme which is asking the poor to pay for the rich's casino banking greed which nearly bankrupted the world. This is one sure way of increasing the numbers of the most vulnerable. Poor people die sooner than rich people – that's an official statistic.

The gluttonous Empire champions measures that take from those who have little, giving to those who have more, making malnutrition and infection more likely. And whilst there is no money in the coffers for the poor, and a corresponding rise in free food charities in the UK, the British government has recently committed half a billion pounds to further the Trident missile programme. What does this say about society?

Poverty seems to be an intrinsic requirement of capitalism and the pharmaceutical industry. It serves the wealthy elite to keep us poor, frightened, malnourished, unhealthy, and more easily controlled. Rather than support the weak, the weak have become cash cows for them. Further, legislation around the world makes it legally acceptable for corporations and the wealthy elite to avoid paying taxes that would benefit the people who are living in poverty – the poor misguided people who are encouraged to submit to their products without full informed consent, and who are most vulnerable to viral disease *and* vaccine damage.

And they lie to us. In order to sell their vaccines, they *have to* lie to us, and resolutely blind themselves to the harm they may cause.

We have witnessed researchers who, noticing deaths in children in Africa following vaccination with a high potency vaccine, deciding that it would be a good idea to see if it might also kill American babies – and the CDC hid the carnage. This is nothing new; it seems so common to hide vaccine adverse effects that it could be considered method. It's methodology that constantly and consistently ignores the Helsinki Declaration – a charter designed to protect basic human healthcare rights.

We've seen scaremongering 'pandemic' vaccines rushed to market and tested in the field (which means your body), and their deathly results. We've seen a willingness to destroy academics and doctors who stand up and speak the truth, and the cosy relationships between industry and academics who might be prepared to bend the truth. And we've witnessed parents being sent to prison after vaccines caused their children's deaths, and government experts, who knew the truth, suppressing evidence.

The Establishment, or political elite and super-rich, are seen to collude with the vaccine industry to hide vaccine adverse effects and limit financial compensation for the people who are harmed: the political system is part of the industry. It grants licenses to vaccines that are barely needed or don't work, but which come with deadly side-effects. Governments even develop and profit from vaccines that have been proven to kill and wreck lives, and own the patent rights to emerging viruses.

We are not being told the truth, and in many cases we are manipulated – not for our own good, but for some other agenda.

It seems to me that the name of the current beast is an ideology that very few have even heard of. It's called 'neoliberalism'. Writing for *The Guardian* on 15 April 2016, George Monbiot said: "Neoliberalism sees competition as the defining characteristic of human relations. It redefines citizens as consumers, whose democratic choices are best exercised by buying and selling, a process that rewards merit and punishes inefficiency. It maintains that "the market" delivers benefits that could never be achieved by planning.

"… Inequality is recast as virtuous: a reward for utility and a generator of wealth, which trickles down to enrich everyone. Efforts to create a more equal society are both counterproductive and morally corrosive. The market ensures that everyone gets what they deserve.

"With the help of sympathetic journalists and political advisers, elements of neoliberalism, especially its prescriptions for monetary policy, were adopted by Jimmy Carter's administration in the US and Jim Callaghan's government in Britain.

"After Margaret Thatcher and Ronald Reagan took power, the rest of the package soon followed: massive tax cuts for the rich, the crushing of trade unions, deregulation, privatisation, outsourcing and competition in public services. Through the IMF, the World Bank, the Maastricht treaty and the World Trade Organisation, neoliberal policies were imposed – often without democratic consent – on much of the world. Most remarkable was its adoption among parties that once belonged to the left: Labour and the Democrats, for example. As Stedman Jones notes, "it is hard to think of another utopia to have been as fully realised."

"Freedom from trade unions and collective bargaining means the freedom to suppress wages. Freedom from regulation means the freedom to poison rivers, endanger workers, charge iniquitous rates of interest and design exotic financial instruments. Freedom from tax means freedom from the distribution of wealth that lifts people out of poverty."

Neoliberalism also means that any benevolent protection of the people has been dismantled. You simply can't expect your government to protect you from corporate healthcare fraud, or any other corporate offering – as many of us have found to our cost.

So now we come to the part of this book where solutions are expected.

The gift of suffering

The first solution, it seems to me, is knowledge: we need to understand what is happening. With an accurate diagnosis we might find an effective cure. There is no getting around the fact that this planet is experiencing a terrible sickness that we can either collectively cure, or collectively ignore.

It seems that the world is currently being ruled by sociopaths and narcissists – that is, people who *don't care* about you or your loved ones. They are supported by apaths – people who aren't shocked by deceit, injustice and suffering, and who aren't motivated to do anything about it:

the ones who yawn and turn away. Apaths make up around 60 percent of society, and sociopaths a further one to ten percent. Narcissists, similar to sociopaths, are thought to represent fewer than 20 percent of us, but the percentage seems to be increasing. So that covers the majority, which essentially adds up to a world that lacks compassion.

However, apathy can be dislodged by a wakeup call. Most wakeup calls, like my own, are catastrophic: someone you love dies, your material comfort is shattered, your reality is rocked. And you start to ask whether there is more to life than your body and possessions. When we are personally affected by a terrible event, we are more likely to act.

This is the Gift of Suffering. Suffering brings wisdom.

But how about acting before tragedy strikes? How about having empathy for others, and working for the good of others before it gets personal? How about education and knowledge making a difference instead? How about creating a society that simply refuses to accept the suffering of others?

My question is: have enough of us suffered yet?

An end to hierarchy

Human beings are *conditioned* to fit in and conform. But we are actually *created* to reform and redefine what it is to be human. We are creating, with every choice, the world we inhabit, and our choices affect the lives of everyone on the planet. If we see our fellow human beings and our beloved animals suffering because of something the human race is collectively doing, surely it is our duty to do something about it? Even if you forget about duty, think about consequences – for you and your loved-ones could be next.

Having lived the problem of vaccine damage for a quarter of a century now, I firmly believe that it's time for the hierarchical structure to end. We are conditioned to put others on a pedestal and let them get on with the work – because they have letters after their names, or they're in a position of power. But you just have to look at the way this is playing itself out. We need to take back our power and, with it, personal responsibility. We simply can't afford blind trust anymore.

I also think it's time for individuals within the scientific community to open their eyes and first seek the truth, then speak the truth. It's time for the scientific community to stop being so pleased with itself and heal from within. Please drop the, "I'm a scientist so I'm superior and know more than you" arrogance, and open your eyes to the truth.

Individuals with letters after their names, or titles before them, routinely make choices to put themselves and their own self-interests before the lives of others, and this shame remains hidden. They don't speak out when they see vaccines, drugs or chemicals causing harm; they accept and minimise that harm. They allow their academic rigor to be sold to the highest bidder; others put company profits before public good; and others still put their new cars and mortgages before truth and life. This isn't just people at the top, by the way – it's every one of us who knows that something is wrong but does nothing about it.

The 'experts' are morally obliged to explain the risks and benefits and allow us to make our own choices. In order to do this, they actually need to know what the truth looks like. And it's up to us to demand truthful information – which rarely comes from the mainstream media or – I'm sad to say – the average vet in practice.

If you combine the love you have for your dogs and children with *knowledge*, those you love will be safer in your hands than in any vet or doctor's hands.

How much do you love? How much are you willing to learn? How hard will you strive to be worthy of your dogs and children?

What will it take to crack the world's heart open, to seek wisdom and have compassion for others; to end victimhood?

What needs to happen before we take our power back?

One thing I know: to become an empath (which means you have grown out of apathy and have compassion for others), you have to experience pain, because the ability to empathise is learned. It comes from having experienced suffering and making the choice to soften your heart. And it is a choice.

Compassion

Someone commented to me that, "this vaccine issue is another form of distraction from our true selves. I look at everything as life lessons and what we came here to experience."

In some ways this is true. There is a purpose to 'life lessons'; they can make us more compassionate to others. So, for example, if you know what it is to be poor, you are less likely to condemn poor people. If you know what it's like to witness someone die from a vaccine they didn't need, you are more likely to be open to knowledge on this subject, and more compassionate when others suffer a similar loss.

However, I don't agree that seeking to help others by sharing the truth can ever be regarded as a distraction from our true selves. In fact, I think this belief is not spirituality, but apathy.

I've been re-reading *The Tibetan Book of Living and Dying* by the Buddhist Master Sogyal Rinpoche. He says how self-grasping (simplistically expressed as greed or self-interest in this context) is at the root of all personal suffering. Ultimately, selfishness and greed do not serve us; they eventually make us miserable. The antidote to self-grasping and self-cherishing, he advises, is nothing other than compassion.

It is compassion, he says, dedicating ourselves to others, taking on their suffering instead of cherishing ourselves, that along with egolessness, destroys completely the attachment to a false self [ego] that is the cause of our misery. "That is why in our tradition," he writes, "we see compassion as the source and essence of enlightenment, and the heart of enlightened activity.

"What is compassion?" he asks. "It is not simply a sense of sympathy or caring for the person suffering, not simply a warmth of heart toward the person before you, or a recognition of their needs and pain. *It is also a sustained and practical determination to do whatever is possible and necessary to help alleviate their suffering.*

"Compassion is not true compassion unless it is active."

It's interesting that this take on compassion should come from a Buddhist teacher, because studies are now showing that mindfulness, or meditation, increase the compassionate response to suffering [1]. Another study claims that mindfulness training can cultivate the gift of compassion in people [2]. We need to start with the children and build a more compassionate society – through the simple techniques of mindfulness and meditation. What a world we could create!

One of the world's most revered spiritual leaders of recent times was also a health activist. Mahatma Ghandi was a fierce opponent of vaccination. He spoke out against the "barbarous practice" of vaccines, calling them a "fatal delusion". He felt that vaccination is unethical and immoral because of the manner in which they are produced: through the great suffering of poisoned animals.

He also said that the income generated through vaccination is the driving reason why the medical profession does not wish to identify problems in safety and efficacy. Sanitation, hygiene, fresh air, water, and clean food are essential for preventing infection and/or helping the infected to recover, he asserted.

How long ago did he say that? Isn't it time we did something?

Reject sacrifice

I am aware that pro-vaccinators strongly believe in the concept of 'the greater good' – that although vaccines may harm some, the vast majority benefit.

I hope they can appreciate that I – and others – reject this view on two counts. The first is that vaccination is not the only way to protect against infection: nutrition and sanitation might be said to be more effective. The second is that we do not accept the concept of lying to people about the necessary sacrifices vaccines demand; we do not even accept the concept of sacrifice. Sacrificing others whilst keeping them ignorant of the truth is, I submit, just a legal form of murder.

Keep speaking truth

In his report to NOAH in 1998 (obtained under the Freedom of Information Act), when I was telling largely closed ears that we don't need to vaccinate our dogs annually, and that vaccines can cause harm, the vet David Holmes wrote:

"If we continue to ignore CHC, these meetings will take place with increased frequency, with the unchallenged message to dog owners that the veterinary profession will not listen to them and is only interested in vaccine revenue. There will be more media events such as last week's 'World in Action' [TV documentary] which will portray us in a bad light. Animals will be left unprotected and disease will occur. We will share blame for this for failing to address the issues …

"As a final comment, having talked about this subject and thought it through as best I can, I am disturbed that Catherine O'Driscoll and CHC should have had to do all this work while in their view being ignored by the profession… We do not have the right to leave our clients in the dark because we have not listened to people who claim to have had problems.

"Catherine has said to me that she would like to close down CHC and get on with her life but only if she and her members could feel confident that the issues were being tackled honestly and openly without influence from commercial pressure.

"Her use of the media and public meetings is a response to the frustration she feels that the problems she has seen with her own eyes or have been reported to her have been ignored by us. The profession is failing if dog owners have to turn to CHC in desperation because vets have not answered their questions or allayed their fears. We must not be afraid to respond to this challenge and be seen to rise above considerations of self interest so that we can retain the confidence of the pet owning public."

Thank you David for writing that, and for your good heart. But this was written over 20 years ago, and vets are still pushing annual shots which are not needed. I look forward to the day when all vets understand the vaccine issue accurately, and relieve me of this task. I am sure that those working in the human vaccine damage field feel the same about medical doctors.

Help alleviate suffering

If you have lost a loved-one to a vaccine reaction, or seen a loved-one suffer – whether human or animal – and you relate that suffering to the suffering of others, then you are being called to act. If you have a heart and a conscience, you don't need to have witnessed vaccine damage first hand: you are also being called to act. There have been vaccine dissenters since vaccines were first invented. Our struggle spans the centuries. We need more than a few lone voices speaking out for us all. Heck, with mandatory vaccination being imposed around the world, you soon won't have a choice. Unless you claim your basic human right to freedom of healthcare choice now, you may not have it in the future.

During 2017, the Royal College of Veterinary Surgeons issued a position statement, influenced by a vet called Danny Chambers and the so-called 'Good Thinking Society' (there's an oxymoron if I've ever seen one). They're using a professional body to gun for homeopathic and holistic vets. Many of our homeopathic vet friends believe that they're trying to ban qualified vets from using complementary and alternative (CAM) therapies. By implication, they could also try prosecuting people like you and me who go first for the natural solutions before resorting to the more damaging and toxic conventional offerings; the Animal Welfare Act might appear to support their stance.

The RCVS wants vets to FIRST use the toxic drugs and, only if they don't work, can gentler therapies be tried. This is the RCVS position statement:

RCVS Council yesterday (Thursday 2 November 2017) approved a new position statement on the veterinary use of complementary and alternative medicines, including homeopathy. The statement is as follows:

"We have recently been asked questions about complementary and alternative medicines and treatments in general and homeopathy in particular.

"We would like to highlight our commitment to promoting the advancement of veterinary medicine upon sound scientific principles and to re-iterate the fundamental obligation upon our members as practitioners within a science-based profession which is to make animal welfare their first consideration.

"In fulfilling this obligation, we expect that treatments offered by veterinary surgeons are underpinned by a recognised evidence base or sound scientific principles. Veterinary surgeons should not make unproven claims about any treatments, including prophylactic treatments.

"Homeopathy exists without a recognised body of evidence for its use. Furthermore, it is not based on sound scientific principles. In order to

protect animal welfare, we regard such treatments as being complementary rather than alternative to treatments for which there is a recognised evidence base or which are based in sound scientific principles. It is vital to protect the welfare of animals committed to the care of the veterinary profession and the public's confidence in the profession that any treatments not underpinned by a recognised evidence base or sound scientific principles do not delay or replace those that do."

The statement comes after long-standing discussions within the veterinary community about the efficacy and ethics of complementary and alternative medicines.

Our President Professor Stephen May said: "It is fair to say that debates on either side of this issue have been passionate and this too has been reflected in the debates that we have had amongst Council members as to how to best articulate the College's position on complementary and alternative medicines.

"What we have is a statement that reinforces the evidence-based and sound scientific foundations of our profession and our commitment to put animal health and welfare at the forefront of all we do.

"I am very pleased that the overwhelming majority of Council members agreed with this statement and that the College has a firm and clear position on this important topic."

Those few paragraphs could be the subject of an entire book of refutes. But has the RCVS shot itself in both its feet and knees, and hung a noose around its own neck? Take these two paragraphs, for example:

"We would like to highlight our commitment to promoting the advancement of veterinary medicine upon sound scientific principles and to re-iterate the fundamental obligation upon our members as practitioners within a science-based profession which is to make animal welfare their first consideration.

"In fulfilling this obligation, we expect that treatments offered by veterinary surgeons are underpinned by a recognised evidence base or sound scientific principles. Veterinary surgeons should not make unproven claims about any treatments, including prophylactic treatments.

Are these people totally lacking in any level of self-awareness? Do they not realise that every time vets recommend, insist, or bully a client into giving yet another unnecessary annual shot they don't need they are potentially committing fraud? Do they know that annual vaccination is not underpinned by any recognised evidence base or sound scientific principles? For presumably intelligent people, they make a lot of unproven claims about pet vaccination, especially with their bogof annual sales jamboree, MSD's Vaccine Amnesty – which has nothing whatsoever to do scientifically with adult animals and vaccines.

Hypocrites! Since when was annual vaccination underpinned by a recognised evidence base or sound scientific principles? NEVER. There is no science to support annual vaccination and there never was. But does the RCVS care? Apparently not. Your corrupt fraudulent vet has the RCVS's blessing if they want to give your dogs vaccines they don't need but which could kill them.

Narcissism is on the increase in our society. Whereas it was once thought to be the result of genes alongside childhood abuse, it's now also thought to be caused by parents who literally spoil their children by telling them that they're superior to others. Narcissists boast, lie, manipulate, devalue others, and have no capacity to empathise. They are apparently without conscience and don't care about anyone other than themselves. They're immune to the suffering of others, and they shift the blame of their own actions onto their victims. This entire book has been about the damage caused by narcissists and even sicker sociopaths. Yes – I've said it. I've named the elephant in the room, or the albatross around all of our necks.

The trouble is, we've allowed the people with severe personality disorders – the narcissists and the sociopaths – to take control of the planet. We bought the lies and stood confused when the consequences arrived. We have allowed evil to reign on the planet.

Change *is* however possible. Don't let anyone tell you it's not. As Margaret Mead wrote, "Never doubt that a small group of thoughtful, committed, citizens can change the world. Indeed, it is the only thing that ever has."

Meanwhile, the task is getting harder. It always does just before a battle is finally won. America and Australia have moved to make vaccines mandatory [3], and Europe appears to be following the trend, with Germany threatening ten years in jail for vaccine dissenters. Brazil is also offering prison to vaccine objectors. Over in Sweden, however, the government has voted against mandatory vaccination, citing both "serious health concerns" and the violation of each citizen's constitutional rights to choose their own healthcare [4].

American veterinarian Stephen Blake commented: "I predicted that it was just a matter of time before OUR bought off government would pass a law of the land, forcing all the children of America to be injected with toxic waste and here it is. In the form of HR 2232. Next step will be every

American no matter how old you are.

"This insane experiment is nothing more than an experiment in eugenics, sold to us as health. The next step after they make vaccines mandatory for all Americans, is to go door to door and drag you and your family out of your homes and inject toxic waste and chips to track you against your will."

As I write, President Donald Trump is being attacked from all sides. He is aware of vaccine harms and promised to sort the mess out, appointing Robert F. Kennedy, Jr to look into the matter from inside government. He is also purported to be putting legislation in place to see an end to mandatory vaccination. Will Trump come up trumps – or will the Establishment see him off? Or is he just another narcissist, telling us what we want to hear with no intention of keeping his word?

Stop Press: A Guardian piece carried in February 2018, stated, "Donald Trump appears to have abandoned plans to investigate the spurious link between childhood immunisations and autism, a move welcomed by experts but condemned by Robert F Kennedy Jr, a vaccine sceptic.

The son of former US attorney general Bobby Kennedy met Trump in New York during the presidential transition in January last year and announced that he had been asked to chair a commission to review vaccine safety.

Scientists warned that it would give credence to debunked theories, while a Trump spokeswoman denied any decision had been made.

Then, a year ago this week, Kennedy told reporters he had met "many times" with members of Trump's transition team, "trading documents about what the commission would look like". But little has been heard of the plan since then.

"I would say there's zero progress," Kennedy told the Guardian last week. "We were told President Trump wanted to meet directly with us. Not only did nothing happen, they've cut off all communication with people who care about this issue. The administration has decided to go in another direction."

If I ruled the world, I would seriously purge government departments which lie, cheat and champion profit over life. When you vote, please consider voting for the party that doesn't put Big Business above life.

The Need for Truth

I will finish by paraphrasing Jordan Peterson, a Canadian clinical psychologist, cultural critic, and professor of psychology at the University of Toronto who's become something of an internet sensation.

"Repression is something like deception, like a lie," he said. "Repression is an attempt to not be conscious about something you should be conscious about. Under UK Common Law, it's a crime. So if you're a CEO and your company secretary is cooking the books and you know, then you're acting illegally. English Common Law says you have an obligation to be conscious of the things you should be conscious of."

I sometimes get accused of vet-bashing. I don't know where that phrase came from, and I think it's a silly accusation. I'm quite rightly, scientifically and legitimately over-vaccination-bashing. It's not a personal insult to anyone. That vaccines come with potential failure as well as potential harm is a fact. The other fact is that our dogs don't need to be vaccinated every year, every three years, or even every seven or eight or nine years … if they're already immune. No-one, and no profession, needs to be worshipped and obeyed irrespective of their actions and omissions. Surely a vet would have to be living in a cave on his own to not have heard that annual vaccination is neither necessary nor safe?

All I ask is that vets fulfil their duties as professional healthcare providers and tell the truth. By doing this, they redeem the profession and make it better for the young people who follow in their footsteps. Do you seriously want to watch the veterinary profession being led by the nose by Big Pharma, moving ever-closer to untruth? Does this serve your clients or even you?

Can we expect the truth from our governments, academia, or the vaccine industry? Yes – insofar as *individuals* within these areas are called to seek the truth and speak the truth. "All it takes for evil to thrive is that good men and women do nothing."

Jordan Peterson continued: "Information propagates in a network manner, so don't under-estimate the power of your speech. Your capacity for speech is divine. It's the thing that turns order from chaos and then sometimes turns pathological order into chaos when it has to. Don't under-estimate the power of truth. There's nothing more powerful. Now, in order to speak what you regard as the truth, you have to let go of the outcome. You have to think, alright, stupid as I am, biased as I am, ignorant as I am, I'm going to state what I think as clearly as I can, and I'm going to live with the consequences, no matter what they are. That's faith.

"Nothing brings a better world into being than the sacred truth. Now you may have to pay a price for that, but that's fine. You're going to pay a price for everything you do or don't do anyway. You get to choose which poison you're going to take. That's it.

"So if you're going to stand up for something, stand up for your truth. It will shape you – because people will respond and object and tell you why you're a biased moron, why you're ignorant, and that if you listened to them ….

"After five years you'll be so tough and articulate and able to withstand pressure that you won't recognise yourself. You'll be a force to contend with."

The alternative, he said (I paraphrase), is to keep your truth to yourself, going to your grave with regrets, never having stretched yourself, ending up as a mealy-mouthed mouse of a human being.

You may wonder why I shared my personal story with you alongside vaccine information. The answer is that I wanted you to turn the page and understand the harm we are doing to our children and our beloved animal friends, and I know that people are interested in people more than they're interested in dry scientific data. I also wanted to demonstrate that you don't have to be fully formed or perfect to stand up for what you believe. Your life doesn't have to be totally in order before you speak the truth, because no-one's life is fully in order! To be human is to be imperfect and fallible.

I have presented the truth as I understand it here in order to prevent or alleviate suffering. You have a right to disagree with me. But please give us proper, verifiable, observable, scientifically established facts to prove that vaccines are safe and effective, and that the fears we have are unnecessary. Give the people informed, unbiased, truthful information so they can make their own choices about their bodies and the bodies of those in their care.

I'm calling upon the scientific community to speak the bloody truth – that's all anyone needs to do to free us from this nightmare.

Just speak the truth.

"This above all – to thine own self be true, and it must follow, as night follows day, thou canst not then be false to any man." (Shakespeare)

Chapter 93

The Simple Solution

Chappie, my first born, taught me that We Are All One. Sometimes Chappie would stick his head around a corner, and I would think I was looking at myself. Our energies had merged, and we were the same being. There was no me and him; there was no separation. We are all One – everything that has life is made of the same Source energy. That Source energy, the energy that holds us all together, is Love. Love is the Creative Principle.

When another living being suffers, we all suffer. My dogs taught me this. In relationship we find ourselves or lose ourselves.

I perceived that something was causing harm and chose to do something about it. Even now, twenty-five years on, I still question myself and wonder whether I've wasted my precious time. The task of cleaning this mess up seems insurmountable, with too many powerful vested interests blocking truth.

But I knew from the work of independent scientists that we do not need to vaccinate our dogs every year. I also knew, again from the work of independent scientists, that vaccines are not without harm. I felt that people needed to know so they and their dogs wouldn't suffer. I can hear pro-vaccinators saying that infectious diseases cause suffering in greater numbers, and vaccines can prevent that. So can better living conditions and real food, and it's a pity that they have to lie to us in order to be able to defend vaccines.

Practically everything you have read in this book is about the human ego. The psychologist Alfred Adler defined the ego as the false self. Eckhart Tolle describes it as the pain body. The ego is essentially all the lies we make up about ourselves and our place in the world. It's the part of us that believes we created ourselves and that we are vulnerable to attack. The ego is fundamentally the part of us that fears. And from that fear comes a propensity to attack others, to take from others, to wish to control others, and to forget that we are all One. Fear blocks compassion, just as cynicism blocks the acquisition of knowledge.

The scientific community has accepted the concept of sacrifice. Science accepts that it's necessary to make animals suffer in laboratory experiments so that shampoo doesn't sting our eyes, or cleaning products and agrichemicals don't give us cancer. Except that, as far as I can see, shampoo still stings and many approved chemicals still give us cancer.

We've accepted that only some of us should be allowed to experience the abundance that this planet offers to us all, yet I'm not alone in believing that there's enough for all of us if some of us would appreciate the far-reaching benefits of benevolence. And we've accepted side-effects and adverse reactions as a necessary part of a paradigm that on the one hand is dedicated to healing, and on the other overlooks and hides the suffering it creates.

We forget that strangers, too, can feel pain.

I appreciate that it is rather idealistic to expect that, one day, we will collectively remember Who we are. But I do expect this.

Elisabeth Kübler-Ross, a doctor who studied thousands of near-death experiences, wrote that many who had died and been brought back felt an indescribable peace, and relayed the message that the only thing that matters in this life is how much we have loved.

Love and kindness are very simple things. These simple things – and not the complex and scientific – have the power to save us all.

However, the inhabitants of this planet are at a juncture. We can close our eyes and yawn as those in power seek to resolve over-population by polluting our food, our homes, and our bodies while raking in the profits, or we can become knowledgeable and share our knowledge about the real causes of health and ill health. We can choose to help ourselves, our loved-ones, and all who have ears to hear.

I keep asking myself whether I've come to the correct conclusion. Are they trying to kill us or, at least, are they immune to our suffering? But when you add all of the facts together, it's hard to deny that something sinister appears to be happening. Or maybe the cock up theory would cover it all … except that if it's a cock up, you'd expect governments to correct their mistakes, which I see no evidence for.

Knowledge is power. We have the remedy for this sickness in our own ordinary hands. Parents and animal lovers around the world are joining together – with love as their motivation – to beat the Establishment.

And it can be done. It will be done.

Truth and love – which are interchangeable – are the two most powerful forces on this Earth. My dogs taught me this.

There are no hard lines in the Cosmic mind. There is no separation. We are not different to one-another at our core, and none of us is better than anyone else, or more deserving. And suffering is suffering, however it's delivered.

Use your voice, your intelligence, your love … and speak the truth for those who will benefit from hearing.

It really is that simple. When we stop buying their damaging products, they can't sell them, can they?

I'm reminded of a passage by AR Orage on love:

Without shame, people will boast that they have loved, do love, or hope to love. As if love were enough, or could cover any multitude of sins. But love, when it is not conscious love – that is to say, love that aims to be both wise and able in the service of its object – is either an affinity or a disaffinity, and in both cases equally unconscious, that is, uncontrolled. To be in such a state of love is to be dangerous either to oneself or to the other or to both. We are then polarised to a natural force (which has its own objects to serve regardless of ours) and charged with its force, and events, are fortunate if we do not damage somebody in consequence of carrying dynamite carelessly. Love without knowledge and power is demoniac. Without knowledge it may destroy the beloved .... Love is not enough.

There was an Ancient Mariner ....

In Coleridge's poem, the Ancient Mariner grasped the hand of a wedding guest and insisted upon telling him his tale of woe and warning. The guest has no idea why the Mariner has picked on him. He feared the Mariner and, after hearing the bad news, the wedding guest was transformed into a sadder but wiser man.

Which essentially means that none of us is keen to listen to dire warnings. Coleridge's wedding guests were having a good time; they didn't want the troubling message the Mariner had for them.

When you run a campaign as I have done, you eventually come to realise that people are getting on with their lives and that your essentially unpleasant message has little attraction (which is why being a rock star is a better bet). I know that people generally don't want someone like me to come along and share scary facts. It's uncomfortable to feel the anxiety associated with vaccine dangers; vaccines are the modern albatross. So people look away, and even hate you for warning them. It's easier to trust the 'experts' and let them take the pain of uncertainty away.

So it's a hard old slog.

But I know that – with knowledge – you can protect yourself and your loved-ones. One person at a time. I think this is as good as it's going to get unless, like all civilisations before this one, it all crashes around our ears. I don't know, but maybe it would ultimately be a good thing to start again, but with a more conscious, aware, society. Maybe this is what the elite are aiming for, blinded to the suffering along the way.

Everything in this world is about balance, or homeostasis. There is currently an imbalance we need to address, but the forces keeping the imbalance in place are strong and powerful. It can only be corrected, in my view, when the silent masses are silent no longer, and the disinterested come to realise that they are here to co-create the world we share. Human beings have the capacity to care for others through conscious love – but it takes work to become conscious.

George Bernard Shaw wrote, "The worst sin against our fellow creatures is not to hate them, but to be indifferent to them; that's the essence of inhumanity."

Despite my many faults and my own messy life; despite all the anger I've attracted whilst sharing this story of unnecessary suffering, and despite the fact that few want to know, some have heard and benefited from this story. Many at least now know that once a dog is immune to the core viral diseases, he doesn't need another bloody vaccine!

For that at least I am glad.

Appendix 1

Chapter 2
1. R Schultz, Dog vaccines may not be necessary, University of Wisconsin-Madison News, March 14, 2003. http://news.wisc.edu/schultz-dog-vaccines-may-not-be-necessary/

Chapter 12
1. Gov.uk,VMD: About Us. https://www.gov.uk/government/organisations/veterinary-medicines-directorate/about

Chapter 15
1. Immunoglobulin E antibodies to pollens augmented in dogs by virus vaccines. *Am J Vet Res*. 1983 Mar;44(3):440-5.

Chapter 19
1. RationalWiki, Anti-vaccination movement, accessed May 2017. http://rationalwiki.org/wiki/Anti-vaccination_movement
2. Rachael Dunlop, The Guardian, Anti-vaccination activists should not be given a say in the media, 16 October, 2013.http://www.theguardian.com/commentisfree/2013/oct/16/anti-vaccination-activists-should-not-be-given-a-say-in-the-media
3. Evgeny Morozov, Slate.com, accessed May 2017. http://www.slate.com/articles/technology/future_tense/2012/01/anti_vaccine_activists_9_11_deniers_and_google_s_social_search_.html
4. Anna Kata, Anti-vaccine activists, Web 2.0 and the post-modern paradigm – An overview of tactics and tropes used on-line by the anti-vaccination movement, *Vaccine*, Volume 30, Issue 25, pages 3778-3789, 28 May 2015. http://www.sciencedirect.com/science/article/pii/S0264410X11019086
5. *Vaccine*. 2012 May 28;30(25):3778-89. doi: 10.1016/j.vaccine.2011.11.112. Epub 2011 Dec 13
6. P Aaby, K Knudsen, T G Jensen, J Thårup, A Poulsen, M Sodemann, M C da Silva, H Whittle. Measles incidence, vaccine efficacy, and mortality in two urban African areas with high vaccination coverage. *J Infect Dis*. 1990 Nov ;162(5):1043-8. PMID: 2230232
7. Inácio M Mandomando, Denise Naniche, Marcela F Pasetti, Xavier Vallès, Lilian Cuberos, Ariel Nhacolo, Karen L Kotloff, Helder Martins, Myron M Levine, Pedro Alonso. Measles-specific neutralizing antibodies in rural Mozambique: seroprevalence and presence in breast milk. *Am J Trop Med Hyg*. 2008 Nov;79(5):787-92. PMID: 18981523
8. L Sekla, W Stackiw, G Eibisch, I Johnson. An evaluation of measles serodiagnosis during an outbreak in a vaccinated community. *Clin Invest Med*. 1988 Aug ;11(4):304-9. PMID: 3168353
9. A J Hall, F T Cutts. Lessons from measles vaccination in developing countries. *BMJ*. 1993 Nov 20;307(6915):1294-5. PMID: 8257878

10. Peter Aaby, Henrik Jensen, Francois Simondon, Hilton Whittle. High-titer measles vaccination before 9 months of age and increased female mortality: do we have an explanation? *Semin Pediatr Infect Dis.* 2003 Jul;14(3):220-32. PMID: 12913835

11. BBC News, Unicef child-death campaign in Africa 'failed,' Jan. 2010. http://news.bbc.co.uk/1/hi/world/africa/8455444.stm

12. T L Gustafson, A W Lievens, P A Brunell, R G Moellenberg, C M Buttery, L M Sehulster. Measles outbreak in a fully immunized secondary-school population. *N Engl J Med.* 1987 Mar 26 ;316(13):771-4. PMID: 3821823

13. R M Davis, E D Whitman, W A Orenstein, S R Preblud, L E Markowitz, A R Hinman. A persistent outbreak of measles despite appropriate prevention and control measures. *Am J Epidemiol.* 1987 Sep ;126(3):438-49. PMID: 3618578

14. B S Hersh, L E Markowitz, R E Hoffman, D R Hoff, M J Doran, J C Fleishman, S R Preblud, W A Orenstein. A measles outbreak at a college with a prematriculation immunization requirement. *Am J Public Health.* 1991 Mar ;81(3):360-4. PMID: 1994745

15. N Boulianne, G De Serres, B Duval, J R Joly, F Meyer, P Déry, M Alary, D Le Hénaff, N Thériault.[Major measles epidemic in the region of Quebec despite a 99% vaccine coverage]. *Can J Public Health.* 1991 May-Jun;82(3):189-90. PMID: 1884314

16. S A de Oliveira, W N Soares, M O Dalston, M T de Almeida, A J Costa. Clinical and epidemiological findings during a measles outbreak occurring in a population with a high vaccination coverage. *Rev Soc Bras Med Trop.* 1995 Oct-Dec;28(4):339-43. PMID: 8668833

17. N Coetzee, G D Hussey, G Visser, P Barron, A Keen. The 1992 measles epidemic in Cape Town--a changing epidemiological pattern. *S Afr Med J.* 1994 Mar ;84(3):145-9. PMID: 7740350

18. Michael Loeffelholz „*J Clin Microbiol.* 2012 Jul; 50(7): 2186–2190. doi: 10.1128/JCM.00612-12 http://www.ncbi.nlm.nih.gov/pmc/articles/PMC3405598/

19. Steven Novella, Lessons from Dunning-Kruger, Neurologica blog, Nov 2014. http://theness.com/neurologicablog/index.php/lessons-from-dunning-kruger/

Chapter 20

1. *Environmental Health Perspectives* 1995;105(11):1214. See also http://www.mdpestnet.org/resources/news2006/

Chapter 27

1. Hirokuni Beppu et al, Lessons learnt in Japan from adverse reactions to the HPV vaccine: a medical ethics perspective, *Indian Journal of Medical Ethics*, accessed May 2017. http://ijme.in/articles/lessons-learnt-in-japan-from-adverse-reactions-to-the-hpv-vaccine-a-medical-ethics-perspective/?galley=html

Chapter 29

1. Thiravat Hemachudha, M.D., et al, Myelin Basic Protein as an Encephalitogen in Encephalomyelitis and Polyneuritis Following Rabies Vaccination, *N Engl J Med* 1987; 316:369–74. http://www.nejm.org/doi/full/10.1056/NEJM198702123160703

Chapter 33

1. Christopher Day, Alternative Veterinary Medicine Centre, accessed May 2017. http://www.alternativevet.org/Clinical%20Trial%20-%20Dogs%20K-C%20WS009-07.pdf
2. Register KB1, Nicholson TL, Misidentification of Bordetella bronchiseptica as Bordetella pertussis using a newly described real-time PCR targeting the pertactin gene, *Journal of Medical Microbiology* 56(Pt 12):1608-10 · January 2008, DOI: 10.1099/jmm.0.47511-0 http://www.researchgate.net/publication/5813441_Misidentification_of_Bordetella_bronchiseptica_as_Bordetella_pertussis_using_a_newly_described_real-time_PCR_targeting_the_pertactin_gene
3. Lakshmi Gopinathan et al, Different mechanisms of vaccine-induced and infection-induced immunity to Bordetella bronchiseptica, *Microbes and Infection*, January 2007, 442e448 http://vbs.psu.edu/research/labs/harvill/selected-publications/2007%20M-I%20Lakshmi%20Vacc%20v%20Infect.pdf
4. Ellis JA, Comparative efficacy of an injectable vaccine and an intranasal vaccine in stimulating Bordetella bronchiseptica-reactive antibody responses in seropositive dogs. *J Am Vet Med Assoc.* 2002 Jan 1;220(1):43-8. https://www.ncbi.nlm.nih.gov/pubmed/12680446
5. Register KB1, Nicholson TLMisidentification of Bordetella bronchiseptica as Bordetella pertussis using a newly described real-time PCR targeting the pertactin gene. . *J Med Microbiol.* 2007 Dec;56(Pt 12):1608-10. https://www.ncbi.nlm.nih.gov/pubmed/18033827
6. Larry J Strausbaugh, Ruth L Berkelman, Human Illness Associated with Use of Veterinary Vaccines. *Clinical Infectious Diseases*, Volume 37, Issue 3, Pp. 407-414. https://academic.oup.com/cid/article/37/3/407/437242/Human-Illness-Associated-with-Use-of-Veterinary

Chapter 35

1. CBC News, Canada, Sept 14, 2011. http://www.cbc.ca/news/canada/swissair-crash-may-not-have-been-an-accident-ex-rcmp-1.1019738
2. Wikipedia Swissair Flight 111. http://en.wikipedia.org/wiki/Swissair_Flight_111
3. Rebecca Smith, Haemophilia patients infected with Hepatitis C and HIV 'should be compensated', *Telegraph*, 20 Feb, 2009. http://www.telegraph.co.uk/health/healthnews/4733810/Haemophilia-patients-infected-with-Hepatitis-C-and-HIV-should-be-compensated.html
4. Nigel Bunyan, Doctor missing for six months is found dead, Telegraph, 8 Jan 2004 http://www.telegraph.co.uk/news/uknews/1451154/Doctor-missing-for-six-months-is-found-dead.html
5. David Kelly (weapons expert) Wikipedia https://en.wikipedia.org/wiki/David_Kelly_(weapons_expert)

6. Malaysia Airlines Flight 370, Wikipedia https://en.wikipedia.org/wiki/Malaysia_Airlines_Flight_370#Passengers
7. Sara C Nelson, MH370: Missing Malaysia Airlines Flight 'Was Hijacked By Secret Extra Passenger', *Huffington Post*, 9 March, 2017 http://www.huffington-post.co.uk/entry/mh370-missing-malaysia-airlines-flight-was-hijacked-by-secret-extra-passenger_uk_58c131b0e4b054a0ea6822e4
8. Malaysia Airlines Flight 17, Wikipedia https://en.wikipedia.org/wiki/Malaysia_Airlines_Flight_17
9. Joep Lang, Wikipedia. https://en.wikipedia.org/wiki/Joep_Lange
10. Pan Am Flight 103, Wikipedia https://en.wikipedia.org/wiki/Pan_Am_Flight_103
11. Mary Dejevsky Cameron's freebie to Apartheid South Africa, *Independent*, 25 April 2009 http://www.independent.co.uk/news/uk/politics/camerons-freebie-to-apartheid-south-africa-1674367.html
12. Huntly Collins, Shankar Vedantam, *Inquirer Daily News*, 20 June, 2011, http://www.philly.com/philly/health/_8_years_and_700_million_later_how_a_better_drug_was_found__.html#vQgUdDAmBKEUQQuD.99
13. Keiron Pim, Lockerbie 'bomber' Megrahi was innocent, says Norfolk man, *Eastern Daily Press*, 21 May 2010 http://www.edp24.co.uk/news/crime/locker-bie_bomber_megrahi_was_innocent_says_norfolk_man_1_1383902
14. Carol Adl, Body Of Doctor Who Linked Vaccines To Autism, Found Floating In River, *YourNewsWire.com* http://yournewswire.com/body-of-doctor-who-linked-vaccines-to-autism-found-floating-in-river/
15. Erin Elizabeth, Holistic Doctor Death Series: Over 60 Dead In Just Over A Year, *Health Nut News*, 12 March 2016 http://www.healthnutnews.com/re-cap-on-my-unintended-series-the-holistic-doctor-deaths/
16. Lynne McTaggart, What Doctors Don't Tell You blog http://www.lynnemctag-gart.com/blog/299-what-you-do-with-the-most-promising-cancer-treatment-to-date also available at http://www.activistpost.com/2015/08/gcmaf-naga-lase-and-the-immune-system.html
17. The World Factbook, CIA https://www.cia.gov/library/publications/the-world-factbook/fields/2111.html
18. Jim Edwards, *CBS MoneyWatch*, 6 May, 2009 http://www.cbsnews.com/news/merck-created-hit-list-to-destroy-neutralize-or-discredit-dissenting-doctors/ and
19. Ben Goldacre, *The Guardian*, 9 May 2009 http://www.theguardian.com/com-mentisfree/2009/may/09/bad-science-medical-journals-companies

Chapter 38

1. Gaskell, Gettinby, Graham, Skilton, Veterinary Products Committee (VPC) Working Group on Feline and Canine Vaccination, May 2001 http://modernveter-inarytherapeutics.com/vpc-feline%20and%20canine%20vaccination.pdf
2. Veterinary Products Committee, About Us https://www.gov.uk/government/or-ganisations/veterinary-products-committee/about

Chapter 39

1. Tom Lonsdale, Oral Disease in Cats and Dogs, *Control and Therapy* Series No. 3128; Mailing No. 163, December1991 http://www.rawmeatybones.com/No_3128.html

Chapter 40

1. Wakefield, Andrew, J, *Callous Disregard*, Skyhorse Publishing, 2010.
2. The MMR Urabe atrocity; various citations http://whale.to/vaccine/mmr15.html
3. Chris Tryhorn, Glaxo brings in James Murdoch, *The Guardian*, 3 February 2009 https://www.theguardian.com/business/2009/feb/03/glaxosmithkline-james-murdoch
4. OffsoreSimple.com, Tax Havens – Neither Illegal nor Immoral http://offshoresimple.com/moral.htm
5. Partnership for New York City, current portfolio http://pfnyc.org/our-investments/current-portfolio/
6. .org – Rupert Murdoch http://www.sourcewatch.org/index.php/K._Rupert_Murdoch
7. Wikipedia, RELX Group (Reed Elsevier) http://en.wikipedia.org/wiki/Reed_Elsevier
8. Wikipedia, Crispin Davis director at GSK: https://en.wikipedia.org/wiki/Crispin_Davis
9. Polly Tommey, Discredited disinformation of Dr Andrew Wakefield, *Age of Autism* January 6, 2010 http://www.ageofautism.com/2010/01/polly-tommey-of-autism-file-magazine-on-discredited-defamation-of-dr-andrew-wakefield.html
10. Reuters, Rupert Murdoch quits GSK Board, Jan 27, 2012 http://www.reuters.com/article/us-glaxosmithkline-idUSTRE80Q0OJ20120127
11. Sir Crispin Davis and James Murdoch leave GSK Board, *Age of Autism*, April 2016 http://www.ageofautism.com/2016/04/best-of-sir-crispin-davis-and-james-murdoch-leave-gsk-board.html
12. James Murdoch criticized by the British Office of Communications, Wikipedia https://en.wikipedia.org/wiki/James_Murdoch
13. Simon Walters, Rebekah vetoed BBC man and told Cameron he should give No10 job to Andy Coulson, *Mail on Sunday*, July 16, 2001 http://www.dailymail.co.uk/news/article-2015573/Rebekah-Brooks-vetoed-BBC-man-told-Cameron-No10-job-Andy-Coulson.html
14. Owen Jones, *The Establishment and How They Get Away With It*, Penguin Books
15. Chris Tryhorn, Glaxo brings in James Murdoch, *The Guardian*, February 3, 2009 https://www.theguardian.com/business/2009/feb/03/glaxosmithkline-james-murdoch
16. Reuters, James Murdoch to quit GSK Board, November 29, 2007 http://www.reuters.com/article/us-glaxosmithkline-idUSTRE80Q0OJ20120127
17. Wikipedia, Jonathan Harmsworth http://en.wikipedia.org/wiki/Jonathan_Harmsworth,_4th_Viscount_Rothermere
18. 132 Research papers supporting vaccine/autism causation, SCRIBD.com https://www.scribd.com/doc/220807175/132-Research-Papers-Supporting-the-Vaccine-Autism-Link

19. Thomas Piketty, *Capital in the Twenty-First Century* – 18 Mar 2014.
20. WikiPedia, Jonathan Harmsworth, https://en.wikipedia.org/wiki/Jonathan_Harmsworth,_4th_Viscount_Rothermere
21. Tom de Castella, Who are the Barclay brothers?, *BBC News Magazine*, 20 February 2015 http://www.bbc.co.uk/news/magazine-31517392

Chapter 41
1. Powerbase, Public Interest Investigations, http://powerbase.info/index.php/MMR
2. Sue Corrigan, *Mail on Sunday*, May 2016khttp://www.dailymail.co.uk/health/article-376203/Former-science-chief-MMR-fears-coming-true.html
3. John Aston, MMR Doctor John Walker-Smith wins High Court Appeal, *Independent*, 7 March 2012 http://www.independent.co.uk/life-style/health-and-families/health-news/mmr-doctor-john-walker-smith-wins-high-court-appeal-7543114.html
4. Leslie Manookian , CDC Whistleblower to Extend MMR Vaccine Fraud , *The Weston A Price Foundation*, May 3, 2016 https://www.westonaprice.org/press/cdc-whistleblower-extend-mmr-vaccine-fraud/
5. Jonathan Benson, MMR vaccines cause 340% increased risk of autism in African American infants, *Naturalnews.com*, August 27, 2014 http://www.naturalnews.com/046622_MMR_vaccine_autism_African_Americans.html
6. TruthWiki, Dr William Thompson http://www.truthwiki.org/dr-william-thompson/
7. Neil Z Miller, A Covert CDC Program Inoculated Black Babies with Deadly, Experimental Measles Vaccines, *Age of Autism*, http://www.ageofautism.com/2014/09/minority-report-a-covert-cdc-program-inoculated-black-babies-with-deadly-experimental-measles-vaccines.html
8. Coursehero.com, WMA Declaration of Helsinki – Ethical Principles for Medical Research Involving Human Subjects https://www.coursehero.com/file/9934829/WMA-Declaration-of-Helsinki-Ethical-Principles-for-Medical-Research-Involving-Human-Subjects/
9. World Medical Association, International Code of Medical Ethics (1949) http://ethics.iit.edu/ecodes/node/4676
10. Brian S Hooker, Measles-mumps-rubella vaccination timing and autism among young African American boys: a reanalysis of CDC data, 27 August 2014 http://www.translationalneurodegeneration.com/content/3/1/16
11. Science-based medicine, Vaccine Whistleblower: BS Hooker and William Thompson try to talk about epidemiology, August 24, 2015 https://sciencebased-medicine.org/tag/william-thompson/
12. Jerome Burne and Sally Beck, *Rescued media*, The MMR vaccine: why it's sensible to worry about the way it has been regulated, 21 February 2017 https://rescuedmedia.org/BeckHuffPoUKMMR.php
13. Sciencblogs.com, The conspiracy circle is complete: Brian Hooker claims "The Man" has gotten to the "CDC whistleblower", April 26, 2016 http://scienceblogs.com/insolence/2016/04/26/the-conspiracy-circle-is-complete-brian-hooker-claims-the-man-has-gotten-to-the-cdc-whistleblower/

See also:

14. Measles inclusion-body encephalitis caused by the vaccine strain of measles virus, *Journal Clin Infect Dis*. 1999 Oct;29(4):855-61.PMID 10589903
15. http://www.ageotautism.com/2014/09/minority-report-a-covert cdc program in oculated-black-babies-with-deadly-experimental-measles-vaccines.html
16. The whistleblower, Dr William Thompson, worked at the American CDC and participated in a cover-up of MMR-induced autism in African-American boys. http://ireport.cnn.com/docs/DOC-1164794.
17. The peer reviewed analysis of the original CDC data showing a 340% increase in autism in African American boys due to the MMR vaccine http://www.translationalneurodegeneration.com/content/3/1/16
18. http://www.naturalnews.com/046599_CNN_censorship_medical_genocide.html
19. DeStefano F, Bhasin TK, Thompson WW, et al. "Age at first measles-mumps-rubella vaccination in children with autism and school-matched control subjects: a population-based study in metropolitan Atlanta." Pediatrics 2004 Feb; 113(2): 259-66.
20. Press Release. "Statement of William W. Thompson, Ph.D., regarding the 2004 article examining the possibility of a relationship between MMR vaccine and autism." August 27, 2014. www.morganverkamp.com
21. Hooker BS. "Measles-mumps-rubella vaccination timing and autism among young African American boys: a reanalysis of CDC data." *Translational Neurodegeneration* 2014 Aug 8; 3: 16.
22. Henderson RH, et al. "Immunizing the children of the world: progress and prospects." Bull WHO 1988; 66: 535-43.
23. Hayden GF, et al. "Progress in worldwide control and elimination of disease through immunization." *J of Pediatrics* 1989; 114: 520-27.
24. Gold E. "Current progress in measles eradication in the U.S." *Infect Med* 1997; 14(4): 297-300; 310.
25. Van Ginneken JK, et al. Maternal and Child Health in Rural Kenya. (London: Croom Helm, 1984).
26. FL, et al. "Geographic variation in infant loss of maternal measles antibody and in prevalence of rubella antibody." *American J. of Epidemiology* 1986; 124: 442-52.
27. Garenne M, et al. "Pattern of exposure and measles mortality in Senegal." *J of Infectious Diseases* 1990; 161: 1088-94.
28. WHO-EPI. "The optimal age for measles immunization." *Weekly Epidemiology Records* 1982; 57: 89-91.
29. JS, et al. "Successful immunization of infants at 6 months of age with high dose Edmonston-Zagreb measles vaccine." *Pediatric Infect Dis* J 1991 April; 10(4): 303-311.
30. Sabin AB, et al. "Successful immunization of children with and without maternal antibody by aerosolized measles vaccine. I. Different results with undiluted human diploid cell and chick embryo fibroblast vaccines." *JAMA* 1983; 249: 2651-62.
31. Sabin AB, et al. "Successful immunization of children with and without maternal antibody by aerosolized measles vaccine. II. Vaccine comparisons and evidence for multiple antibody response." *JAMA* 1984; 251: 2363-71.

32. Whittle HC, et al. "Immunisation of 4-6 month old Gambian infants with Edmonston-Zagreb measles vaccine." *Lancet* 1984; ii: 834-37.
33. Whittle HC, et al. "Trial of high-dose Edmonston-Zagreb measles vaccine in The Gambia: antibody response and side-effects." *Lancet* 1988; ii: 811-814.
34. Aaby P, et al. "Trial of high-dose Edmonston-Zagreb measles vaccine in Guinea-Bissau: protective efficacy." *Lancet* 1988; i: 809-811.
35. Garenne M, et al. "Child mortality after high-titre measles vaccines: prospective study in Senegal." *Lancet* 1991; 338: 903-7.
36. Whittle HC. "Effect of dose and strain of vaccine on success of measles vaccination of infants aged 4-5 months." *Lancet* 1988; i: 963-66.
37. Khanum S, et al. "Comparison of Edmonston-Zagreb and Schwartz strains of measles vaccine given by aerosol or subcutaneous injection." *Lancet* 1987; i: 150-53.
38. Tidjani O, et al. "Serological effects of Edmonston-Zagreb, Schwartz, and AIK-C measles vaccine strains given at ages 4-5 or 8-10 months." *Lancet* 1989; ii: 1357-60.
39. Markowitz LE, et al. "Immunization of six-month-old infants with different doses of Edmonston-Zagreb and Schwartz measles vaccines." *NEJM* 1990; 332: 580-87.
40. Awadu KO. Outrage! How Babies Were Used as Guinea Pigs in an L.A. County Vaccine Experiment. (Long Beach, CA: *Conscious Rastra Press*, 1996).
41. Weiss R. "Measles battle loses potent weapon." *Sci* 1992 Oct. 23: 546-47.
42. 1Cimons M. "CDC says it erred in measles study." *L.A. Times* (June 17, 1996).
43. Autism following congenital rubella infection. *J. Autism Dev. Disord.* 1971;1:33-47
44. Autistic spectrum disorder after brain inflammation caused by measles virus. *Arch Dis Child.* 1975;50:115-119
45. Measles and mumps exposure linked to autism: *American Journal of Epidemiology.* 1979;109:628-638
46. Cases of meningitis after Urabe MMR reported in Japan. *Jpn. Ju. Infect. Dis.* 2002;55:101-111.
47. Allergic reactions to MMR vaccine (anaphylaxis). *Pediatrics;* 1992, 89:168-9.
48. Autism and known medical conditions; myth and substance (linking vaccines to autism). *J. Child psycho. Psychol. Psychiat.* 1994;35;311-322.
49. Gait disturbances (ataxia) after measles mumps rubella vaccine. *Lancet* 1995;345-316.
50. Ring et al link measles infection to autism in Israel. Pathophysiology. 1997;4:1485-8.
51. Acute encephalopathy followed by permanent brain injury or death associated with further attenuated measles vaccines. A review of claims submitted to the National Vaccine Injury Compensation Program. *Paediatrics.* 1998;101:383-387.
52. Plesner – follow up study of MMR complications. Confirms that severe ataxias are associated with residual cognitive deficits in some children. *Acta Paediatrica* 2000;89:58-63.
53. *The Journal of Pediatrics November* 1999; 135(5):559-63
54. *The Journal of Pediatrics* 2000; 138(3): 366-372

55. *Journal of Clinical Immunology* November 2003; 23(6): 504-517
56. *Brain, Behavior and Immunity* 1993; 7: 97-103
57. *Pediatric Neurology* 2003; 28(4): 1-3
58. *Neuropsychobiology* 2003; 31.77-85
59. *The Journal of Pediatrics* May 2005;146(5):605-10
60. *Autism Insights* 2009; 1: 1-11
61. *Canadian Journal of Gastroenterology* February 2009; 23(2): 95-98
62. *Annals of Clinical Psychiatry* 2009:21(3): 148-161
63. *Journal of Child Neurology* June 29, 2009; 000:1-6
64. *Journal of Autism and Developmental Disorders* March 2009;39(3):405-13
65. *Medical Hypotheses* August 1998;51:133-144.
66. *Journal of Child Neurology* July 2000; ;15(7):429-35
67. *Lancet.* 1972;2:883–884.
68. *Journal of Autism and Childhood Schizophrenia* January-March 1971;1:48-62
69. *Journal of Pediatrics* March 2001;138:366-372.
70. *Molecular Psychiatry* 2002;7:375-382.
71. *American Journal of Gastroenterolgy* April 2004;598-605.
72. *Journal of Clinical Immunology* November 2003;23:504-517.
73. *Neuroimmunology* April 2006;173(1-2):126-34.
74. *Prog. Neuropsychopharmacol Biol. Psychiatry* December 30 2006;30:1472-1477.
75. *Clinical Infectious Diseases* September 1 2002;35(Suppl 1):S6-S16
76. *Applied and Environmental Microbiology*, 2004;70(11):6459-6465
77. *Journal of Medical Microbiology* October 2005;54:987-991
78. *Archivos venezolanos de puericultura y pediatría* 2006; Vol 69 (1):
79. *Gastroenterology.* 2005:128 (Suppl 2);Abstract-303

Chapter 42
1. O'Driscoll, C, Vets on vaccines, Dogs Naturally magazine,=http://www.dogsnaturallymagazine.com/vets-on-vaccines/

Chapter 43
1. *Tizard's Veterinary Immunology*, 4th edition.
2. "Vaccine-Associated Immune-Mediated Haemolytic Anaemia (IMHA) in the Dog". *Journal of Veterinary Internal Medicine* (Vol 10, No 5 (September-October) 1996)

Chapter 45
1. David Feinstein PhD, 'Acupoint stimulation in treating psychological disorders: Evidence of efficacy, *Review of General Psychology*, 16, 364-380. doi:10.1037/a0028602.

Chapter 48
1. Dr Bob Rogers DVM, Critteradvocacy.org, Complaint To The Texas Veterinary Board of Medical Examiners http://www.critteradvocacy.org/State%20Board%20Complaint.htm

Chapter 49

1. Michael D Innis. Autoimmunity and Non-Accidental Injury in Children. *Clinical Medicine Research.* Vol. 2, No. 3, 2013, pp. 40-44.doi: 10.11648/j. cmr.20130203.15

2. What killed Sally Clark's child? *The Spectator*, 16 May 2007 https://www.spectator.co.uk/comic/what-killed-sally-clarks-child/#

3. Brian Deer, The vanishing victims, *The Sunday Times Magazine*, November 1 1998 http://briandeer.com/dtp-dpt-vaccine.htm

4. Colin R. Paterson1 and Elizabeth A. Monk, Temporary brittle bone disease: relationship between clinical findings and judicial outcome, *Pediatr Rep.* 2011 Jun 30; 3(3): e24. http://www.ncbi.nlm.nih.gov/pmc/articles/PMC3207312/

5. Colin R. Paterson, Elizabeth A. Monk, Temporary brittle bone disease: association with intracranial bleeding, *J Pediatr Endocr* Met 2013

See also:

6. Hirtz DG, Nelson KB, Ellenberg J H, "Seizures following childhood immunizations", *Pediatr* 1983 Jan; 102(1):14-18.

7. Cherry JD, Holtzman AE, Shields WD, Buch D, Nielsen, "Pertussis immunization and characteristics related to first seizures in infants and children," *J Pediatr* 1993 Jun;122(6):900-903.

8. Coplan J, "Seizures following immunizations," *J Pediatr* 1983 Sep;103(3):496.

9. Barkin RM, Jabhour JT, Samuelson J S, "Immunizations, seizures, and subsequent evaluation," *JAMA* 1987 Jul 10;258(2):201.

10. Griffin MR, et al, "Risk of seizures after measles-mumps-rubella immunization," *Pediatrics* 1991 Nov;88(5):881-885.

11. Griffin MR, et al, "Risk of seizures and encephalopathy after immunization with the diphtheria-tetanus-pertussis vaccine," *JAMA* 1990 Mar 23-30;263(12):1641-1645.

12. Cizewska S, Huber Z, Sluzewski W, "[Prophylactic inoculations and seizure activity in the EEG]," *Neurol Neurochir Pol* 1981 Sep-Dec;15(5-6):553-557. [Article in Polish]

13. Huttenlocher PR, Hapke RJ, "A follow-up study of intractable seizures in childhood." *Ann Neurol* 1990 Nov; 28(5):699-705.

14. Blumberg DA, "Severe reactions associated with diphtheria-tetanus-pertussis vaccine: detailed study of children with seizures, hypotonic-hypo-responsive episodes, high fevers, and persistent crying."*Pediatrics* 1993 Jun; 91(6):1158-1165.

15. Prensky AL, et al, "History of convulsions and use of pertussis vaccine," *J Pediatr* 1985 Aug; 107(2):244-255.

16. Baraff LJ, "Infants and children with convulsions and hypotonic-hypo-responsive episodes following diphtheria-tetanus-pertussis immunization: follow-up evaluation," *Pediatrics* 1988 Jun; 81(6):789-794.

17. Jacobson V, "Relationship of pertussis immunization to the onset of epilepsy, febrile convulsions and central nervous system infections: a retrospective epidemiologic study," Tokai *J Exp Clin Med* 1988;13 Suppl: 137-142.

18. Cupic V,et al, "[Role of DTP vaccine in the convulsive syndromes in children]," Lijec Vjesn 1978 Jun; 100(6):345-348. [Article in Serbo-Croatian (Roman)]

19. Pokrovskaia NIa, "[Convulsive syndrome in DPT vaccination (a clinico-erimental study)]," *Pediatriia* 1983 May;(5):37-39. [Article in Russian]
20. Ballerini, Ricci, B, et al, "On Neurological Complications of Vaccination, With Special Reference to Epileptic Syndromes," *Rlv Neurol*, Jul Aug 1973, 43:254-258. Wolf SM, Forsythe A, "Epilepsy and mental retardation following febrile seizures in childhood," *Acta Paediatr Scand* 1989 Mar;78(2):291-295.
21. AIP McCandlish et al state: "Post-vaccinal encephalitis is a recognised complication of the administration of certain strains of live attenuated canine distemper vaccine (Hartley 1974, Bestetti and others 1978, Cornwell and others 1988)." *Veterinary Record*, 1992 (130, 27-30),
22. Viera Scheibner, PhD, Shaken Baby Syndrome Diagnosis On Shaky Ground, *J. Aust. Coll. Nutr. & Env. Med.* Vol. 20 No. 2 (August 2001) pages 5-8, 15
23. Buttram, Harold E., M.D., "Shaken Baby Syndrome or Vaccine-Induced Encephalitis?" Originally published in the Medical Sentinel 2001;6(3):83-89. Association of American Physicians and Surgeons, http://aapsonline.org/jpands/hacienda/buttram.html

Chapter 50
1. American Animal Hospital Association (AAHA) Canine Vaccination Task Force, 2011 AAHA Canine Vaccination Guidelines (with reference to 2003 guidelines) https://www.aaha.org/public_documents/professional/guidelines/caninevaccine-guidelines.pdf

Chapter 53
1. 31 vets call for an end to annual vaccination, *Veterinary Times*, accessed via http://www.dogs4sale.com.au/Notice_Board_Dogs_World_UK.htm

Chapter 54
1. http://www.researchgate.net/
2. *Lancet*, Volume 383, Issue 9913, Pages 257 – 266, 18 January 2014
3. Ari Levy, Bill Gates Joins $35 Million Funding in Startup ResearchGate, *Bloomberg*, 4 June 2013 https://www.bloomberg.com/news/articles/2013-06-04/bill-gates-joins-35-million-investment-in-startup-researchgate
4. Sayer Ji, Gates Foundation Funds Surveillance of Anti-Vaccine Groups, Greenmedinfo.com, Aug 29 2010 http://www.greenmedinfo.com/blog/gates-foundation-funds-surveillance-anti-vaccine-groups
5. Gary Null, Ph.D. and Richard Gale, HPV Vaccines: Unnecessary and Lethal, *Educateyourself.org* http://educate-yourself.org/vcd/garynullrichardgaleHPVlethal08apr14.shtml
6. Demicheli V, Jefferson T, Al-Ansary LA, Ferroni E, Rivetti A, Di Pietrantonj C, Vaccines to prevent influenza in healthy adults, *Cochrane.org*, 13 March 2014 http://www.cochrane.org/CD001269/ARI_vaccines-to-prevent-influenza-in-healthy-adults
7. Gates.org, Polio Strategy Overview http://www.gatesfoundation.org/What-We-Do/Global-Development/Polio
8. Neetu Vashishti, Jacob Puliyel1, Polio programme: let us declare victory and

move on, *Indian Journal of Medical Ethics* Vol IX No 2 April-June 2012 15. http://ijme.in/wp-content/uploads/2016/11/1769-5.pdf

9. WikiPedia, Poliomyelitis https://en.wikipedia.org/wiki/Poliomyelitis
10. Dean Nelson, Ending polio in India is world's greatest health achievement, says Bill Gates, *Telegraph*, 12 Feb 2014, http://www.telegraph.co.uk/news/worldnews/asia/india/10632759/Ending-polio-in-India-is-worlds-greatest-health-achievement-says-Bill-Gates.html
11. Mohammadi D, Polio-like disease in the news: much ado about nothing?, *Lancet Neurol*. 2014 Jul;13(7):650-1. doi: 10.1016/S1474-4422(14)70132-2. http://www.ncbi.nlm.nih.gov/pubmed/24943341#cm24943341_10417
12. Healthimpactnews.com, The Vaccine Myth of "Polio-free" Status – Polio Vaccine Caused 53,000 Paralysis Victims in India Last Year, http://healthimpactnews.com/2014/the-vaccine-myth-of-polio-free-status-polio-vaccine-caused-53000-paralysis-victims-in-india-last-year/
13. Fergus Walsh, Bill Gates: The world can defeat polio, BBC News online, 28 January 2013 http://www.bbc.co.uk/news/health-21207601
14. Anubhuti Vishnoi, Centre shuts health mission gate on Bill & Melinda Gates Foundation, *Economic Times*, Feb 9, 2017 http://economictimes.indiatimes.com/news/politics-and-nation/centre-shuts-gate-on-bill-melinda-gates-foundation/articleshow/57028697.cms?from=mdr&utm_source=contentofinterest&utm_medium=text&utm_campaign=cppst
15. Douglas L. Leslie1, Robert A. Kobre, Brian J. Richmand, Selin Aktan Guloksuz and James F. Leckman, Temporal Association of Certain Neuropsychiatric Disorders Following Vaccination of Children and Adolescents, *Front. Psychiatry*, 19 January 2017 http://journal.frontiersin.org/article/10.3389/fpsyt.2017.00003/full
16. Robert F Kennedy Jnr, New CDC Research Debunks Agency's Assertion That Mercury in Vaccines Is Safe, *Ecowatch.com*, 1 February 2017 http://www.ecowatch.com/cdc-mercury-vaccines-kennedy-2226257805.html

Chapter 55

1. WikiPedia, Margaret Sanger Eugenics, https://en.wikipedia.org/wiki/Margaret_Sanger#Eugenics
2. Transcript – Bill Moyers interviews Bill Gates, pbs.org http://www.pbs.org/now/printable/transcript_gates_print.html
3. Press statement by the catholic health commission of kenya – kenya conference of catholic bishops on the ongoing national tetanus vaccination campaign in 60 districts in Kenya, March 26, 2014 http://www.kccb.or.ke/home/com/statements-com/press-statement-by-the-catholic-health-commission-of-kenya-kenya-conference-of-catholic-bishops-on-the-ongoing-national-tetanus-vaccination-campaign-in-60-districts-in-kenya/
4. Steve Weatherbe, Kenyan gvmt launches probe into claim UN is using vaccines for 'mass sterilization', Lifesitenews.com, Nov 12, 2014, https://www.lifesitenews.com/news/kenyan-gvmt-launches-probe-into-claim-un-is-using-vaccines-for-mass-sterili
5. Joylene Sing'oei, Catholic Church questions ongoing tetanus vaccination target-

ing women aged between 14-49 years, Standard Media, 26 March, 2014 http://www.standardmedia.co.ke/mobile/?articleID=2000107916&story_title=Catholic%20Church%20questions%20ongoing%20tetanus%20vaccination%20targeting%20women%20aged%20between%2014-49%20years/lifestyle/

6. Jennifer Ip, Petition, Forcechange.com, Stop Forced Sterilization of Low-Income Women in India, http://forcechange.com/135413/stop-forced-sterilization-of-poor-women/

7. IAP Statement on Population Growth, 1994, http://www.interacademies.net/10878/13940.aspx

8. Gates Notes http://www.gatesnotes.com/

9. Our 2017 Annual Letter, Bill and Melinda Gates, February 14, 2017 https://www.gatesnotes.com/2017-Annual-Letter

10. CJ Duncan, et al, The effects of population density and malnutrition on the dynamics of whooping cough. *Epidemiol Infect*. Oct 1998; 121(2): 325–334.

11. Duncan CJ, Duncan SR, Scott S, Whooping cough epidemics in London, 1701-1812: infection dynamics, seasonal forcing and the effects of malnutrition, *Proc Biol Sci*. 1996 Apr 22;263(1369):445-50. http://www.ncbi.nlm.nih.gov/pubmed/8637925 –

12. Peter Katona, Judit Katona-Apt, The Interaction between nutrition and infection, *Clinical Practice*, 2008: 46, (15 May) http://health120years.com/cn/pdf/Nutrition_Infection-Interaction.pdf

13. Huiming Y, Chaomin W, Meng M, Vitamin A for treating measles in children (Review), Wiley reprint, 2005, http://www.measlesrubellainitiative.org/wp-content/uploads/2013/06/Vitamin-A-for-measles-children.pdf

14. Tuula E. Tuorma, Adverse Effects of Zinc Deficiency: A Review from the Literature, *Journal of Orthomolecular Medicine*, Vol. 10, No. 3 & 4, 1995 http://www.orthomolecular.org/library/jom/1995/pdf/1995-v10n0304-p149.pdf

15. Mitsuyoshi Urashima, et al, Randomized trial of vitamin D supplementation to prevent seasonal influenza A in schoolchildren, *Am J Clin Nutr,* May 2010 vol. 91 no. 5 1255-1260

16. Ethan Will Taylor1 and Chandra Sekar Ramanathan, Theoretical Evidence that the Ebola Virus Zaire Strain May Be Selenium-Dependent: A Factor in Pathogenesis and Viral Outbreaks? *The Journal of Orthomolecular Medicine Vol. 10, No.2, 1995* http://orthomolecular.org/library/jom/1995/articles/1995-v10n0304-p131.shtml

17. Peter Katona Judit Katona-Apte, Interactions of nutrition and infection, *Clinical Infectious Diseases*, Volume 46, Issue 10, Pp. 1582-1588. http://cid.oxfordjournals.org/content/46/10/1582.abstract

18. John Hoddinott Mark Rosegrant Maximo Torero, Challenge Paper, Hunger and Malnutrition, Copenhagen Concensus 2012 http://www.copenhagenconsensus.com/sites/default/files/hungerandmalnutrition.pdf

19. Stuart Winter, Environment Editor, 'I give my badgers vitamins to stop TB', Express, 21 July 2011 http://www.express.co.uk/news/uk/262162/I-give-my-badgers-vitamins-to-stop-TB

20. English RM, Badcock JC, Giay T, Ngu T, Waters AM, Bennett SA, Effect of nutrition improvement project on morbidity from infectious diseases in preschool

children in Vietnam: comparison with control commune, *BMJ* 1997;315:112 http://www.ncbi.nlm.nih.gov/pmc/articles/PMC2127738/

21. Zaman MM, Yoshiike N, Rouf MA, Haque S et al, Association of rheumatic fever with serum albumin concentration and body iron stores in Bangladeshi children: case control study, *BMJ* 1998;317:1287-8 http://www.ncbi.nlm.nih.gov/pmc/articles/PMC28708/http://www.ncbi.nlm.nih.gov/pmc/articles/PMC2127738/

22. Wolff CG, Schroeder DG, Young MW, Effect of improved housing on illness in children under 5 years old in northern Malawi: a cross sectional study, *BMJ* 2001;322:1209-12. http://www.ncbi.nlm.nih.gov/pmc/articles/PMC31618/

23. Sebastian L Johnston, Peter J M Openshaw, The protective effect of childhood infections, *BMJ*. Feb 17, 2001; 322(7283): 376–377 https://www.ncbi.nlm.nih.gov/pmc/articles/PMC1119618/

24. Dr Viera Scheibner, Vaccinations 100 Years of Orthodox Research shows that vaccines represent a Medical Assault on the Immune System, Paperback – 1 Dec 1993

25. Elisabeth Kernbauer, Yi Dingand& Ken Cadwell, An enteric virus can replace the beneficial function of commensal bacteria, *Nature* 516, 94–98 (04 December 2014): http://www.nature.com/nature/journal/vaop/ncurrent/pdf/nature13960.pdf

26. A.W. Taylor-Robinson, Multiple Vaccination Effects on Atopy, Can vaccines cause immune dysfunction resulting in allergies, asthma and anaphylaxis? *Allergy* April 1999, Volume 54, pp. 398-399 http://vaccinechoicecanada.com/health-risks/multiple-vaccination-effects-on-atopy/

27. Poverty Matters blog, Why is the Gates foundation investing in GM giant Monsanto?, *Guardian* http://www.theguardian.com/global-development/poverty-matters/2010/sep/29/gates-foundation-gm-monsanto

28. Christina Sarich, Big Owner of Monsanto Shares: Does Bill Gates Want Population Control?, NaturalSociety.com, 18 May 2014 http://naturalsociety.com/big-owner-monsanto-shares-bill-gates-depopulation-agenda-exposed/

29. http://www.unicef.org/mdg/poverty.html

30. F. William Engdahl,, "Doomsday Seed Vault" in the Arctic – Bill Gates, Rockefeller and the GMO giants know something we don't, GlobalResearch.ca, December 2007 http://www.globalresearch.ca/doomsday-seed-vault-in-the-arctic-2/23503

Chapter 56

1. Global Health Watch, Bill Gates http://www.ghwatch.org/sites/www.ghwatch.org/files/d1.3.pdf

2. Gopal Dapade, Jacob Puliyel, Bill & Melinda Gates Foundation's grant-making programme for global health. *Lancet* 2009; 373: 1645-1653; http://www.thelancet.com/journals/lancet/article/PIIS0140-6736(09)60571-7/fulltext

3. Guest: Critics say Gates Foundation's agriculture program won't help poor farmers, *Humanosphere*, 13 Oct 2014 http://www.humanosphere.org/social-business/2014/10/critics-say-gates-foundations-agriculture-program-wont-help-poor-farmers/

4. John Vidal, Why is the Gates foundation investing in GM giant Monsanto?, *Guardian*, 29 September 2010 https://www.theguardian.com/global-development/poverty-matters/2010/sep/29/gates-foundation-gm-monsanto

5. The flip side to Bill Gates' charity billions, *New Internationalist*, April 2012 https://newint.org/features/2012/04/01/bill-gates-charitable-giving-ethics/
6. Anne Hendershott, The Ambitions of Bill and Melinda Gates: Controlling Population and Public Education, Crisis magazine, 25 March 2013 http://www.crisismagazine.com/2013/the-ambitions-of-bill-and-melinda-gates-controlling-population-and-public-education
7. Bill & Melinda Gates Foundation Trust stocks, Gurufocus.com http://www.gurufocus.com/StockBuy.php?GuruName=Bill+Gates
8. David Bank and Rebecca Buckman, Gates Foundation Buys Stakes in Drug Makers, Wall Street Journal,17 May 2002 http://www.wsj.com/articles/SB1021577629748680000
9. Charles Piller, Edmund Sanders, Robyn Dixon, Dark cloud over good works of Gates Foundation, *Los Angeles Times*, 7 Jan 2007 http://www.latimes.com/news/la-na-gatesx07jan07-story.html
10. Jacob Levich, Big Pharma and the Gates Foundation: "Guinea Pigs for the Drug Makers" *Global Research*, May 2014 http://www.globalresearch.ca/big-pharma-and-the-gates-foundation-guinea-pigs-for-the-drugmakers/5384374?print=1
11. Gopal Dabade, Joseph Puliyel, Correspondence, The Lancet, Vol 373, 27 June 2009 http://www.thelancet.com/pdfs/journals/lancet/PIIS0140-6736(09)61184-3.pdf
12. Ruben Rosenberg Colorni, Bill Gates, Big Pharma, Bogus Philanthropy, *News Junkie Post*, 7 June 2013 http://newsjunkiepost.com/2013/06/07/bill-gates-big-pharma-bogus-philanthropy/

Chapter 57

1. Vaccine Safety (?), a possible etiology of autoimmune disease, William La Rosa, Trustee, Hayward Foundation, http://www.omegadanes.com/purdue_university_and_hayward_foundation_study_on_vaccines.htm

See also:
1. Yehuda Shoenfeld and M. Eric Gershwin MD, *Autoantibodies*, 27 Nov 2006, Elsevier Publishing. The authors stated : "Following six initially euthyroid [normal thyroid function] brothers and sisters for a decade we found that a high proportion who were antibody positive later developed biochemical evidence of impaired thyroid function … the presence of autoantibodies even in clinically normal individuals may sometimes represent an early warning signal of impending disease."
2. Benedict J. Chambers, Norman W. Klein, Role of laminin autoantibodies on the embryo toxicity of sera from mercuric chloride treated brown Norway rats, *Reproductive Toxicology,* Volume 7, Issue 4, July–August 1993, Pages 333-341 http://www.sciencedirect.com/science/article/pii/089062389390022Y: "These observations suggested the possibility that an environmental pollutant such as mercury could cause the formation of embryotoxic autoantibodies that could persist in the body as embryotoxic factors for extended periods of time.
3. E Druet, J C Guery, K Ayed, B Guilbert, S Avrameas, and P Druet, Characteristics of polyreactive and monospecific IgG anti-laminin autoantibodies in the rat

mercury model. *Immunology* Nov 1994; 83(3): 489–494. "This study shows that polyreactive anti-laminin antibodies are produced during this autoimmune disease, and indicates that they may have pathogenic potential." http://www.ncbi. nlm.nih.gov/pmc/articles/PMC1415045/

4. Patricia G. Wolff, Uwe Kühl, Heinz-Peter Schultheiss, Laminin distribution and autoantibodies to laminin in dilated cardiomyopathy and myocarditis, *American Heart Journal*, Volume 117, Issue 6, June 1989, Pages 1303–1309. "Seventy-eight percent of 91 patients with dilated cardiomyopathy and 73% of 41 patients with myocarditis exhibited significantly elevated anti-laminin antibody levels compared with 68 apparently healthy persons."

5. Carine J. Peutz-Kootstra, Kim Hansen, Emile De Heer, Christine K. Abrass, Differential expression of laminin chains and anti-laminin autoantibodies in experimental lupus nephritis., *Journal of Pathology*, 24 July 2000: "These changes in anti-laminin chain autoantibodies, with concomitant alterations in the glomerular expression of laminin chains, may aggravate progressive immune injury in this model for lupus nephritis."

6. Terry K Means, et al, Human lupus autoantibody-DNA complexes activate DCs through cooperation of CD32 and TLR9, *J Clin Invest*. 2005 Feb;115(2):407-17: "These data demonstrate that endogenous DNA-containing autoantibody complexes found in the serum of patients with SLE activate the innate immune system and suggest a novel mechanism whereby these ICs contribute to the pathogenesis of this autoimmune disease." https://www.ncbi.nlm.nih.gov/pmc/articles/ PMC544604/

7. Revolvy.com. "Anti-cardiolipin antibodies (ACA) are antibodies often directed against cardiolipin and found in several diseases, including syphilis, antiphospholipid syndrome, livedoid vasculitis, vertebrobasilar insufficiency, Behçet's syndrome, idiopathic spontaneous abortion, and systemic lupus erythematosus (SLE)." https://www.revolvy.com/main/index.php?s=Anti-cardiolipin%20antibodies&item_type=topic

8. Hull RG, Harris EN, Gharavi AE et al. 1984. "Anticardiolipin antibodies: occurrence in Behçet's syndrome". *Ann. Rheum. Dis.* 43 (5): 746–748. doi:10.1136/ ard.43.5.746. PMC 1001520. PMID 6497467.

9. Petri M, Golbus M, Anderson R, Whiting-O'Keefe Q, Corash L, Hellmann D 1987. "Antinuclear antibody, lupus anticoagulant, and anticardiolipin antibody in women with idiopathic habitual abortion. A controlled, prospective study of forty-four women". *Arthritis Rheum.* 30 (6): 601–606. doi:10.1002/art.1780300601. PMID 3111489.

10. Harris EN, Gharavi AE, Boey ML et al. 1983. "Anticardiolipin antibodies: detection by radioimmunoassay and association with thrombosis in systemic lupus erythematosus". *Lancet* 2 (8361): 1211–1214. doi:10.1016/S0140-6736(83)91267-9. PMID 6139567.

11. Harris EN, Gharavi AE, Loizou S et al. 1985. "Crossreactivity of antiphospholipid antibodies". *Journal of clinical & laboratory immunology* 16 (1): 1–6. PMID 3981615.

12. Keane A, Woods R, Dowding V, Roden D, Barry C 1987. "Anticardiolipin antibodies in rheumatoid arthritis". *Br. J. Rheumatol.* 26 (5): 346–350. doi:10.1093/

rheumatology/26.5.346. PMID 3664159.

13. Malia RG, Greaves M, Rowlands LM et al. 1988. "Anticardiolipin antibodies in systemic sclerosis: immunological and clinical associations". *Clin. Exp. Immunol.* 73 (3): 456–60. PMC 1541778. PMID 2974767.

14. McNeil HP, Simpson RJ, Chesterman CN, Krilis SA 1990. "Anti-phospholipid antibodies are directed against a complex antigen that includes a lipid-binding inhibitor of coagulation: beta 2-glycoprotein I (apolipoprotein H)". *Proc. Natl. Acad. Sci.* U.S.A. 87 (11): 4120–4124. doi:10.1073/pnas.87.11.4120. PMC 54059. PMID 2349221.

15. Proven A, Bartlett RP, Moder KG, et al: Clinical importance of positive test results for lupus anticoagulant and anticardiolipin antibodies. *Mayo Clin Proc* 2004;79:467-475

16. Wilson WW, Gharavi AE, Koike T, et al: International consensus statement on preliminary classification criteria for definite antiphospholipid syndrome. *Arthritis Rheum* 1999;42(7):1309-1311

17. *J Am Vet Med Assoc* 2002;221:515–52, "Conclusions and Clinical Relevance— Recent vaccination may result in increased anti-canine thyroglobulin antibodies. Whether these antibodies have a deleterious effect on canine thyroid function is unknown."

18. Michael Day, chairman of the WSAVA vaccine guidelines group, and professor within the Department of Pathology and Microbiology, University of Bristol. IgG subclasses of canine anti-erythrocyte, antinuclear and anti-thyroglobulin autoantibodies, *Res Vet Sci.* 1996 Sep;61(2):129-35: "The mAbs are widely applicable to the study of the pathogenesis of canine autoimmune disease."

19. Jennifer Fiala, Rabies vaccine increases antibodies, study shows, DVM360 magazine, 1 October 2002: http://veterinarynews.dvm360.com/rabies-vaccine-increases-antibodies-study-shows

Chapter 58

1. Ian Tizard, Richard M. Schubot, Susan L. Payne, Active Immunization, *MSD Veterinary Manual*, on-line, accessed May 2017 http://www.merckmanuals.com/vet/pharmacology/vaccines_and_immunotherapy/active_immunization.html

2. Harry Yorke, Dog owners' concerns over dog death, Telegraph, 2 July 2016 http://www.telegraph.co.uk/news/2016/07/02/dogs-dying-after-having-protective-vaccine-owners-claim/

3. David Woodmansey, VMD offers reassurance over vaccine concerns, *Veterinary Times*, 20 March, 2017 https://www.vettimes.co.uk/news/vmd-offers-reassurance-over-vaccine-concerns/

Chapter 60

1. Yehuda Shoenfeld and M. Eric Gershwin MD, *Autoantibodies*, 27 Nov 2006, Elsevier Publishing http://www.amazon.co.uk/Autoantibodies-Yehuda-Shoenfeld/dp/0444563784/ref=dp_ob_image_bk#reader_0444563784

2. Janeway CA Jr, Travers P, Walport M, et al, *Immunobiology: The Immune System in Health and Disease.* 5th edition. Garland Science; 2001 http://www.ncbi.nlm.nih.gov/books/NBK27155/

3. Michael Day, *In Practice*, Vol 20 No 2, Feb 1998
4. Jennifer Fiala, Rabies vaccine increases antibodies, study shows, *DVM360 Magazine*, Oct 01, 2002 *http://veterinarynews.dvm360.com/rabies-vaccine-increases-antibodies-study-shows*
5. *The Truth About Drug Companies – how they deceive us and what to do about it,* Dr Marcia Angell, Random House 2004
6. FDA Officially Belongs to Big Pharma With Senate Confirmation of Dr. Robert Califf, February 2016 http://www.ecowatch.com/fda-officially-belongs-to-big-pharma-with-senate-confirmation-of-dr-ro-1882179798.html
7. Martha Rosenberg, AlterNet, The FDA now officially belongs to Big Pharma , February 2016 http://www.salon.com/2016/02/27/the_fda_now_officially_belongs_to_big_pharma_partner/
8. Martha Rosenberg, The Strange Career of Scott Gottlieb, Counterpunch.org, December 2007 http://www.counterpunch.org/2007/12/26/the-strange-career-of-scott-gottlieb/
9. Ibid. http://ecowatch.com/2016/02/25/fda-big-pharma-califf/

See also:

1. 'ASIA'-Autoimmune/inflammatory syndrome induced by adjuvants. *J Autoimmun* 2011; 36: 4–8.
2. Vaccines and autoimmunity. *Nat Rev Rheumatol* 2009; 5: 648–52.
3. The new H1N1 and HPV vaccines and old fears. *Curr Opin Rheumatol* 2010; 22: 431–436.
4. Adjuvants and autoimmunity. Lupus 2009; 18: 1217–1225.
5. Towards an understanding of the adjuvant action of aluminium. *Nat Rev Immunol* 2009; 9: 287–293.
6. Alum adjuvant boosts adaptive immunity by inducing uric acid and activating inflammatory dendritic cells. *J Exp Med* 2008; 205: 869–882.
7. Crucial role for the Nalp3 inflammasome in the immunostimulatory properties of aluminium adjuvants. *Nature,* 2008; 453: 1122–1126.
8. Manifestations of systemic autoimmunity in vaccinated salmon. *Vaccine* 2010; 28: 4961–4969.
9. Human adjuvant disease induced by foreign substances: a new model of ASIA (Shoenfeld's syndrome). *Lupus* 2012; 21: 128–135.
10. Influenza vaccination can induce new onset anticardiolipins but not β2-glyco-protein-I antibodies among patients with systemic lupus erythematosus. *Lupus,* 2012; 21: 168–174.
11. Autoimmune response following influenza vaccination in patients with autoimmune inflammatory rheumatic disease. *Lupus,* 2012; 21: 175–183.
12. Systemic Lupus Erythematosus following HPV Vaccination. *Lupus,* 2012; 21: 158–161.
13. Autoimmunity following Hepatitis B vaccine as part of the spectrum of ASIA "Autoimmune (auto-inflammatory) Syndrome Induce by Adjuvants" – analysis of 93 cases. *Lupus,* 2012; 21: 146–152.
14. The Gulf War Syndrome as a part of the autoimmune (auto-inflammatory) syndrome induced by adjuvant (ASIA). *Lupus,* 2012; 21: 190–194.

15. Vaccine model of antiphospholipid syndrome induced by tetanus vaccine. *Lupus*, 2012; 21: 195–202.

16. Mechanisms of aluminum adjuvant toxicity and autoimmunity in pediatric populations. *Lupus,* 2012; 21: 223–230.

17. Aluminum as an adjuvant in Crohn's disease induction. *Lupus,* 2012; 21: 231–238.

18. http://www.scribd.com/doc/220807175/86-Research-Papers-Supporting-the-Vaccine-Autism-Link

Chapter 61

1. *Clinical Immunology and Immunopathology*, Volume 7, Issue 3, May 1977, Pages 311–314.

Chapter 62

1. United States Senate Committee on Finance, February 6, 2008, Senator Charles E Grassley – search Victoria Hampshire via http://www.finance.senate.gov/

2. |Jeff Donn, FDA vet blows whistle, pays price, Associated Press, *LA Times*, 13 May 2007 http://articles.latimes.com/2007/may/13/news/adna-watchdog13/2

3. GAP, Government Accountability Project, Senator Grassley's Letter to Wyeth Pharmaceuticals, 17 November 2005 https://www.whistleblower.org/senator-grassleys-letter-wyeth-pharmaceuticals

4. US Senate Committee on Finance, Senator Grassley letter to U.S. Department of Health and Human Services and FDA, 6 February 2008 http://docshare.tips/hampshire-investigation_57686678b6d87fb2918b4c86.html

5. AAVP Newsletter, page 15 Volume 29, Number 2, June 2007, page 15 http://www.aavp.org/documents/2012/03/aavp-june-2007-newsletter.pdf – Glickman doing a heartworm talk

6. Nadler & Associates, custom marketing services, Larry Glickman Epidemiological study presentation, client: Fort Dodge: http://nadlerassociates.com/videoevent/videoevent.html

7. No longer available at this link: http://www.fda.gov/AdvisoryCommittees/CommitteesMeetingMaterials/VeterinaryMedicineAdvisoryCommittee/ucm208444.htm but available here: https://wayback.archive-it.org/7993/20170113195526/http://www.fda.gov/AdvisoryCommittees/CommitteesMeetingMaterials/VeterinaryMedicineAdvisoryCommittee/ucm208444.htm

8. Bridget M. Kuehn, Fort Dodge recalls ProHeart 6, citing FDA safety concerns, *JAVMA News*, 1 October 2004 https://www.avma.org/News/JAVMANews/Pages/041015a.aspx

9. George E. Moore, Lawrence T Glickman et al, *Adverse events diagnosed within three days of vaccine administration in dogs* JAVMA, October 1, 2005, Vol. 227, No. 7, Pages 1102-1108 https://doi.org/10.2460/javma.2005.227.1102

10. Gardasil: One More Girl – documentary, watch it online: https://www.youtube.com/watch?v=3N0KTZZOrD4

Chapter 63

1. Proheart 6 datasheet, Zoetis: http://www.proheart6.com/pdf/DirectDeposit03_12. pdf

Chapter 64

1. Patrick Holford and Jerome Burne, *Food is Better Medicine Than Drugs*, Piatkus Books, 2006 https://www.holfordirect.com/food-is-better-medicine-than-drugs-patrick-holford.html
2. Jon Cruddas and Zoe Gannon, *A Bitter Pill to Swallow, Drugs for people, not just for profit,* Compass – Direction for the Democratic Left Ltd. http://www.compass-sonline.org.uk/wp-content/uploads/2013/05/compass-bitter-pill-WEB-2.pdf
3. IFAH, representing companies engaged in research, development and manufacturing of veterinary medicines, vaccines and other animal health products in Europe. *Facts and figures about the European animal health industry*, http://www.bft-online.de/fileadmin/bft/publikationen/Facts_and_Figures_2008.pdf
4. Cathy J Tralau-Stewart, et al, *New Models for Industry-Academic Partnerships*, Drug Discovery Today 14(1-2):95-101 · December 2008 http://www.research-gate.net/publication/23459557_Drug_discovery_new_models_for_industry-academic_partnerships
5. http://nconehealthcollaborative.weebly.com/uploads/8/6/0/4/8604842/larry_glickman_bio.pdf
6. Pfizer, Public Private Partnerships http://www.pfizer.com/responsibility/grants_contributions/medical_and_academic_partnerships/public_private_partnerships
7. Medical and Educational Goods and Services (MEGS) grants paid by Pfizer in 2013 to UK Organisations, Associations and Institutions that are comprised of health professionals and /or that provide healthcare or conduct research http://www.pfizer.co.uk/sites/g/files/g10018861/f/201403/SHS129e%20MEGS%20 2013%20disclosure%20report%20.pdf
8. Robert Mendick, How Tony Blair Inc spent £57 million in four years, *The Telegraph*, 11 Jan 2015 http://www.telegraph.co.uk/news/politics/to-ny-blair/11337856/How-Tony-Blair-Inc-spent-57-million-in-four-years.html
9. Sarah Boseley, *Blair sides with drug giants*, Guardian, 31 March 2001 http://www.theguardian.com/politics/2001/mar/31/uk.eu
10. Pfizer Political Action Committee and Political Contributions Report http://www.pfizer.com/about/corporate_governance/political_action_committee_report
11. Pace Environmental Law Review, volume 28 http://digitalcommons.pace.edu/pelr/vol28/
12. Scott Klinger, Sarah Anderson, Javier Rojas, Institute for Policy Studies, Corporate Tax Dodgers, 10 companies and their corporate tax loopholes, 2013 Report http://www.americansfortaxfairness.org/files/Corporate-Tax-Dodgers-Report-Final.pdf
13. Project Censored, Richest global 1 percent hide trillions in tax havens, 30 September 2013 http://projectcensored.org/2-richest-global-1-percent-hide-trillions-tax-havens
14. Gerald F. Jr. Combs, The Role of Selenium in Nutrition, Elsevier, 2 Dec 2012 https://books.google.co.uk/books?id=vLnRg5gfqOUC&pg=PA402&lp-

g=PA402&dq=sheffey,+et+al,+vaccination&source=bl&ots=SNQjGBki4_
&sig=jqQVf6pHKKeVsjm1xu9xngLyYok&hl=en&sa=X&ei=oXbPVM-
YMYS1Ud7mgPgB&ved=0CFUQ6AEwBw#v=onepage&q=
sheffey%2C%20et%20al%2C%20vaccination&f=false

Chapter 68

1. Was available at: http://www.vmd.defra.gov.uk/vet/vaccines_letters.aspx but now on PWA website – http://www.petwelfarealliance.org/campaign-to-end-over-vaccination.html
2. Jordan Michael Smith, Vote all you want. The secret government won't change. *Boston Globe*, October 19, 2014 https://www.bostonglobe.com/ideas/2014/10/18/vote-all-you-want-the-secret-government-won-change/jVSkXrENQlu8vNcBf-Mn9sL/story.html
3. National Security and Double Government, Michael J. Glennon, Oxford University Press 2015
4. Vaccines for Dogs and Cats – Advice for Owners, VMD website https://www.gov.uk/government/uploads/system/uploads/attachment_data/file/368589/PCDOCS-_305476-v3-VMD_Leaflet_012_A_-_Vaccines_for_dogs_and_cats_-_Advice_for_Owners.PDF

Chapter 69

1. Isolation of an Infectious Endogenous Retrovirus in a Proportion of Live Attenuated Vaccines for Pets, Journal of Virology, April 2010, p. 3690-3694, Vol. 84, No. 7. http://jvi.asm.org/cgi/content/full/84/7/3690
2. See also *Applied Biosafety*, 9(2) pp. 68-75 © ABSA 2004, Introduction for "Safety Considerations for Retroviral Vectors: A Short Review", Donald E. Mosier
3. Ellerman, C., and O. Bang. 1908. *Centralbl. Bakteriol.* 46:595–609.
4. Rous, P. 1911. J. Exp. Med. 13:397–411. http://centennial.rucares.org/index.php?page=Cancer
5. Michael Specter, Darwin's Surprise, New Yorker, 3 December 2007 http://www.newyorker.com/magazine/2007/12/03/darwins-surprise
6. Robin A. Weiss, Retroviruses and cancer, *Current Science*, Vol. 81, No. 5, 10 September 2001 http://www.iisc.ernet.in/currsci/sep102001/528.pdf
7. Missing link (taken down – but you can ask the VMD for it): http://www.vmd.defra.gov.uk/pdf/vaccines_retrovirus_RD114.pdf
8. Try this instead: CVMP Risk Management Strategy – Managing the risk of the potential presence of replication competent endogenous retrovirus RD114 in starting materials and final products of feline and canine vaccines, European Medicines Agency, 16 February 2017 EMA/CVMP/IWP/592652/2014 Committee for Medicinal Products for Veterinary Use (CVMP) http://www.ema.europa.eu/docs/en_GB/document_library/Regulatory_and_procedural_guideline/2017/02/WC500222260.pdf
9. Yoshikawa, R., Shimode, S., Sakaguchi, S. et al. Arch Virol (2014) 159: 399. doi:10.1007/s00705-013-1809-1 Mar https://link.springer.com/article/10.1007/s00705-013-1809-1 ch 2014, Volume 159, Issue 3, pp 399–404 https://link.springer.com/article/10.1007/s00705-013-1809-1

10. Ian Tizard, Risks Associated with use of live vaccines, *JAVMA*, vol 196, No 11, pages 1851-1858, 1990

11. Barbara Loe Fisher, The Emerging Risks of Live Virus & Virus Vectored Vaccines: Vaccine Strain Virus Infection, Shedding & Transmission, National Vaccine Information Center http://www.nvic.org/CMSTemplates/NVIC/pdf/Live-Virus-Vaccines-and-Vaccine-Shedding.pdf

12. CDC: *measles cases and outbreaks* https://www.cdc.gov/measles/cases-out-breaks.html

13. Sayer Ji, Greenmedinfo.com, January 2015 http://www.greenmedinfo.com/blog/disney-measles-outbreak-mousetrap-ignorance

14. Sir Philip Hampton's 2005 review, Department for Business Innovation and Skills: http://webarchive.nationalarchives.gov.uk/+/http:/www.bis.gov.uk/policies/better-regulation/improving-regulatory-delivery/assessing-our-regulatory-system

15. The Veterinary Medicines Directorate, A Hampton Implementation Review Report http://webarchive.nationalarchives.gov.uk/20121212135622/http://www.bis.gov.uk/assets/biscore/better-regulation/docs/10-693-veterinary-medicines-directorate-hampton-implementation-review

16. The National Archives, VMD history http://webarchive.nationalarchives.gov.uk/20140909095303/http://vmd.defra.gov.uk/business/history.aspx

Chapter 73

1. Markets and markets.com Veterinary/Animal Vaccines Market http://www.marketsandmarkets.com/Market-Reports/animal-veterinary-vaccines-market-1233.html

2. Statitica: Top 10 biotech and pharmaceutical companies worldwide based on market value in 2016 (in billion U.S. dollars) http://www.statista.com/statistics/272716/global-top-biotech-and-pharmaceutical-companies-based-on-market-value/

3. Wikipedia, UK national debt https://en.wikipedia.org/wiki/United_Kingdom_national_debt

4. http://www.bloomberg.com/news/2013-10-28/merck-profit-beats-analysts-estimates-on-gardasil-sales.html

5. BMJ Case Reports 2012; doi:10.1136/bcr-2012-006879 http://casereports.bmj.com/content/2012/bcr-2012-006879.abstract

6. Sharyl Attkisson, Gardasil Researcher Speaks Out, *CBS* 19 August 2009 http://www.cbsnews.com/news/gardasil-researcher-speaks-out/

7. Wikipedia, Gardasil: https://en.wikipedia.org/wiki/Gardasil

8. NIH: NIH Technology Licensed to Merck for HPV Vaccine http://www.ott.nih.gov/nih-technology-licensed-merck-hpv-vaccine

9. Gavi.org: HPV vaccine inventor Ian Frazer sees his idea become reality http://www.gavi.org/library/news/gavi-features/2012/hpv-vaccine-inventor-ian-frazer/

10. Hirokuni Beppu et al, Lessons learnt in Japan from adverse reactions to the HPV vaccine: a medical ethics perspective, *Indian Journal of Medical Ethics* Vol II No 2 April-June 2017 http://ijme.in/articles/lessons-learnt-in-japan-from-adverse-reactions-to-the-hpv-vaccine-a-medical-ethics-perspective/?galley=html

Chapter 74

1. MarketWatch.com, Vaccine makers rally in wake of pandemic declaration June 12, 2009 http://www.marketwatch.com/story/biotech-stocks-slide-as-euro-vaccine-makers-gain

2. Kalorma.com, New Report Forecasts More than Doubling of Vaccine Sales by 2013, Press Release Jun 11, 2009 http://www.kaloramainformation.com/about/release.asp?id=1402

3. GPs reeling as RCGP draws up damning dossier of swine flu chaos, Pulse, 2009 http://www.pulsetoday.co.uk/gps-reeling-as-rcgp-draws-up-damning-dossier-of-swine-flu-chaos/11009754.article#.VgFpBZiFPcs

4. HRSA, National Vaccine Injury Compensation Program http://www.hrsa.gov/vaccinecompensation/vaccinetable.html

5. The History of Vaccines.org, College of Physicians of Philadelphia, Vaccine injury compensation programs https://www.historyofvaccines.org/content/articles/vaccine-injury-compensation-programs

6. Gov.uk, Vaccine damage payment https://www.gov.uk/vaccine-damage-payment/overview

7. HRSA, National Vaccine Injury Compensation Program, injury table https://www.hrsa.gov/vaccinecompensation/pre03202017-vaccineinjurytable.pdf

8. Bloomberg.com. May 13, 2009

9. CTV News, Baxter admits flu product contained live bird flu virus, 27 February 2009 http://www.ctvnews.ca/baxter-admits-flu-product-contained-live-bird-flu-virus-1.374503

10. FiercePharma.com: Baxter: Vax products contained bird flu virus, 11 March 2009 http://www.fiercevaccines.com/story/baxter-vax-products-contained-bird-flu-virus/2009-03-11

11. Sam Marsden, Juliet Conway, Press Association/Independent, Swine flu outbreak cost UK £1.2 billion, 1 July 2010 http://www.independent.co.uk/life-style/health-and-families/health-news/swine-flu-outbreak-cost-uk-pound-12bn-2015429.html

12. Medicalxpress.com Kids' Swine flu shots recalled; not strong enough, 15 December 2009 https://medicalxpress.com/news/2009-12-kids-swine-flu-shots-recalled.html

13. Boston.com, Kids' Swine flu shots recalled; not strong enough, 15 December 2009 http://archive.boston.com/news/health/articles/2009/12/15/kids_swine_flu_shots_recalled_not_strong_enough/

14. CDC: Summary of 2009 monovalent H1N1 vaccine data – vaccine adverse events reporting system, data through November 2009 http://vaers.hhs.gov/resources/2009H1N1Summary_Nov25.pdf

15. Haruka Nakada et al, Risk of Fatal Adverse Events after H1N1 Influenza Vaccination, *Clin Infect Dis* (2010) 50 (11): 1548-1549. https://academic.oup.com/cid/article-lookup/doi/10.1086/652719

16. Wow.com: 2009 flu pandemic vaccine http://www.wow.com/wiki/2009_flu_pandemic_vaccine#cite_note-75

17. Lakemedelsverket.se, A Swedish registry based cohort study provides strengthened evidence of an association between vaccination with Pandemrix and narco-

lepsy in children and adolescents March 29, 2011 http://www.lakemedelsverket.
se/english/All-news/NYHETER-2011/A-Swedish-registry-based-cohort-study-
provides-strengthened-evidence-of-an-association-between-vaccination-with-
Pandemrix-and-narcolepsy-in-children-and-adolescents-/

18. "Review Shows Safety of H1N1 Vaccine, Officials Say" *New York Times,* 4
December 2009. http://www.nytimes.com/2009/12/05/health/05flu.html

19. Transcript of virtual press conference with Dr Marie-Paule Kieny, Director,
Initiative for Vaccine Research World Health Organization. 19 November 2009
http://www.who.int/mediacentre/vpc_transcript_19_november_09_kieny.pdf?ua=1

20. NHS Choices: when to have vaccines http://www.nhs.uk/Conditions/vaccina-
tions/Pages/vaccination-schedule-age-checklist.aspx

21. Brain-Damaged UK Victims of Swine Flu Vaccine to Get £60 Million
Compensation, International Business Times, 2 March 2014 http://www.ibtimes.
co.uk/brain-damaged-uk-victims-swine-flu-vaccine-get-60-million-compensa-
tion-1438572)

22. Globalresearch.ca, If Vaccines Don't Cause Brain Damage, Why Is
GlaxoSmithKline Paying Out $63 Million to Vaccine Victims? http://www.
globalresearch.ca/if-vaccines-dont-cause-brain-damage-why-is-glaxosmithkline-
paying-out-63-million-to-vaccine-victims/5463716?print=1

23. Reuters, Insight – Evidence grows for narcolepsy link to GSK swine flu shot,
22 January 2013 http://uk.reuters.com/article/uk-narcolepsy-vaccine-pandem-
rix-idUKBRE90L07F20130122

24. European Medicines Agency, European Medicines Agency recommends re-
stricting use of Pandemrix 21 July 2011 http://www.ema.europa.eu/ema/index.
jsp%3Fcurl=pages/news_and_events/news/2011/07/news_detail_001312.
jsp%26murl=menus/news_and_events/news_and_events.jsp%26mid=W-
C0b01ac058004d5c1

25. Luisa Dillner, Is the government wrong about giving children the nasal spray
flu vaccine? Guardian, 5 October 2014 http://www.theguardian.com/lifeand-
style/2014/oct/05/government-wrong-nasal-spray-vaccine

26. Health Impact News, Guillain Barré Syndrome is #1 Side Effect of Vaccine
Injury Compensations due to Flu Shots http://healthimpactnews.com/2014/guil-
lain-barre-syndrome-is-1-side-effect-of-vaccine-injury-compensations-due-to-flu-
shots/#sthash.cxsqzfO6.dpuf

27. Irving Nachamkin et al, The *Journal of Infectious Diseases*, volume 198, issue 2,
2008, had been looking into 'Anti-Ganglioside Antibody Induction by Swine (A/
NJ/1976/H1N1) and Other Influenza Vaccines: Insights into Vaccine-Associated
Guillain-Barré Syndrome'. https://www.researchgate.net/profile/John_Iskander/
publication/51398909_Anti-Ganglioside_Antibody_Induction_by_Swine_
ANJ1976H1N1_and_Other_Influenza_Vaccines_Insights_into_Vaccine-
Associated_Guillain-Barre_Syndrome/links/564ca4ed08ae635cef2a7b52.pdf

Chapter 75

1. Vaccines for preventing influenza in healthy adults. The Cochrane Database of
Systematic Reviews. 1, 2006. http://www.cochrane.org/CD001269/ARI_vac-
cines-to-prevent-influenza-in-healthy-adults

2. Lone Simonsen et al, Impact of influenza vaccination upon seasonal mortality in the US elderly population, *Archives of Internal Medicine, 2 April 2005* http://jamanetwork.com/journals/jamainternalmedicine/fullarticle/486407

3. American Thoracic Society, Children Who Get Flu Vaccine Have Three Times Risk Of Hospitalization For Flu, Study Suggests *Science Daily May 20, 2009* https://www.sciencedaily.com/releases/2009/05/090519172045.htm

4. Kate Devlin, Swine flu: Ministers 'preparing to offload millions of unwanted vaccines', *Telegraph*, 9 Jan 2010 http://www.telegraph.co.uk/news/health/swine-flu/6952793/Swine-flu-Ministers-preparing-to-offload-millions-of-unwanted-vaccines.html

5. The Star.com, Indian health authorities grappling with deadly flu, 22 Feb 2015 http://www.thestar.com/news/world/2015/02/22/indian-health-authorities-grappling-with-deadly-flu.html

6. Times of India, H1N1: Lack of policy on vaccination raises concern, 23 Feb 2015 http://timesofindia.indiatimes.com/city/chennai/H1N1-Lack-of-policy-on-vaccination-raises-concern/articleshow/46336692.cms

7. Parliamentary Assembly (PACE), The handling of the H1N1 pandemic: more transparency needed, provisional version http://assembly.coe.int/CommitteeDocs/2010/20100604_H1N1pandemic_e.pdf

8. Fiona Godlee, Conflicts of interest and pandemic flu, BMJ, 4 June 2010 http://www.bmj.com/content/340/bmj.c2947

9. Swine flu advisers' ties to drug firms, *Daily Mail*, 13 Aug 2010 http://www.dailymail.co.uk/health/article-1302505/WHO-swine-flu-advisers-ties-drug-firms-Experts-linked-vaccine-producers.html

10. Tom Jefferson, Of influenza, flu, potions and key opinion leaders, *The Conversation*, 2 June 2013 http://theconversation.com/of-influenza-flu-potions-and-key-opinion-leaders-14003

11. Chris Del Mar, The Tamiflu saga shows why all research data should be public, *The Conversation*, 4 June 2013 https://theconversation.com/the-tamiflu-saga-shows-why-all-research-data-should-be-public-13951

Chapter 76

1. Lucija Tomljenovic, PhD, The vaccination policy and the Code of Practice of the Joint Committee on Vaccination and Immunisation (JCVI): are they at odds? *BSEM* March 2011 The Health Hazards of Disease Prevention https://nsnbc.me/wp-content/uploads/2013/05/BSEM-2011.pdf

2. Wakefield, Andrew J., Callous Disregard: Autism and Vaccines – The Truth behind a Tragedy, Skyhorse Publishing, New York, 2011, ch. 3

3. Polly Tommey, "Discredited Defamation of Dr. Andrew Wakefield", *Age of Autism* http://www.ageofautism.com/2010/01/polly-tommey-of-autism-file-magazine-on-discredited-defamation-of-dr-andrew-wakefield.html

4. Oxford Vaccine Group, Department of Paediatrics: https://www.paediatrics.ox.ac.uk/research/vaccine-and-infectious-diseases-research

5. Martha Rosenberg, The FDA now officially belongs to Big Pharma, Alternet.org, 24 Feb 2016 http://www.alternet.org/news-amp-politics/fda-now-officially-belongs-big-pharma

6. Sabrina Tavernise, F.D.A. Nominee Califf's Ties to Drug Makers Worry Some, New York Times, 19 Sept 2015 https://www.nytimes.com/2015/09/20/health/fda-nominee-califfs-ties-to-drug-industry-raise-questions.html?_r=0

Chapter 77
1. Cathereine O'Driscoll, Star-spangled Spangler, *Dogs Today*, June 2006 http://chchealth.weebly.com/uploads/3/0/3/6/3036695/vaccines_2.pdf
2. Hsin-Yi Cohen, A Shot in the Dark, *Dogs Today*, Nov 2006 http://chchealth.weebly.com/uploads/3/0/3/6/3036695/dogs_today_lepto_article_nov_2006.pdf
3. Defra Zoonosis Report, UK 2012 https://www.gov.uk/government/uploads/system/uploads/attachment_data/file/236983/pb13987-zoonoses-report-2012.pdf
4. Public Health England PHE Surveillance Report (Summary) Report no 4 (Summary) Covering period 20.02.14 (00:01) to 24.02.14 (23:59) https://www.gov.uk/government/uploads/system/uploads/attachment_data/file/390489/Summary_Surveillance_report_4_FINAL_20140226_.pdf
5. Gov.uk, The characteristics, diagnosis and epidemiology of infections caused by spirochaetes of the genus Leptospira (Leptospires). 19 December 2016 https://www.gov.uk/leptospirosis

Chapter 79
1. Singh VK, Warren RP, Odell JD, Warren WL, Cole P. Antibodies to myelin basic protein in children with autistic behavior. *Brain Behav Immun.* 1993 Mar;7(1):97-103.
2. Mostafa GA, El-Sayed ZA, El-Aziz MM, El-Sayed MF Serum anti-myelin-associated glycoprotein antibodies in Egyptian autistic children.. *J Child Neurol.* 2008 Dec;23(12):1413-8.
3. Weizman A, Weizman R, Szekely GA, Wijsenbeek H, Livni E Abnormal immune response to brain tissue antigen in the syndrome of autism.. *Am J Psychiatry.* 1982 Nov;139(11):1462-5.

The following seem potentially relevant to individuals with aluminium hypersensitivity and/or weak alleles which participate in aluminium detoxification (clearance):
4. *Frontiers in Neurology* doi: 10.3389
5. *Journal of Medical Case Reports* February 10, 2104
6. *Medical News Today* February 13, 2014
7. *Journal of Alzheimer's Disease* 2010;20(1):17-30
8. *Aljazeera* October 6, 2014
9. *New England Journal of Medicine* September 4, 2014; 371:973-974
10. Evans PH, Yano E, Klinowski J, Peterhans, Oxidative damage in Alzheimer's dementia, and the potential etiopathogenic role of aluminosilicates, microglia and micronutrient interactions. Cornucopia Institute October 6, 2014, E. EXS. 1992;62:178-89. Review.
11. Shigematsu K, McGeer PL, Accumulation of amyloid precursor protein in damaged neuronal processes and microglia following intracerebral administration of aluminum salts.. *Brain Res.* 1992 Oct 9;593(1):117-23
12. Verstraeten SV, Golub MS, Keen CL, Oteiza PI. Arch Biochem Biophys, Myelin

is a preferential target of aluminum-mediated oxidative damage. 1997 Aug 15;344(2):289-94.

13. Itoh M, Suzuki Y, Sugai K, Kozuka N, Ohsawa M, Otsuki T, Goto Y. Progressive leukoencephalopathy associated with aluminum deposits in myelin sheath. *J Child Neurol*. 2008 Aug;23(8):938-43

14. Bergfors E, Björkelund C, Trollfors B. Nineteen cases of persistent pruritic nodules and contact allergy to aluminium after injection of commonly used aluminium-adsorbed vaccines. *Eur J Pediatr*. 2005 Nov;164(11):691-7

Chapter 82

1. Harry Yorke, Dog owners' concerns over dog deaths, *Telegraph* 2 July 2016 http://www.telegraph.co.uk/news/2016/07/02/dogs-dying-after-having-protective-vaccine-owners-claim/

2. Catherine O'Driscoll, WSAVA new puppy vaccine guidelines, WSAVA www.petwelfarealliance.org/uploads/3/0/3/6/3036695/new_puppy_owner_vaccination_guidelines_may_2013.pdf

Chapter 85

1. NOAH issues statement on canine vaccination – only a press statement. The NOAH statement on canine vaccination itself has been taken down. http://www.noah.co.uk/noah-issues-statement-canine-vaccination/. Contact NOAH's press office; they might let you see it.

2. Ajay R Bharti, Leptospirosis: a zoonotic disease of global importance, *Lancet*, Infectious Diseases Volume 3, No. 12, p757–771, December 2003

3. MSD, CICADA – The companion animal disease survey http://uk.cicadasurvey.com

4. Dana Scott, Leptospirosis Vaccine Protection And Dogs: What You Need To Know, Dogs Naturally http://www.dogsnaturallymagazine.com/leptospirosis-vaccine-protection-and-dogs-what-you-need-to-know/

5. Andre-Fontaine G, Branger C, Gray AW, et al. Comparison of the efficacy of three commercial bacterins in preventing canine leptospirosis. Vet Rec 153:165-169, 2003.

6. Patricia Jordan DVM, Smoke and Mirrors, the problem with the leptospirosis vaccine, *Dogs Naturally*, March/April 2010 http://www.dogsnaturallymagazine.com/leptospirosis-vaccine/

7. Tomljenovic L1, Shaw CA, Mechanisms of aluminum adjuvant toxicity and autoimmunity in pediatric populations. Lupus February 2012 vol. 21 no. 2 223-230 https://www.ncbi.nlm.nih.gov/pubmed/22235057

8. This web link is no longer available. The VMD should be able to furnish enquirers with a copy. Email postmaster@vmd.defra.qsi.gov.uk

Chapter 86

1. Julie E. Martin et al, A DNA Vaccine for Ebola Virus Is Safe and Immunogenic in a Phase I Clinical Trial, *Clin Vaccine Immunol*. 2006 Nov; 13(11): 1267–1277. https://www.ncbi.nlm.nih.gov/pmc/articles/PMC1656552/

2. A notice by the National Institutes of Health, Prospective Grant of Exclusive

License: Multivalent Vaccines for Rabies Virus and Ebola and Marburg (Filoviruses) https://www.federalregister.gov/articles/2014/03/31/2014-07023/prospective-grant-of-exclusive-license-multivalent-vaccines-for-rabies-virus-and-ebola-and-marburg

3. Leonard P. Ruiz: "Age Dependence of the Risk of Intussusception Following Tetravalent Rhesus-Human Reassortant Rotavirus Tetravalent Vaccine: Is it Beyond Doubt?" *Am J Epidemiol* (2010) 172 (7): 864. 2 Aug 2010 http://aje.oxfordjournals.org/content/172/7/864.1.full

4. NHS Choices: Diarrhoea and vomiting (gastroenteritis) http://www.nhs.uk/conditions/rotavirus-gastroenteritis/Pages/Introduction.aspx#close

5. Gov.uk New vaccine to help protect babies against rotavirus https://www.gov.uk/government/news/new-vaccine-to-help-protect-babies-against-rotavirus

6. Sayer Ji, Rotavirus Vaccines Still Contaminated With Pig Virus DNA, greenmedinfo.com 30 March 2010 http://www.greenmedinfo.com/blog/rotavirus-vaccines-still-contamined-pig-virus-dna

7. George E. Armah, Albert Z. Kapikian, Timo Vesikari, Nigel Cunliffe, Robert M. Jacobson, D. Bruce Burlington, and Leonard P. Ruiz, Jr, Efficacy, Immunogenicity, and Safety of Two Doses of a Tetravalent Rotavirus Vaccine RRV-TV in Ghana With the First Dose Administered During the Neonatal Period, *J Infect Dis.* 2013 Aug 1; 208(3): 423–431 http://www.ncbi.nlm.nih.gov/pmc/articles/PMC3699001/

8. Rotavirus Vaccine: NIH Office of Technology Transfer https://www.ott.nih.gov/sites/default/files/documents/pdfs/casestudy13.pdf

9. Opinion by Dr. Roger I. Glass, Fogarty International Center New Indian rotavirus vaccine provides hope, May / June 2013 | Volume 12, Issue 3 letter [PDF 4.9M] http://www.fic.nih.gov/news/globalhealthmatters/may-june-2013/pages/roger-glass-opinion-rotavirus-vaccine.aspx

10. ClinicalTrials.gov, A Phase III Clinical Trial to Evaluate the Protective Efficacy of Three Doses of Oral Rotavirus Vaccine (ORV) 116E (ROTAVAC) https://www.clinicaltrials.gov/ct2/show/NCT01305109?term=NCT01305109&rank=1

11. Leonard P Ruiz Inventprise consultant, http://inventprise.com/whoweare2.html

Chapter 87

1. Jon Cohen, Ebola vaccines racing forward at record pace, *Sciencemag.org* Sep. 9, 2014 http://news.sciencemag.org/health/2014/09/ebola-vaccines-racing-forward-record-pace

2. National Institute of Allergy and Infectious Disease, Vaccine Research Center Mission and History https://www.niaid.nih.gov/about/vaccine-research-center-mission-and-history

3. Patent, Human Ebola virus species and compositions and methods thereof CA 2741523 A1 http://www.google.com/patents/CA2741523A1?cl=en

4. The Common Sense Show.com, The CDC, NIH & Bill Gates Own the Patents On Existing Ebola & Related Vaccines: Mandatory Vaccinations Are Near http://www.thecommonsenseshow.com/2014/09/17/the-cdc-nih-bill-gates-own-the-patents-on-existing-ebola-related-vaccines-mandatory-vaccinations-are-near/

5. Horowitz, Leonard G., DMD, Emerging Viruses: AIDS & Ebola: Nature,

Accident or Intentional?, Medical Veritas, 1996, ch. 2,http://www.bibliotecap-leyades.net/ciencia/ciencia_viruses02.htm

6   Tizard, Ian, Risks associated with use of live vaccines, *Veterinary Medical Association*, Vol 196, No. 11, pages 1851-1858 https.//www.ncbi.nlm.nih.gov/pubmed/2190963

7.   Seigl G. Canine parvovirus, Origin and significance of a new pathogen. In: Bers Kl, ed The Parvovoruses, New York: Plenum Press, 1984;363-387.

8.   Parrish CR, Aquadro CF, Carmichael LE. Canine host range and specific epitope map along with variant sequences in the capsid protein gene of canine parvovirus and related feline, mink and raccoon parvoviruses. *Virology* 1988;166:293-307.

9.   "Hemorrhagic fever viruses as biological weapons: medical and public health management". *Journal of the American Medical Association* 287 (18): 2391–405. doi:10.1001/jama.287.18.2391. PMID 11988060. May 2002.

10.   Salvaggio MR, Baddley JW (July 2004). "Other viral bioweapons: Ebola and Marburg hemorrhagic fever". *Dermatologic clinics* 22 (3): 291–302, vi. doi:10.1016/j.det.2004.03.003. PMID 15207310.

11.   Zubray, Geoffrey (2013). Agents of Bioterrorism: Pathogens and Their Weaponization. New York, NY, USA: Columbia University Press. pp. 73–74. ISBN 9780231518130.

12.   Jim Robbins, The ecology of disease, New York Times, 14 July 2012 http://www.nytimes.com/2012/07/15/sunday-review/the-ecology-of-disease.html?pagewanted=all&_r=0

13.   Aid worker security database https://aidworkersecurity.org/incidents/report/summary

14.   David Scales, At Least Nine Polio Workers Killed in Nigeria, Disease Daily, 11 Feb 2013 http://healthmap.org/site/diseasedaily/article/least-nine-polio-workers-killed-nigeria-21113

15.   Harriet A Washington, Why Africa Fears Western Medicine, NY Times, 31 July 2007 http://www.nytimes.com/2007/07/31/opinion/31washington.html?_r=1&

16.   Horowitz, op. cit., ch. 3, http://www.bibliotecapleyades.net/ciencia/ciencia_viruses03.htm

17.   Pilger, John, *The New Rulers of the World*, Verso, London, 2002, 2003, pp. 69, 71

18.   Horowitz, ch 2 http://www.bibliotecapleyades.net/ciencia/ciencia_viruses02.htm

19.   Norman M Covert, *Cutting Edge, a history of Fort Detrick*, 1993 https://archive.org/details/cuttingedgeahist00fort

20.   Medical Research Council, Patent: Improvements relating to influenza vaccine WO 1986004242 A1 https://google.com/patents/WO1986004242A1?cl=pt

21.   Ethan A. Huff, CDC owns patent on Ebola virus; agency to collect royalties on all future Ebola vaccines, *NaturalNews*, September 19, 2014 http://www.natural-news.com/046941_Ebola_virus_patents_vaccines.html

22.   Patent: Human Ebola virus species and compositions and methods thereof https://www.google.com/patents/CA2741523A1?cl=en

23.   Anne Dachel, 7 Minutes on CDD, Age of Autism http://www.ageofautism.com/2017/01/7-minutes-on-cdc.html

24.   Government Statement in response to investigations into the probable release of FMD virus from Pirbright http://webarchive.nationalarchives.gov.

uk/20130402151656/http://archive.defra.gov.uk/foodfarm/farmanimal/diseases/atoz/fmd/documents/govstatement_fmd2007.pdf

25. Foot & Mouth, caused by government, still suffered by farmers, *Prison Planet Forum*, 18 October 2009 http://forum.prisonplanet.com/index.php?topic=140624.0

26. David Schley, Laura Burgin, John Gloster, Predicting infection risk of airborne foot-and-mouth disease, *Jnl Royal Soc Interface*, 29 August 2008. DOI: 10.1098/rsif.2008.0306 http://rsif.royalsocietypublishing.org/content/6/34/455

27. World Population: The Silent Explosion. Department of State Bulletin, Fall 1978. http://rsif.royalsocietypublishing.org/content/6/34/455

28. National Security Study Memorandum NSSM 200: Implications of Worldwide Population Growth For US Security and Overseas Interests (The Kissinger Report), December 10, 1974 https://pdf.usaid.gov/pdf_docs/PCAAB500.pdf

29. Horowitz, op. cit., ch. 10, pp. 177-78

Chapter 88

1. ibid ch 87 ref 24

2. Foot-and-mouth cover-up claims dismissed, Mail Online http://www.dailymail.co.uk/news/article-32268/Foot-mouth-cover-claims-dismissed.html

3. Ibid ch 87 ref 26

4. Ian Sample, Revealed: 100 safety breaches at UK labs handling potentially deadly diseases, Guardian, 4 Dec 2014 http://www.theguardian.com/science/2014/dec/04/-sp-100-safety-breaches-uk-labs-potentially-deadly-diseases

5. David Wahlberg, UW-Madison flu studies raise risk more than prevent it, biosafety panelist says, Madison.com, 29 Jun 2014 http://host.madison.com/news/local/health_med_fit/uw-madison-flu-studies-raise-risk-more-than-prevent-it/article_c4fb6927-e6de-5162-a276-48c4603213fa.html#ixzz3D6T3gUHT

6. David Wahlberg, UW steps up bio research safety, Madison.com, 21 Feb 2012 http://host.madison.com/news/local/education/university/uw-steps-up-bio-research-safety/article_3320c7cd-0cda-5fbc-9b9a-f3921231705c.html

7. Erin Elizabeth, 30 Million Dead: Bill Gates Sees a Genetically Engineered Bioweapon Triggering the Next Global Pandemic, HealthNut News, 16 Mar 2017http://www.healthnutnews.com/30-million-dead-bill-gates-sees-genetically-engineered-bioweapon-triggering-next-global-pandemic/

8. Report by the Policy Planning Staff , TOP SECRET, [Washington,] February 24, 1948. Review of Current Trends U.S. Foreign Policy https://www.scribd.com/document/29552945/George-Kennan-Policy-Paper-23

9. Pilger, John, The New Rulers of the World, Verso, London, 2002, 2003, pp. 69, 71

10. Future of Healthcare Investor Forum Highlights Investment Opportunity in UK Life Sciences, UK BioIndustry Association, 29th January 2015 http://www.bioindustry.org/newsandresources/bia-news/future-of-healthcare-investor-forum/

Chapter 89

1. Paola Scommegna, Clean Water's Historic Effect on U.S. Mortality Rates Provides Hope for Developing Countries, Population Reference Bureau, May 2005 http://www.prb.org/Publications/Articles/2005/

CleanWatersHistoricEffectonUSMortalityRates
ProvidesHopeforDevelopingCountries.aspx

2. David Cutler, Grant Miller, The Role Of Public Health Improvements In Health Advances: The 20th Century United States, National Bureau of Economic Research, May 2004 http://www.nber.org/papers/w10511.pdf

3. World Economic Forum, Access to simple technologies can reduce poverty, 17 Oct 2002 https://www.weforum.org/agenda/2012/10/access-to-simple-technolo-gies-can-reduce-poverty/

4. Oxfam, Even it Up: Time to end extreme inequality, 29 Oct 2014 http://poli-cy-practice.oxfam.org.uk/publications/even-it-up-time-to-end-extreme-inequali-ty-333012

5. Guest post: time to tackle inequality, *Financial Times* https://www.ft.com/con-tent/45dba5d9-521d-3f8b-a6e5-9f512f96b771

6. Simon Bowers, French legal firebrand turns her attention to corridors of power, Guardian, 4 Feb 2011 http://www.theguardian.com/business/2011/feb/04/eva-jo-ly-interview

7. Scott Carney, Testing Drugs on India's Poor, Wired.com, 19 Dec 2005 http://ar-chive.wired.com/medtech/drugs/news/2005/12/69595?currentPage=all

8. Andrew Buncombe, Nina Lakhani, Without Consent: how drug companies ex-ploit Indian 'guinea pigs', Independent, 14 Nov 2011http://www.independent.co.uk/news/world/asia/without-consent-how-drugs-companies-exploit-indi-an-guinea-pigs-6261919.html

9. Helsinki Declaration https://www.wma.net/policies-post/wma-declaration-of-hel-sinki-ethical-principles-for-medical-research-involving-human-subjects/

10. Miloud Kaddar, Health Economist, WHO, IVB, Geneva, Presentation http://who.int/influenza_vaccines_plan/resources/session_10_kaddar.pdf

11. Stein, R. Medical Groups Promoted HPV Vaccine Using Funds Provided by Drugmaker. *The Washington Post.* 19 August 2009 http://www.washingtonpost.com/wp-dyn/content/article/2009/08/18/AR2009081803325.html

12. Judicial Watch.org press releases http://www.judicialwatch.org/blog/tag/gardasil/

13. Savita Verma, Indian Council of Medical Research endorsed 'illegal' US vaccine, *Mail Online India*, 30 Aug 2003 http://www.dailymail.co.uk/indiahome/indian-ews/article-2407569/Indian-Council-Medical-Research-endorsed-illegal-US-vaccine.html

14. Bill Gates Funded Group Accused of Breaking Law in HPV Vaccine Trials in India Resulting in Fatalities, HealthImpact News http://healthimpactnews.com/2013/bill-gates-funded-group-accused-of-breaking-law-in-hpv-vaccine-tri-als-in-india-resulting-in-fatalities/

15. Parliament of India: Alleged Irregularities in the Conduct of Studies us-ing Human Papilloma Virus (HPV) Vaccine by Path in India (Department of Health Research, Ministry of Health and Family Welfare) 30 Aug 2013 http://164.100.47.5/newcommittee/reports/EnglishCommittees/Committee%20on%20Health%20and%20Family%20Welfare/72.pdf

16. Statement from PATH: cervical cancer demonstration project in India, 3 Sep 2013 http://www.path.org/news/press-room/642/

17. Reuters: Special Report: Food, beverage industry pays for seat at health-policy

table http://www.reuters.com/article/2012/10/19/us-obesity-who-industry-idUS-BRE89I0K620121019

Chapter 90
1. *Journal of Clinical and Vaccine Immunology*, Aug. 2006, p. 821–829 Vol. 13, No 8; http://cvi.asm.org/content/13/8/821
2. SumofUs.org petition to the UK government, updated Dec 2014 https://actions.sumofus.org/a/weapons-NHS
3. *Private Eye.* "Rothermere's patriot games"
4. http://www.rollingstone.com/politics/news/inside-the-koch-brothers-toxic-empire-20140924

Chapter 91
1. Andrew Maniotis PhD, How to Predict Epidemics http://www.ddponline.org/epidemics.pdf
2. http://www.wma.net/en/30publications/10policies/b3/ (not available, not sure what it is)

Chapter 92
1. Paul Condon, et al, Meditation increases compassionate response to suffering, *Psychol Sci*, 21 Aug 2013 http://journals.sagepub.com/doi/abs/10.1177/0956797613485603
2. Helen Y Weng et al, Compassion training alters altruism and neural responses to suffering, *Psychol Sci.* 2013 Jul 1; 24(7): 1171–1180. Published online 2013 May 21. https://www.ncbi.nlm.nih.gov/pmc/articles/PMC3713090/
3. 30 States Move to Enact Vaccine Bills Including Tracking and Mandatory Vaccines, Vaccineimpact.com http://vaccineimpact.com/2017/30-states-move-to-enact-vaccine-bills-including-tracking-and-mandatory-vaccines/
4. Erin Elizabeth, Sweden Bans Mandatory Vaccinations Over 'Serious Health Concerns', 15 May 2017 http://www.healthnutnews.com/sweden-bans-mandatory-vaccinations-serious-heath-concerns/

Appendix 2

Vaccines and Unexplained Diseases:

1. Hiner, E E, Frasch, C E, "Spectrum of Disease Due to Haemophilus Influenza Type B Occurring in Vaccinated Children", J Infect Disorder, 1988 Aug; 158(2): 343-348.
2. Olin P, Romanus, V, Storsaeter, J, "Invasive Bacterial Infections During an Efficacy Trial of Acellular Pertussis Vaccines --Implications For Future Surveilance In Pertussis Vaccine Programmes", Tokai J Exp Clin Med, 1988; 13 Suppl: 143-144
3. Storsaeter, J, et al, "Mortality and Morbidity From Invasive Bacterial Infections During a Clinical Trial of Acellular Pertussis Vaccines in Sweden", Pediatr Infect Disorder J, 1988 Sept; 7(9):637-645.
4. Vadheim, CM, et al, "Effectiveness and Safety of an Haemophilus Influenzae type b Conjugate Vaccine (PRP-T) in Young Infants. Kaiser-UCLA Vaccine Study Group," Pediartics, 1993 Aug; 92(2):272-279. [The vaccines caused fevers, irritability, crying, and seizures, but were declared to be "safe and ... effective ... ".]
5. Stickl, H, "Estimation of Vaccination Damage", Med Welt, Oct 14, 1972, 23:1495-1497.
6. Waters, VV, et al, "Risk Factors for Measles in a Vaccinated Population", JAMA, Mar 27, 1991, 265(12): 1527.
7. Stickl, H, "Iatrogenic Immuno-suppression as a Result of Vaccination", Fortschr Med, Mar 5, 1981, 99(9);289-292.
8. Abnormal measles-mumps-rubella antibodies and CNS autoimmunity in children with autism. http://www.ncbi.nlm.nih.gov/pubmed/12145534
9. http://livelovefruit.com/still-vaccinating-25-questions-former-pro-vaccine-advocate/#UyQbscPYr3mmfkH2.99

Vaccines Cause the "Prevented" Disease:

1. Nkowane, et al, "Vaccine-Associated Paralytic Poliomyelitis, US 1973 through 1984, *JAMA*, 1987, Vol 257:1335-1340.
2. Quast, et al, "Vaccine Induced Mumps-like Diseases", nd, Int Symp on Immun, *Development Bio Stand*, Vol 43, p269-272.
3. Green, C et al, "A Case of Hepatitis Related to Etretinate Therapy and Hepatitis B Vaccine", *Dermatologica*, 1991, 182(2):119-120.
4. Shasby, DM, et al, "Epidemic Measles in Highly Vaccinated Population", *NEJM*, Mar 1977, 296(11): 585-589.
5. Tesovic, G et al, "Aseptic Meningitis after Measles, Mumps and Rubella Vaccine", *Lancet*, Jun 12, 1993, 341(8859):1541.
6. Johnson, RH, et al, "Nosocomial Vaccinia Infection", West J Med, Oct 1976, 125(4):266-270.
7. Malengreau, M, "Reappearance of Post-Vaccination Infection of Measles, Rubella, and Mumps. Should Adolescents be re-vaccinated?" *Pedaitric*, 1992;47(9):597-601 (25 ref)

8. Basa, SN, "Paralytic Poliomyelitis Following Inoculation With Combined DTP Prophylactic. A review of Sixteen cases with Special Reference to Immunization Schedules in Infancy", *J Indian Med Assoc*, Feb 1, 1973, 60:97-99.

9. Landrigan, PJ et al, "Measles in Previously Vaccinated Children in Illinois", Ill *Med J, Arp* 1974, 141:367-372.

10. NA, "Vaccine-Associated Poliomyelitis", *Med J Aust*, Oct 1973, 2:795-796.

Vaccine Failures:
1. Hardy, GE, Jr, et al, "The Failure of a School Immunization Campaign to Terminate an Urban Epidemic of Measles," Amer J Epidem, Mar 1970; 91:286-293.

2. Cherry, JD, et al, "A Clinical and Serologic Study of 103 Children With Measles Vaccine Failure", J Pediatr, May 1973; 82:801-808.

3. Jilg, W, et al, "Inoculation Failure Following Hepatitis B Vaccination", *Dtsch Med wochenschr*, 1990 Oct 12; 115(41):1514-1548.

4. Plotkin, SA, "Failures of Protection by Measles Vaccine," *J Pediatr,* May 1973; 82:798-801.

5. Bolotovskii, V, et al, "Measles Incidence Among Children Properly Vaccinated Against This Infection", ZH *Mikrobiol Epidemiol Immunobiol*, 1974; 00(5):32-35.

6. Landrigan, PJ, et al, "Measles in Previously Vaccinated Children in Illinois", Ill *Med J,* Apr 1974; 141:367-372.

7. Strebel, P et al, "An Outbreak of Whooping Cough in a Highly Vaccinated Urban Community", *J Trop Pediatr*, Mar 1991, 37(2): 71-76.

8. Forrest, JM, et al, "Failure of Rubella Vaccination to Prevent Congenital Rubella," *Med J Aust*, 1977 Jan 15; 1(3): 77.

9. Jilg, W, "Unsuccessful Vaccination against Hepatitis B", *Dtsch Med Wochenschr*, Nov 16, 1990, 115(46):1773.

10. Coles, FB, et al, "An Outbreak of Influenza A (H3N2) in a Well-Immunized Nursing home Population," *J Am ger Sociologist*, Jun 1992, 40(6):589-592.

11. Jilg, W, et al, "Inoculation Failure following Hepatitis B Vaccination," *Dtsch Med Wochenschr*, Oct 12, 1990, 115(41):1545-1548.

12. Hartmann, G et al, "Unsuccessful Inoculation against Hepatitis B," *Dtsch Med Wochenschr*, May 17, 1991, 116(20): 797.

13. Buddle, BM et al, "Contagious Ecthyma Virus-Vaccination Failures", *Am J Vet Research*, Feb 1984, 45(2):263-266.

14. Mathias, R G, "Whooping Cough In Spite of Immunization", *Can J Pub Health*, 1978 Mar/Apr; 69(2):130-132.

15. Osterholm, MT, et al, "Lack of Efficacy of Haemophilus b Polysacharide Vaccine in Minnesota", *JAMA*, 1988 Sept 9; 260(10:1423-1428.

16. Johnson, RH, et al, "Nosocomial Vaccinia Infection", West *J Med*, Oct 1976, 125(4):266-270.

17. Favez, G, "Tuberculous Superinfection Following a Smallpox Re-Vaccination", Praxis, July 21, 1960; 49:698-699.

18. Gilchrist, A, "To Vaccinate is Not Always to Immunize", Med J Aust, May 6, 1991, 154(9):638.

19. Daniel, J C, "The Polio Paradox, One of the Two Polio Vaccines Has Been Largely Abandoned in the US; The other is the Leading Cause of the Disease", Science, April 1986, p 37-39.
20. http://www.greenmedinto.com/blog/vaccines-dont-work malig nant-mumps-mmr-vaccinated-children-12

Vaccines Causing Another Vaccinal Disease:
1. Basa, SN, "Paralytic Poliomyelitis Following Inoculation With Combined DTP Prophylactic. A review of Sixteen cases with Special Reference to Immunization Schedules in Infancy", *J Indian Med Assoc*, Feb 1, 1973, 60:97-99.
2. Pathel, JC, et al, "Tetanus Following Vaccination Against Small-pox", *J Pediatr*, Jul 1960; 27:251-263.
3. Favez, G, "Tuberculous Superinfection Following a Smallpox Re-Vaccination", *Praxis*, July 21, 1960; 49:698-699.
4. Quast, Ute, and Hennessen, "Vaccine-Induced Mumps-like Diseases", Intern Symp on Immunizations , *Development Bio Stand*, Vol 43, p 269-272.
5. Forrest, J M, et al, "Clinical Rubella Eleven months after Vaccination," *Lancet,* Aug 26, 1972, 2:399-400.
6. Dittman, S, "Atypical Measles after Vaccination", *Beitr Hyg Epidemiol*, 19891, 25:1-274 (939 ref)
7. Sen S, et al, "Poliomyelitis in Vaccinated Children", *Indian Pediatr*, May 1989, 26(5): 423-429.
8. Arya, SC, "Putative Failure of Recombinant DNA Hepatitis B Vaccines", *Vaccine*, Apr 1989, 7(2): 164-165.
9. Lawrence, R et al, "The Risk of Zoster after Varicella Vaccination in Children with Leukemia", *NEJM*, Mar 3, 1988, 318(9): 543-548.

Vaccines and Death:
1. Na, "DPT Vaccination and Sudden Infant Death – Tennessee, US Dept HEW, MMWR Report, Mar 23, 1979, vol 28(11): 132.
2. Arevalo, "Vaccinia Necrosum. Report on a Fatal Case", Bol Ofoc Sanit Panamer, Aug 1967, 63:106-110.
3. Connolly, J H, Dick, G W, Field, CM, "A Case of Fatal Progressive Vaccinia", Brit Med Jour, 12 May 1962; 5288:1315-1317.
4. Aragona, F, "Fatal Acute Adrenal Insufficiency Caused by Bilateral Apoplexy of the Adrenal Glands (WFS) following Anti-poliomyelitis Vaccination", Minerva Medicolegale, Aug 1960; 80:167-173.
5. Moblus, G et al, "Pathological-Anatomical Findings in Cases of Death Following Poliomyelitis and DPT Vaccination", Dtsch Gesundheitsw, Jul 20, 1972, 27:1382-1386.
6. NA, "Immunizations and Cot Deaths", Lancet, Sept 25, 1982, np.
7. Goetzeler, A, "Fatal Encephalitis after Poliomyelitis Vaccination", 22 Jun 1961, Muenchen Med Wschr, 102:1419-1422.
8. Fulginiti, V, "Sudden Infant Death Syndrome, Diphtheria-Tetanus Toxoid-Pertussis Vaccination and Visits to the Doctor: Chance Association or Cause and Effect?", Pediatr Infect Disorder, Jan-Feb 1983, 2(1): 7-11.

9. Baraff, LJ, et al, "Possible Temporal Association Between Diphtheria-tetanus toxoid-Pertussis Vaccination and Sudden Infant Death Syndrome", Pediatr Infect Disorder, Jan-Feb 1983, 2(1): 5-6.
10. Reynolds, E, "Fatal Outcome of a Case of Eczema Vaccinatum", Lancet, 24 Sept 1960, 2:684-686.
11. Apostolov. et al, "Death of an Infant in Hyperthermia After Vaccination", J Clin Path, Mar 1961, 14:196-197.
12. Bouvier-Colle, MH, "Sex-Specific Differences in Mortality After High-Titre Measles Vaccination", Rev Epidemiol Sante Publique, 1995; 43(1): 97.
13. Stewart GT, "Deaths of infants after triple vaccine.", Lancet 1979 Aug 18;2(8138):354-355.
14. Flahault A, "Sudden infant death syndrome and diphtheria/tetanus toxoid/pertussis/poliomyelitis immunisation.", Lancet 1988 Mar 12;1(8585):582-583.
15. Larbre, F et al, "Fatal Acute Myocarditis After Smallpox Vaccination", Pediatrie, Apr-May 1966, 21:345-350.
16. Mortimer EA Jr, "DTP and SIDS: when data differ", Am J Public Health 1987 Aug; 77(8):925-926.

Vaccines and Metabolism:

1. Deutsch J, " [Temperature changes after triple-immunization in infant age]," Padiatr Grenzgeb 1976;15(1):3-6. [Article in German]
2. NA, "[Temperature changes after triple immunization in childhood]," Padiatr Grenzgeb 1976;15(1):7-10. [Article in German] Considering that the thyroid controls our Basal Metabolism, it would appear that vaccines altered (depressed) thyroid activity.]

Vaccines Altering Resistance to Disease:

1. Burmistrova AL, "Change in the non-specific resistance of the body to influenza and acute respiratory diseases following immunization diphtheria-tetanus vaccine," Zh Mikrobiol *Epidemiol Immunobiol* 1976; (3):89-91. [Article in Russian]

Vaccines and Kidney Disorders:

2. Jacquot, C et al, "Renal Risk in Vaccination", *Nouv Presse Med*, Nov 6, 1982, 11(44):3237-3238.
3. Giudicelli, et al, "Renal Risk in Vaccination", *Presse Med*, Jun 11, 1982, 12(25):1587-1590.
4. Tan, SY, et al, "Vaccine Related Glomerulonephritis", *BMJ*, Jan 23, 1993, 306(6872):248.
5. Pillai, JJ, et al, "Renal Involvement in Association with Post-vaccination Varicella", *Clin Infect Disorder*, Dec 1993, 17(6): 1079-1080.
6. Eisinger, AJ et al, "Acute Renal Failure after TAB and Cholera Vaccination", *B Med J*, Feb 10, 1979, 1(6160):381-382.
7. Silina, ZM, et al, "Causes of Postvaccinal Complications in the Kidneys in Young Infants", *Pediatria*, Dec 1978, (12):59-61.
8. Na, "Albuminurias", *Concours Med*, Mar 1964, 85:5095-5098. [vaccination adverse reactions]

9. Oyrl, A, et al, "Can Vaccinations Harm the Kidney?", *Clin Nephrol*, 1975, 3(5):204-205.
10. Mel'man Nia, "[Renal lesions after use of vaccines and sera]." *Vrach Delo* 1978 Oct;(10):67-9, [Article in Russian]
11. Silina ZM, Galaktionova TIa, Shabunina NR, "[Causes of postvaccinal complications in the kidneys in young infants]." *Pediatriia* 1978 Dec;(12):59-61, [Article in Russian]
12. Silina EM, et al, "[Some diseases of the kidneys in children during the 1st year of life, following primary smallpox vaccination and administration of pertusis-diphtheria-tetanus vaccine]." *Vopr Okhr Materin Det* 1968 Mar; 13(3):79-80, [Article in Russian]

Vaccines and Skin Disorders:

1. Illingsworth R, "Skin rashes after triple vaccine," Arch Dis Child 1987 Sep; 62(9):979.
2. Lupton GP, "Discoid lupus erythematosus occurring in a smallpox vaccination scar," *J Am Acad Dermatol*, 1987 Oct; 17(4):688-690.
3. Kompier, A J, "Some Skin Diseases caused by Vaccinia Virus [Smallpox]," *Ned Milt Geneesk* T, 15:149-157, May 1962.
4. Weber, G et al, "Skin Lesions Following Vaccinations," *Deutsch Med Wschr*, 88:1878-1886, S7 Sept 1963.
5. Copeman, P W, "Skin Complications of Smallpox Vaccination," *Practitioner*, 197:793-800, Dec 1966.
6. Denning, DW, et al, "Skin Rashes After Triple Vaccine," *Arch Disorder Child*, May 1987, 62(5): 510-511.
7. Sterler, HC, et al, "Outbreaks of Group A Steptococcal Abcesses Following DTP Vaccination", Pediatrics, Feb 1985, 75(2):299-303.
8. DiPiramo, D, et al, "Abcess Formation at the Site of Inoculation of Calmette-Guerin Bacillus (BCG)," Riv Med Aeronaut Spaz, Jul-Dec 1981, 46(3-4):190-199.
9. Edwards, K, "Danger of Sunburn Following Vaccination", Papua New Guinea Med J, Dec 1977, 20(4):203.

Vaccines and Shock:

1. Caileba, A et al, "Shock associated with Disseminated Intravascular Coagulation Syndrome following Injection of DT.TAB Vaccine, *Prese Med*, Sept 15, 1984, 13(3):1900.

Various Citations:

1. Pathel, JC, et al, "Tetanus Following Vaccination Against Small-pox", *J Pediatr*, Jul 1960; 27:251-263.
2. Bonifacio, A et al, "Traffic Accidents as an expression of "Iatrogenic damage", *Minerva Med,* Feb 24, 1971, 62:735-740. [But officer I was just vaccinated!]
3. Baker, J et al, "Accidental Vaccinia: Primary Inoculation of a Scrotum", *Clin Pediatr (Phila)*, Apr 1972, 11:244-245.
4. Stroder, J, "Incorrect Therapy in Children", *Folia Clin Int (Barc)*, Feb 1966, 16:82-90. [Agreed.]

5. Wehrle PF, "Injury associated with the use of vaccines," *Clin Ther* 1985;7(3):282-284.
6. Alberts ME, "When and where will it stop", Iowa Med 1986 Sep; 76(9):424. [When!]
7. Breiman RF, Zanca JA, "Of floors and ceilings--defining, assuring, and communicating vaccine safety", *Am J Public Health* 1997 Dec;87(12):1919-1920.
8. Stewart, AM, et al, "Aetiology of Childhood Leukaemia", *Lancet*, 16 Oct, 1965, 2:789-790.
9. Nelson, ST, "John Hutchinson On Vaccination Syphilis (Hutchinson, J)", *Arch Derm*, (Chic), May 1969, 99:529-535.
10. Mather, C, "Cotton Mather Anguishes Over the Consequences of His Son's Inoculation Against Smallpox", *Pediatrics*, May 1974; 53:756.
11. Thoman M, "The Toxic Shot Syndrome", *Vet Hum Toxicol*, Apr 1986, 28(2):163-166. Johnson, RH, et al, "Nosocomial Vaccinia Infection", *West J Med*, Oct 1976, 125(4):266-270.
12. Heed, JR, "Human Immunization With Rabies Vaccine in Suckling Mice Brain," *Salud Publica*, May-Jun 1974, 16(3): 469-480.
13. Tesovic, G et al, "Aseptic Meningitis after Measles, Mumps and Rubella Vaccine", *Lancet*, Jun 12, 1993, 341(8859):1541. [AM has same symptoms as poliomyelitis!]
14. Buddle, BM et al, "Contagious Ecthyma Virus-Vaccination Failures", *Am J Vet Research*, Feb 1984, 45(2):263-266.
15. Freter, R et al, "Oral Immunization And Production of Coproantibody in Human Volunteers", *J Immunol*, Dec 1963, 91:724-729. [copro = Feces]
16. NA, "Vaccination, For and Against", 1964, *Belg T Geneesk*, 20:125-130
17. Sahadevan, MG et al, "Post-vaccinal Myelitis", *J Indian Med Ass*, Feb 16, 1966, 46:205-206.
18. Castan, P et al, "Coma Revealing an acute Leukosis in a child, 15 days after an Oral Anti-poliomyelitis Vaccination," *Acta Neurol Bekg*, May 1965, 65:349-367. [Coma from vaccines!]
19. Stickl, H, et al, "Purulent [pus] meningitides Following Smallpox Vaccination. On the Problem of Post-Vaccinal Decrease of Resistance", *Deutsch Med Wschr*, Jul 22, 1966, 91:1307-1310.
20. Haas, R, et al, "Studies on the Occurrence of Viremia Following Oral Poliomyelitis Vaccination with Sabin Type I Strain LSC2ab", *Deutsch Med Wschr*, Mar 4, 1968, 91:385-389.
21. Converse, J L, et al, "Control of Tissue Reactions in monkeys vaccinated with Viable Coccidioides immitis by prevaccination with killed Coccidioides immitis", *J Bact*, Sept 1965, 90:783-788.
22. Motelunas, LI et al, "The Potential Epidemiological Hazard of Parental Transmission of Epidemic Hepatitis as the Result of Vaccination," *Zh Mikrobiol*, Nov 1965, 42:105-108.
23. Krudusz, J, "Effect of Vaccinotherapy on the Sedimentation Rate and On the Hematocrit", Klin Oczna, 1967, 37:191-195.
24. Pop, A, "Production of Laboratory Animals for the Production of Serums and Vaccines," *Arch Roum Path Exp Mocrobiol*, 1967, 23:423-430. [Animal research

for vaccine production!]

25. Espmark, A, "The Composition of Vaccines With Reference to Potentially Injurious Allergens", *Lakartidningen*, Nov 3, 1965, 62:3662-3667.

26. DeRenzi, S, et al, "Damage Caused by Vaccine Therapy and Serotherapy", *Clin Ter*, Sept 30, 1966, 38:497-500.

27. Lewis, J, "Iatrogenic Malaria," *New Zeal Med* J, Feb 1970, 71:88-89.

28. Prakken, JR, "Syphilization", *Nederl T Geneesk*, Jun 13, 1970, 114:1019-1023.

29. Damert, C et al, "Hygenical and Bacteriological Inspection of the Execution of Vaccination," *Z Gesamite Hyg*, Jul 1974, 20(7):439-442.

30. Na, "Sibling Accidentally Vaccinates other Following Inoculation", *Can Med Assoc J*, Aug 4, 1973, 109:237.

31. Opitz, B et al, "Prevention of Iatrogenic Infections Following Vaccination", *Dtsch Gesundheltsw*, Jun 15, 1972, 27:1131-1136.

32. Raff, MJ, "Progressive Vaccinia (Vaccinia Gangrenosum)", *J Ky Med Assoc*, Feb 1973, 71:92-95.

33. Hanissian, AS et al, "Vasculitis and Myositis Secondary to Rubella Vaccination", *Arch Neurol,* Mar 1973, 28:202-204.

34. Cho, CT, et al, "Panencephalitis Following Measles Vaccination", *JAMA*, May 28, 1973, 224:1299.

35. Rubin, R H, et al, "Adverse Reactions to Duck Embryo Rabies Vaccine. Range and Incidence," *Ann Intern Med*, May 1973, 78:643-649.

36. Gunderman, JR, "Guillain-Barre Syndrome. Occurrence Following Combined Mumps-Rubella Vaccine", *Am J Disorder Child*, Jun 1973, 125:834-835. [GBS is paralysis!]

37. Hale, MS et al, "Carpal Tunnel Syndrome Associated With Rubella Immunization", *Am J Phys Med*, Aug 1973, 52:189-194.

38. Provost, A et al, "Inopportune Cattle Mucosal Diseases Associated With Rinderpest Vaccine", *Bull Epizoot Afr*, Dec 1972, 20:265-267.

39. Budal, J, "Hazards of Prophylactic Vaccination," *Orv Hetil,* Sept 10, 1972, 113:2237-2240.

40. Levenbuk, IS, et al, "A Morphological Study of the Harmlessness of Live Dysentery Vaccines From Streptomycin Dependent Mutants of Sh. Flexnert", ZH *Mikrobiol Epidemiol Immunobiol*, Feb 1972, 49:18-22.

41. Arnold, H, "Our Vaccination Service is Sick", *Oeff Egsundheitswes*, Feb 1974, 36:133-134.

42. Spless, H, "Sterility of Vaccination Guns", *Dtsch Med Wochenschr*, Jun 27, 1975, 100(26):1445-1446.

43. Redey, B, "Self-Experiments with the Ingestion of Various Bacteria", *Acta Microbiol Acad Sci Hung*, 1974, 21(1-2):45-62.

44. Webster, AC, "The Adverse Effect of Environment on the Response to Distemper Vaccination", *Aust Vet J*, Oct 1975, 51(10): 488-490.

45. NA, "Vaccines Made From House-Dust Mites", *Drug Ther Bull*, Apr 23, 1976, 14(9):35-36. [Sic!]

46. Levaditi, JC et al, "Local Tolerance of Vaccines Adsorbed on Immuno-Stimulating Substances", *Sem Hop Ther*, Feb 1975, 51(2):117-118.

47. Borsche, A, "What are the Hazards of Vaccinations in Childhood?" *ZFA,* May 10,

1976, 52(13):666-674.

48. Starke, G, et al, "Requirements for the Control of a Dog Kidney Cell-adapted Live Mumps Virus Vaccine", *J Biol Stand*, Apr 1974, 2(2):143-150. [DKC = Dog Kidney Cells]

49. Garlick, P et al, "Stimulation of Protein Synthesis and Breakdown By Vaccination", *Br Med J*, Jul 26, 1980, 281(6235):263-265.

50. Weissmann, G, "In Quest of Fleck: Science From the Holocaust", *Hosp Pract*, Oct 1980, 15(10):48-49.52, 54-55 passim.

50. Williams, Go, "Vaccines in Older Patients: Combating the Risk of Mortality", *Geriatrics*, Nov 1980, 35(11):55-57, 63-64.

52. Sun, M, "Compensation for Victims of Vaccines", *np*, Feb 27, 1981, 211(4485):906-908.

53. Frerichs, GN et al, "Estimation of Residual Free Formaldehyde in Biological Products", *J Biol Stand* 1980; 8(2):139-144. [Formaldehyde is a carcinogen.]

54. Ambs, E et al, "Tuberculous Abcess of the Upper Arm With Regional Lymphadenitis as a Consequence of Injection in Two Siblings", *Med Klin*, July 7, 1967, 62:1050-1054.

55. Davis, LE, "Communicating Hydrocephalus in New born Hamsters and Cats Following Vaccinia Virus infection", *J Neurosurg*, Jun 1981, 54(6):767-772. [Hydrocephalus is similar to brain swelling.]

56. Simon, J et al, "A new Model of Multiple Sclerosis. Experimental Vaccinia Infection in the Monkey", *Forschr Med*, Nov 6, 1980, 98(41):1607-1611. [Links between vaccines and MS.]

57. Stickl, H, "Discussion on the Most Favorable Age For Primary Smallpox Vaccination of Children", *Monatsschr Kinderheilkd*, Sept 1970, 118:541-544.

58. Daugaard, J, "Adverse Effects of Vaccination. The Liability of Physicians and The objective Liability," *Nord Med*, Jun 1972, 87:183-184.

59. Nosov, SD, et al, "Systematization of Reactions Developing After Prophylactic Vaccination", *Pediatria*, Feb 1972, 51:10-15.

60. Remsey, "Iatrogenic Disease Caused by Vaccination", *Orv Hetil,* Sept 1971, 112:2245.

61. Stickl, H, "Estimation of Vaccination Damage", *Med Welt*, Oct 14, 1972, 23:1495-1497.

62. Millichap JG, et al, "Etiology and treatment of infantile spasms: current concepts, including the role of DPT immunization," *Acta Paediatr Jpn* 1987 Feb; 29(1):54-60.

63. Mason, MM et al, "Toxicology and Carcinogenesis of Various Chemicals Used in the Preparation of Vaccines", np, Jun 1971, 4:185-204.

64. Michiels, J, "Harmful Effects of Common Drugs on the Vital Apparatus. Agents of Immunity." *Bull Sociologist Beige Ophtalmol*, 1972, 160:467-483.

65. Knudsen, Rc, et al, "Difference in the Protective Immunity of the tongue and feet of Guinea Pigs Vaccinated with Foot-and-Mouth Disease Virus Type A12 Following intradermolingual and Footpad [foot and mouth] Challenge", *Vet Microbiol*, May 1982, 7(2):97-107.

66. Elliman, D, "Vaccination and Professional Confusion", *Br Med J*, Sept 15, 1990, 301(675):551.

67. NA, "Risk Language Preferred By Mothers in Considering a Hypothetical New Vaccine For Their Children", 1991, np.

68. Stickl, H, "No Negligence in Preventive Vaccinations", *Fortschr Med*, July 20, 1989, 107(21):14-15.

69. Donaldson, AI, et al, "Transmission of Foot-and-mouth Disease by Vaccinated Cattle Following Natural Challenge", Research *Vet Sci*, Jan 1989, 46(1):9-14.

70. Spier, RE, "Democratic Governments and Vaccines", *Vaccine*, Nov 1994, 12(15):1363.

71. Vaccines and the military, Spier RE. *Vaccine*. 1993;11(5):491

72. Spier R. Vaccines and biotechnology, *Vaccine* 1984 Mar,2(1):58

73. Cichutek, K, Nucleic Acid Immunizations", *Vaccine*, Dec 1994, 12(16):1520-1525 (23 ref). [Gene therapy could make autoimmune diseases increase.]

74. http://www.cmaj.ca/content/167/4/363.full – The Arrogance of Preventative Medicine

75. Alexander, NJ, et al, "Contraceptive Vaccine Development", *Reprod Fertil Development*, 1994, 6(3):273-280.

76. Allen, JM, "Over-the-counter Sale of Drugs and Vaccines, *J AM Vet Med Assoc*, Feb 1, 1995, 206(3):286.

77. Harte, PG et al, "Failure of Malaria Vaccine in Mice Born to Immune Mothers", *Clin Exp Immunol*, Sept 1982 49(3):509-516.

78. Editorial, "Are We Vaccinating without Reason?", *Lakartidningen*, Nov 27, 1974, 71(48):4915.

79. Na, "The Hen's Egg versus the Horse's Brain: ..." 1988, np,

80. Bonard, EC, "Is Vaccination Still Necessary?" , *Rev Med Suisse Romande*, Oct 1987, 107(10):781-782.

81. Forrester, HL, et al, "Inefficacy of Pneumococcal vaccine in a High Risk Population," *Am J Med*, Sept 1987, 83(3): 425-430.

82. NA, "Protection for AIDS Vaccine Suits", *NJMed*, May 1989, 86(5):338.

83. NA, "AIDS Vaccines: Is Optimism Justified? *Fortschr Med*, Jul 20, 1989, 107(21):13.

84. Perez Diaz R, et al, "[Post-vaccinal Pericarditis. Report of 2 Cases]", *Rev Cuba Med*, 1:49-54, Jul-Aug 1962.

85. Larbre, F et al, "Fatal Acute Myocarditis After Smallpox Vaccination", *Pediatrie*, Apr-May 1966, 21:345-350.

86. http://www.puliclub.org/CHF/AKC2007Conf/What%20Everyone%20Needs%20to%20Know%20About%20Canine%20Vaccines.htm – Schultz

87. http://www.ncbi.nlm.nih.gov/pubmed/23902317

Lungs:
1. Chudwin, DS, et al, "Lung Involvement in Progressive Vaccinia", West J Med, May 1981, 134(5):446-448.

Liver:
1. Lilic, D, et al, "Liver Dysfunction and DNA Antibodies after Hepatitis B Vaccination", Lancet, Nov 5, 1994, 344(8932):1292-1293.

Eyes:
1. Goldman, A, "Occular Vaccinia: A Case Report and Review of Treatment," Med J Aust, Nov 30, 1968, 2:921-922.
2. Rennie, AG et al, "Occular Vaccinia," Lancet, Aug 3, 1974, 2:273-275.

Appendix 3

Vaccine damage / information networks

http://www.canine-health-concern.org.uk/
http://www.petwelfarealliance.org/
http://dr-jordan.com/
http://www.dogs4dogs.com/
http://www.dogsnaturallymagazine.com/
http://thinktwice.com/allvacs.htm
http://over-vaccination.net/
http://vran.org/
http://healthimpactnews.com/2014/dr-brian-hooker-father-of-vaccine-damaged-child-and-his-relentless-pursuit-to-expose-fraud-at-cdc/
http://www.homstudy.net/Vaccine%20Damaged%20Children/
http://www.vaccination.co.uk/questions/q5.htm
http://www.jabs.org.uk/
http://www.cheeseslave.com/vaccine-injuries-will-your-child-be-next/
http://www.whale.to/vaccines/damage.html
http://vaccinefree.wordpress.com/vaccine-injury-homeopathic-detox-mn-cease/
http://vaccine-injury.info/
http://vactruth.com/
http://www.thedoctorwithin.com/autism/psychology-of-vaccine-injury-awareness/
http://www.shirleys-wellness-cafe.com/Vaccines/Vaccines.aspx
http://www.animalnaturopathy.org/
www.gesundheit-und-impffreiheit.de
http://www.nrbreedersassociation.org
http://www.thewholedog.org
www.rabieschallengefund.org
http://ascas.org/
www.fundaciontrifolium.org
www.k9-rescue.org.uk/
info@centerforpetsafety.org

Films

http://vaxxedthemovie.com/
https://thetruthaboutcancer.com/
https://www.youtube.com/watch?v=8h66beBrEpk&feature=share
https://www.youtube.com/watch?v=K1m3TjokVU4&feature=youtu.be